Principles for Management of Fisheries and Wildlife

Principles for Management of Fisheries and Wildlife

THE MANAGER AS DECISION-MAKER

First Edition

Larkin Powell

University of Nebraska—Lincoln

Bassim Hamadeh, CEO and Publisher
Kristina Stolte, Senior Field Acquisitions Editor
Susana Christie, Developmental Editor
Alisa Munoz, Project Editor
Jess Estrella, Senior Graphic Designer
Alexa Lucido, Licensing Manager
Natalie Piccotti, Director of Marketing
Kassie Graves, Vice President of Editorial
Jamie Giganti, Director of Academic Publishing

Printed in the United States of America.

To Kelly and Tristan, for all of those nights when I was in the other room writing.

Contents

Chapter 2 Global Models of Wildlife Management 33

SECTION II

MAKING TOUGH MANAGEMENT DECISIONS 73

Chapter 3 Decision-Making Frameworks 75

SECTION III

POPULATION MANAGEMENT 173

SECTION IV

THREATENED AND ENDANGERED SPECIES RECOVERY 257

Acknowledgments

NICHOLAS HARTWIG, WILLIAM Clark, Erwin Klaas, Michael Conroy, and David Krementz engaged me as advisers throughout my degree programs. They pushed me to learn more about wildlife ecology and provided opportunities for me to learn practical skills from wildlife managers. Advising is an investment of time and energy, for which I am grateful. I will forever be indebted to Walter Schacht and Mark Vrtiska, two colleagues who, upon my arrival at the University of Nebraska-Lincoln, unveiled what lay beneath the sea of grass in the Nebraska Sandhills. Walter and my colleague Mary Bomberger Brown also taught me how to work with private landowners, and that set of lessons led to the inclusion of private lands in this textbook. B. Ken Williams always had time for a chat when I was a young graduate student, and our conversations through the years gave this textbook its subtitle on decision-making. I appreciate Ken's encouragement to write this textbook. Mark Ryan introduced me to the world of problem-based learning, which changed my approach to teaching forever. His influence is responsible for the short problem cases at the start of each chapter. Drew Tyre and I have been comparing notes on our sequences of courses for over a decade, and he provided important feedback as I started to flesh out an outline for this project.

Mark Pegg and Kevin Pope reminded me on too many occasions that fish are wildlife too, and the even-handed inclusion of fisheries management you will find between the covers is largely their fault. Walter, Mary, Drew, Mark, and Kevin are just a few of many important colleagues in the applied ecology area of the School of Natural Resources at the University of Nebraska-Lincoln who enjoy talking about teaching and learning, while contributing impactful research for management of wildlife. Our interactions have been one of the joys of my career, and I can trace much of the material in this book back to one of these good people. I have also enjoyed the riches of supportive colleagues in many state and federal agencies and NGOs in Nebraska, the Great Plains, and beyond, who gave me insights into management to supplement the mere three months I have worked outside of academia in the field of wildlife management. I am grateful for their patience.

Students in my NRES 311 Wildlife Ecology and Management course for the past two decades have provided feedback in the form of facial expressions, verbal reactions, and end-of-year evaluations that continually refined much of the development of material that made its way from lecture and learning activities into this textbook. Kelly Powell taught the course for three years, which provided for useful feedback on learning exercises. The book is better for her input, which is more than I bargained for when I asked her to marry me almost 30 years ago.

I also owe a debt of gratitude to those who allowed me time to think and write, and this textbook would still be a rough outline if not for John Carroll and Tiffany Heng-Moss. My colleagues at the Game and Wildlife Conservation Trust in the UK, Julie Ewald and Nicholas Aebischer, provided important feedback as I wrote chapters and thought about wildlife management outside of the USA. Lastly, I am grateful for the support I have received from Alisa Muñoz and her team at Cognella, Inc. Most critically, I thank my lucky stars that Susana Christie, the Developmental Editor at Cognella, became a part of my life. Her support for writing a textbook that engaged students with purpose has resulted in much of the structure that you will find in the text. It was beyond my expectation that I would have pedagogical discussions with an editor who matched my enthusiasm for teaching and learning. Thank you, everyone.

Preface

ISSUES RELATED TO wildlife and their interactions with people are all around us. A career in this field can be personally rewarding, but the future of our country and our earth depends on the next generation of innovative wildlife managers.

Wildlife issues are constantly in the news. As an introduction to some of the issues we will cover in this book, let me share with you four topics that seem to come up each year at my extended Powell family Christmas.

I live in eastern Nebraska, and my father's extended family lives in western Iowa, along the Missouri River. We gather each year for a meal over the holidays. My uncle's family farms in the flood plain of the Missouri River, and their land was greatly affected by remarkable flooding in 2011. As a result, these relatives have strong opinions about the balance of priorities for management of the river for endangered species and the landowners who farm along its banks. In this text, we will explore issues of threatened and endangered species and methods to make complex decisions by incorporating diverse concerns of stakeholders.

Christmas comes during hunting season for ring-necked pheasants in Iowa, and nearly every year one of my cousins asks me why there are so few pheasants. That is a good question, and many members of the public focus on the lack of game during their hunts in the last few years. Is the state wildlife agency to blame? Here, we will consider how private lands play a large role in habitat management in many states, and we will gain insight by looking at a longer history of our landscapes and changes in wildlife habitat. Perhaps this perspective informs solutions for the future.

Predators are returning to many regions. Gray wolves, mountain lions, and black bears have been reported in or close to Iowa and Nebraska in the recent decade. Another cousin of mine has two daughters, and they live on a farm. When they were smaller, they used to ask their mom to close the garage door before they opened the car door after returning home because of the "M.L." (mountain lion). I did not grow up with mountain lions, and their presence is as new to me as it is to my cousin's daughters. Four to five generations of people in most regions of our country have not had to think about large predators on the landscape. That has since changed. We should discuss the potential for human-wildlife conflict.

That same cousin—the one with the two daughters—is a manager at a large bank. About 20 years ago, the bank built a 45-story skyscraper, which provided the perfect roosting habitat for European starlings during the winter. My cousin knew that I was a wildlife biologist, and we talked about their many attempts to solve this obnoxious problem. The bank was spending thousands of dollars every week to clean up bird feces to protect their workers. There are many ways to approach human-wildlife conflicts, and we will provide you with some decision frameworks to use as a manager.

Perhaps your family is not as wildlife-centered as my extended family, but I would guess your family talks about issues related to hunting, angling, and the presence of wildlife in your region. My hope is that your course and this textbook will be useful to help you provide some answers at your own holiday meals!

Introduction

The Format of Our Chapters

I developed this textbook while teaching a wildlife ecology and management course at the University of Nebraska-Lincoln. The order of chapters and topics is the way I feel most comfortable taking my class through an introduction to wildlife management. I have prepared the information in this text to serve as the basis for your learning experiences, which will be unique depending on your region and state of residence. Your instructor may rearrange the order, skip portions, and build on the information in these chapters.

Certainly, wildlife management issues vary across our nation. Some of you are studying in western states with large amounts of public lands, such as national parks and national forests. These will most likely be your employers, so understanding the structure and function of public lands is important. Others are reading this textbook in states dominated by private land ownership in which the land is used for private forestry, livestock grazing, or row crop agriculture. To have a successful career in these states, you will need to understand the goals of private landowners, and you will not be able to manage wildlife populations by depending on public lands. Through applied scenarios in each chapter, I have provided an assortment of examples of management decisions that cover the diversity of our nation's habitats and state-specific contexts for management. Your instructor will be able to supplement this text with local examples that will be important learning experiences for you.

Each chapter starts with five key sections: a list of learning outcomes, a summary of the chapter, a description of principles of ecology and management, a short problem scenario for you to consider, and definitions of terms you will encounter in the chapter. While you are reading, you will see questions to check your comprehension. Each chapter ends with several application scenarios, and the textbook concludes with a final challenge section.

Learning Outcomes

It is impossible to get to our destination without a map. Learning outcomes provide a map to your learning experiences in this textbook. This textbook is designed to include only information that will help you reach the learning outcomes—there is no sense in reading material that is only included to make the book bigger or more impressive or expensive. Every paragraph in this book helps us reach our learning outcomes.

Overview of the Chapter

I was late to class a few times as a student. I worked late on the college newspaper, and sometimes I overslept. I would have really enjoyed a one-minute summary of the chapter that I was supposed to have read before class. Just remember that your exam will most likely cover more than the summary!

Principles for Your Toolkit

The field of wildlife management relies on key concepts, theories, and frameworks. As you become a professional, these principles form an important toolkit for you to use as you encounter new problems. We will explore when and how to use each tool in the text, but you should review these principles before you jump into the chapter. Reviewing the principles may also be time well spent before a quiz or test.

Problem Scenarios

I have placed a problem for you at the beginning of each chapter. Each problem description is based on real-life situations but uses fictitious characters. The practice of problem-based learning suggests that we learn better when we learn in context. So, rather than give you information and wait to provide an application or case study at the end, you have a problem to consider as you read. Can you solve the problem before you get to the end of the chapter?

Terms and Definitions

Scan this section before you tackle the chapter, so that you will be able to keep reading as you encounter new terminology. A review of this section may be useful before an exam.

Comprehension Checks

As you read the chapter, you will find questions to challenge you. Do you need to review the previous section before going forward? Was the message clear? In the hierarchy of learning, comprehension is the first critical step before we can apply knowledge to new situations, perform analyses, synthesize ideas with other information, or evaluate an argument. Use these comprehension checks to ensure you are ready to use the information in the chapter. Your instructor might use these comprehension check questions as in-class discussion material during lectures or to guide a flipped classroom conversation.

Decision-Making on the Ground

What situations do real biologists and managers find themselves in? How do the issues in each chapter come to life in the real world? At the end of each chapter, I have placed one, two, or three application scenarios to challenge you to apply and synthesize concepts. In some cases, you will be asked to evaluate a real-life argument or scenario. Take advantage of these challenges to test yourself and improve your ability to use the concepts in the chapter. Your instructor could use these situations to guide a role playing exercise or in-class discussion.

For Further Study

If you want further experience working with the topics in a chapter, go to the back of the textbook to this section to find further challenges. Your instructor might use this section for homework assignments or in-class problem-solving. Some of these challenges might make good exam questions, so see if you can solve problems in preparation for these assessments.

The Philosophy behind the Structure of This Textbook

This textbook addresses a problem: students in a typical wildlife ecology and management course are not taught to manage. If your professor's experience is like mine, they received a graduate degree from a program that was very good at teaching ecology and population dynamics. However, university professors who teach wildlife courses are often not trained in decision theory or a diversity of management frameworks. Professors have often not worked for state or federal agencies where daily decisions are made to manage wildlife. Our textbooks have reflected this for several generations: we have focused on ecological and evolutionary theory while we labeled our courses as wildlife management courses. In this text, we return to the applied nature of Aldo Leopold's first textbook on game management, which placed management approaches in the context of biological principles.

Why is there a need for a radical change in an introductory wildlife management textbook? Our management agencies report that new employees often lack basic management understanding and skills. Universities receive complaints about students' lack of applied training in communication and planning. agencies and NGOs spend inordinate amounts of money on training basic management skills that should be taught to students during their degree. You need to learn problem-solving skills to use in our rapidly changing world. Your success depends on learning to be a manager.

This textbook was developed as the solution to this problem. We will cover management frameworks in addition to ecological theory that underpins our management decisions. My goal is to provide experiences with problem-solving and decision-making skills by providing basic frameworks and principles used by successful managers of wildlife (which includes fish!).

The objectives for this textbook are to provide learning experiences so that students (1) can describe how history, society, and politics influences our approach to wildlife management, (2) will use biological principles to predict how a natural system will respond to management actions, and (3) can use basic decision frameworks to make management decisions. If we are successful, you have a bright career ahead of you!

Looking Forward

Fisheries and wildlife management is a science, and it is complex. This textbook will support your learning experiences by building purposefully from basic principles to decision frameworks to allow you to confront the complexities created by history and socio-political situations.

Section I is a review of paradigms of fisheries and wildlife management. The section begins with an overview of the history and social development of fisheries and wildlife management in **chapter 1**. We cover the legal foundations of the field and look at the complexities of our federal system of politics in the United States. In **chapter 2**, we continue with an in-depth examination of management principles that are found in the North American Model for wildlife management. We evaluate the pillars of this model, and we compare its tenets to characteristics of models for wildlife management for other countries around the world. How is wildlife managed elsewhere?

In **section II**, we address decision-making frameworks that are critical principles for management. **Chapter 3** is an overview of various forms of decision-making systems, including structured decision-making and adaptive management. We also discuss situations for which decision-making processes must be simple, quick, and perhaps less structured. **Chapter 4** applies the principles found in chapter 3 to management planning. We learn the formal cycle of management and apply decision-making to the development of a management plan. We also consider the implications of personal beliefs and values on our decision processes in **chapter 5**. Wildlife biology, as a profession, has unique professional ethics, and we will use a set of cases from real situations in our profession to examine how we should behave as professionals.

Section III has a focus on management of fisheries and wildlife populations. We start in **chapter 6** with an introduction to population growth models and concepts of population limitation and regulation, competition, and predation. These biological principles will form the basis for management decisions with regard to harvest of game populations found in **chapter 7**. We address assumptions often found in management principles of sustainable yield and models for species of fish or wildlife that may reflect additive or compensatory responses to harvest. We explore a bit of the politics of setting harvest regulations at state, national, and international levels.

In **section IV**, we look at threatened and endangered species recovery starting in **chapter 8** with the review of conditions that may lead to endangerment. We review genetic principles that cause concern during management planning for species with small populations. In **chapter 9**, we explore the management processes of the Endangered Species Act and international system of rating species by the International Union for Conservation of Nature. We look at the management principles found in recovery plans for threatened and endangered species. We also discuss the pros and cons of taking animals from the wild for breeding programs in zoos and aquariums, and describe the Species Survival Plans used by captive facilities to support conservation.

Management of species with populations deemed too large or too invasive is the focus of **section V**, and we begin in **chapter 10** with the complex management principles associated with decisions related to introduced and invasive species. In **chapter 11**, we venture farther into contentious issues related to situations where native animals are found in numbers that are deemed too high by a segment of society. We compare management principles used to solve wildlife-livestock conflicts, and we discuss principles for resolution of conflict resolution during decision-making.

Section VI concludes the textbook with a focus on habitat management. We start the discussion in **chapter 12** with a review of biological principles that predict how wildlife respond to soil quality, cover, food, and water within landscapes. We evaluate basic biological and ecological principles that form the frameworks used to manage terrestrial wildlife habitat with fires, grazing, and flooding. In addition, we explore how the geological processes of sedimentation, hydrology, and soil formation underlie processes of succession in terrestrial and aquatic environments. The chapter also includes a review of some of the most common alternatives for managing wetlands, grasslands, forests, rivers, and reservoirs. In **chapter 13**, we assess the political and social dichotomy of public and private land management in the United States. We explore the toolboxes available to managers in each situation, and review the critical considerations that guide day-to-day management decisions by biologists working in private and public lands.

SECTION I

Management Paradigms

CHAPTER ONE

Public Trust Doctrine in the United States

Learning Outcomes

After participating in learning experiences related to this chapter, students should be able to:

- Describe events in key periods in the history of wildlife management in the United States.
- Describe how the Public Trust Doctrine shapes approaches to wildlife management in the United States.
- Describe and compare legislation that affects management of wildlife in the United States.
- Decide who is responsible for management of wildlife in unique situations.
- Provide three reasons why it is legal for states in the US to discriminate against out-of-state hunters.

A One-Minute Summary

Wildlife (vertebrate, non-domestic animals) can be managed by managing their habitat, managing the people who interact with wildlife, or managing the population directly. Wildlife management, as a set of human decisions and actions that affect wildlife populations, is math- and science-based.

The management of wildlife by humans has a long history. Modern wildlife management in the United States has developed with influences of Roman and European laws. Currently, the legal structure defining the approach to wildlife management in the United States is a combination of state and federal statutes passed by legislatures, case law from court decisions that interpret state and federal statutes, and common law that has developed over time from a body of court decisions, customs, and traditional practices.

The Public Trust Doctrine is the principle of common law that describes who owns and manages natural resources in the United States. Private individuals, state governments, and the federal government all play a role, but our unique history dictates that wildlife are owned by the people of a state and managed in the public trust by the state. Effectively, this means that state fish and wildlife agencies have the responsibility to work with state legislatures to make decisions to manage wildlife on behalf of the residents of the state. In cases of threatened and endangered species, as well as migratory species, the federal government has been given the responsibility for management. The story of the development of our system of wildlife laws and management principles requires an understanding of history.

Principles for Your Toolkit

Wildlife management is a three-legged stool. Managers may affect populations by:

- Managing the habitat of wildlife
- Managing the wildlife population through direct intervention
- Managing the people who interact with the wildlife population

Any management decision typically has alternative actions in each of the three categories (Figure 1.1), and few wildlife management scenarios may be successful without consideration of all three categories of influence.

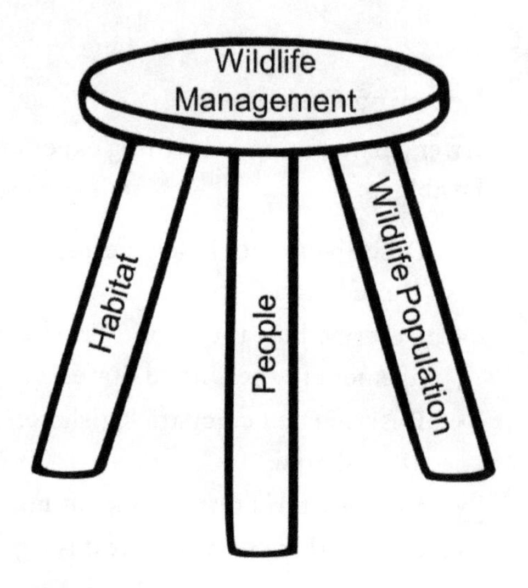

FIGURE 1.1 The three-legged stool of wildlife management: alternatives for any management problem may involve management of habitat, people, or the wildlife population.

External influences on wildlife management: Wildlife managers consider the biological and ecological context of each decision they make, but many decisions are affected greatly by political, social, or economic considerations (Figure 1.2). For example, private landowners make decisions on the use of their land that are socially acceptable to neighbors and support the investment the landowner has made in his or her land; politics play a limited role in private land decisions. However, on public lands such as National Wildlife Refuges, decisions are made by governmental agencies that are, by definition, political. Social influences of surrounding landowners or visitors to the public lands are important, but economic considerations are not as important on public lands. Lastly, incentives for conservation such as the Farm Bill are approved by Congress (political) and have economic considerations for how taxpayer dollars are spent. Social concerns are relatively less important to the creation of incentive

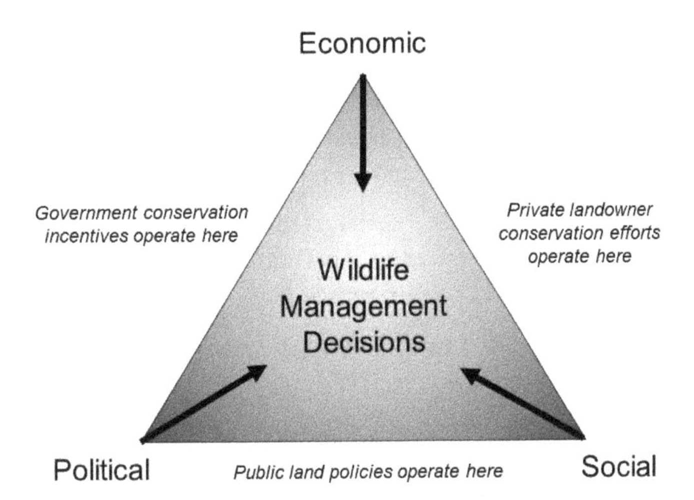

FIGURE 1.2 The context of wildlife management decisions includes economic, political, and social considerations.

programs. Therefore, the training for wildlife biologists includes a broad spectrum of topics beyond biology and ecology.

A Problem: The Rancher and the Box Turtle

The Anderson family owns a 20,000-acre ranch in the Great Plains. On the ranch, the family often find ornate box turtles. The family has collected box turtles from the ranch to sell them pet stores in Kansas City for $200 each. If they found ten of them, they could pay for their vacation each year—or maybe they could use the money to pay a bit of tuition for their daughter who is headed to college to become a wildlife biologist.

Now, the state of Nebraska has passed a law that prohibits the sale of most reptiles and amphibians as pets. In fact, it is only legal, now, to have three box turtles as pets at one time, and sales are illegal.

Of course, this new law impacted the family, and made Mr. Anderson quite upset. He believed that these were "his" box turtles on his land, and the state just told him he couldn't make money from them anymore. As he is headed out the door to go talk to his lawyer, his daughter (thinking of a discussion in her first wildlife management course at university) tells him, "Dad, these are not your box turtles."

Who is correct? The rancher or his daughter? Who owns box turtles in Nebraska? What will the lawyer tell him? What do you need to know to solve the problem? By the time you finish this chapter, you should know the answer.

Terms and Definitions

Bag limit: A regulation imposed on anglers and hunters that restricts the number of animals within a species or group of species that they may harvest and keep during a certain time period.

Ballot initiatives: A means by which citizens may bring about a public vote on a proposed statute, generally achieved through obtaining a required minimum number of signatures of registered voters with a petition.

Game animals: Species of animals that may be legally hunted or fished in a given jurisdiction.

Game Management: The first textbook written on the topic of wildlife management, authored by Aldo Leopold in 1933.

Habitat: The place where a wildlife population lives, including the time-specific and species-specific physical and biological resources necessary to maintain a population (McComb 2008).

Law, case: The body (or cumulative weight) of court decisions interpreting statutory and common law.

Law, common: The body of court decisions deriving from custom and traditional practices.

Law, statutory: Laws enacted by city, state, or federal legislative body.

Magna Carta: An English charter, written in 1215, that served as a fundamental guarantee of certain rights and privileges.

Population: All individuals of the same species, which live in a particular geographical area at a particular time.

Public Trust: A concept central to democratic governance that elected and appointed government officials must respect the trust that the public places upon them, as the true power of a society lies within the public.

Public Trust Doctrine: The common law, legal principle that certain natural and cultural resources, including but not limited to wildlife, are intended for public use, and that the government owns and must protect and maintain these resources for the public's use.

***Ratione privilegii*:** Latin, a right relating to wild animals, in which, by a specific franchise anciently granted by the English crown, a person may kill and take animals on another person's land.

***Res nullis*:** Latin, a reference to Roman law in which an object (such as a wild animal) belonged to no one because ownership was never appropriated but acquirable by appropriation.

Wildlife: Vertebrate, non-domestic animals.

Wildlife management: A human decision and action that affects a wildlife population.

Wildlife and Wildlife Management

We define **wildlife** as all "**vertebrate, non-domestic animals**." Aldo Leopold concentrated his early textbook, *Game Management,* on hunted populations of mammals and birds—**game animals**. Others have defined wildlife as "free-ranging birds and mammals" (Sinclair et al. 2006) or "native fauna of a region." Consider the differences and potential policy implications of each definition.

- *Would a fish be considered wildlife?*
- *Would a feral house cat be considered wildlife?*
- *Are captive tigers in zoos considered wildlife?*
- *Is a butterfly considered wildlife?*
- *Would a feral horse be considered wildlife?*

Certainly, house cats and horses are domesticated species, and feral individuals are not wildlife by the strict definition we will use in this text. Cats and horses are a part of ecosystems because of human actions. However, some wildlife managers still have to make decisions that affect and are affected by feral cats and feral horses. But, the definition for wildlife is important as agencies take legal mandate for management of all animals in the definition. We also prioritize which species receive attention in different circumstances, and we may use legal definitions to decide whether introduced animals like feral horses should exist on public land areas such as national parks.

Consider fish, feral cats and horses, captive tigers, and butterflies as you consider the following legal definitions of wildlife as defined by selected state and federal statutes. What types of species are included? Why do you think the definition of wildlife varies?

LEGALLY DEFINING "WILDLIFE"

From United States Code Annotated, Title 16, Conservation, Chapter 5B, Wildlife Restoration (commonly known as the Pittman-Robertson Wildlife Restoration Act):

> The term "wildlife" means any species of wild, free-ranging fauna including fish, and also fauna in captive breeding programs the object of which is to reintroduce individuals of a depleted indigenous species into previously occupied range.

From the Endangered Species Act, Section 3:

The term "fish or wildlife" means any member of the animal kingdom, including without limitation any mammal, fish, bird (including any migratory, nonmigratory, or endangered bird for which protection is also afforded by treaty or other international agreement), amphibian, reptile, mollusk, crustacean, arthropod or other invertebrate, and includes any part, product, egg, or offspring thereof, or the dead body or parts thereof.

From the Code of Federal Regulations, Title 50, Chapter I, United States Fish and Wildlife Service, Department of the Interior, Subchapter B, Part 10, Subpart B, §10.12:

Fish or wildlife means any wild animal, whether alive or dead, including without limitation any wild mammal, bird, reptile, amphibian, fish, mollusk, crustacean, arthropod, coelenterate, or other invertebrate, whether or not bred, hatched, or born in captivity, and including any part, product, egg, or offspring thereof.

From the Code of Federal Regulations, Title 36, Chapter I, National Park Service, Department of the Interior, Part 1, Section 1.4:

Wildlife means any member of the animal kingdom and includes a part, product, egg or offspring thereof, or the dead body or part thereof, except fish.

From British Columbia, Canada's Wildlife Act (RSBC 1996), Chapter 488:

Wildlife (a) means raptors, threatened species, endangered species, game and other species of vertebrates prescribed by regulation, and (b) for the purposes of sections 3 to 5, 7, 8, 84 (6.1) to (6.4), 97.1 to 98.1 and 108 (2) (v), includes fish, but does not include controlled alien species.

From California Codes, Fish and Game Code, Division 0.5, General Provisions and Definitions, Chapter 1, General Definitions, §89.5:

"Wildlife" means and includes all wild animals, birds, plants, fish, amphibians, reptiles, and related ecological communities, including the habitat upon which the wildlife depends for its continued viability.

From Georgia Code, Title 27, Game and Fish, Chapter 1, General Provisions § 27-1-2 –(2010):

"Wildlife" means any vertebrate or invertebrate animal life indigenous to this state or any species introduced or specified by the board and includes fish, except domestic fish produced by aquaculturists registered under Code Section 27-4-255, mammals, birds, fish, amphibians, reptiles, crustaceans, and mollusks or any part thereof.

From Texas Parks and Wildlife Code, Title 1, General Provisions, Chapter 1, General Provisions, Subchapter C:

"Wild," when used in reference to an animal, means a species, including each individual of a species that normally lives in a state of nature and is not ordinarily domesticated. This definition does not include exotic livestock defined by Section 161.001(a)(4), Agriculture Code.

From Montana Code 87-5-702, Definitions:

(a) "Wildlife" means any wild mammal, bird, reptile, amphibian, fish, mollusk, crustacean, or other wild animal or the egg, sperm, embryo, or offspring of the wild animal. (b) The term does not include domestic animals.

From Maine Revised Statutes, Title 12: Conservation, Part 13: Inland Fisheries and Wildlife, Subpart 1: General Definitions, Chapter 901: Definitions:

"Wildlife" means any species of the animal kingdom, except fish, that is wild by nature, whether or not bred or reared in captivity, and includes any part, egg or offspring of the animal, or the dead body or parts of the animal. "Wildlife" includes wild animals and wild birds.

From Missouri Statutes, Title XVI, Conservation, Resources and Development, Chapter 252, Department of Conservation—Fish and Game, 252.020 Definitions:

The word "wildlife" shall mean and include all wild birds, mammals, fish and other aquatic and amphibious forms, and all other wild animals, regardless of classification, whether resident, migratory or imported, protected or unprotected, dead or alive; and shall extend to and include any and every part of any individual species of wildlife.

We will define **wildlife management** in simple terms as *a human decision and action that affects a wildlife population*. We should be clear that when we discuss wildlife management, we refer to human decisions and human actions. These decisions should be made to achieve an objective, and the management action is typically set in the context of human social and political constraints (Figure 1.2).

Leopold defined **game management** as *the art of making land produce sustained annual crops of wild game for recreational use*. More recently, others have described a wildlife biologist's job as the "art and science of wildlife management" (Anderson 2002). But, is management really an art form? Art is a human activity that creates a product that expresses the author's imaginative or technical skill, and art is intended to be appreciated for its beauty or emotional power. Although it is true that decisions for management are often based on gut-based predictions rather than research-based predictions, our gut responses as managers are based on sets of scientific principles that describe how animals and vegetation grow and function. With apologies to Leopold and others, wildlife management is not art! A close look at the curriculum you are required to take as a wildlife student should confirm this point! Wildlife management is a decision-making process that draws heavily upon mathematics and the applied sciences.

The wildlife manager must evaluate the current level of the population as they work to achieve management goals. If we judge there to be too many animals—like Canada geese in urban areas—perhaps we want to make the population decrease. If we are working with a harvested species like channel catfish, we want to make sure there are enough left to keep the population going for future years. Or, perhaps our management of a species is a decision to really do nothing—to leave it alone and keep track of its population levels. We do this for many species—for example, very few people manage for fox squirrels, eastern spadefoot toads, northern cardinals, or common garter snakes. In fact, the grand majority of species probably fit into this category: not a priority or not judged to be a problem at the present time.

FEDERAL AGENCIES' MISSION STATEMENTS

National Park Service: The ***National Park Service*** preserves unimpaired the natural and cultural resources and values of the national park system for the enjoyment, education, and inspiration of this and future generations.

US Fish and Wildlife Service: Working with others to conserve, protect, and enhance fish, wildlife, plants, and their habitats for the continuing benefit of the American people.

US Forest Service: To sustain the health, diversity, and productivity of the nation's forests and grasslands to meet the needs of present and future generations.

Wildlife managers can take different approaches to management. We see this in the different missions of federal agencies. The National Park Service tends to be a custodial agency. Their mission is typically to preserve, and they may be more likely to let nature take its course than use active management. In contrast, an agency like the US Fish and Wildlife Service tends to actively manage wildlife populations. Similarly, the US Forests Service also actively manages forests with productivity as a primary goal.

Direct manipulation includes the harvest of animals through hunting and angling, or the capture and translocation of animals, such as the introduction of gray wolves to Yellowstone National Park.

Indirect manipulation includes the provision of habitat such as pumping water into wetlands for waterfowl during migration or planting food plots for deer. Indirect manipulation does not directly change a population level by introduction or harvest.

Instead, the size of the population may change as you improve habitat conditions or add/subtract habitat area.

One of the basic frameworks for a wildlife manager is known as the **three-legged stool of wildlife management**. This framework describes actions we can take to manage wildlife by one of three means (Figure 1.1):

- We can **manage habitat** (e.g., prescribed fires in grasslands or provision of cover habitat for larval fish in a pond)
- We can **manage people** (e.g., regulations that keep people from entering an area, or limit harvest)
- We can **manage the animal population** directly (e.g., harvest of waterfowl or stocking fish in a reservoir).

Every time a biologist asks, "How can we manage the population?" these are the only three options to consider. All choices fall under one of these three categories.

QUICK COMPREHENSION CHECK

The lesser prairie-chicken is a bird that needs large landscapes with grass cover. It is currently legal to harvest lesser prairie-chickens in Kansas. However, the US Fish and Wildlife Service is considering a petition to add the species to the Endangered Species List. Can you think of one possible way to manage lesser prairie-chickens in Kansas under each of the legs of the management stool?

History: Early Managers

Who were the first wildlife managers? We know that humans, more than 10,000 years ago, influenced Pleistocene animal populations, such as giant ground sloths, saber tooth tigers, giant bison, and mammoths in North America. In fact, humans may have contributed to these large mammals' extinctions, in concert with changing climates (Lorenzen et al. 2011).

The first wildlife regulations or laws were most likely ancient societal norms or taboos. Leopold (1933) wrote:

> The tribes observing (hunting) taboos which were biologically effective in preserving the game supply were more likely to survive and prosper ... hunting customs, like plant and animal species, were evolved by a process of selection, in which survival was determined by successful competition. Game laws grew out of these hunting customs.

Mosaic Law in the Bible records the first written wildlife law (Krausman 2002) to protect breeding stock in Deuteronomy 22:6:

> If a bird's nest be before thee ... with young ones or eggs, and the dam sitting upon the young ... let the dam go, but the young thou mayest take unto thyself.

The story of Marco Polo, *The Book of the Marvels of the World*, written circa 1300, contained a note that the Great Kublai Khan managed wildlife (Komroff 2013):

> There is an order which prohibits every person throughout all the countries subject to the Great Khan, from daring to kill hares, roebucks, fallow deer, stags, or other animals of that kind, or any large birds, between the months of March and October. This is that they may increase and multiply.

Marco Polo was also reported to have found winter feeding and cover control for quail on Khan's reserves. Khan ruled the Mongol Empire during 1259–1294. So, we have been managing wildlife through governments for about 700 years! Although the travels of Marco Polo may be fictional (Vogel 2012), the mention of wildlife management in a book published near 1300 demonstrates the deep history associated with wildlife management throughout the world.

History: Europe's Influence

Roman law viewed wildlife as *res nullis*. This translates to "no one's property," or the property of the commons. Game species, therefore, were property of whoever captured them for food or other uses.

The English changed Roman Law. Under English common law, wildlife were viewed as *ratione privilegii*—the wildlife belonged (or were "rationed") to the "privileged" or the crown. Nobility were given rights by the king to game species, no matter who owned the land. The mythical Robin Hood, you will remember, was always getting in trouble for taking the king's deer.

Although our system has changed from the system of *ratione privilegii*, the special rights to the king's game animals are the origins of today's hunting and angling licenses, by which every state in the United States provides opportunity for its residents and some nonresidents to hunt and fish.

St. Hubert is a person that escapes the history books in many discussions of wildlife management. St. Hubert is the patron saint of hunters. He was the son of a nobleman in the late 600s in Europe, which meant that Hubert had access to wildlife. Hubert was out hunting one day (one version of the story says he was skipping church on Good Friday), when he saw an image of a white stag with a cross between its antlers. This experience changed his life, and he devoted himself to the church after that experience (Ausubel 2002). He raised hunting dogs in the monastery and was the first person to caution against over-hunting by suggesting that hunting mortality might be "additive" to natural mortality.

Today, we find St. Hubert's symbol, the floating cross between the antlers of a stag, on the label for bottles of Jägermeister. The label is edged with the following statement, written in German: "It is the hunter's honor that he Protects and preserves his game, Hunts sportsmanlike, honors the Creator in His creatures."

The Norman kings in England set aside royal forests to protect deer and wild boar for hunting, and at the height of their use in the 11th and 12th centuries, royal forests of England covered over one-third of southern England. That meant one-third of the region was off limits to the average person. Monarchs were only ones with rights to wildlife in royal forests, and the forests often surrounded towns and villages.

The **Magna Carta**, produced in 1215, signified a rebellion against the dictatorial powers of the king. Among many changes to the way royalty operated, the document expressed that kings could no longer grant fishing rights to nobles; the landowners now had rights. Of course, few members of the public were landowners, but the transfer of ownership from the crown to the people is important to our modern wildlife laws.

Other significant landmarks in English history that affect our modern wildlife laws include:

- Henry VII (late 1400s): granted right of landowner to give permission to hunt (illegal to hunt on other's land without permission)
- Henry VIII (1500s): established closed seasons for conservation purposes for waterfowl and eggs (May 31 to August 31)

In many countries of present-day Europe, landowners retain some form of ownership of wildlife on their property, and hunters purchase rights to hunt on land. As we will see, this is very different than how wildlife law has evolved in the United States, but our European heritage established the path forward.

History: Wildlife Management in the US

Our wildlife laws and management strategies are the result of a long history of society's interactions with wildlife. The approach in the United States is unique in many aspects among the countries across the globe. Each society has evolved with regard to how they think about and legally manage wildlife.

Historians often divide our history of interactions with wildlife (in the US) into discrete time periods (Shaw 1985):

- Era before European influence (~12000 YBP[1]–1600[2])
- Era of Abundance (1600–1850)
- Era of Exploitation (1850–1900)
- Era of Protection (1900–1929)

---

[1] Years Before Present

[2] Format for years used in this text are Common Era

- Era of Game Management (1930–1960)
- Era of Environmental Management (1960–present)

Native Americans were managing wildlife long before Europeans arrived. Indians used fire and grazing to promote certain habitats, and they cleared areas near villages to attract game. The effect of humans on local and regional populations of wildlife varied according to the size, diet, and mobility of populations. For example, the **arrival of the horse**, around 1600, changed the way that Indians hunted. Prior to the horse, mobility and annual hunting trips were much more localized.

As we progress through the rest of the history of management of wildlife in the United States, we acknowledge that all lands of the present-day United States were once the home to multiple tribes and nations of people who were forcibly removed from their traditional lands.

Era of Abundance (1600–1850)

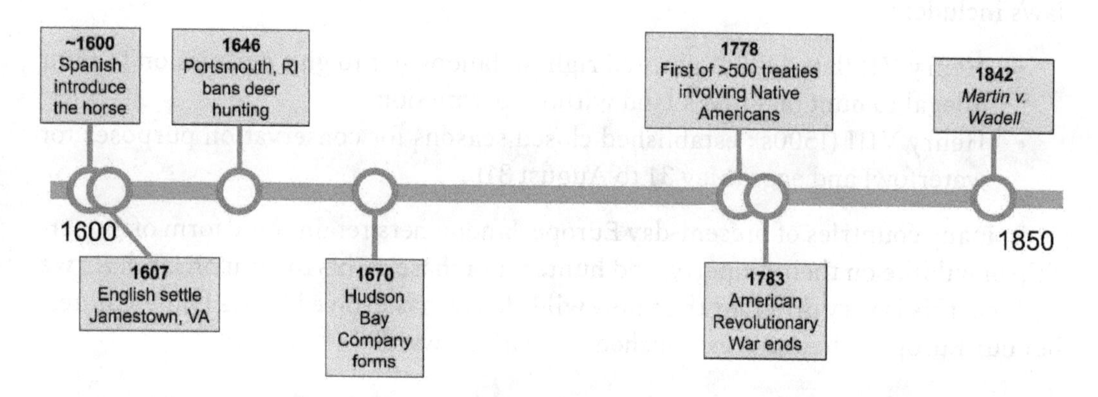

When Columbus arrived in the Americas in 1492, historians estimate that the passenger pigeon's population size was three to five billion strong. It is difficult to imagine that this bird became extinct in 1914 (Schorger 1955). That is symbolic of the Era of Abundance. There were so many resources in North America that no one expected them to become scarce. Europeans were arriving to abundance—Europe was overpopulated, and Europe's wildlife resources had been "used up" many times over, prior to 1600.

This time period marked the start of market hunting. Wildlife was used as commerce. Native Americans traded bird plumes and pelts for steel knives and guns. Trappers/hunters were providing materials used in the US and Europe—supporting the needs of two continents. This was also the time period that European traders spread diseases such as small pox to Native Americans (Wishart 1992), which dramatically reduced their population and set the stage for a massive transition in the type of people who lived and used the resources in the US. This, in turn, had a dramatic impact on wildlife.

Brown (2007) describes the impact of the arrival of Europeans in North America on wildlife:

> As early as 1607, Captain John Smith reported that the French were shipping 25,000 beaver pelts per year to Europe, and by 1650, much of the beaver had been eliminated from the entire east coast. The exploitation of the fur bearers in the northeast and Canada was by the French and by England's Hudson's Bay Company. In the Pacific Northwest, the Russian-American Fur Company took seals and sea otters, and by 1768 had extirpated the Steller's sea cow. Bird populations suffered from being taken both for meat and for the plumage, which was used for ladies' hats in Europe. Deer and wild turkey populations also declined, again, largely due to market hunting. In 1748 alone, South Carolina shipped 160,000 deer pelts to England. As wildlife populations declined, the settlers at first blamed it on predators. In 1630 the Massachusetts Bay Colony offered a bounty of one shilling for each wolf killed. When the deer did not rebound, the city of Portsmouth, Rhode Island enacted the first closed season on deer hunting in 1646.

During the English claim to America, wildlife was under the ownership of the crown—just like in the "home country" of England. However, the American Revolution changed politics in the US. The change in politics, in turn, put wildlife in legal limbo.

In 1842, a landmark court case, known as **Martin v. Wadell**, was held. In the case, a New Jersey landowner argued he could prevent others from taking oysters from his mudflats along the Raritan River. The title of the land had been given to the Duke of York by King Charles II in 1664. The US Supreme Court ruled that the people of New Jersey were the successors to the king and the Parliament of England. Therefore, the "state" owned the wildlife. Private individuals could not control use of wildlife. The landowner lost his case. Why was this important? It established **states** as successors to the

QUICK COMPREHENSION CHECK

Who do you think should have inherited the rights to wildlife in the United States after the English king's claim was erased by the results of the Revolutionary War? State government? The US president? Residents of the US? Residents of each state? Why?

crown's claim to wildlife. It was the first step towards establishing the principle of the **Public Trust Doctrine** (Brown 2010).

Market hunting continued during this period, and a good living could be made as a market hunter. Historical records show that from 1903 to 1909, 400 men in the Currituck, NC area made a combined $100,000 annually by market hunting, with canvasback ducks commanding the highest price at $7 per pair (Oldys 1910; Bureau of Sport Fisheries and Wildlife and Others 1965).

By [1830], most of the beaver were gone from the country, and silk had replaced beaver for the manufacture of men's hats. The former trappers became buffalo hunters. In 1833 alone, the American Fur Company shipped 43,000 buffalo hides, mostly traded for from the Native Americans. Buffalo meat was also used for camp towns and for crews building railroads to the west. There was wanton wastefulness, with many buffalo being killed solely for their tongues, which were considered a delicacy. By the mid-1840s a noticeable decline in buffalo numbers was already evident (Brown 2007).

Era of Exploitation (1850–1900)

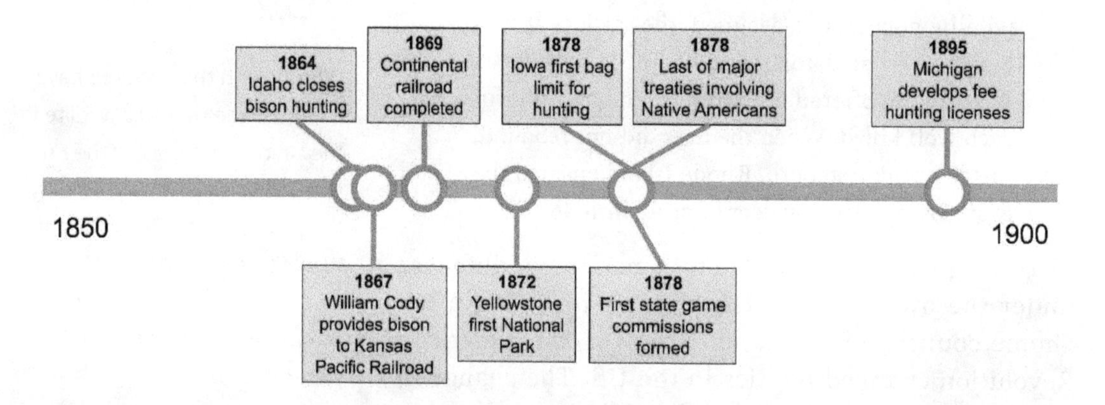

The US expanded to the West during this period marked by the social construct of Manifest Destiny. People hunted for sustenance as they traveled west, and American bison ("buffalo") were used by soldiers and wagon trains. Forests and grassland and wetlands were replaced and fragmented by agriculture. Brown (2007) described hunting during this period:

> The famous "Buffalo Bill" Cody, a hunter for the railroad, once killed 69 in a single day, and 4,240 in an 18-month period. Other hunters were actually more successful than he. The annual kill in 1865 was 1 million; by 1871 was 5 million/year. Most bison were taken just for their hides, with the rest of the carcass being left to rot. In 1864 Idaho imposed the first closed season on bison hunting, and Colorado and Kansas followed in 1875.

The Golden Spike that connected the Union Pacific Railroad to the Central Pacific Railroad was hammered on May 10, 1869. The event was critical to the future of wildlife in the western US, as the country was now connected by train. Market hunters increased their reach into the Great Plains and the Rockies as it was now possible to quickly ship game birds and bison products anywhere. Bison herds were decimated, which contributed to the demise of the native people in the Great Plains and western US, and changed the roles of responsibility for wildlife management in the region.

During this Era of Exploitation, some protection was beginning. In 1872, Yellowstone became the first national park before the surrounding region of Wyoming became a state. New regulations in Yellowstone stipulated no local hunting. States began to protect wildlife, and California and New Hampshire were the first two states to form wildlife agencies, or "game commissions." By 1900, 17 states had developed similar state agencies for wildlife. Iowa was the first state to have bag limits on hunting: In 1878, Iowa hunters were limited to 25 greater prairie chickens per day. Michigan may have been the first state to institute a system of hunting licenses. In 1895, Michiganders were charged 50 cents for a license to hunt deer, while nonresidents paid $25.

Hunting was becoming a "sport," rather than only for sustenance (Figure 1.3). Sport hunting rivaled habitat changes as the largest cause of population declines. However, hunting clubs offer the first examples of conservation efforts, as noted by Brown (2007):

> One cannot understate the influence of the formation of sportsmen's clubs, conservation organizations, scientific societies and the print media as part of the American conservation movement. Magazines such as the American Sportsman

FIGURE 1.3 Duck hunters return to camp in 1899 in an unknown location in the United States carrying "all they can stagger under." Original photo published by T.W. Ingersoll; Library of Congress collection LC-USZ62-98284.

(1871), Forest and Stream (1873), Field and Stream (1874) and the American Angler (1881) informed readers of both the bounty and the plight of western wildlife. Attitudes of the public changed, as they saw some species of wildlife disappear due to market hunting. They came to realize that natural resources in America were not unlimited, and that conservation efforts should be employed.

Era of Protection (1900–1929)

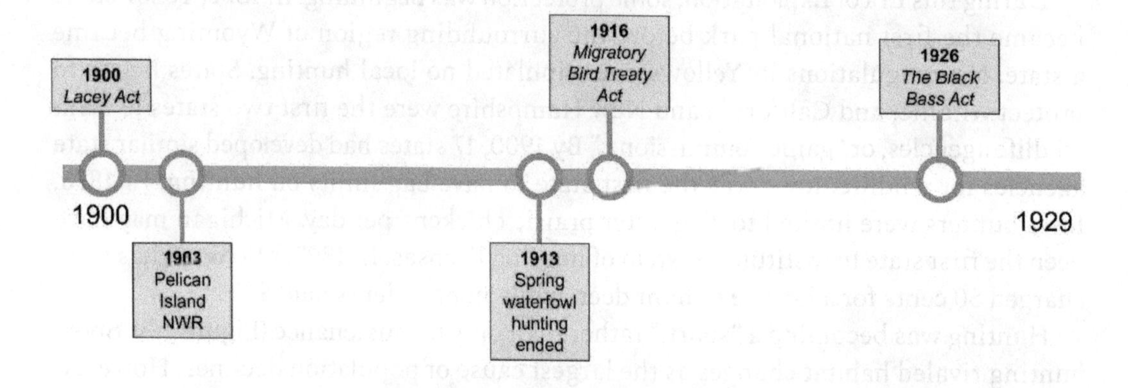

The Era of Protection was a period of many new laws that protected wildlife and their habitats. There are three general types of law that may apply to wildlife management:

Statutory laws: laws enacted by Congress, such as the Lacey Act (1900) and the Migratory Bird Treaty Act (1918) during this time period. Later statutory laws include the Clear Air Act, Water Pollution Control Act, National Wildlife and Scenic River Act.

Case law: court decisions interpreting statutory and common law, such as the authority of federal government to control commerce in wildlife. For example, in **Missouri v. Holland** the state wanted to prevent enforcement of Migratory Bird Treaty Act (1918). But, the court ruled birds were a human food supply that crossed state borders, which meant migratory birds were under federal purview.

Common law: the body (or cumulative weight) of court decisions deriving from custom and traditional practices. For example, landowners' right in the United States to prevent access for hunting or fishing is not written as a law; the right is derived from many court cases that have ruled in favor of landowners.

The Era of Protection was ushered in by a landmark US Supreme Court case in 1896. The case was known as **Geer v. Connecticut**, and it dealt with **game birds.** Geer had been convicted of illegally planning to transport killed game birds out of state, which was a violation of Connecticut law. The court decided that wildlife was the *property of the state*, not the landowner—Geer could not do as he wished with the game birds. Instead, he had to abide by state law. Justice Edward White wrote that states had the "right to control and regulate the common property in game," which was to be exercised "as a **trust for the benefit of the people**." This case law reinforced our developing Public Trust Doctrine.

MORE ABOUT GEER V. CONNECTICUT

Although Geer v. Connecticut was a critical case in our history, a portion of the Geer decision was actually overruled in 1979 by **Hughes v. Oklahoma**. Oklahoma law had prohibited catching native minnows and transporting for sale out of state. Hughes challenged that law because he believed he had a right to run a business and make a living. The Supreme Court ruled in Hughes' favor, stating that the state's rights (which Geer v. Connecticut had supported) cannot conflict with the constitutional authority of Congress to regulate interstate commerce. That is, the state cannot impose a law on something that the federal government regulates.

The implication to the Hughes ruling is that states may manage wildlife within their borders but cannot limit use to only their citizens (Hughes can take native minnows out of the state of Oklahoma). In addition, the case allowed federal wildlife law to overrule state law in specific situations. Regardless, the Geer decision remains a foundation of general state ownership and responsibility for wildlife in the United States.

The Public Trust Doctrine grew in scope during this period, as it became clear that some level of federal oversight was important to manage wildlife-related interstate transport by humans and migratory birds. Scale of movement was the argument used to extend the management of the public trust to the federal level (Brown 2010):

- 1900: *The Lacey Act* created an additional federal penalty for interstate transport of game killed illegally within any state.
- 1903: Pelican Island became the first National Wildlife Refuge, and thus federal laws applied within the new refuge's borders in Florida.
- 1913: Spring waterfowl hunting was ended in all states by federal mandate.
- 1916: Migratory Bird Treaty Act was an agreement between the United States, Canada, and Great Britain. Migratory birds were now under federal jurisdiction instead of the states.

The Lacey Act was a critical piece of legislation, as it was the first major federal wildlife law. Previously, wildlife law was confined to hunting and fishing permit rules or more broadly to the establishment of national parks or national forests. Officially, the "Lacey Act" was the *Game and Wildlife Birds Preservation and Disposition Act of 1900*, introduced by Congressman John Lacey. The act prohibited transportation of illegally killed animals across state lines, curbed sale of plumages and other wildlife products, and gave federal government regulatory rights over introduced and exotic species (to protect agriculture). The current enforcement penalty is $10,000 and/or one year in jail.

The Lacy Act served to halt unregulated market hunting. However, the Lacy Act only applied to terrestrial wildlife, and it was over 25 years until *The Black Bass Act of 1926* regulated importation and transportation of species of black bass and other fish.

Era of Game Management (1930–1955)

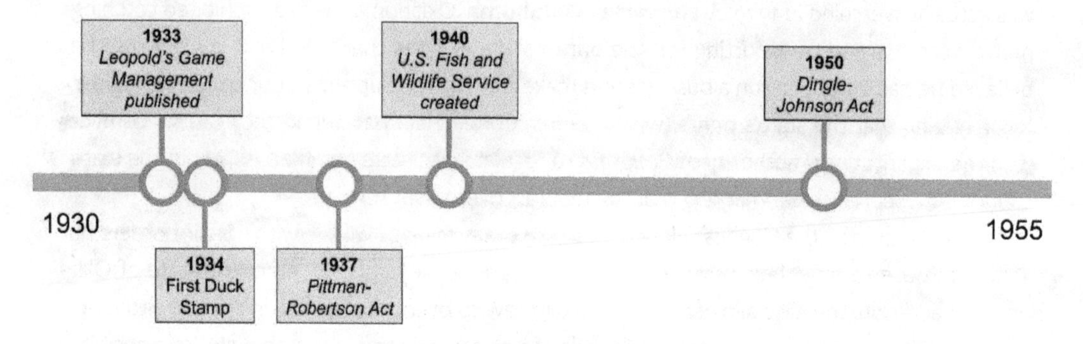

Wildlife populations had declined dramatically through the late 1800s and early 1900s, which led to political energy to provide support to active management beyond simple harvest management, establishment of seasons, and public land designations. Wildlife professors were hired at universities, the ranks of wildlife managers grew in state agencies, and active habitat management and research began. Some pivotal events during this period included (Brown 2010):

- 1933: Aldo Leopold completes the first wildlife textbook: *Game Management.*
- 1934: The first duck stamps are sold to duck hunters with proceeds to wetland habitat preservation. These stamps now generate more than $25 million per year, and over six million acres have been acquired for public use with duck stamp funds.
- 1937: Habitat Restoration Act of 1937, **Pittman-Robertson (P-R) Act.**
- 1940: The US Fish and Wildlife Service is created in the Department of the Interior by merging the United States Bureau of Fisheries and the Bureau of Biological Survey.
- 1950: Habitat Restoration Act of 1950, **Dingle- Johnson (D-J) Act.**

The P-R (for hunting) and D-J (for angling) Acts are responsible for the excise tax placed on hunting and fishing equipment. If you purchase a gun, ammunition, or fishing equipment, you pay an 11% tax, above the normal sales tax. These funds go back to the US Fish and Wildlife Service, and they are then distributed to the states for research and habitat management for fish and game species. Fish and wildlife research projects in your state may be supported by P-R or D-J funds.

Passage of the Pittman-Robertson Act was an incredible political achievement—consider the strength of the gun lobby today. The Great Depression was gripping the US in the 1930s, but gun and ammunition manufacturers still agreed to allow an 11% tax to be placed on their products. Why? Wildlife populations had gotten so small, and society placed the blame squarely on over-hunting. Social pressure was heavy, but the gun manufacturers also had another problem—if wildlife disappeared, there would be no more hunting, and no hunters would buy their guns and ammunitions. These political and social pressures brought the gun manufacturers to the table, and they worked to promote this new funding source for wildlife agencies across the country. Through this mechanism, hunters and anglers now fund the majority of wildlife conservation projects in each state.

Era of Environmental Management (1960–present)

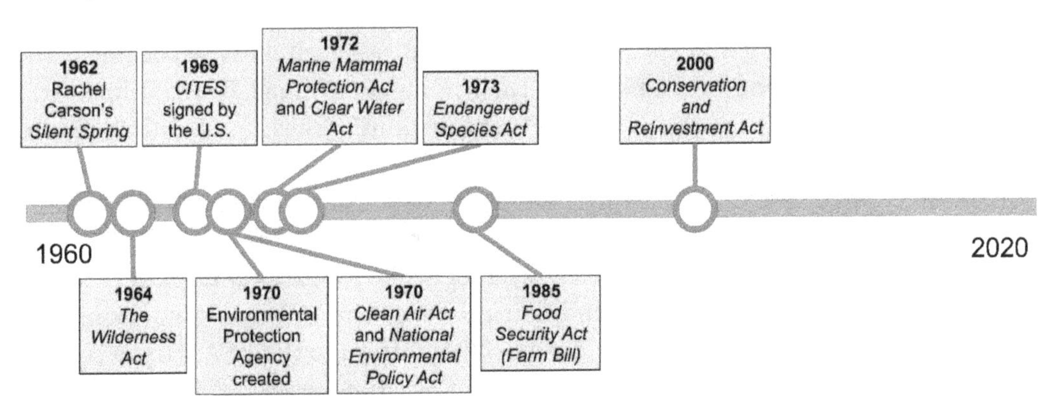

Many environmental concerns led to the Era of Environmental Management. One of the key events was a reaction to the use of DDT for insecticide. Rachel Carson's *Silent Spring* raised awareness of the environment by documenting how DDT worked through the food chain to birds. Brown (2007) describes what followed Carson's book:

> In 1962, a former USFWS editor, Rachel Carson, published her book, *Silent Spring*, documenting the impact of these chemicals on the environment, especially on wildlife. She predicted a future of spring seasons when no birds would be heard. This resonated with the public. No book before or after has had as great an effect on arousing the American public's awareness of environmental concerns. It literally set the stage for the future environmental movement for the next three decades. Chemical companies tried to discredit Carson, but President Kennedy defended her and made the environment part of his political platform. He also signed the Land and Water Conservation Fund to acquire land for scenic, recreational and public values. In 1964 President Lyndon B. Johnson passed the *Wilderness Act*, incorporating areas of 5,000 or more roadless acres into Wilderness Areas to

remove them from the National Forest inventory and placing them into national parks and wildfire refuges. Next, Johnson signed the *Wild and Scenic Rivers Act*, setting aside seven major rivers for recreational and conservation purposes.

Concerns over pesticide toxins led eventually to more concern over predator control techniques. Common methods for killing predators included the use of sodium floroacetate (Compound 1080), and "coyote getters," explosive shells filled with cyanide pellets, as well as the use of strychnine and thallium poisons. These devices and poisons killed all manner of small mammals, hawks and even eagles. In response to public outcry over the potential loss of our national bird, the Bald Eagle, in 1969 Congress passed the *Endangered Species Conservation Act*, but it had little in the way of enforcement power or funding. Congress followed with a tougher *Endangered Species Act* (ESA) in 1973. The ESA defined and divided species and subspecies into threatened versus endangered. It eliminated all commercial traffic in live, dead, parts, or products from endangered species, and it funded research on why species were becoming threatened and how to recover them. The act defined "critical habitat," included harassing wildlife to be a "taking," set substantial fines, and required teams of scientists and managers to develop recovery plans for each endangered species. The ESA is often touted as the most significant conservation legislation ever enacted in the United States. It continues to be the basis and the source of funding for wildlife research, though the funding is far below what is needed for this enterprise.

Surprisingly to many, the Nixon administration was one of the most environmentally progressive of all American presidencies. In addition to the ESA, Nixon signed the *Marine Mammal Protection Act*, the *National Environmental Policy Act* (NEPA), the *Clean Air Act*, and the *Clean Water Act*, and he established the Environmental Protection Agency. These acts, taken together, had a monumental impact on guiding what could and could not be done with America's natural resources, and clearly established the environment as an issue of national importance. The NEPA led to the Council on Environmental Quality, which requires environmental impact statements on all government projects (such as the construction of a federal building). It also requires open hearings for public input, thus making environmental decision-making a democratic process. The EPA is now one of the major funding sources for wildlife research, in addition to being an environmental enforcement and research agency. In 1969, the United States signed the *Convention on International Trade in Endangered Flora and Fauna Species Act* (CITES) making it illegal to import or export items made from endangered species.

We should note that not all legislation related to wildlife makes biological sense—social, political, and economic pressures may influence legislation. An example is the *Wild and Free-Roaming Horses and Burro Act (1971)*. This federal legislation was brought about by special interest groups. It requires that feral horses and burros be treated as an "integral part of the natural system of public lands." The act places restrictions on removing animals and has directly resulted in overpopulation, habitat degradation, and competition with native grazing wildlife.

In 1985, Congress passed the *Food Security Act* in the midst of an economic crisis for farmers in the United States. This bill has become known as the *Farm Bill*. The 1985 version introduced a unique incentive program for private landowners, the Conservation Reserve Program (CRP). Over the past three decades, landowners have enrolled 20–35 million acres in this voluntary program that removes land from crop production to be placed in a type of cover to protect soil, water, and wildlife.

States gained more capacity to support nongame species of wildlife for management after passage of the *Conservation and Reinvestment Act* in 2000. Through this mechanism, the US Fish and Wildlife Service provides annual grants to states to protect species of concern. To be eligible, states must file a comprehensive wildlife conservation plan.

The Public Trust Doctrine: Who Manages Wildlife?

Many legal battles have been waged over who has the right to manage wildlife. In this chapter, we have explored the history of court cases and common law that have established the **Public Trust Doctrine** as the key principle used as the basis for wildlife laws and management strategies in the United States. Under the Public Trust Doctrine, wildlife is property of the state. States are made up of people, but we cannot literally each own a bit of each deer or turtle or catfish. Therefore, wildlife is held in public trust by the state for its residents, and the state is obligated to manage them for the good of the public. As elected representatives of the people, state legislatures are the acting trustees for wildlife. The legislatures provide the structure for creation and financial support of a state wildlife agency that hires biologists and planners to carry out the task of wildlife management. Examples of state wildlife agencies are the Iowa Department of Natural Resources, Texas Parks and Wildlife Department, Florida Fish and Wildlife Conservation Commission, and Montana Department of Fish, Wildlife, and Parks.

However, we have also provided examples of situations where the federal government has been given responsibility in preference over states. These situations are generally limited to (1) birds or fish that migrate between or across states, (2) species that are so imperiled as to need federal coordination for their protection through the Endangered Species Act, a federal law, or (3) situations involving commerce or illegal activity that occurs as animals are sent across state lines.

States Flex Their Muscles: Nonresident Discrimination

A by-product of the Public Trust Doctrine's influence in the United States is the unequal, or discriminatory, treatment of state residents and nonresidents under rules for hunting and angling license sales. States typically charge their residents much less for these permits.

TABLE 1.1 *Examples of Montana resident and nonresident permit fees (2017)*

SPECIES	RESIDENT / NONRESIDENT
Pronghorn	$19 / $205
Black bear	$19 / $350
Migratory bird	$6.50 / $50
Moose	$125 / $1250
Turkey	$14 / $115
Angling, season	$31 / $111

What reasons do states give for this discrimination of nonresidents? The most commonly cited reason is that residents of each state provide tax support to state government to assist with the management of wildlife in the state. Thus, the higher fees for nonresidents may be viewed as an attempt to level the playing field and have the out-of-state guests pay their share of the total costs for wildlife management. Additionally, higher fees for nonresidents are supported to prevent a "tragedy of the commons" that could be created by an influx of out-of-state hunters and anglers. By reducing the out-of-state hunter and angler pool through higher fees, the state limits the mortality pressure on the game species.

Through this legal, discriminatory practice, states feel justified that they are protecting their resource for the benefit of their citizens, and directly meeting their obligation to manage the wildlife resource as a public trust. Of course, the states also benefit from the higher fees paid by the nonresident hunters and anglers, and these fees further support wildlife management.

Why does the federal government allow states to discriminate against each other? Indeed, the term "discriminate" might be seen with a negative connotation. Typically, we create laws in the United States to end discriminatory practices with regard to religion, gender, or racial issues. Why is discrimination allowed in the case of wildlife?

The answer is found in our **federal system of government** in the United States, in which power is shared between the national (the federal government) and state levels. When states have power, there is always tension between states' rights to make laws for the benefit of their residents and the common, national interest of shared laws for all citizens of the country. Such is the case with wildlife law, including the power for states to set regulations that provide for higher fees or other exclusions for hunting and angling for nonresidents. When does the national good overcome the rights for states to set such policies? In theory, there are three constitutional platforms under which the federal government could argue to end discrimination of nonresidents for hunting and angling permits (Janecek 2006):

Equal Protection Clause

The Fourteenth Amendment to the Constitution of the United States, which took effect in 1868, prohibits states from denying protection provided by laws to any person in its jurisdiction. However, the courts have avoided granting claims of discrimination based on this line of reasoning, because hunting or fishing in another state is not defined as an important right to balance against the discrimination.

Privileges and Immunities Clause

Article IV of the United States Constitution prevents states from discriminating against residents of another state. However, the courts have allowed states to discriminate if they have a substantial reason. "State residents pay taxes to support wildlife in our state" is typically used as the reason to discriminate against nonresidents.

Dormant Commerce Clause

Article I of the United States Constitution provides that states cannot pass a law that prevents or burdens interstate commerce, which is established as a function of the federal government. In the past, the economics of nonresidents traveling to another state to hunt and fish has been successfully argued in the courts as commerce. But, the states' purpose for discrimination on license sales has typically been enough to dispel challenges. To successfully halt discrimination in license sales, the challenge of the higher fees to commerce would need to be deemed as critical, and most courts have not interpreted recreational hunting commerce as critical. However, in 2002, the Ninth Circuit ruled that Arizona's nonresident hunting regulations violated the Dormant Commerce Clause. In response, the United States Congress drafted and passed Public Law Number 109-13, which reaffirmed states' rights to regulate hunting.

QUICK COMPREHENSION CHECK

Why do you think that federal legislators worked very quickly to give power back to the states with the passage of Public Law Number 109-13? Why wouldn't a US Senator want federal control of hunting and fishing permit sales?

Why should states have the legal ability to force nonresidents to pay higher fees for hunting and fishing licenses?

The Public Flexes Its Muscle at the Ballot Box

Ballot initiatives are a growing trend for legislation. State ballot measures are placed to the public after petitioners gather signatures, rather than legislators arguing their merits. Supporters of ballot initiatives say that the people are making the rules—real democracy! Opponents argue that sentimental advertising campaigns may result in unwise legislation and most people do not understand the implications of the law being considered. Whatever you believe, ballot initiatives are here to stay, and wildlife managers must learn to work within that system.

There were 56 state-level ballot initiatives related to animal rights between 1990 and 2016. Animal rights advocates squared off against factory farmers, hunters, and other animal industries, and these groups won 38 ballot campaigns (Humane Society 2016). The new regulations included restrictions on trapping methods as well as a ban on dove hunting in Michigan, airborne hunting of predators in Alabama, mountain lion hunting in California, the use of dogs, and methods of hunting bears.

Many states are encountering ballot initiatives that limit the consumptive use of wildlife. One reason for the success of these initiatives—the portion of the population who hunts and fishes is declining. Further, the overwhelming majority of Americans do not engage in hunting or fishing. In fact, the northern Great Plains region has the highest proportion of its population engaged in hunting (12% of the regional population) and fishing (21% of the regional population). Along the Pacific coast and in New England, which include dense urban areas, less than 5% of the population hunts and about 10% of the population fishes. Wildlife agencies are spending a lot of time and money on campaigns to increase participation in hunting and fishing, but societal trends suggest that hunters and anglers will continue to be in the minority in the future (USFWS 2006).

WRAPPING UP

Based on the information provided in this chapter, do you believe the rancher in our problem case owns the box turtles on his ranch?

Given the dramatic impact of history on the political, social, and economic influence on wildlife management in the US, would you predict that other countries' wildlife management strategies and laws are similar to those in the US? Why?

Decision-Making on the Ground

1: The Public Trust Doctrine, a State Wildlife Agency, and Prairie Dogs

Black-tailed prairie dogs live in colonies in the western United States (Figure 1.4). Currently, the species is not listed as threatened or endangered by the Endangered Species Act, but the populations have declined substantially.

In 2003, the commissioners of the Nebraska Game and Parks Commission were under political pressure from agricultural organizations and the governor to resist a multi-state effort to develop a black-tailed prairie dog recovery plan. Thus, the Commission voted to not allow their biologists to do any management of prairie dogs—biologists were not supposed to answer questions about prairie dogs, write plans for prairie dog conservation, or develop harvest management plans for prairie dogs.

In western states, prairie dogs are a controversial species, and the commission appeared to want to create some political breathing room by ignoring the species (The Grand Island Independent 2003). However, at their next meeting, the commissioners were forced to rescind their original vote, after consultation with their legal team.

FIGURE 1.4 Black-tailed prairie dogs at the entrance to a burrow. Public domain photo, Pixabay.

APPLICATION, ANALYSIS, SYNTHESIS, AND EVALUATION

Based on your knowledge of the Public Trust Doctrine, would you predict that state or federal agencies are responsible for prairie dog management planning?

Describe how the principles in the Public Trust Doctrine prevailed to force the NGPC to rescind their earlier vote. Why was their earlier vote not a legal option for them to consider?

What do you feel caused the NGPC to initially move to prohibit their biologists from working with prairie dogs?

2: Who Manages Fish in the BWCA Wilderness?

The Boundary Waters Canoe Area (BWCA) Wilderness includes lands managed by the US Forest Service in northeastern Minnesota. The wilderness area is over one million acres within the Superior National Forest, and the area became a part of the National Wilderness Preservation System in 1964. There are over 1,000 lakes in the BWCA Wilderness, and visitors may fish with proper angling permits.

APPLICATION, ANALYSIS, SYNTHESIS, AND EVALUATION

Who would you predict is responsible for the management of fish in this federal wilderness area?

Would you expect to have to purchase a state or federal fishing license to fish in the BWCA Wilderness?

Given the ideals of the Public Trust Doctrine, what type of species of fish would you expect to be found at a federal fish hatchery, such as the Genoa National Fish Hatchery in Genoa, Wisconsin?

Why would the species of fish raised at the National Fish Hatchery (federal) differ from the species propagated by the state wildlife agency at the Kettle Moraine Springs Hatchery in Adell, Wisconsin? Do some research to find the answers to these questions!

3: The Montana Ballot Initiative: Big Game Licenses

> *When Montanans voted Tuesday to abolish the outfitter set-aside big game licenses, they declared for all to see how seriously they take their hunting privileges.*
>
> —Great Falls Tribune, November 4, 2010

Hunting and angling have the potential to provide a measurable value for wildlife. Of course, the history of wildlife management in North America includes a reaction to unregulated market hunting of species such as bison, passenger pigeons, waterfowl, and herons. Generally, the reaction to market hunting led to a practice of removing value from wildlife to protect them, which worked. As a result, many species recovered.

Now, over 100 years later, a new paradigm has emerged—the potential to use direct value to manage wildlife. Private landowners control much habitat within a state, so the state may encourage management for wildlife if the landowner benefits from the wildlife. As an example, Texas has bitten on this idea and is chewing hard. Game farms, with fences that prohibit movements to neighboring lands, occupy much of the landscape in many regions of Texas. Hunters with cash may find highly managed areas to have the hunt of a lifetime. Landowners are investing their private funds in the public resource and are benefiting from their investment. However, not all citizens believe that the public resource should be used for gain by private individuals.

Outfitters and guides fill a gray niche in the new paradigm. These entrepreneurs bring tourism to a state and engage many out-of-state hunters and anglers. Some outfitters and guides are landowners, while others operate with leases on private and public land. There is a catch to being an outfitter who relies on nonresident hunters or anglers: your business only works if your hunters and anglers have licenses. For some species, especially big game like elk, bear, deer, or pronghorn, licenses are limited (angling licenses are rarely limited). If the outfitter's clients miss the opportunity to obtain a license, the outfitter can't provide their client with a hunt.

So, to ensure that outfitters will be able to maintain their businesses, some states have begun to provide outfitters with a guaranteed set of permits. In Montana, prior to 2010, nonresident hunters were allocated 5,500 outfitter-sponsored big game licenses. That is, out-of-state hunters had to contact outfitters who were the only people who could access these licenses. Some local residents felt that this practice automatically favored wealthy out-of-state hunters who could afford to use outfitters over the interests of resident hunters. It was easier, in some cases, for a nonresident hunter to obtain a permit from an outfitter than for a resident to obtain the same type of limited-issue permit in a lottery (Tipton and Nickerson 2011).

In 2010, Montana residents successfully used a ballot initiative to replace the 5,500 outfitter sponsored big game licenses with 5,500 additional general nonresident big game licenses (Ballotpedia 2010). The ballot initiative also raised the price of a nonresident big game combination license fee from $628 to $897 and the nonresident deer combination license fee from $328 to $527. Now, outfitters and their clients are in the pool with all other resident or nonresident hunters. The Great Falls Tribune wrote: "This was another chapter in the continuing struggle over commercialization of a public resource."

What will change? Montana residents may have more access to their state's wildlife. This also means that some outfitters may go out of business. Outfitters also argued that their services are key to maintaining high revenues for the state wildlife agency, which makes more money from out-of-state hunters than in-state hunters. It is clear that Montanans do not want to be like Texans, but the issue of commercialization of wildlife is far from settled in the United States.

APPLICATION, ANALYSIS, SYNTHESIS, AND EVALUATION

How do you believe the Public Trust Doctrine informs this conflict?

Can you find the hunting and angling permit prices on the web page for the wildlife agency in your state? How different are the permit fees for residents and nonresidents?

How would you have voted in the ballot initiative in Montana? Why?

Should outfitters be allocated a certain number of hunting permits for their out-of-state big game hunting clients?

Ironically, the motto of the state of Montana is Oro y Plata ("gold and silver"). How do you think this issue will be decided in your state? Will economics play a role in how this issue is resolved?

Citizens of Montana and surrounding states have different perspectives and opinions about the issue of big game licenses for outfitters and their clients. In a role-playing exercise, consider this issue from the following perspectives:

- The Montana Governor's office of economic development
- A private landowner in Montana
- A Montana state wildlife management biologist
- An out-of-state hunter, desiring to hunt in Montana
- An outfitter/guide in Montana

Sources of Information and Further Reading

Ausubel, J. H. "Maglevs and the Vision of St. Hubert—Or the Great Restoration of Nature: Why and How." In *Challenges of a Changing Earth*, 175–182. Springer Berlin Heidelberg, 2002.

Ballotpedia, "Montana Hunter Access Funding, I-161." 2010. Accessed October 29, 2017. https://ballotpedia.org/Montana_Hunter_Access_Funding,_I-161

Brown, R. D. "A History of Wildlife Conservation and rResearch in the United States—with Implications for the Future." *In Proceedings of the Taiwan Wildlife Association*, 1–30. Taipei: Taiwan National University, 2007.

Bureau of Sport Fisheries and Wildlife and Others. "Back Bay-Currituck Sound Data Report." In *Waterfowl Studies Volume II*, 1965.

Humane Society. "*Initiative and Referendum History—Animal Protection Issues.*" 2016. Accessed online October 31, 2017. http://www.humanesociety.org/assets/pdfs/legislation/ballot_initiatives_chart.pdf

Janecek, J. A. "Hunter v. Hunter: The Case for Discriminatory Nonresident Hunting Regulations." *Marquette Law Review* 90 (2006): 355–382.

Komroff, M. *The Travels of Marco Polo*. Read Books, Ltd., 2013.

Leopold, A. *Game Management*. New York: Charles Scribner's Sons, 1933.

Lorenzen, E. D., Nogués-Bravo, D., Orlando, L., Weinstock, J., Binladen, J., Marske, K. A., Ugan, A., Borregaard, M. K., Gilbert, M. T. P., Nielsen, R., and Ho, S. Y. "Species-specific responses of Late Quaternary megafauna to climate and humans." *Nature* 479, no. 7373 (2011): 359–364.

Loyn, H. R. *Anglo Saxon England and the Norman Conquest*. Routledge, 2014.

Oldys, H. "The Game Market of Today." *US Department of Agriculture Yearbook* (1910): 243–254.

Schorger, A. W. *The Passenger Pigeon: Its Natural History and Extinction*. Madison, WI: University of Wisconsin Press, 1955.

Simson, G. J. "Discrimination Against Nonresidents and the Privileges and Immunities Clause of Article IV." *University of Pennsylvania Law Review* 128 (1979): 379–401.

Tipton, M.and Nickerson, N. P. "Assessment of Hunter Access on Montana Private Lands." *Institute for Tourism and Recreation Research Publications* 210 (2011). Accessed on October 29, 2017. http://scholarworks.umt.edu/itrr_pubs/210

The Grand Island Independent. "Nebraska sees its first ban on prairie dog hunting." *The Grand Island Independent* (2003). Accessed on October 29, 2017. http://www.theindependent.com/news/nebraska-sees-its-first-ban-on-prairie-dog- hunting/article_4a2b9afd-85d3-5f96-9bca-32bb8b99176a.html

US Fish and Wildlife Service. "National Survey of Fishing, Hunting, and Wildlife-Associated Recreation." US Department of the Interior, Fish and Wildlife Service, and US Department of Commerce, US Census Bureau, 2006.

Vogel, H. U. *Marco Polo Was in China: New Evidence from Currencies, Salts and Revenues*. Brill, 2012.

Wishart, D. J. *The Fur Trade of the American West: 1807–1840; a Geographical Synthesis*. University of Nebraska Press, 1992.

Image Credits

Fig. 1.3: Source: https://www.loc.gov/item/89715710/.

Fig. 1.4: Source: https://pixabay.com/en/prairie-dogs-pups-cute-wildlife-938578/.

CHAPTER TWO

Global Models of Wildlife Management

Learning Outcomes

After participating in learning experiences related to this chapter, students should be able to:

- Describe the pillars of the North American Model of wildlife management that are unique, compared with other models from around the world.
- Explain how the North American Model relates to potential funding sources for state wildlife agencies in the United States.
- Contrast the manner in which countries approach the economics and commercialization of fish and wildlife.
- Explain the historical paths that led countries to adopt their current models of management.
- Describe how private individuals may benefit economically under the models of fish and wildlife management from around the world.

A One-Minute Summary

Wildlife is a resource that has value, and there are direct and indirect economic benefits that may be extracted from the resource. However, commercialization of wildlife is either illegal or absent in the system of wildlife management used in the United States, known as the North American Model. The three unique qualities of wildlife management in the United States are (1) our general lack of ownership of wildlife as derived from the Public Trust Doctrine, (2) limited markets for game and wildlife, and (3) availability of public lands for hunting, fishing, and wildlife viewing.

The funding for state wildlife agencies is dependent on the users of our system of wildlife management. Funds from taxpayers fund less than one-fifth of state agency expenses. Excise taxes on hunting and angling equipment are critical sources of revenue, but the funds may only be used for game species. New funding streams for non-game species are on the horizon.

A comparison of wildlife management in the United States with five other countries emphasizes the affluence of society in the United States, which provides support for funding as well as allocation of lands for access to natural resources. History and culture have created contrasting approaches to wildlife management around the globe. In general, other global systems provide more rights to landowners, relative to the United States. Government efforts in other countries often lack funding, compared to the levels of funding that state agencies in the United States received from license fees and hunting/angling excise taxes. The stability of governments, the level of decentralization of decisions for wildlife management, and the rights of lower-income people who rely on wildlife for food are important factors when assessing global models for wildlife management.

Principles for Your Toolkit

Wildlife management options are guided by history and constrained by culture: The management options that may be considered by wildlife biologists vary from country to country. The history of each country sets a powerful precedent for the current legal framework. For example, the experience of the United States with unregulated market hunting has led to current laws that reduce the commercialization of wildlife. Concurrently, countries in southern Africa have used commercialization as a tool to successfully save species of wildlife from local extinction. Cultural characteristics of society, such as religion and shared worldviews, have the potential to limit options for wildlife managers. In Thailand, consideration of legal hunting is not an option because of religious views towards nature.

Decentralization of responsibility for wildlife: One revealing method to contrast global models for wildlife management is to assess at what level(s) responsibility for wildlife exists. Are most wildlife management decisions made at the national level, the state or regional level, or at the landowner level? Often, economic benefits of wildlife follow the decentralization trend for a country. If a nation allows the landowner to make decisions on their land, often the landowner may receive more economic benefits from those decisions than landowners in countries that have a strong national- or state/regional-level management model (Figure 2.1).

Funding flows define models of wildlife management: Global models for wildlife management may be defined by the economic relationships between the national government, the state or region, the landowner, and the user (hunter, angler, or nature viewer). As the old saying goes, "Show me the money!" Do users provide funds through

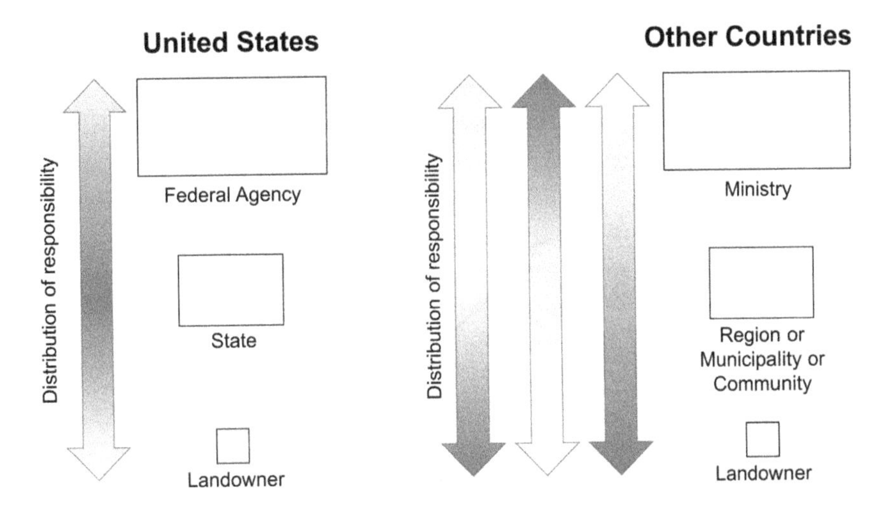

FIGURE 2.1 Distributions of responsibility among the public (landowners), state, and federal agency in the United States, and potential distributions of responsibility for similar levels of control for other countries. Darker shading represents more responsibility.

license fees to the state? Do substantial income, property, or sales taxes come from landowners and users to pay for government initiatives? The answers to these questions may often reveal strengths or weaknesses in a model of wildlife management—stress points that managers face (Figure 2.2). As you review the international models in this chapter, consider the presence and strength of each of the arrows in the diagram. Wildlife management depends on incentives to landowners and funding of government programs, and the sources of these funds vary from country to country in illuminating ways.

A Problem: Access to Hunting in the UK

Angela, an accomplished bow hunter from Michigan, was planning a trip of a lifetime to the United Kingdom. Besides visiting historical sites, national parks, and her ancestral roots, Angela decided to include a deer hunting experience. Perhaps she could find some public hunting areas to visit on a few mornings as the rest of her family visited cathedrals? What were the laws that governed the import of her bow?

As Angela began to research the laws and opportunities in southern England, her jaw dropped. "Bow hunting is illegal?" she gasped. "How can that be?"

Her problems continued. "Why can't I find any public hunting areas? I don't want to pay over $2000 for three days of hunting on a large estate! What is going on in the UK?"

What do you need to know to help Angela plan her hunting trip? By the time you finish this chapter, you should know the answer.

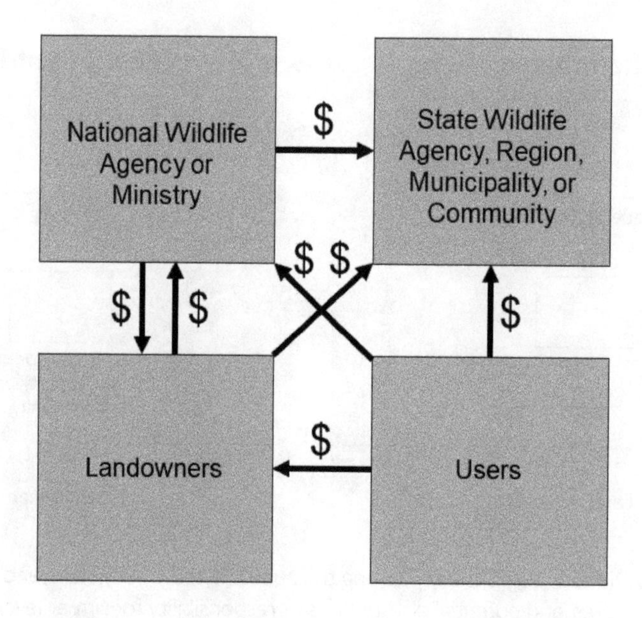

FIGURE 2.2 Potential flows of funds to support conservation of wildlife among national agencies, state agencies, landowners, and land users.

Terms and Definitions

Angler: A person who attempts to catch fish with a rod and line.

Bag limit: A regulation imposed on anglers and hunters that restricts the number of animals within a species or group of species that they may harvest and keep during a certain time period.

Commercialization: The management of an enterprise for financial gain.

Federal Wildlife and Sport Fish Restoration Programs: A program of the US Fish and Wildlife Service that provides targeted grant programs designed to benefit fish and wildlife to states and territories of the United States. The program is authorized by the Pittman-Robertson Wildlife Restoration Act (passed in 1937) and the Dingell-Johnson Sport Fish Restoration Act (1950). Funds are derived from taxes on hunting and angling equipment.

Flyway: A route regularly used by large numbers of migratory birds.

Hunter: A person who pursues and attempts to kill a wild animal for sport or food.

IUCN Red List of Threatened Species: A comprehensive inventory of the global conservation status of plant and animal species, based on scientific criteria that is used to evaluate the extinction risk of thousands of species and subspecies.

North American Model: A recent definition by a segment of the wildlife management community of the set of principles used for management of terrestrial wildlife species with emphasis on the United States and Canada.

Paradigm: A pattern or model that constrains choices in a given situation.

Privatization: The transfer of an enterprise or activity from the public sector (government) to the private sector.

Tragedy of the Commons: A situation in a shared-resource system where individuals act according to their self-interest and thus contrary to the common good of all users; the resource is then depleted through collective action.

Wildlife Is a Global, Natural Resource with Value

As students of wildlife management in the United States, we typically have a lifetime of experiences that provide us with the context of how we think wildlife management and conservation generally operates. We understand the opportunities available, the laws, and the benefits of wildlife management in the United States. Look at a popular sporting magazine, and it is easy to find an article in which the writers trumpet the successes of wildlife management in the United States and North America. Often, the conclusion is that we have the best system of wildlife management anywhere in the world. Is that true?

Wildlife management occurs around the globe. It is often a surprise, even for seasoned, professional wildlife biologists, to learn that our **paradigm**, or model, for wildlife management is very different from the system used in other countries. In this chapter, we explore the model used in the United States, and we compare it some representative models from around the world. As we explore the variety of approaches to management of wildlife, we will pay special attention to how wildlife management agencies are funded and how private individuals may benefit economically from wildlife under the different models.

Wildlife is a natural resource, and every species has a value of some type, ranging from functional value to ecosystem dynamics to aesthetic values to direct, economic value. Societies decide, through their laws, how their citizens may use the resource and how much economic value may be placed on it.

Some modern conservation groups list the **commercialization of wildlife**, the potential for economic benefit from wildlife, as one of the biggest threats to modern wildlife management and conservation. For example, in 2018 the North Carolina Wildlife Federation (NCWF) stated on their web page, "NCWF views the commercial exploitation of our fish and wildlife resources—be it the sale of our turtles to Asia or the farming of white-tailed deer and elk—as a serious deterioration of public trust resource management."

Over-harvest of turtles and game farming are serious issues that pose complex decisions to managers. However, it is an overstatement to say that any type of commercial exploitation of wildlife is negative. In fact, it is difficult to avoid commercialization of wildlife in some manner. The 2016, the **National Survey of Fishing, Hunting, and Wildlife-Associated Recreation** (US Fish and Wildlife Service) estimated that hunters, anglers, and wildlife-watchers spend $156.3 billion annually in the US to purchase equipment, licenses, services, and travel. The money spent on wildlife-related activities equates to 1% of Gross Domestic Product. The industry surrounding hunting and angling supports 1.5 million jobs, which include boat makers, hunting and fishing guides, optics companies, and camouflage clothing designers.

Is it possible to assign real, economic value to some wildlife species? The income from hunting licenses, bird viewing guide fees, and hotels has a positive impact on the infrastructure needed to manage the species. In addition, the economic value has the potential to have a positive effect on the attitude of local residents towards wildlife as a beneficial resource. Admittedly, hunting, angling, and birdwatching are most likely not what the North Carolina Wildlife Federation was referencing in their statement about commercial exploitation.

We can establish a gradient of commercialization from indirect to direct economic benefit. Perhaps it is clear how commercialization may be considered acceptable and beneficial on one end of the gradient, but less acceptable by some people towards the other end of the gradient:

- Purchase of gear for self-guided angling, hunting, or non-consumptive, nature-based recreation
- Purchase of angling or hunting license from the state
- Indirect payments to outfitters for amenities and services
- Fee-hunting (direct payments to landowner for access and recreation)
- Direct sale of wildlife products such as meat and antlers
- Direct sale of live wildlife

This gradient illustrates that the choice between "commercial" or "not commercial" is a red herring, or a false choice. In most states in the US, the only position in the gradient not legalized is the last step, the sale of live wildlife. All other activities are legal in some manner, and these activities are often used to show the value in the species we are trying to conserve. Potential concerns occur because some consider the gradient of commercialization as a "slippery slope" that may lead to over-commercialization of wildlife.

Descriptions of the current paradigm for wildlife management in North America tends to be loaded with anti-commercial messages. Americans typically find ethical problems with commercial use of wildlife because of our history. We fear a reversion to the problems encountered in the United States in the late 1800s during the period of unregulated market hunting, which resulted in loss of passenger pigeons, along with a massive reduction in bison and waterfowl and other migratory birds (chapter 1).

History is important to consider. We will see, as we explore further in this chapter, that the history of other countries did not include market hunting as we experienced it, so their laws and regulations are unique. No matter a country's history, it is true to state that wildlife is a natural resource, and it has a value. The true choice of a society is how to use that potential value for the purpose of conservation.

QUICK COMPREHENSION CHECK

Define "commercialization of wildlife" in your own words and provide examples.

The United States and the "North American Model"

Population: 326,625,791
Area: 9,833,517 sq. km
Population Density: 33.2 people/sq. km
Percent Protected Areas: 14%
Gini Index/Rank (1: most disparity): 41.5/39th of 157
Average Annual Salary: $60,154
Unemployment rate: 4%

The use of the phrase ***North American Model of Wildlife Conservation*** is a recent phenomenon. Since the turn of the twenty-first century, professionals concerned with **privatization** and **commercialization** of wildlife in North America have used the phrase to describe the traditional framework for how we manage wildlife in Canada and the United States. The model describes, in broad strokes, the current legal, social, and ethical relationship with wildlife in North America. However, the language of the model and its pillars contain implicit bias that includes anti-privatization and anti-commercialization rhetoric as well as a limited focus on game animals and terrestrial wildlife.

Still, the **paradigm** set forth by the North American Model is useful for general comparisons with other models for wildlife management around the globe. In reality, the approach used in the United States has unique features, but we also share many core characteristics with management systems in other countries.

The Seven Pillars of the North American Model

Proponents of the North American Model of Wildlife Conservation have developed seven pillars, or tenets, that describe how we manage wildlife. Some wildlife professionals claim that these seven pillars make us unique (Organ et al. 2012), so we will examine them critically.

1. *Wildlife as a Public Trust*
2. *Elimination of Markets for Game*
3. *Allocation of Wildlife by Law*
4. *Kill only for Legitimate Purpose*
5. *Wildlife as International Resource*
6. *Science-based Wildlife Policy*
7. *Democracy of Hunting*

Wildlife Is Held as a Public Trust

This pillar is certainly substantial and true. The legal precedents of the Public Trust Doctrine dictate that wildlife generally cannot be owned by individuals in the United States, and the state and federal government play key roles in making management decisions. In states of the US that are dominated by private land ownership, we face a challenge because the public resource exists on private lands. Without landowner permission, the public cannot access wildlife.

Have We Eliminated Markets for Game?

Although the pillar's claim may be generally true, the restrictions usually apply only to the sale of meat from certain species. Regulations may vary by state, but it is often legal to sell the antlers, hide, and hooves of a legally shot deer. Although it is not legal to sell the meat as a private individual, it is possible to obtain a permit to establish a **game farm**. With this permit, an individual may sell deer or elk meat (look in your local sporting goods store, and you will find elk jerky near the cash register). Further, it is clear, by the use of the term "game," that the advocates of the North American Model are terrestrial wildlife professionals. Commercial fishing operations are very common in the United States, both commercial fishing of wild fish in rivers and lakes (with commercial permits) and aquaculture in artificial tanks and ponds. In fact, one proposed solution to halt the rapid increase in size of Asian carp populations in the Mississippi River depends on commercial fishing to remove fish if demand can be established to support a market for Asian carp.

Wildlife is Allocated by Law

It is true that we have structured, effective, and thorough laws regulating use of wildlife in the US State and federal agencies employ active game wardens or conservation officers. However, we are not unique in this feature, especially in developed countries. Countries who are unable to fund their wildlife agencies at adequate levels sometimes have fewer laws or poor enforcement of existing laws.

Wildlife Is Taken Only for Legitimate Purpose

This pillar is an ethical stance, and perhaps we should view this statement as a reflection of a meritorious desire. Taking meat from ungulates (deer, moose, elk), waterfowl (ducks, geese), upland game birds, and fish for consumption at the dinner table is a very common activity, upon which this pillar is based. However, there have always been blatant exceptions and gray areas in this regard. Early American colonists placed bounties on wolves. Modern hunters may legally shoot American crows, which have high bag limits, and leave the carcasses in the field (e.g., Kansas [*Code 115-20-1*] has a five-month season with no daily bag limits or possession limit, and "may be disposed of in any manner"). Similarly, most people who hunt prairie dogs in the western United States may be more properly classified as "shooters," using the animals for target practice, which is typically justified by prairie dogs' status as a pest species in many states. Rattlesnake roundups have occurred ever since American and European immigrants invaded the West, and these events still occur.

As new professionals, it is important for you to understand that society, as a whole, may not agree with the justifications used in situations that degrade this pillar's ethical stance. Certainly, many hunters do not agree with the regulations allowed for some species or the uber-harvest that occurs legally in these situations. In chapter 5, we will explore the ethics of sport hunting, and we will see that this pillar of the North American Model can be especially tricky to interpret and implement.

Wildlife Is an International Resource

The US does have strong treaties with its neighbors, such as the ***Migratory Bird Treaty Act***, that we use to enforce laws to protect species that move between countries. However, we are not the only country to have treaties with neighbors about migratory animals. For example, migratory birds in Europe are protected under ***The Convention on the Conservation of European Wildlife and Natural Habitats*** (the Bern Convention), which was adopted in Bern, Switzerland in 1979. The International Union for Conservation of Nature (IUCN), created in 1948, provides the well-known **IUCN Red List of Threatened Species** around the world. The IUCN facilitates conservation efforts on an international scale.

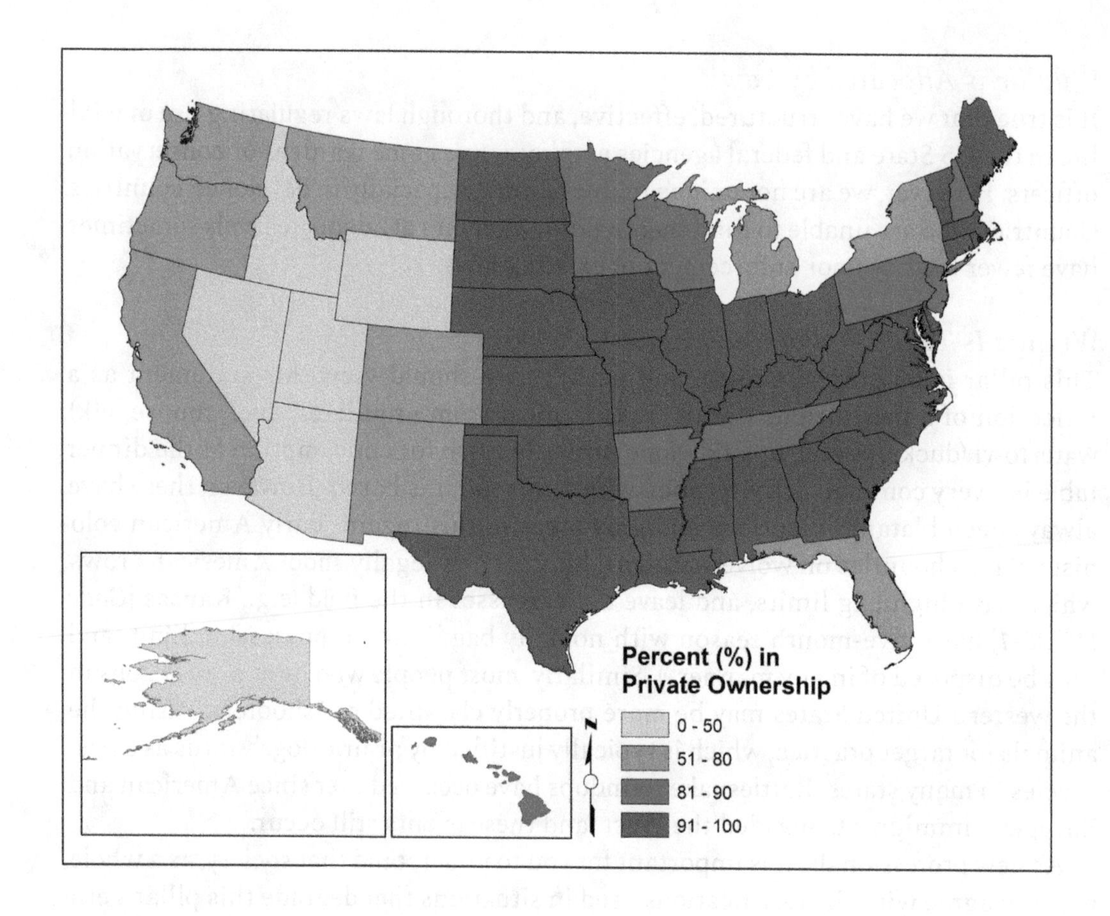

FIGURE 2.3 Percentage of each state of the United States in private ownership.

Our Wildlife Policy Is Based on Science

In an ideal situation, all wildlife management decisions in the US would be based on information from scientific monitoring, and the decision processes would resemble those that we will cover in chapter 3. However, many decisions are made based on politics or without rigorous, scientific decision-making processes. The decision to harvest predators, for example, could stall because of public opinion, even though population models suggest that hunting is sustainable. Consider that Nebraska is the only state in the **Central Flyway** that does not have a sandhill crane hunting season. The decision to not harvest cranes in the fall is purely a social and political decision that is affected by local opinion from the massive influx of cranes in the spring; the cranes are a local favorite for birdwatchers, and a fall hunting season would never be approved by the state legislature. Therefore, it is true that the United States has put a structure of state and federal government agencies in place to provide support for science-based management. However, not all decisions are based on science. It is probably best to see this pillar as another ideal expressed by proponents of the North American Model.

Democracy of Hunting

Do all people have access to wildlife for hunting? We do have an incredible set of public lands in the United States, and many are open to angling or hunting. Our public resource of wildlife is distributed on private lands (Figure 2.3), which dominate the landscape in many states. However, every state has public wildlife management areas or other public lands. It may be worth noting that this pillar does not mention angling, which is further evidence that The North American Model was developed in the context of terrestrial wildlife. However, we can broaden the statement to ask if we provide access to all people for hunting, angling, and wildlife viewing? The answer is, "yes."

The democracy of hunting pillar, most critically, emphasizes that the North American Model has developed in the context of game animals that are hunted for consumption. There is a mismatch, therefore, between recent advances in the conservation of non-game species and the North American Model, which is somewhat discouraging because the use of the "Model" paradigm evolved in literature during the last two decades after many advances in non-game management were established. It is clear that the North American Model has biases, which reflect our biases as a profession (Leopold's first textbook was titled *Game Management*). State and federal agencies currently lack funding to support conservation and management of non-game species, compared to game species.

In summary, all seven pillars describe an approach to wildlife management in the United States. With critical analysis, we can narrow the pillars down to **three real unique qualities of North American management**, compared to the rest of the world. Restated to apply to the breadth of conservation and wildlife management, these distinctive, core pillars are:

- The Public Trust Doctrine, and the general lack of wildlife ownership.
- Limited, regulated markets for fish and game.
- Availability of public lands for hunting, fishing, and nature viewing.

QUICK COMPREHENSION CHECK

How did early, mostly unregulated market hunting and over-harvest in the United States affect the eventual principles captured in our model of conservation?

Funding for State Agencies under the North American Model

The Public Trust Doctrine in the United States provides that states must manage wildlife species on behalf of their citizens. State wildlife agencies collectively manage over 464 million acres of land in the United States, and funding is critical for the agencies to accomplish their missions. Indeed, state agency budgets in the United States totaled $5.6 billion in 2017 (Voyles and Chase 2017). Similar state/province and national/federal agencies or ministries around the world have similar funding needs. Employees must be paid, tractors need petrol, and aquatic law enforcement agents must have boats. Where do those funds come from?

There is a connection between our model of wildlife management and funding. If we did not allow hunting, our state agencies would have much less money to spend on wildlife habitat projects and research to inform decisions. On the expense side of the ledger, the public access areas for hiking, hunting, and angling come with costs for maintenance and habitat management. Our management model carries with it true costs and benefits.

Some of the public trust missions carried out by state agencies have specific revenue sources, such as entrance fees, excise taxes, or license fees. Subsequently, many of these funding sources have restrictions as to how the funds may be spent. As many state administrators like to say, "The color of the money is important." That is, funds derived for one purpose often cannot be used to fund another purpose, even within the same agency (Figure 2.4).

The budget sources shown in Figure 2.4 are for a hypothetical wildlife agency that also manages state parks. Not all state wildlife agencies include a parks management division, but the illustration provided shows how funds must stay true to their purposes for which they were received from citizens of the state. For example, state park fees cannot be used to pay for wildlife habitat improvement projects on wildlife management areas owned and managed by the agency. Similarly, funds obtained through state waterfowl hunting stamps (an additional charge when purchasing a waterfowl hunting license) cannot be used to manage the state parks.

The legislature of each state provides funds for the state wildlife agency in two ways. First, most states provide a base allocation of state funds, derived from tax payers in the state, to the agency for its use. Second, the legislature often approves the process for setting hunting and fishing license fees and other similar fees charged by the state wildlife agency.

The funds allocated by the legislature from the tax payers are typically a very small percentage of the overall agency budget. A recent survey of state agencies (Voyles and Chase 2017) reported that, on average, state agencies derive only 16% of their funding from the taxpayers of the state, as designated by the legislature. Users and federal reimbursement to the state through **federal wildlife and sport fish restoration programs** (Pittman-Robertson [PR] for terrestrial wildlife and Dingle-Johnson [DJ] for fish) support the other 84% of the budget. The users include visitors of state parks who pay entrance fees and use the concessions at cost. Other users include people who buy hunting and fishing permits. Federal reimbursement income, PR and DJ funds, comes from excise taxes paid by people who purchase guns and ammunition or fishing equipment; these funds are labeled as reimbursements because the state receives a potential allocation from the US Fish and Wildlife Service for these excise taxes, collected nationally. The states must then propose uses for the funds, and the funds are received after federal approval.

State agencies typically establish funds, such as the Game Fund or Habitat Fund, that receive money from specific sources and pay for specific types of expenses. These funds are a key framework used to manage the government's fiscal operations—the funds clearly demark the "color" of the money received and where it is used. For example, funds obtained from sales of the terrestrial wildlife habitat stamp that is required when purchasing a hunting license in many states, must be used to fund terrestrial wildlife habitat improvement projects. Similarly, the funds from aquatic habitat stamps sold to anglers must be used for aquatic habitat projects. These funds cannot be used to support new lodges at state parks.

Of the funds shown in Figure 2.4, only the General Fund has relatively constant funding levels. Income to all of the other funds may vary annually. As the number of hunters and anglers dropped in the early twenty-first century, the budgets of many state wildlife agencies have shrunk markedly because of lower receipts from fishing

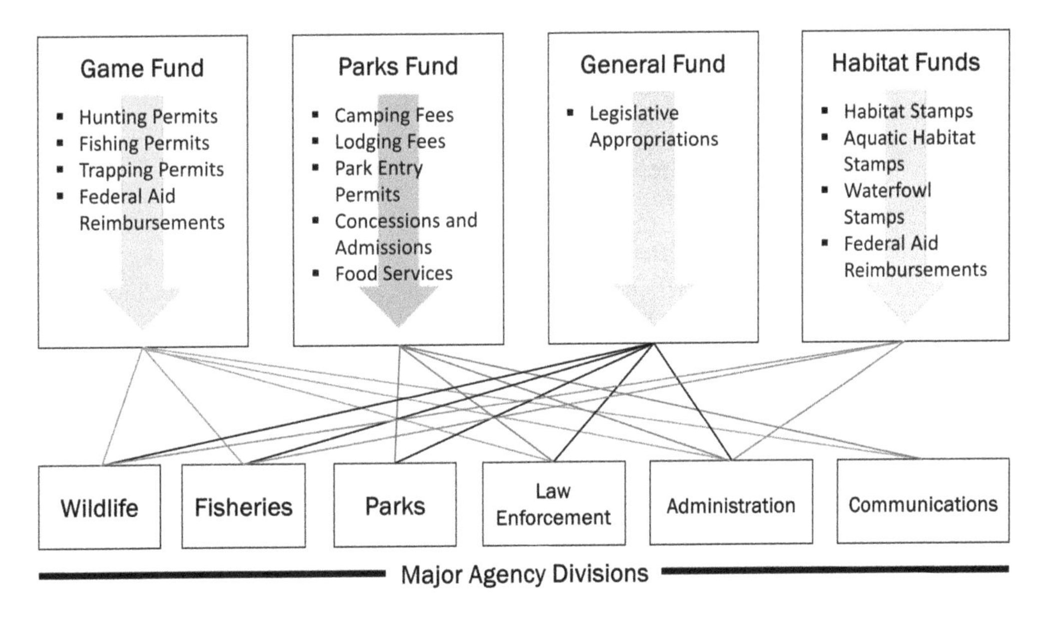

FIGURE 2.4 Funding streams to support divisions within a state wildlife agency. Some funding sources are specific to the type of expenditures for which they may be used. Agency divisions and funding sources may vary from state to state (after information provided by J. Douglas and P. Cole).

and hunting permits. That income supports staff salaries and programming, which had to be adjusted in the face of less income to those funds. Similarly, since gun and ammunition purchases vary from year to year, the money coming from PR funds varies. In the past decade, the news coverage of many mass shootings in the United States has been followed by an increase in gun sales. Hobby gun owners, fearful that specific types of ammunition or guns may be outlawed in the wake of mass shootings, make purchases. This unusual dynamic has led to higher-than-normal funding for wildlife habitat management and research at the state level. However, fisheries habitat management projects did not benefit, as PR funds may only be used on terrestrial game animals. Again, the source of money matters.

On average, states report that the majority of the funding, 59%, for their budgets comes from hunting- and fishing-related activities such as license and stamp sales or the excise taxes on hunting and angling equipment. Hunters and anglers have traditionally been the primary funding source for conservation efforts by state wildlife agencies, but the funding sources are diversifying. In fact, **the Recovering America's Wildlife Act** was introduced in Congress for action during 2017. This legislation would provide a new source of funding for states that would increase the amount spent on non-game species through each state's conservation plan.

A NEW FUNDING SOURCE FOR WILDLIFE?

What: Recovering America's Wildlife Act, H.R.4647, a bill to support conservation of species at risk by providing funds to state wildlife agencies.

Where: Introduced in the US House of Representatives by Representative Jeff Fortenberry (R-Neb.) and Debbie Dingell (D-Mich.).

Who: Support for the act originated with Alliance for America's Fish and Wildlife, a partnership represented by the outdoor recreation retail and manufacturing sector, the energy and automotive industries, private landowners, educational institutions, conservation organizations, sporting groups, and state and federal fish and wildlife agencies.

When: Introduced to US House of Representatives of the 115th Congress in December 2017. The bill was not acted upon, but the bill was re-introduced to the House of Representatives in the 116th Congress in July 2019.

Why: States and politicians appear to support the legislation as it will help at-risk species before they require listing under the Endangered Species Act, which moves management to the federal level.

How: Funds for state wildlife conservation would come from existing mineral and energy royalties from federal lands.

It is clear that funding for conservation is important, which requires attaching value to wildlife and the opportunity to hunt, fish, and participate in outdoor activities. The North American Model of wildlife management, as defined by its promoters, stipulates some beliefs and ethics about the commercialization of wildlife. However, at its core the North American Model is a model for how we approach management, which includes how we pay for management. As you review the models used in other countries, think of how their funding sources might be different than those sources used in the United States.

QUICK COMPREHENSION CHECK

Scenario for consideration: The wildlife habitat fund of a state agency received an unusually large amount of funds from PR sources, and the law enforcement division of the same agency needed to hire a new game warden to perform covert operations to protect against poaching. Would you predict the habitat fund would be able to pay for the new game warden's salary? What funding options are available for law enforcement?

A Model of an Affluent People

Earlier in this chapter, we analyzed and provided clarification for pillars of the North American Model. Truly, there are distinct characteristics of the approach used for wildlife management in the United States. We hold wildlife in trust as a people, we have given up direct value of wildlife in many cases because of our experiences with market hunting, and we pay taxes to support the management of public lands for recreation. Our model is a model of an affluent people who generally do not need wildlife for our livelihood; we can buy our food at the grocery with money we make at our job. We have low unemployment rates. We value the opportunity for consumptive and non-consumptive use of wildlife. We may even spend a significant portion of our annual salary on a holiday trip just to view wildlife and appreciate the landscapes in a national park. However, much of the rest of the world differs from our experience in many ways.

The history and culture of the United States have molded our unique approach. Teer (1999) stated:

> The increasing affluence of the United States beginning with the industrial revolution, made the conservation movement possible. Without these two conditions—the growing appreciation of wildlife resources and the affluence to afford conservation—the movement could not have advanced so rapidly or so far.

Consideration of how we value natural resources, including wildlife, is a useful mental exercise and may prompt vigorous discussions. Our view of the world affects our stance on commercialization, or valuation, of natural resources. As we turn to models of fisheries and wildlife management from other countries around the globe, it is useful to think of the reaction of Native Americans to European and American immigrants to the western US Native Americans gave value to the land and resources, as they fought wars over hunting grounds. However, the idea of claiming secure ownership was an overwhelming new idea. When Chief Seattle was asked to sell his lands to the United States government, he is reported to have said:

> How can you buy or sell the sky, the warmth of the land? The idea is strange to us. If we do not own the freshness of the air and sparkle of the water, how can you buy them? Every part of this earth is sacred to my people ... The earth does not belong to man; man belongs to the earth.

QUICK COMPREHENSION CHECK

Why should students of wildlife management in the United States study other models for wildlife conservation?

We must appreciate the context of our North American Model for wildlife conservation. The United States is a relatively affluent country with a unique history. Other countries differ in their historical, cultural, and economic contexts, and their models have derived from their history.

International Models of Wildlife Management

Wildlife managers make decisions differently in countries around the world, and there are stark contrasts in management paradigms. Politics, history, culture, and availability of scientific information can constrain possible management options.

Europe and the United States are similar in terms of the economic prosperity of the citizens. As we look at issues, such as the commercialization or privatization of wildlife, we tend to look at the issue from our US- or Euro-centric viewpoints.

For example, if we consider the destruction of the rainforest and the loss of many forest-dependent species of wildlife in Latin America, we might wonder (as an American) how a country could allow such destruction. However, if we delve into the culture and society, our view may change. Most countries in Latin America are facing urgent problems that relate to the function and structure of their country: health, education, and basic economic development (Ojasti 1984). Therefore, these basic, urgent factors are top priority for their governments, and rainforest area or species of conservation concern are not an immediate concern. Unless a wildlife or other natural resource has large monetary returns, they will be outcompeted for attention or space on the landscape by mining, logging, or agriculture.

Similarly, as we look at wildlife conservation in Africa, it is easy to wonder why critical national parks are shrinking in size or why farmers shoot cheetahs. Surely, these people understand how important their wildlife is to global biodiversity? However, as we investigate the dynamics in African countries, we learn that the need for food for a growing population is driving the need for space, so protected natural habitats disappear in favor of crop fields and pastures. Economic pressures at the ranch scale are responsible for farmers' decisions to shoot predators, and economic pressures may also be responsible for the overhunting of elephants and rhinos. Local villagers are sometimes easily convinced with a sum of money equal to many months' salary to provide information on the location of a rhino, for example, that eventually leads to its poaching.

It is clear that we must consider the context of decisions made by managers for fish and wildlife around the world (Figure 2.5). Throughout the next section, you will be provided with basic statistics to describe five countries for comparison to the United States. These countries were chosen for their geographic distribution around the world, as well as their contrasting approaches to management.

QUICK COMPREHENSION CHECK

In what way does economics play a role in conservation problems in developing countries?

How does economics play a role in the United States with regard to land use and conservation issues?

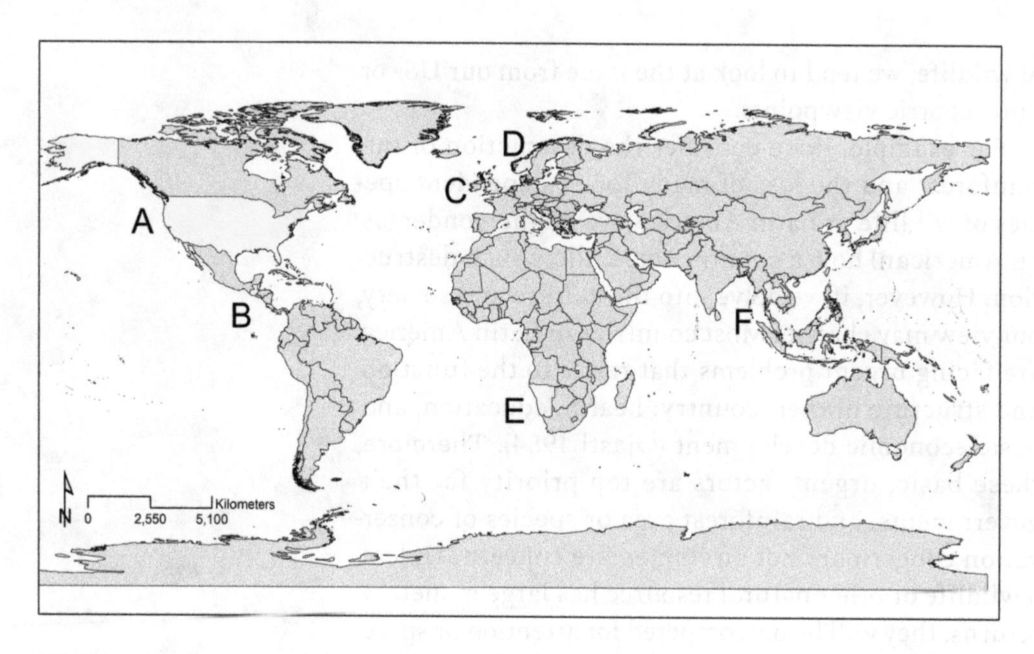

FIGURE 2.5 Location of countries considered in this chapter: A) United States of America, B) Guatemala, C) United Kingdom, D) Norway, E) Namibia, and F) Thailand.

Western Europe: United Kingdom

Population: 64,769,452
Area: 243,610
Population Density: 265 people/sq. km
Percent Protected Areas: 28%
Gini Index/Rank (1: most disparity): 32.4/111st of 157
Average Annual Salary: $42,835
Unemployment Rate: 4%

The United Kingdom has been a constitutional monarchy since 1688. Although previous kings and queens had unrestricted power, the laws of the constitution (created by a representative Parliament) bind the current queen. Scotland, England, Wales, and Northern Ireland, as countries within the United Kingdom, act as administrative divisions with some government functions. Counties or council areas within each country provide a lower level of government administration. However, wildlife law is created at the national level by the British Parliament, the supreme legislative body of the United Kingdom.

The deep history of wildlife management in the United Kingdom continues to be flavored by the presence of the monarchy, the king and queen, and an upper class of elite landowners who traditionally received their status (and therefore lands) from the crown. Prior to the Magna Carta in 1215, only the king could provide access to game, and those found taking the king's animals had committed a high crime. The Magna Carta weakened the king's hold on wildlife to some extent, but the common peasant typically did not have access. For example, the Game Laws of 1671 restricted use of game for hunting to men with a rental income over £100 (Tapper 1992). Of the approximately 300,000 landowners at the time, only 16,000 squires were allowed access. During the next 200 years, poaching became a serious offense, and Longrigg (1977) estimates that one-third of prisoners in England in 1823 had been convicted of offenses under the Game Laws.

Economic failures in the nineteenth century resulted in many landowners selling their farms, which were purchased by the wealthiest estate owners. Many of the resulting estates reached sizes of 10,000 acres (4,000 ha). Around 1900, changes in agriculture forced many traditional estate owners to sell or divide their estates, many of which were purchased by wealthy businessmen who had made their fortunes in the city. Few of the new landowners were interested in agriculture as an economic pursuit, but they saw the advantages of lives of leisure on their estates, marked with hunting opportunities. The prestige of a sporting lifestyle led to an immense popularity in "shooting." Estate owners valued high bag numbers during shoots, and they employed gamekeepers to reduce predators, raise supplemental birds, and manage the estate for high production of game animals.

In the modern UK, hunting (we use the American term, the British term is **shooting** and hunting is the pursuit of game with hounds) only occurs with permission of estate owners. There are no public hunting areas in the UK, and there are no hunting licenses as we know them in the US. Landowners have legal authority to hunt or invite hunters onto their land as long as the person using a firearm has a valid certificate for shotgun or firearm. The government sets legal species of game and seasons, but there are no daily bag limits or quotas in the UK. Deer **stalks** (the UK term for ground hunting of deer) may cost $500–$1,500 per day on an estate, depending on how many deer (and of what species) are taken. **Gamebird shoots** on estates may cost upwards of $10,000 per weekend, and the shoots are advertised by the bag that the shooter may anticipate (often in the range of 50–250 birds per weekend, per person). In the tradition that goes back centuries (Figure 2.6), shooters stand in place, often assisted with loading of extra shotguns, and birds are driven towards the shooters by beaters who walk through the fields to flush the birds. Control of predators (e.g., foxes and crows) is the duty of the gamekeeper on many estates, which improves nesting success. Birds driven towards the shooters often consist of many pen-reared birds that were released as young to acclimatize to the environment, in contrast to pen-reared birds released minutes before the hunt on regulated game farms in the United

FIGURE 2.6 A member of Lord Woolavington's House Party, with a gamekeeper in a hide during a grouse shoot in 1922 on Mannock Moors in the Scottish Highlands. Photo by W. G. Phillips.

States. Typically, about one-third of birds released on estates for driven shooting are eventually taken by UK shooters during the course of the season.

The high level of harvest of game-birds is supported by the intense management effort on each estate that produces, in the field and supplemented by artificial means, high numbers of game birds. In addition, the presence of estates and shoots for hundreds of years often means that records of birds shot are available as **indices** to population levels. Although monitoring by the Breeding Bird Survey in the United States, started in 1966, is considered to be one of the US' longest long-term monitoring efforts, the records from estates that are now compiled in the National Gamebag Census in the UK date back to 1793.

Other unique features of management in the UK:

- **Royal privilege:** In 1215, the Magna Carta spread access of game from the king or queen to noble landowners, but some unique traditions continue in wildlife law in the UK. For example, mute swans belong to the king or queen. Traditionally, the birds were considered to be such special creatures that only the monarchs could use them as the centerpiece for a feast. Today, that royal ownership continues. The "King's deer" of Robin Hood yore is no longer a phenomenon, but at present, even Robin Hood would do best not to mess with the "Queen's swans."

- **Grant of access:** Lords of manors may deputize their gamekeepers or others to take game for the purposes of the manor or any other purpose deemed fit by the Lord.
- **Ownership of game:** Wild animals are the property of no one, but once hunted and killed become the property of the landowner. Common sale of meat of deer and game (defined as "hares, pheasants, partridges, grouse, heath or moor game, black game") is prohibited by the 1991 Deer Act and 1831 Game Act, but landowners (or those permitted by the landowner) may sell deer or game to licensed game dealers. Licenses for dealers are approved by justices of the peace in each county, and the license allows the dealer to sell from game meat at one storefront or location.
- **Definition of "wildlife":** "Wild animal" means any animal (other than a bird) which is (before it was killed or taken) or was living wild; "wild bird" means any bird of a species which is ordinarily resident in or is a visitor to the European territory of any member state in a wild state but does not include poultry or ... any game bird; "game bird" means any pheasant, partridge, grouse (or moor game), black (or heath) game or ptarmigan (Wildlife and Countryside Act 1981).
- **Bow hunting:** Hunting with a bow and arrow has been illegal in the UK since 1965. Bow hunting is not considered ethical by the majority of the British public.

Scandanavia: Norway

Population: 5,320,045
Area: 323,802 sq. km
Population Density: 16 people/sq. km
Percent National Parks: Norway: 29%
Gini Index/Rank (1: most disparity): Norway: 26.8/139th of 157
Average Annual Salary: Norway: $53,643
Unemployment Rate: 4%

Norway, like the United Kingdom, is a constitutional democracy. At the national level, the current king enjoys mostly ceremonial roles in government. Laws are created in the Storting, the representative parliament of Norway. Local government includes over 400 municipalities, each led by a council. Norway has shifted a substantial amount of power from the national level to the municipalities. The empowerment of local boards, or **decentralization** of power, is similar, in some ways, to the powers given to states in the United States.

The Ministry of the Environment is the national agency that is tasked with issues of nature conservation and wildlife management. In the past decade, the ministry has created local conservation boards to create and revise management plans. The boards are composed of elected politicians from municipalities. As such, the boards are responsive to local residents and to the ministry, which has final power for approval of plans (Hongslo et al. 2016).

Wildlife law changed in Norway in 1899, when landowners were given exclusive hunting and fishing rights to all game on their property. Prior to this decision, the public had more access to wildlife, and over-harvesting was occurring in a real-life example of the **tragedy of the commons**. Power was given to landowners as a management decision to protect wildlife (Brainerd and Kaltenborn 2010).

Despite the hunting and fishing rights enjoyed by landowners, living wildlife in Norway are considered a public resource and the property of the state. Landowners are granted permission to hunt animals on their property through hunting licenses that are property-specific. That is, the license is given to a landowner only for use on their land. The number of permits is decided by the local conservation boards with information provided by regional wildlife managers. A state-owned company, Statskog, is responsible for management and permissions to harvest wildlife on 20% of the land base of Norway, which is state-owned forests or high altitude, treeless areas. Hunters must pay a fee to hunt in these areas, but they represent lands available to the public for hunting.

As in the United Kingdom, counts of harvested wildlife have been kept in Norway for almost two centuries. New monitoring programs have been added for predators and other non-game animals. Landowners in Norway are more involved in the management process than most landowners in the United States. Hunters must report days afield and total harvest to avoid fines and loss of ability to purchase a license in the future. Norwegian landowners collect harvest and count data used to make decisions by the local boards, and in August hunters train their dogs by participating in over 7,500 km of voluntary transect surveys that provide indices for monitoring of ptarmigan and other game birds.

Once an animal has been legally harvested, the carcass becomes the property of the landowner, and this dynamic becomes important in the management of wildlife. For example, it is common for a landowner to charge a group of hunters for access to their land for moose hunting. Once the group has killed the moose, the landowner gives the rights to the carcass to the hunters, who may use it for their own purposes. They may sell some of the meat to local meat markets or to friends. Moose meat is advertised for sale in the newspaper. Quite often, the hunters receive more for the meat than they paid for the permission to access the land. Therefore, moose may

FIGURE 2.7 A Saami man with child and domesticated reindeer in Norway c. 1890.

be effectively managed, and hunters dependably remove the number of moose that biologists decide to allow. Eating moose and other game animals is an important part of the culture, which also brings hunters from cities to rural landscapes in search of opportunities to hunt.

Hunting and fishing access to private lands requires permission, but Norway's trespass laws for other purposes are similar to other European countries. These laws stand in contrast with trespass laws in the United States. The Norwegian public may legally trespass (from the Latin "*to pass beyond*") on private lands for specific purposes, such as hiking, camping, and berry picking. Local trails cut through private pastures and fields, but cultivated crops are off-limits to hikers until the harvest has occurred.

The native Saami people of northern Norway have strong coastal fishing and reindeer herding traditions. Norway's International Covenant on Civil and Political Rights (1966) gives control of land and natural resources, including wildlife, to the Saami people. Most reindeer in Norway are semi-domesticated (herded, Figure 2.7), and only the Saami may engage in herding (Tyler et al. 2007).

Other unique features of management in Norway:

- **Quotas for hunting:** Local boards consider the size of the wildlife population, the condition of the habitat, and the amount of damage caused by the species when setting local quotas for landowners.
- **Killing for legitimate reasons:** Landowners may kill wildlife in self-defense or in defense of property. Otherwise, hunting is strictly for acquisition of meat.
- **Hunting for all:** Statistics suggest that hunters in Norway are representative of the population. Hunting is not an activity reserved for an elite class. All hunters must pass annual, obligatory shooting tests before obtaining permission to hunt.
- **License and quota fees:** The fee for a hunting license and the fee charged for each moose, deer, and reindeer permitted to be shot are paid into a Wildlife Fund that promotes management of wildlife.
- **"Wildlife" means:** "Wildlife" means all wild terrestrial mammals, birds, amphibians and reptiles (from the Wildlife Act 1981)."

QUICK COMPREHENSION CHECK

In Norway, the public was over-harvesting game in the 1800s. Contrast Norway's approach to solving the problem with the approach used by the United States.

Southern Africa: Namibia

Population: 2,484,780
Area: 824,292 sq. km
Population Density: 3.0 people/sq. km
Percent Protected Areas: 38%
Gini Index/Rank (1: most disparity): 59.7/7th of 157
Average Annual Salary: $6,626
Unemployment Rate: 28%

Namibia's history includes a rich heritage of more than ten indigenous tribes. During the colonial period in Africa, Germany claimed the area, known as German

South West Africa. Many indigenous people were killed and displaced during this period. Following Germany's loss in World War I, the country was given as a protectorate to South Africa, which marked the beginning of a long legal battle and war for independence for the region that was now known as Namibia. Namibia was established as an independent nation in 1990, just as apartheid was ending in South Africa and Namibia. Today, the government (including the president) is representative of the majority of the population, which is black.

Namibian wildlife managers are proud to note that Namibia is distinct for having conservation directly specified in its constitution:

> The State shall actively promote and maintain the welfare of the people by adopting, inter alia, policies aimed at the following: ... (l) maintenance of ecosystems, essential ecological processes and biological diversity of Namibia and utilization of living natural resources on a sustainable basis for the benefit of all Namibians, both present and future ... (Chapter 11, Principles of State Policy, Article 95 Promotion of the Welfare of the People).

The ministry that manages wildlife in Namibia is the Ministry of Environment and Tourism, and the name of the ministry may give a clue as to the importance of wildlife to Namibia. Tourists come to Namibia to see the "Hairy and Scary," or the Big Five: Cape buffalo, black and white rhino, African elephants, lions, and leopards. Plains game animals such as zebra, oryx, springbok, common eland, kudu, and hartebeest are plentiful on farms and in national parks. Relative to other African countries, these species have larger populations and are less threatened in Namibia.

However, many species of wildlife were almost eradicated in Namibia in the mid-20th century. 40–50 years prior to Namibian independence, white livestock farmers commonly shot predators on their ranches to reduce predation of their cattle, sheep, and goats. In addition, farmers also killed all of the grazing and browsing wildlife, such as zebra, oryx, and kudu, that competed with their cattle, goats, and sheep for forage in this semiarid country. In fact, farms were sold with "wildlife free" labels if all game and predators had been removed. The farm would then sell for premium price, as it guaranteed a better income for the new owner.

By the 1970s, people in Namibia became concerned as the trend of wildlife eradication spread across the landscape. The country was losing its wildlife, and in 1975, Namibia passed the Nature Conservation Ordinance. The new set of laws allowed farmers to establish ownership of huntable game animals, which could be sold as live animals to other farmers or sold as meat to butchers and grocers. If you visit a butcher shop in Namibia, you will find the traditional beef, lamb, and pork, but you may also find zebra, oryx, common ostrich, and springbok steaks.

The dynamic now in place in Namibia is an example of **privatization** of wildlife, as the landowner owns individual animals and makes decisions as to their fate. Further, Namibia is an example of full **commercialization** of wildlife, as animals are given economic value in markets. The regulated strategy worked for conservation. Now, kudu and oryx compete for space with cattle on the ranch, because the farmer may make money on both. In the driest parts of Namibia, wildlife was much more adapted to the dry landscape than cattle or sheep, and some farmers today have removed livestock from their farms or severely reduced their domestic livestock herds in favor of wild animals. Farmers have constructed lodges for hunters and nature seekers, and ecotourism in Namibia competes with mining and agriculture for the top industry in the country. Wildlife is back on the landscape, and Namibia is considered a true conservation success story (Powell 2010). In fact, wildlife biologists estimate that 80% of all wildlife in Namibia now exists outside of national parks and other protected areas (Schalkwyk et al. 2010).

There are potential benefits to tourism for the funding of government's wildlife management actions in Namibia as well, but these are not currently realized. Two decades ago, the Ministry of Environment and Tourism received 25% of the admission fees to national parks, such as the world-famous Etosha National Park. The remaining 75% of the admission fees simply went to the general treasury of Namibia. Planners called for an increase in the proportion of entrance fees that were returned to be directly invested in conservation. However, as global economic crises emerged, the government changed the ministry's allocation of entrance fees to 0%.

Funds generated from international hunters are split among three main destinations. The hunting guide and landowner or communal group receive the largest portion of the income from hunts, but a portion of any revenue from wildlife and wildlife products is allocated to the Game Products Fund (Game Products Fund Act, 1997). These funds are used for wildlife conservation and community-based conservation programs. However, the amount of funding returned to the ministry pales in comparison to the levels of funding enjoyed by license sales in the US. This decentralized funding for conservation is a characteristic of Namibian wildlife management that incentivizes landowners to care for wildlife, but the system does not provide for support of extensive management programs that might be directed by the ministry. Plans for the future to support national parks and other government-level action plans for wildlife in Namibia call for more efficient use of funds by government officials, an increase in the proportion of entrance fees that come back to the agency, and development of new funding streams for the ministry.

When Namibia became independent, the new government established **communal conservancies**, regional communal lands for indigenous Namibians. Namibia now has 83 designated conservancies, which are registered with the Ministry of Environment and Tourism. A local, elected committee makes decisions on behalf of all community members, and in many cases the sale of meat and safari hunts of wildlife on the conservancy supports at least half of the income used for schools, roads, and other conservancy projects. Similar to the group ownership of wildlife by residents of states in the US, conservancy members are vested with joint responsibility for their

FIGURE 2.8 Skulls and horns in the process of preparation for taxidermy mounts in Windhoek, Namibia. Photo by the author.

wildlife resource. Individuals cannot access the wildlife for their own purposes unless permitted by the group. Wildlife is a critical resource for residents, so meat provided by trophy hunting on the conservancy is distributed to its members. Through this process, poaching in conservancy areas has dramatically decreased, and populations of game animals have increased on communal conservancies.

Some Americans may be initially repulsed at the photo of preparations in a taxidermy shop in Namibia (Figure 2.8). Certainly, the photo is evidence of the grand scale at which hunting takes place in Namibia. However, you now know the entire story, and this photo may represent a success story in Namibia. It is a story of high-intensity management, with much more wildlife monitoring than takes place in the United States on private farms and ranches. Namibian ranches are often over 7,000 ha (17,000 acres), so even wildlife behind the tallest border fences are still "wild." But farmers pay attention to their animals, and they manage them by supplementing salt and rotating active water points to encourage rotational grazing.

Farmers can make money from the wildlife on their farm from consumptive and non-consumptive uses. On the consumptive side of the ledger, wildlife are used in the regulated, safari hunting industry each year. The system is sustainable because no farmer wants their kudu to disappear, just as a cattle farmer would never sell their entire herd of cattle (Schalkwyk et al. 2010). Sustainable wildlife populations on farms ensure continual income from meat sales, hunts, and non-consumptive ecotourism such as photo safaris and wildlife viewing.

Other unique features of management in Namibia:

- **Quotas for hunting:** Farmers and groups of indigenous people who live on "communal conservancies" monitor their wildlife with game counts each year. The counts are reported to the ministry, which then provides a quota for each species that may be hunted. Licensed guides, called "professional hunters," bring foreign hunters to farms for hunts that may involve costs of $300–$500 per day for guiding and $400–$2000 for each game animal hunted.
- **Controversial rhino, elephant, and lion hunts:** Namibia has been in the news during recent years because of opportunities for international hunters that bring large sums of money to local community conservation efforts yet target species of international concern. In 2013, a North American hunter paid $350,000 for a black rhino hunt. The rhino was a wild, older, post-breeding male that was not useful for breeding efforts in Namibia. Opponents argued that killing a species of conservation concern was not logical, or that the animal could have been used to support tourism income by moving it to a private nature reserve for use in photo safaris.
- **No public hunting areas:** Namibia has many national parks. In fact, it claims to be the only country in the world with 100% of its coastline protected as a national park. However, there are no public hunting areas in Namibia. Locals must find a farmer who will let them hunt for meat. A license is not required. Although the farmer has ownership of their wildlife, they must have permission from the ministry to remove a specific number of animals based on the farmers' game count data.
- **Fence types establish ownership:** Namibia's laws allow ownership of huntable wildlife on farms, but ownership depends on the type of fence. On farms with a normal, 1 meter fence, the landowner owns the game animals that cannot jump over the fence (non-jumping game include springbok, hartebeest, and oryx). Farmers may double the height of the fence to 2 meters ("game fence," or "high fence"). These farmers now own all game animals on their land. The reasoning for this rule is that farmers with short fences could potentially overhunt animals such as greater kudu or common eland that can easily jump normal fences and enter from the neighbors' property. In effect, the fence law is based on whether a farmer has an open or closed population of a species on their land. Game fences are expensive to build, and a landscape with tall fences inhibits natural movement of wildlife.
- **Definition of wildlife:** "'Wild animal' ... means any vertebrate (including any bird, fish and reptile), whether kept or bred in captivity or elsewhere,

belonging to a non-domestic species and the habitat of which is in the Republic of South Africa or Namibia" (from the Namibian Conservation Ordinance of 1975).

Southeast Asia: Thailand

Population: 68,414,135
Area: 513,120 sq. km
Population Density: 133 people/sq. km
Percent National Parks: 19%
Gini Index/Rank (1: most disparity): 45.0/43rd of 157
Average Annual Salary: $3,277
Unemployment Rate: 0.7%

Thailand is a progressive country in Southeast Asia, characterized by a dense population and intense agriculture that occurs on farm plots of <8 ha. The Thai people have a deep and complex history, marked most significantly by the influence of Buddhism as a religion and way of life.

Thailand sits in the middle of the Indo-Burma biodiversity hotspot, recognized because of high biodiversity and loss of native, tropical wildlife habitat.

Thailand is a constitutional monarchy, and it is not possible for an outsider to understand the depth to which the Thai people respect their kings. Still, the actual government in Thailand has been led by a series of military-appointed leaders, each promoted following a coups d'etat. Through the chaotic political dynamics, the military has stayed loyal to the king, and the general structure of government has remained similar. Voting in elections is compulsory, but frequent charges of vote buying give a unique flavor to democracy in Thailand.

In 1896, Thailand formed the Royal Forest Department, which evolved into the modern Department of National Parks, Wildlife, and Plant Conservation. This

QUICK COMPREHENSION CHECK

How did ownership of wildlife in Namibia affect landowners' decisions about shooting and removing wildlife from their ranches?

Would the Namibian model be politically acceptable in the United States? Explain why or why not.

Why do you think private landowners in the United States are less likely to conduct counts of wildlife on their property than Namibia landowners?

agency carries out the mission for management of wildlife in Thailand. In the 1960s, national parks were set aside to reduce loss of forests. Almost 25% of forests in Thailand are protected by law, but over one million people live within the boundaries of the protected areas and rely on the forest for food and resources. Such needs are at odds with the legal distinction for national parks, which states that no economic benefit may be derived from protected lands.

There is no legal hunting in Thailand, which stems from the high population density and lack of any potential game animals outside of the protected national parks. Fishing with a rod does not require a permit, so the main source of income for the management of wildlife and national parks is the entrance fees associated with national parks (Laungaramsri 2002). Mismanagement and corruption often mean that fees do not reach their intended destination.

Attitudes toward wildlife and natural habitats are heavily influenced by culture and religion in Thailand. Early Thai people saw forests as mystical, unordered areas, and the culture rewarded a person who worked to clear the forest for useable agriculture or urban areas (Johnson 1992). The mystical nature of forests can be seen in the

FIGURE 2.9 Anglers legally fish at a reservoir without permits and with multiple rods and reels in Thailand. Photo by the author.

reverence for the life of the Buddha, who was in natural forests for the main events of his life. Trees became a sacred symbol, and Buddhists tend to see other objects (including plants and animals) as having souls. A news story from 2016 exemplifies the Buddhist regard for animals: A Bangkok resident was sitting on a toilet in his house when a large python emerged from the plumbing and bit the man in a rather tender area of his body. Although this episode might have ended with the snake's death in the United States, neighbors and emergency staff managed to separate man and snake. Workmen destroyed the toilet so that the snake could be freed, and the python was released in a local park.

The respect for other animals is promoted in this selection from the Dhammapada, a collection of poetic Buddhist scriptures:

> *All living things fear being beaten with clubs. All living things fear being put to death.*
>
> *Putting oneself in the place of the other, Let no one kill nor cause another to kill.*
>
> —Dhammapada 129

In modern Thailand, we see evidence of the conflict between traditional culture and the modern world, which is often at odds with Buddhist philosophy. Economic benefit drives a lucrative poaching and illegal pet trade that exists in the view of the public in markets in Bangkok.

Since the 1960s, in an attempt to be progressive, national parks in Thailand have been managed in "set aside" ways that mimicked the national park system in the US. The flaw in that approach has been that large groups of Thai people lived within the borders of the national parks when they were established. By initially ignoring the needs of their rural citizens in favor of establishing the parks for more wealthy citizens and international visitors, the government created conflict and most likely caused local extirpations of wildlife species that had been goals of the land protection program. Thailand's government maintains a very powerful grip on the country from the national level, but some efforts since the 1990s to decentralize conservation decisions in a limited number of situations has given more power to local residents (International Centre for Environmental Management 2003). The future of wildlife conservation in Thailand will most likely revolve around the ability to provide economic security for lower-income, rural residents and the effectiveness of enforcing wildlife law under the dynamic political system.

Other unique features of management in Thailand:

- **Tourism impact:** The ecotourism industry has grown by 10–15% per year since the 1990s and represents a growing source of income for private and government investment in conservation.
- **NGO presence:** Non-governmental organizations, or NGOs, mainly the World Wildlife Fund and Wildlife Conservation Society, play a large role in monitoring species of conservation concern in Thailand. NGOs are more numerous in neighboring countries, but foreign efforts to mobilize local conservation scientists outside of the low-capacity government agencies are important for conservation in Thailand. The organizations also play vital roles in the facilitation of many community-based conservation efforts with local groups.
- **Lack of legal backing for management plans:** One unique feature of Thai wildlife law is that it is largely a list of prohibitions (no hunting, no logging forests, no wildlife trade, etc.). There is little legal context to require the management of habitat to support species of conservation concern. When a management plan is developed, it may be left unimplemented. Park managers, who are often assigned for political reasons, operate in an ad hoc fashion, and then may be quickly replaced. The dynamic leaves little opportunity for a true management process (planning, action, and monitoring) to occur.
- **Definition of wildlife:** "'Wild Animals' refers to all kinds of animals including terrestrial, aquatic, and winged animals as well as insects, which by nature are born and live in the forest or water" (from the Wild Animal Reservation and Protection Act 1992).

QUICK COMPREHENSION CHECK

Explain how religious beliefs in Thailand result in lower funding for wildlife management?

Central America: Guatemala

Population: 16,342,900
Area: 108,889 sq. km
Population Density: 150 people/sq. km

Percent Protected Areas: 32%
Gini Index/Rank (1: most disparity): 53.0/11th of 157
Average Annual Salary: $2,740
Unemployment Rate: 2.4%

Guatemala is nestled in the middle of the Mesoamerica biodiversity hotspot, so named by conservation organizations because of its high species richness, threatened by levels of habitat loss of over 80% of the native habitat. "Guatemala" has its derivations in Mayan words that describe a "place of many trees."

Guatemala's representational democracy has the trappings of a modern democratic system, but corruption and power struggles within the political ranks have led the Guatemalan system to be labeled a "hybrid regime." Such nations experience critical irregularities during elections that regularly move the system from a fair and free democracy. The Guatemalan government is known to have applied pressure on political opponents, and the result is widespread corruption and often anemic law enforcement. The latter characteristics affect the enforcement of wildlife laws as well.

The Mayan indigenous culture is important to understanding the structure of wildlife management and conservation in Guatemala. Guatemala is home to over 20 unique groups with Mayan heritage that share an intrinsic bond with nature, which shapes the way individuals see forests and natural resources. Personal autonomy is a cultural tradition. A common Guatemala expression is "Cada cabeza es un mundo" (each person's head is its own world). That is, it is difficult to understand the motivations of others, so it is important to respect the other's independence and ability to make decisions without constraint.

Hunting is regulated by the General Hunting Law (*Ley General de Caza*) and the Law of Protected Areas (*Ley de Áreas Protegidas*). Wildlife or wildlife products (including meat) cannot be traded without authorization. Landowners may register with the government to legally hunt on their land, but the process to hunt legally is quite convoluted and devolved. Guatemala does not have regional or national daily bag limits for game species, so landowners must submit annual requests to The National Council for Protected Areas (Consejo Nacional de Áreas Protegidas, CONAP) to take a specified number of individual game animals. Landowners are then able to permit others to hunt on their land, including international guests who pay for the privilege. The fees for the permits and portions of the access fees for guests are returned to a fund for CONAP to use in management. Although higher-end hunting guides may follow most of the regulations because of their visible activities, many landowners do not register when hunting for their own use.

One-third of Guatemala is now set aside as national parks as part of a concerted effort to provide corridors through Mesoamerica (Grandia 2007). The Mayan Biosphere Reserve covers the northern one-fifth of the country. The national laws prohibit hunting within the national parks, biological reserves, and biotopes, the core areas of the biosphere reserves, natural monuments, cultural monuments, historical parks, scenic views and some private natural reserves. Hunting in Guatemala is generally an ancestral, subsistence practice, which is decreasing as the rural communities become modernized. Subsistence hunting is allowed within the "multiple-use zones" of protected areas. CONAP requires subsistence hunters to register, like estate owners, but law enforcement is lacking. Illegal hunting, trapping and trading of wild species, such as the endangered scarlet macaw, is one of the largest threats to biodiversity in Guatemala.

Guatemala is not an affluent country. Government agencies tasked with managing natural resources do not have large budgets, and most government initiatives are currently severely underfunded. Unlike the United States, the amount of money received for hunting and angling license fees is relatively small. Even entrance fees to national parks in Guatemala are relatively inexpensive (Fujisaki 2002), and the trickle of funds do not support the management of the parks. The Guatemalan government agencies tasked with wildlife management typically focus on protected areas. CONAP, the National Institute of Forests (Instituto Nacional de Bosques, INAB), and the National Fund for the Conservation of Nature (Fondo Nacional para la Conservación de la Naturaleza, FONACON) all have important yet underfunded roles in management decisions for habitat and wildlife. These agencies function as the top-down administration of wildlife management.

Another model for wildlife management in Guatemala is a "bottom-up" model: local communities are often empowered (remember the cultural emphasis on autonomy) to set wildlife policy and planning at the regional or community level. The strain on national-level agency budgets means that most of the sources of funding for wildlife management and conservation in Guatemala come from the private sector (including tourism) as well as international partners and donors (e.g., European Union, USAID, and Norwegian Agency for Development Cooperation).

Non-governmental organizations (NGOs), such as the World Wildlife Fund, the Nature Conservancy, Wildlife Conservation Society, and Conservation International, have taken leadership roles in Guatemala as well. These NGO initiatives for wildlife management and conservation routinely pour millions of dollars toward community-based projects; in essence, NGOs co-manage many protected areas with the government agencies. Guatemalan-based NGOs (e.g., Defenders of Nature Foundation and Foundation for Ecodevelopment and Conservation) receive international funds for important projects within the country as well. Such a model is useful in countries where government corruption and bureaucracy have the potential to mismanage funds directed towards top-down approaches.

Other unique features of management in Guatemala:

- **Funding wildlife research and protection:** The Private Protection and Development Fund (El Fondo Privativo de Protección y Fomento) for wildlife receives funds from permit sales, fines from illegal hunting, seizures from illegal wildlife trafficking, donations, and the general legislative budget process. Money from the fund may only be used for the formation of reserves, habitat restoration, biological research, and similar activities that support the "preservation of the resource."
- **Red List:** Similar to the IUCN Red List at the international level, Guatemala's wildlife management agency, CONAP, publishes a Red List of threatened wildlife and plant species whose harvest, commercialization, and transportation is prohibited.
- **National bird**: Guatemala protects the resplendent quetzal (a member of the trogon family) from capture. Even with protection, the species is listed as "near threatened" by the IUCN because of forest habitat loss.
- **Definition of wildlife:** "'Wildlife' includes: animals that live under natural, native and migratory conditions that subsist freely and outside the control of man, within the national territory" (from Ley General de Caza (General Hunting Law), Decreto Número 8–70).

Back to the United States

Our world is incredibly unique and complex. Biologists work around the globe in pursuit of very similar goals—maintaining and supporting populations of wildlife. But, as you have seen, we have developed contrasting approaches for wildlife management in a variety of cultural, political, and historical situations.

Perhaps international conservation work sounds thrilling to you. If so, you clearly should have knowledge of the complexities of international wildlife management and the diverse approaches taken to achieve a common goal. Biologists should be well-versed in the laws, traditions, and assumptions made in the context of management decisions for wildlife in their local country, but knowledge of global models may be advantageous in our modern era of global communication and connectivity.

Might ideas from other countries have use in the United States? Consider the dynamic of predators such as mountain lions, wolves, and bears that are returning to many landscapes in the United States. For many wildlife biologists, the emergence of predators is a new situation and decision context. A prudent step during the development of management options in the US might include an assessment of how our colleagues in other countries deal with human-wildlife conflict in predator situations.

Acknowledgements for reviews of international overviews: Brett Sandercock, Nils Odendaal, Heidi Bass, Sigi Bass, Gabriella Palomo, Lucia Corral, George Gale, Mike Swan, Wanlop Chutipong, and Dusit Ngoprasert.

QUICK COMPREHENSION CHECK

How has southern Africa worked to manage predator interactions? Would landowners in the United States tolerate the presence of mountain lions if they could benefit from people coming to hunt them or view them?

WRAPPING UP

Based on the information we have covered in this chapter, how would you advise Angela in our problem case as she considers the UK and other international destinations for hunting?

How would you respond to someone who claims the North American Model is the best model of wildlife management in the world?

Decision-Making on the Ground

1: Elephants and Ivory: Strategies to Control Poaching

African elephants were listed as an Appendix 1 (the most threatened level) species on CITES in 1990. Since then, elephants in four countries (Botswana, Namibia, Zimbabwe, and South Africa) have been upgraded to Appendix 2. Elephant populations are threatened by poaching. Poachers kill elephants for their tusks to sell as ivory products.

The regulations on ivory trade are complex. International trade from countries for which elephants are listed as CITES Appendix 1 is banned, but domestic trade within countries is not governed by CITES. Countries such as the United States have bans on the import of ivory from any country, with the exception of legally obtained hunting trophies. However, the United Kingdom does not currently ban the import of ivory.

Conservation biologists have conflicting views on the approach to use to reduce poaching, with regard to ivory sales. The conflicting views all boil down to interpretations of simple economic (supply and demand) forecasting. Some conservationists believe that the ivory ban has driven up prices, which has made poaching very lucrative—thus, the answer would be to lower the ban and allow ivory from elephants that have died of natural causes to create a market with lower prices because of higher supply. Opponents of this theory point to the response to a legal bulk sale of ivory in 2008 that was designed to flood the market, which should have reduced poaching. In fact, poaching increased immediately after the 2008 sales event. Economists on this side of the argument suggest that removing the ban will create new markets for ivory, and poaching will continue to be a lucrative endeavor.

APPLICATION, ANALYSIS, SYNTHESIS, AND EVALUATION

Consider the countries where elephants are still found. Describe your perception of the decentralization of their wildlife management model. Do they have strong national ministries with good law enforcement teams?

How might the economic reward for assistance given to a poacher affect the decision of a poor rural resident to provide the locations of species of wildlife such as rhinos or elephants?

What do you feel is the answer to the ivory ban issue? Should the UK ban ivory? Should all countries drop the ban on ivory? Explain your answers in light of economic pressures.

2: International Fisheries: Building Collaborations in Open Waters?

Compared to terrestrial wildlife and protected areas, ocean fish have very little protection. In terms of area, 1.2% of the area of the world's oceans has received the status of Marine Protected Areas. The status does not effectively protect fish, because 90% of the Marine Protected Areas allow fishing. From a regulatory perspective, fisheries regulations worldwide are inadequate to protect many species of fish. Sustainable levels of harvest are often exceeded.

The "High Seas" further complicate the regulation and area deficiencies of fish protection. The high seas exist beyond the narrow strip of ocean that falls within the territories and Exclusive Economic Zones of coastal countries. 64% of the world's ocean area is classified as high seas, which are international waters used as a commons. A few agreements have been established for High Seas use, but there are few regulations for commercial fishing on the High Seas. If you think law enforcement is difficult on land, welcome to the high seas where law enforcement is difficult, and many nations turn a blind eye to fishing activities.

Countries are required to cooperate to manage fish stocks in the high seas, and a recent political structure has been developed for this purpose—**regional fisheries management organizations**. These regional collaborations between countries that share areas of the High Seas allows protection strategies to be developed. Of course, the strategies and their effectiveness are only as good as the efforts from the participating countries.

APPLICATION, ANALYSIS, SYNTHESIS, AND EVALUATION

Consider the economic forces that we described within individual countries under various models of wildlife management. Now, apply the principles to a multi-nation effort. Where would the power and responsibility for decisions lie? Where would funding come from?

Assume you are a team member from the United States attending a regional fisheries management organization meeting for the Northwest Atlantic Fisheries Organization. You notice that the Republic of Korea is a member of this organization, and Korean ships are involved in fishing in the High Seas in the region. Review what you know about the government and people of Korea. Consider their interests in securing fish for their country and exports to sustain the country. What are some key factors that you might list as a way of getting to know your partners and understand their potential positions in debates? What do you imagine the Koreans are listing about the United States?

Sources of Information and Further Reading

Beddington, J. R., Agnew, D. J., and Clark, C. W. "Current problems in the management of marine fisheries." *Science* 316, no. 5832 (2007): 1713–1716.

Brainerd, S. M., and Kaltenborn, B. "The Scandinavian model: A different path to wildlife management." *The Wildlife Professional* 4, no. 3 (2010): 52–56.

Central Intelligence Agency. *The World Factbook, 2017.* Washington, DC: Central Intelligence Agency, 2017.

Fisheries and Oceans Canada. "Regional Fisheries Management Organizations." 2016. http://www.dfo-mpo.gc.ca/international/dip-rfmo-eng.htm

Fujisaki, I. "Management of Resources-Based Tourism at Tikal National Park in Northern Guatemala." *The George Wright Forum* 10, no. 2 (2002): 77–86.

Grandia, L. "Between Bolivar and Bureaucracy: The Mesoamerican Biological Corridor." *Conservation and Society* 5 (2007): 478–503.

Hongslo, E., Hovik, S., Zachrisson, A., and Aasen Lundberg, A. K. "Decentralization of conservation management in Norway and Sweden—Different translations of an international trend." *Society & Natural Resources* 29, no. 8 (2016): 998–1014.

International Centre for Environmental Management. "*Lessons learned in Cambodia, Lao PDR, Thailand and Vietnam.*" *Review of Protected Areas and Development in the Lower Mekong River Region, Indooroopilly, Queensland, Australia.* 2003.

Johnson, L. K. "The Buddhist Perception of Nature: Implications for Forest Conservation in Thailand." *The Trumpeter, Journal of Ecosophy* 9, no. 1 (1992).

Laungaramsri, P. "On the Politics of Nature Conservation in Thailand." *Kyoto Review of South-East Asia* 2, no. 10 (2002).

Longrigg, R. *English Squire and his Sport*. London: Michael Joseph, Ltd., 1977.

Naidoo, R., Weaver, L. C., Stuart-Hill, G. and Tagg, J. "Effect of biodiversity on economic benefits from communal lands in Namibia." *Journal of Applied Ecology* 48 (2011): 310–316.

Organ, J. F., Geist, V., Mahoney, S. P., Williams, S., Krausman, P. R., Batcheller, G. R., Decker, T.A., Carmichael, R., Nanjappa, P., Regan, R., Medellin, R. A., Cantu, R., McCabe, R. E., Craven, S., Vecellio, G. M., and D. J. Decker. "The North American model of wildlife conservation." *The Wildlife Society Technical Review* 12, no. 4 (2012).

Organisation for Economic Co-operation and Development. "*OECD Statistics*." 2017. Accessed 15 February 2018. http://stats.oecd.org/

Powell, L. A. *Farming with wildlife: conservation and ecotourism on private lands in Namibia*. Lincoln, NE: Lulu Publishing, 2010.

Schalkwyk, D. L. V., McMillin, K. W., Witthuhn, R. C., and Hoffman, L. C. "The Contribution of Wildlife to Sustainable Natural Resource Utilization in Namibia: A Review." *Sustainability* 2, no. 11 (2010): 3479–3499.

Seguya, A., Martin R., Sekar N., Hsiang S., Di Minin E., and MacMillan D. "Debate: Would a legal ivory trade save elephants or speed up the massacre?" *The Guardian* (2016). https://www.theguardian.com/environment/2016/oct/01/debate-can-legal-ivory-trade-save- elephants

Tapper, S. *Game heritage: an ecological review from shooting and gamekeeping records*. Fordingbridge, UK: Game Conservancy, Ltd., 1992.

Teer, J. G. "Trends in ownership of wildlife resources: who owns wildlife anyway?" In *Tenure and sustainable use*. Cambridge, UK: IUCN (1999): 63–70 .

Tyler, N. J. C., Turi, J. M., Sundset, M. A., Bull, K. S., Sara, M. N., Reinert, E., Oskal, N., Nellemann, C., McCarthy, J. J., Mathiesen, S. D. and Martello, M. L. "Saami reindeer pastoralism under climate change: applying a generalized framework for vulnerability studies to a sub-arctic social-ecological system." *Global Environmental Change* 17, no. 2 (2007): 191–206.

United States Fish and Wildlife Service. "CITES & Elephants: What is the 'global ban' on ivory trade?" 2013. https://www.fws.gov/le/pdf/CITES-and-Elephant-Conservation.pdf

United States Fish and Wildlife Service. "National Survey of Fishing, Hunting, and Wildlife-Associated Recreation: National Overview." Department of Interior, US Fish and Wildlife Service. 2016.

Voyles, L., and L. Chase. "The State Conservation Machine. Association of Fish & Wildlife Agencies and the Arizona Game and Fish Department." 2017.

World Bank. "Terrestrial protected areas." 2017. Accessed 15 February 2018. https://data.worldbank.org/indicator/ER.LND.PTLD.ZS

World Wildlife Fund. "Blue Planet: Open Ocean." 2017. http://wwf.panda.org/about_our_earth/blue_planet/open_ocean/#high_seas

Image Credits

Fig. 2.3: Source: https://www.nrcm.org/documents/publiclandownership.pdf.

Fig. 2.5: Source: http://www.pacgeo.org/layers/geonode:tm_world_borders_0_3.

Fig. 2.6: Source: https://commons.wikimedia.org/wiki/File:August-1922-m-mcdonald-a-member-of-lord-woolavingtons-house-party-a-picture-id3432611.jpg.

Fig. 2.7: Copyright © Nasjonalbiblioteket (CC by 2.0) at https://commons.wikimedia.org/wiki/File:Lapper_og_Reinsdyr.jpg.

SECTION II

Making Tough Management Decisions

CHAPTER THREE

Decision-Making Frameworks

Learning Outcomes

After participating in learning experiences related to this chapter, students should be able to:

- Select the decision-making processes most appropriate to specific situations ranging from sudden emergencies to recurring situations.
- Describe common human tendencies that stand in the way of making robust decisions.
- Propose methods that a manager may use to develop a team that works effectively to make useful decisions for a wildlife management agency.
- Develop a simple expert decision system.
- Incorporate uncertainties and utility values into a decision tree system.
- Describe the concept of adaptive management and propose techniques to improve the success of an adaptive management system.

A One-Minute Summary

Wildlife management involves decision-making, and decisions in natural resource management may be complex. Managers often consider multiple alternatives at the same time, and society may ascribe socioeconomic values to outcomes that must be incorporated in the decision-making process. In some situations, a manager may be uncertain about how a management action will affect the ecosystem or wildlife population.

Humans are prone to making poor decisions, but a manager may adopt behaviors that account for human behavior and result in more effective decisions. Many decisions can be made with guided intuition, while a small set require formal processes to reach a justified, robust decision. Wildlife biologists may pull from decision frameworks used in business and the military to solve similarly complex scenarios. A decision process, known by the acronym *PrOACT*, requires decision-makers to define a problem and set objectives before considering alternative actions and the consequences or tradeoffs involved with those potential responses. A manager should use basic PrOACT ideals during quick, intuitive decisions, and a formal decision process may be used when time is available to evaluate a high-risk decision.

Decisions made by "gut," or intuition, may be improved by developing useful networks of colleagues to check consequences of initial ideas, taking the opportunity to learn from past experiences, and practicing with scenarios as part of training for management positions. In an extreme emergency decision context, the process of satisficing requires the user to find one alternative that meets minimum requirements but does not require extensive comparisons of alternatives to find the most optimal response.

Structured decision-making is useful for complex situations that allow for more time and resources. Expert systems may guide decisions in contexts that have little uncertainty, while decision trees account for uncertainty and values in a decision process. Adaptive management is a type of structured decision-making process that relies heavily on monitoring and learning during recurring, complex decisions.

Principles for Your Toolkit

The decision process: The six-step decision process that may be applied to management scenarios is known by its acronym, *PrOACT*. The steps prior to making and implementing a decision include problem identification, stating objectives, identifying alternatives, describing consequences, and considering tradeoffs (Figure 3.1).

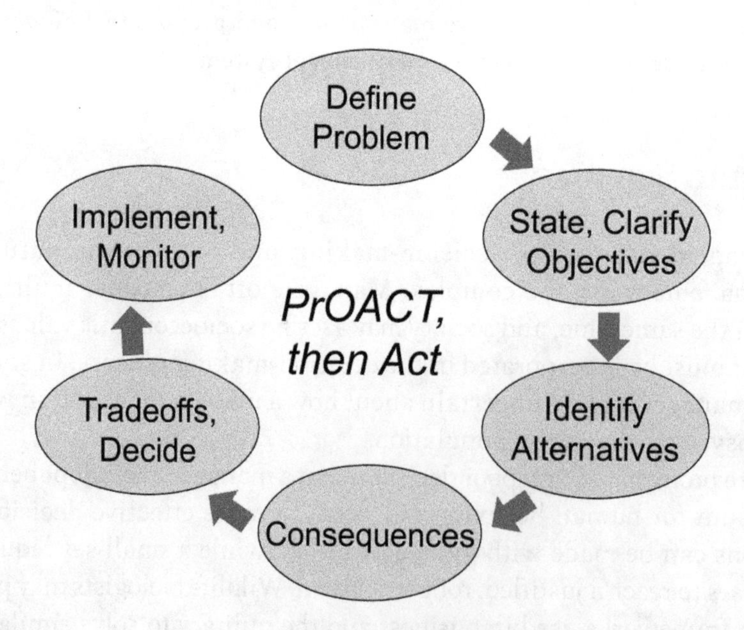

FIGURE 3.1 A six-step, structured decision process, known as PrOACT.

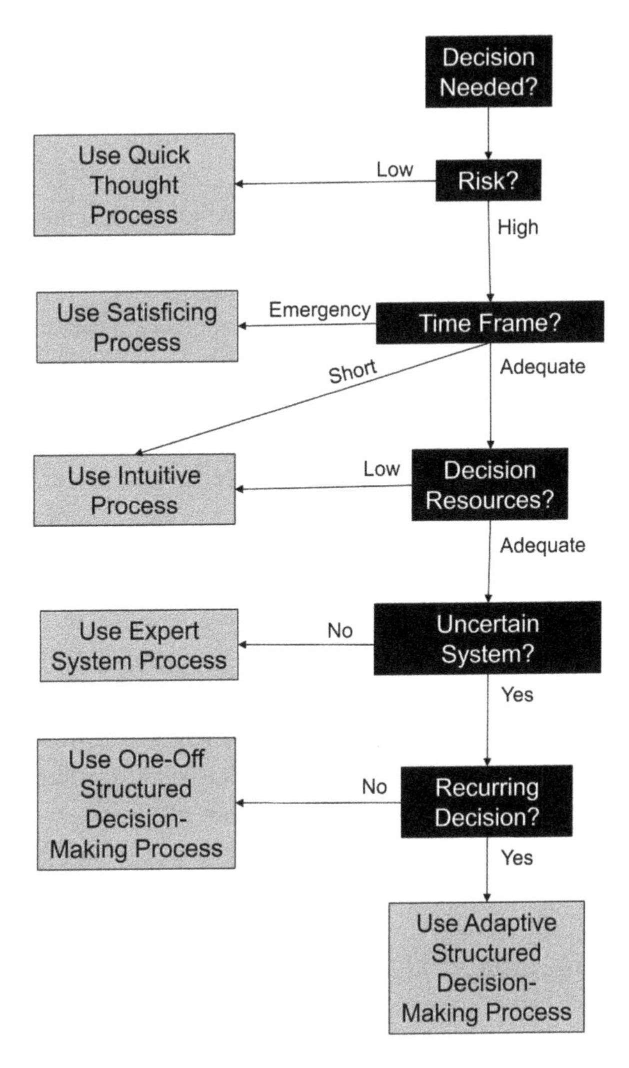

FIGURE 3.2 A decision key to determine which type of decision-making process should be used in a management situation.

Frameworks for any situation: Decision scenarios come in all flavors. Depending on the risk involved, time allowed, resources available, the amount of uncertainty, and the potential for recurrence of the decision in the future, a manager has many choices for decision frameworks (Figure 3.2). All of these processes result in decisions that are more effective, transparent, and defendable than off-the-cuff decisions.

A Problem: Adaptive Management at the Refuge?

Sara Whitefeather was on her first day as manager of the Pond Creek National Wildlife Refuge in Arkansas. She understood that the refuge's primary purpose was to provide habitat for migratory birds, especially waterfowl. After a thorough tour of the refuge, Sara was going through notes in files she received from the previous refuge manager, who was known for leaving short, cryptic messages. Two notes stood out:

> *"Priority One. Emergency Situation. Need to move quickly on a method to removal feral hogs from the refuge. Should have been done last year."*

> *"Move to formal adaptive management for bottomland hardwood forest wetlands."*

Normally, Sara was a methodical thinker, so the "emergency" note gave her a panic—she had never worked with feral hogs before, so how could she choose between possible responses so quickly? Her graduate intern peeked over her shoulder and saw the notes. "What is an 'adaptive management' process?" he asked.

Sara had been involved in an adaptive management plan in the forests of the Pacific Northwest, but this plan involved wetland water levels.

"Sit down," she told her intern. "We need to get started on both of these issues, today."

What would you need to know if you were the graduate intern to offer advice to the refuge manager on making an emergency decision about feral pigs? What information would you need if, like Sara, you were charged with setting up an adaptive management plan? By the time you finish this chapter, you should know the answer.

Terms and Definitions

Adaptive management: Structured, iterative process of robust decision-making in the face of uncertainty, with an aim to reduce uncertainty over time via system monitoring.

Anchoring: The use of an initial piece of information to make subsequent judgments.

Complexity (system): The state of having interconnecting parts or elements.

Decision trees: A structured decision support process that uses a tree-like model of a decision and its possible consequences and utilities.

Decision support system (DSS): Generally, the process and data required to assist with analysis and decision-making within an organization; in practice, DSS are often constructed in the form of an expert system.

Expert system: A process that makes use of expert knowledge to select a decision action.

Heuristic: A method used to enable a person to learn something.

Management: The process of setting strategies to deal with or control things or people.

Predictive models: A mathematical representation of the most important features of an ecological system that may be used with relative reliability to predict ecological states in the future.

Satisficing: A decision-making strategy in which the decision-maker searches through available alternatives until an acceptability threshold is met.

Stakeholder (management): A party that has interest in a decision or process.

Stereotyping: Use of a form of categorization that helps to simplify and systematize information.

Stochastic: A process that was randomly determined.

Structured Decision-Making: An approach to identifying alternatives, evaluating tradeoffs, and making decisions in complicated situations.

Tradeoffs (management): Qualities that increase or decrease depending on the selected management action.

Utility value: The relative satisfaction received from a given management outcome, often represented by the symbol, *R*.

Wildlife Management as Decision-Making

What do a businessperson, a farmer, and a wildlife biologist have in common? All are managers, and all have to make sets of decisions. The businessperson has to allocate human and financial resources to meet the company's objectives. The farmer is also running a business and makes many decisions that involve uncertainty. What price will corn receive in the fall? What will the cattle market do next year? When will the next disease threat emerge?

The job of a wildlife manager may be unique in the opportunities to engage with nature, but at its core, the management of a wildlife refuge, a fish hatchery, or a private lands office may be described as a continual set of decisions that are made to reach an objective. Those decisions can either be made well or poorly.

> *"Should we list a species as 'endangered'?"*
> *"How should we remove cedar trees to create open grasslands for songbirds?"*
> *"What harvest regulations should we set for an invasive fish species?"*

Managers make decisions when they contemplate how to design a management approach, develop the project, engage with their staff, and implement management action. A good resource manager makes decisions that are effective in reaching the goal. That is, **we will evaluate a decision by assessing the eventual outcome**.

Natural resource management decisions can be complex, which makes decision-making more difficult (Conroy and Carroll 2009):

- **There are often multiple decision options.** With regard to harvest of a fish species, should we allow take? If so, when? How many fish per day?
- **There are often subjective values to the decision.** How much do we value a particular species of marine fish? How much do we value the opportunity to view the coral reef community off the coast of St. Thomas while snorkeling? Is that value higher than the expense of upgrading the island's sewage system so that effluent does not damage the reef?
- **There are often uncertainties associated with our decisions.** If we spend tax dollars to attempt to introduce gray wolves into new areas, will we be successful? Do we understand what caused the decline of the species during previous years, so that we can be effective in the recovery plan?

Aldo Leopold, the father of modern wildlife management, never took a decision-making course, and some might argue that wildlife biologists have been making adequate decisions since the early part of the 20th century. Why, then, do we need to focus on special processes for decision-making?

Wildlife management has traditionally behaved in ways that suggested that our field was different than business or other high-stakes industries. In Leopold's era, wildlife managers were taught biology and given a set of management tools (e.g., prescribed burning, predator control) to apply in various situations, but their jobs often involved more administration and management than biology. Our profession hoped for the best—Leopold referred to game management as an "art" (defined as "creating something with imagination or skill"), an unfortunate choice of words that still echoes today (chapter 1)). Perhaps Leopold was trying to capture the range, from good to bad, of results of management decisions made by biologists who were not trained to use a decision process. In that context, wildlife management appeared to be an art form like drawing or painting; some biologists were naturally good managers, and some were not.

Decision-making is taught to students entering business or the military, and it is now a part of the modern wildlife curriculum. Fortunately, untrained decision-makers can become informed decision-makers through training and guided practice. Today's wildlife management profession is a high-stakes career choice. Tax funds must be spent wisely. Species recovery plans must be effective, or species may become extinct. As habitat disappears from the landscape, at levels of removal of which Leopold never dreamed, how we manage the remaining streams, wetlands, grasslands, and forests is highly critical to the presence of wildlife now and in the future. Many modern wildlife management decisions have high risk.

Acknowledging Human Tendencies

The fact of the matter is that people do not naturally make good decisions (Gregory and Keeney 2002). The first step to better decision-making is to acknowledge the dynamics that often stand in the way of good decisions. Social scientists have documented the following attributes about human behavior and decision-making. See if any of these apply in your personal life:

- **We tend to overestimate the probability of highly visible or sensational events.** For example, we are much more likely to purchase flood insurance after a 100-year flood event, when the likelihood of another flood is actually very low. But, our experience with a flood causes us to make a decision that is not logical. As humans, we tend to be too cautious.
- **We tend to give too much credence to previous efforts 'sunk' into projects.** Consider your family's oldest vehicle. You have spent a lot of money on that car or truck. So, we tend to decide to keep fixing it, rather than sell it and buy a new one. Our human tendency is to stay-the-course rather than admit we need to take a different approach.
- **We tend to think that decisions made by groups are good.** Keep this in mind during your team discussions in courses at university! In fact, many group decisions are not made in a logical manner—group decisions may be swayed by vocal idiots! Most people tend to become **anchored** on other's opinions—we may be swayed by public opinion, for example.
- **We do not learn from experience.** Social scientists find that time after time, people make decisions that do not build on past experiences. Our tendency to stay-the-course may be compounded when there are short time frames between decisions, or when there is a lack of adequate feedback. As an example of a time lag problem, if data from the 2017 hunting season is

QUICK COMPREHENSION CHECK

Consider recent decisions that you have made. Do you see any connections to the descriptions of human characteristics listed here?

not processed before decisions must be made for the 2018 hunting season, the time lag in availability of data creates a problem for decision-makers.

Our decision-making processes need to include frameworks that avoid these pitfalls, and we need to be able to take information from past decisions to guide future decisions. Since the 1990s, the wildlife management profession has embraced frameworks of **Structured Decision-Making** (SDM). One framework for SDM is **adaptive management**, which is relatively simple in concept but complex in application. SDM, as we will learn, provides a structured path to decision-making, which may improve the effectiveness of decisions that are complex.

However, not all decisions require full application of the formal frameworks that we will explore in this chapter (Keeney 2004). In fact, the vast majority of decisions that we make as human beings or wildlife managers have such **small consequences** that they require little or no thought, such as which route do you drive to get to school or what kind of paper should you purchase for the office copy machine (Figure 3.3). Other decisions are **no-brainers**, reflex decisions like remembering to brush your teeth in the morning or open the visitor center at the wildlife refuge at 8:00am each morning.

Our focus in this chapter is on the 10% of decisions that remain—decisions where we get stuck and pause to think about the proper way forward (Figure 3.3). Three possible missteps may happen at this point:

- We may procrastinate and extend the decision process until we have to make the decision too quickly with less thought than it deserves

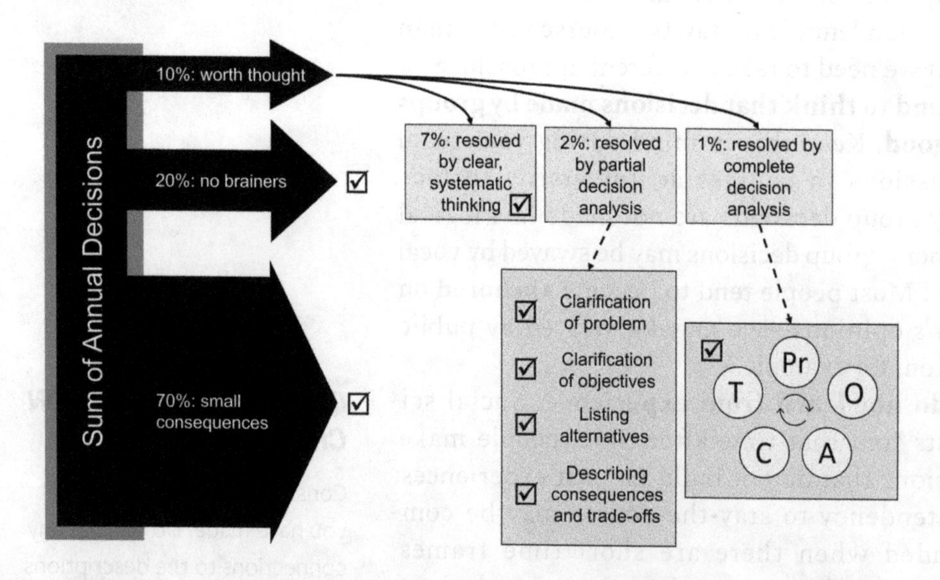

FIGURE 3.3 Hypothetical percentage of decision processes used to resolve decisions encountered by managers. Only a small percentage of decisions require formal, structured decision-making. Modified from Keeney (2004).

- We may make the decision quickly and not allow the appropriate time for reflection and consideration
- We may make the decision without clearly thinking through our goals, various options, tradeoffs, and consequences

It is important to note that psychologists and behavioral scientists suggest that ~7% of these remaining decisions may be solved just by thinking clearly about the decision—taking appropriate time and thinking through options and what they mean to your team (Figure 3.3). The remaining small portion (~3%) require application of either a portion of a formal decision-making process or a full decision-making process (SDM).

How do we recognize which decisions need our full attention? How to you think *more clearly*? We may start by evaluating decision situations by two important factors:

- How much risk is involved with the decision?
- How often do we have to make the decision?

Typically, decisions that we make daily or weekly or monthly (e.g., crew assignments) have less risk than decisions we make each year or every five years (e.g., updating endangered species status). However, not all long-interval decisions are risky (Figure 3.4).

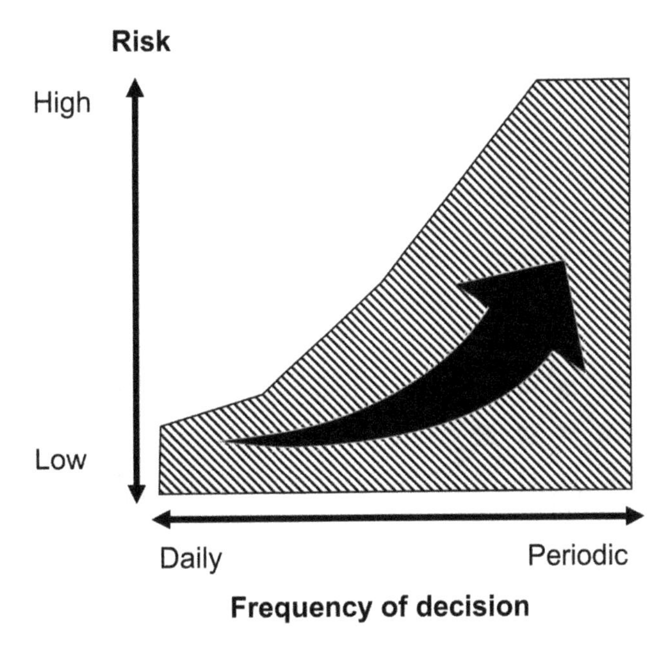

FIGURE 3.4 Relationship between risk and the frequency of decisions. Most decisions made daily have low risk, while periodic decisions may be low- or high-risk depending on circumstances.

Non-Linear Decisions: Using Your Gut

The universe often conspires to create emergency situations in which high- or low-risk decisions need to be made quickly, and many of these decisions must be made without perfect information. Wildlife management may borrow from other professions that face similar situations. The military, for example, needs their officers and commanders to make quick, high-stakes decisions on a regular basis in battle, and military leaders are trained to make good decisions using their gut. Battle-based decisions do not allow for time to implement a formal decision-making process, and often decisions in battle are made with less-than-perfect information (Figure 3.5). However, the decision must be made, as the risk for not taking action may be catastrophic.

Military leaders separate planning into three levels: **tactics**, **operations**, and **strategy** (Jablonsky 2001). This separation is a useful principle for wildlife managers. On the battlefield, "assault" or "ambush" are two examples of tactics, the combination of tools and forces designed for a particular situation and desired result. Wildlife biologists usually refer to tactics as **techniques**, which might include forest thinning or clear cutting. Operations describe when, where, how, and which tactics are to be carried out to meet an objective, and the overall, long-term objective is the strategy. For wildlife management, an agency might have a long-term strategy to increase the population size of a species of conservation concern that lives in forests, and the operations would describe how the agency can use management tools or tactics to achieve the population goal. It is critical for wildlife managers to learn strategic and operational planning, in addition to learning a set of tactics.

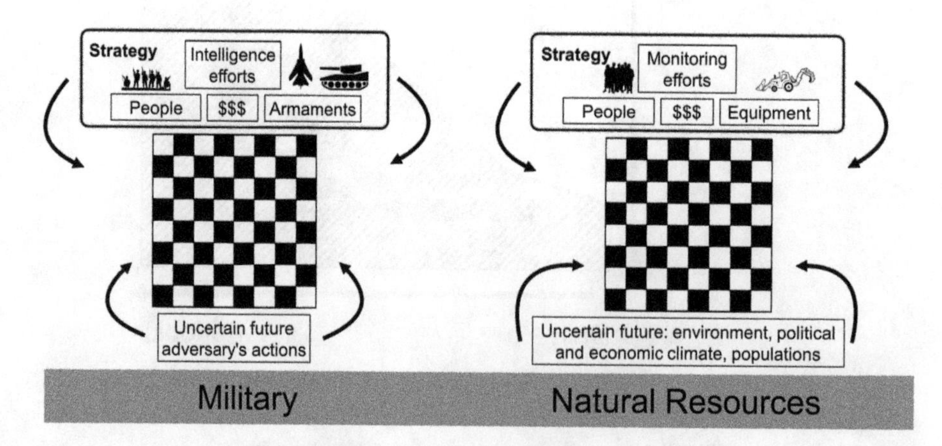

FIGURE 3.5 Comparison between strategies and resources available to military and natural resources decision-makers in their chess-like encounters with new problems and uncertain futures.

Under Fire: Effective, Quick Decisions in the Military

Satisficing is a common method for quick, effective decision-making by military leaders in an emergency situation. When time and logistical resources allow, it may be possible to use the SDM techniques we discuss later in the chapter to make a decision that is nearly perfect—one that provides an outcome that is as close to the desired objective as possible. Satisficing takes a different approach: the decision-maker sets some minimum level of aspiration and searches until an alternative is found that meets the minimum criteria. The leader rejects alternatives that do not help move past a threshold. Thus, the decision meets the quick deadline and makes forward progress; the decision may not be optimal, but it is robust and moves toward the goal. When making decisions in a fast-paced environment in this manner, it is therefore important to know the long-term goal and an acceptable timetable of movement towards the long-term goal. Satisficing eliminates the need to compare all possible alternatives and rank them by their potential outcomes (Franke 2011).

You most likely have used the method of satisficing if you have played video games. You and your team members may be engaged in a strategy to take a castle when, out of nowhere, a flying gremlin appears in front of your team. As your video character dives for cover to escape the balls of fire from the gremlin, you make a quick decision: what can I throw at the gremlin to eliminate this problem? Your choice of weapon in the video game may not be the optimal weapon to destroy gremlins, but your choice is most likely something that is at hand and that will do the job quickly before the gremlin reduces your health level to zero.

The Corporate Battlefield: Effective, Quick Decisions in Business

Corporations often need to make decisions quickly to keep ahead of competitors, to adjust in the face of a public relations crisis, or to take advantage of an emerging trend. A study of the decision speed of technology-based corporations described five characteristics of teams that make fast decisions, relative to teams that took longer to make similar decisions (Eisenhart 1989):

- Fast teams used more **real-time information.**
- Fast teams considered a greater number of **decision alternatives** at the same time.
- Fast teams had an **experienced expert or counselor** as a key member of the team (recognized and used expertise, so all members were not equal).
- Fast teams addressed possible conflicts during the decision-making process with **active conflict resolution techniques** (consensus with qualification technique ... CEO made the decision if the group did not agree).

- Fast teams **integrated related decisions into the decision-making process**, rather than methodically working through each in turn (e.g., had Plan B ready to go if Plan A did not work).

It turned out that teams that made faster decisions in a high-velocity environment tended to make better decisions. Therefore, the characteristics of teams that were organized to make quick decisions also led them to be more successful at meeting their goals.

The speed of decisions was based on (1) accelerating the speed of cognitive processing, (2) constructing smooth group dynamics, and (3) having the confidence to act upon the decision.

Teams improved the speed of cognitive processing during decisions with the use of real-time information, the discussion of alternatives, the presence of experts, and integrated discussions of related decisions. Smooth group dynamics were more likely because of the use of real-time information, acknowledgement of wisdom from experts/counselors, and an active process to address conflicts. Confidence in decisions was heightened by considering as many alternatives as possible, relying on experienced experts, and integrating multiple decisions into a decision process.

Drama in the workplace is often the theme of social media memes, and personal interactions can be important to decision-making. A framework of decision-making that embraces and acknowledges human emotion is critical to efficient decision-making. Frustration, distrust, loyalty, confidence, and anxiety may affect the speed at which the decision-making process occurs. Emotional biases could be relieved by addressing conflicts, establishing experts, and following a process that assessed alternatives and by-products of the present decision (Eisenhart 1989). Clearly, the most important role of the leader of a decision-making team may be to establish the process by which the team will function.

QUICK COMPREHENSION CHECK

If you were asked to lead a group of five biologists to make a management decision, what are three actions you could take as you form the group and work with your team members to improve the decisions made by your group?

Gutting It out with Heuristics

How do military and business leaders make quick, effective decisions with imperfect information? Individuals who routinely make decisions in the presence of uncertainty or incomplete information rely on **heuristics**, a process of mental shortcuts designed to reduce complexity to create a simpler decision environment (Franke 2011). Wildlife managers may also use these processes to their advantage, but only if we keep the potential pitfalls of these methods in mind. These shortcuts result in a form of intuition or "common sense," which must be structured properly to avoid the human tendencies to make poor decisions we covered earlier in this chapter.

Intuition may be necessary for wildlife managers who often lack complete research or monitoring data to guide an emergency decision. Heuristics that humans tend to use to make decisions in complex and uncertain situations may include:

- **Anchoring and adjustment:** In a complex or uncertain situation, it is common for people to start with a reference point (the anchor) that they either recognize or have recommended to them. Then, the decisions are made based on the anchor. This may lead to quick decisions, but it may also lead to poor decisions. The quality of the anchor is key.
- **Representativeness:** As we try to reduce the effects of uncertainty on our decisions, one method is to determine what future conditions may be the most representative conditions to expect. This might lead a riparian forest manager to ignore the effects of floods, for example, if floods happen infrequently. Thus, the method may lead to effective decisions in most years, but very poor decisions in a small number of years.
- **Stereotyping or availability**: We use information that is available to us and ignore information that may not be available to us. Because we use limited amounts of information to make a quick decision, we use stereotypes. The use of stereotypes may work, especially for people with years of experience that have broadened their perspective on the world. However, this method may have undesired consequences. For example, a newly-hired private lands biologist might see all ranchers as rich and conservative, based on a small number of ranchers with whom the biologist has interacted. Or, a forest manager may assume a prescribed burn will always remove an invasive woody species based on one successful experience in his or her past.
- **Affect**: We may respond intuitively based on the emotional feelings that a decision-making situation causes, such as fear or pleasure. Fear is an especially strong emotion that may lead away from an alternative that, in fact, might be the best alternative.

Such methods enhance the speed of the decision but create critical flaws if the decision-maker is not aware of how our brains are wired to respond. The development of intuition that leads to effective decisions may be improved by the same methods that led to effective team decisions in the previous section including discussing alternatives with experts, assessing any previous information, and generating more than one alternative before moving forward. These quick steps may improve our use of heuristics.

The military offers us one last lesson about decision-making in high-pressure situations: the importance of team structure and function. Military leaders train to develop their team so that they can more effectively use their gut or intuition to make decisions. Officers must develop the ability to spot emerging patterns (even though incomplete) and work with their counterparts to make decisions that can achieve their goal in light of the current situation, as they perceive it. Executives in business must use the same tactics (Stewart 2002), and wildlife managers have the same needs. How do we not fall prey to our own human nature to make poor intuitive decisions? Good, intuitive decision-makers spend time on team-building and team function. Well-structured and highly functional teams are able to reduce complexity and/or uncertainty in decision contexts (Paparone et al. 2008) by:

- **Relationship building:** Develop connections and network with people who make similar decisions or who are engaged in your decision environment. The most beneficial relationships are those that lead to critical, constructive feedback and those that may correct improper anchoring and stereotyping.
- **Forming loosely coupled teams:** Micromanagement and overly strict supervising structures may lead lower-level team members to not contribute ideas during quick searches for alternatives that may meet minimum standards.
- **Building sense of purpose:** Team members should have a shared vision of the long-term goal and their organization's purpose. In contrast, teams who do not understand the goal will encounter this as an additional uncertainty during an already complex decision process.
- **Learning:** Decisions made by people who are part of organizations that frequently share information and knowledge will allow better anchoring, the establishment of norms or representativeness, and a clearer perception of the environment in which the decision must be made.
- **Improvising:** The loss of a leader, an unexpected fire, or equipment failure may create momentary panic and stall the decision process if an organization or team is not developed in a way to allow for improvisation. Stuff happens, so be ready to adapt.
- **Emergent thinking:** When quick decisions are needed in complex or uncertain environments, the more traditional and linear formal processes of decision-making and planning are not useful. In fact, adherence to these techniques may stall a situation and cause damage to occur when a decision is not

made by a deadline. Team members should be encouraged to be creative and to develop innovative thinking skills.

- **Practice with case studies and scenarios:** Perhaps the best way to increase the effectiveness of intuitive decisions is frequent practice using case examples and scenarios (similar to those at the end of each chapter in this book). Practice with realistic cases will enhance your ability to develop a more logically-based intuition (Franke 2011). Team-based exercises in wildlife management courses may lead to important communication and leadership skills needed to form the types of teams described here.

Today's wildlife manager must be prepared to use formal decision processes, which we will cover in the next section of this chapter. However, the majority of decisions made by managers may require them to properly use their intuition. In recent years, the wildlife profession has moved forward with a focus on the need for better decision-making. Much of that focus has been to encourage formal, step by step processes that have linear start and end points, such as an endangered species listing decision process or a harvest management process. However, it is just as vital to recognize that wildlife managers are frequently faced with decisions that have short turnaround times, which we refer to as "nonlinear" circumstances. The simple act of taking a moment to clarify thoughts, remember objectives, and consider any personal biases or other human tendencies that could be clouding the decision process may suffice to improve many decisions that managers routinely make in the course of his or her day.

In a true emergency situation (decision needed now), a manager may find the satisficing method (working with his or her team to find one appropriate method that will allow initial response to the emergency) to be a quick way forward. For non-emergency situations that allow for a little more time and discussion, it is clear that managers and their agencies must develop practices that allow for good, intuitive decisions to be made routinely. The dynamics of a decision team and practice with scenarios are key components for agencies to incorporate. Short time frames and low resources are the hallmarks of situations that call for intuitive decision-making, and these decisions may be similar in complexity to the controlled, linear, step by step processes that we will cover next. Your knowledge of frameworks for making intuitive decisions can make you a valuable employee in the future.

Structured Decision-Making

Formal, linear decision-making processes used in longer duration, higher-risk situations go by many names. You may have encountered the terms **decision analysis** or **adaptive management** or **decision science** or **decision support systems**. All of these terms describe methods that enable us to make better, more effective decisions.

As a broad term to describe a formal approach, we will use the phrase, **structured decision-making**, or **SDM**.

SDM is the carefully organized analysis of problems to reach decisions that achieve fundamental objectives. The process usually splits a tough decision into **elements**. The goal of an SDM process is to inform difficult choices, and to make them more transparent and efficient.

> *"SDM is the formal application of common sense to situations too complicated for the informal application of common sense."*
>
> Ralph Keeney, Harvard Business School

The SDM Process

The formal, six-step decision process used by wildlife managers is the same structured process used in business, the military, and other endeavors. That is, these steps may apply to solving any problem in which there is time and resources to conduct a structured approach. SDM users refer to the process with the acronym, PrOACT (Hammond et al. 2015, Figure 3.1).

Step One: Clarify the Problem and the Decision Context

What is the problem? Most decisions are triggered by a problem or issue that arises. The first step in good decision-making involves defining what question or problem is being addressed and why. Further, there is no reason to take a management action if there is no problem! What decision needs to be made? Is this a one-time decision, or a recurring decision that will be made each month or year?

Perhaps most importantly, who will make the decision? Are you or your team the decision-makers, or are you only in charge of creating a recommendation that is passed to someone else to make the decision? If the latter, the decision-maker needs to be involved in the decision-making process. This may seem obvious, but, in reality, this issue can be a break-down point in many management decision-making processes. For example, in many state wildlife agencies, biologists provide recommendations to their director or politically appointed commissioners for approval.

Step Two: Define Objectives

The core of SDM is a set of well-defined objectives. The objectives define what matters about the decision and drive the search for creative alternatives. The objectives become the framework for comparing alternatives. In creating objectives, the decision team must consider legal, regulatory mandates and stakeholder goals.

For example, our problem may be that we need to make a decision about the harvest of wild turkeys. What are we trying to accomplish with turkey management? Perhaps we want to maintain stable populations of turkeys. Perhaps we want the turkey population to get smaller. Perhaps we are responding to turkey hunters who want more recreational opportunities to hunt turkeys. Each objective or combination of objectives would lead to a different decision about hunting regulations. In chapter 4, we will discuss objectives further, because they are so critical to the process.

Step Three: Develop Set of Alternatives

What management options do we have to accomplish our objective? During this step, the team outlines the range of creative management alternatives that could address the objectives. The alternatives may be very different approaches, and they represent the choices that will be considered. We always start our list with "do nothing," which is a default decision. For turkey hunting, to provide more opportunity for hunters (a potential objective), biologists could (1) do nothing, (2) increase the season length, (3) increase the types of legal weapons used to take turkeys, or (4) increase the bag limit. These alternatives will be discussed in steps four and five, and some alternatives may be eliminated by the end of the decision process, but all possible alternatives should be listed, to enable the decision team to be transparent about what they considered during their decision process.

Step Four: Estimate Consequences

This step is an analytical exercise in which the outcome of each alternative is predicted and considered. If we have option A and option B, what will happen to turkey populations under each option? Information or expert opinion is needed to inform this step. During this step, the decision team may decide that there is considerable uncertainty in their predictions for either management option. Such uncertainty is important to acknowledge during the decision process.

Step Five: Evaluate Tradeoffs and Select Action

Examination of tradeoffs is a critical step in decision-making. Many methods can formally help the decision-makers evaluate the predictions under each possible scenario. The value for each consequence, or outcome, of each alternative action is important to consider. What will it cost? Will we be able to enforce such a regulation? How will stakeholders react? Do we have the people to carry this out? If one management alternative has very little chance of helping to reach our objectives, and it is not popular with stakeholders, the team will probably not select it. In contrast, if an alternative seems quite likely to help us reach our objective, and it meets with perceived stakeholder approval, we are likely to value that alternative.

Later in this chapter, we will discuss expert systems and decision trees: two methods that may be used to select a management direction, given a set of consequences and tradeoffs.

QUICK COMPREHENSION CHECK

Can you find the components of the PrOACT acronym in the six-step process?

What are the dangers of skipping each step in the PrOACT process? What might happen if you fail to define the problem? What might happen if you fail to clearly state the objectives? Consequences? Tradeoffs? Monitoring?

Step Six: Implement and Monitor

The last step in the decision process is to implement the decision made in step five. In addition, because we need to determine if our choice worked, we need to identify a plan to monitor our population or habitat. The response of the population or habitat to our management will help us improve future decisions (Nichols and Williams 2006, Lyons et al. 2008).

Why Structured Decision-Making Is Useful to Managers

Structured decision-making has been a viable method to support wildlife management since the 1990s (Nichols and Williams 2006). Why do wildlife managers find the formal decision process to be useful?

As noted previously, today's wildlife managers are encountering complex issues. SDM provides a framework to **focus the decision on management objectives.**

SDM also makes use of scientific data and **increases stakeholder involvement.** When stakeholders (such as the landowners surrounding a wildlife refuge) have a chance to provide input on objectives and the decision-making process, they will usually be much happier with the final decision.

SDM provides transparency to the decision-making system, as well. Unfortunately, it is becoming more common for managers to be sued by private interest groups. For example, the US Forest Service was sued over their forest management plans 729 times between 1989 and 2002 (Keele et al. 2006). Natural resource biologists were summoned to court during litigation in Oregon over northern spotted owl management plans (Noon and Murphy 1997). State legislators may challenge state wildlife agencies over new policies and decisions. Litigation, therefore, may elevate decisions to high-risk status, and decisions made using a formal process are easier to defend. A manager may detail in transparent fashion how a team selected a specific option from a group of alternatives.

Some SDM methods **allow a manager to address uncertainty.** Complex decisions often bring with them the certainty that we are uncertain about many things. We may not know how a species will respond to habitat changes. We may not be able to predict how many hunters will purchase tags to harvest turkeys. Decision-makers have developed SDM processes that allow evaluation of when predictions are far from certain. The decision process provides a way to move forward and learn, rather than closing your eyes and guessing.

Lastly, and maybe most importantly for a manager, **SDM improves planning and utilization of limited resources** such as time, money, and people. Supervisors reward managers for effective use of resources and results of decisions. As state and federal budgets grow tighter and tighter, the importance of SDM becomes more and more relevant to management efficiency (Lyons et al. 2008).

Decisions about How to Make Decisions

So, when is using SDM appropriate? When is using our gut sufficient? In Figure 3.2, we introduced the concept that the optimal decision process is context-specific. The choice of decision process depends on the risk involved with the decision, the amount of time and decision resources available, the complexity of the system, and the recurring nature of the decision.

In the final portion of the chapter, we will discuss techniques used to make decisions when there is high risk, suitable resources, and time for making the decision. These are the big decisions that cause us to wake at night. These are the decisions that need effective, efficient use of funds. It is important to remember, however, that these types of decision make up a very small proportion of a manager's total decisions, as depicted earlier in the chapter. However, these are the types of decisions that make the evening news and Twitter feeds when things go wrong!

As a prelude to formal decision-making processes, we should note that some decision contexts demand some preliminary work that we will discuss further in chapter 4 (Figure 3.6). Look at diagram for the six-step (PrOACT) decision process (Figure 3.1). What happens if you get to step two (setting objectives), and your group of stakeholders for the decision cannot agree on the objectives? For example, what if loggers in Washington do not agree with an objective that describes sustainable logging practices that would provide nesting territories for threatened birds and less turbid streams for native fish? Certainly, the loggers know that lowering the levels of logging will affect their family's income, so they will object to any objective that they foresee will result in possible management actions to reduce timber harvest?

As Figure 3.6 suggests, a situation in which stakeholders do not agree on the goals for a project calls for either **conflict resolution** or **negotiation**. A similar situation developed around the introduction of gray wolves into the Yellowstone ecosystem in recent decades. The planning process was at a standstill, because nearby ranchers did not agree with the long-term goal of having wolves in the landscape. Negotiations resulted in an NGO, the Defenders of Wildlife, offering to pay ranchers for cattle that were documented losses to wolf predation (Nyhus et al. 2003). Negotiation worked, and the decision-making continued.

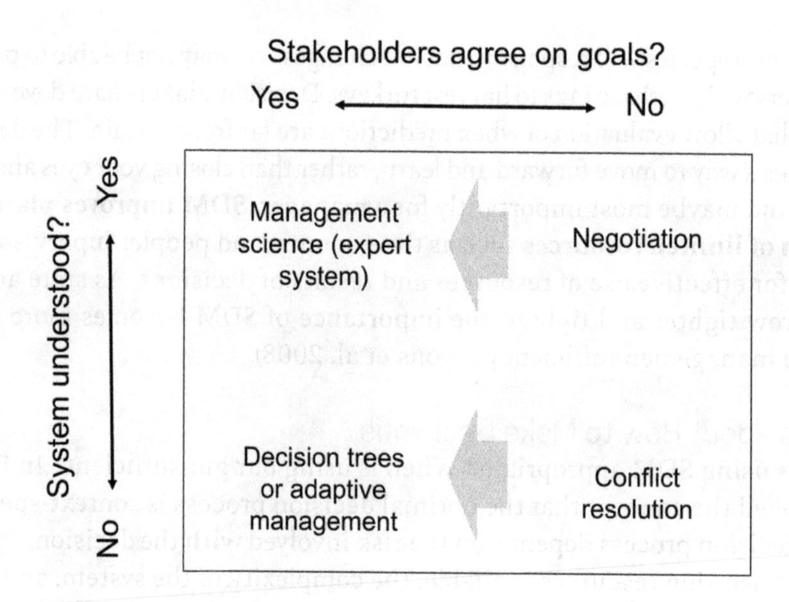

FIGURE 3.6 Context-specific comparison of structured decision-making processes used under a range of stakeholder agreement and system understanding. Arrows indicate movement to a new state following negotiation or conflict resolution. Modified from Williams et al. (2002).

The knowledge of the system is also important as we decide what type of structured decision-making model to use. Do we understand how this wetland system works as we try to manage it for multiple purposes, including waterfowl hunting and shorebird migratory use?

If all stakeholders can agree on objectives and the system is understood, we can use a more prescribed process known as an **expert system**, or **decision support system**. If the goals are agreed upon, but we do not understand the system, we need to take uncertainties into account; we just don't know exactly what is going to happen if we deploy a specific management tool such as a prescribed burn. So, we will use decision tools such as **decision trees** or **adaptive management** that allow us to include uncertainty in the process (Figure 3.6).

Expert Systems, or Decision Support Systems

Expert Systems are also known as **Decision Support Systems** (DSS) in some agencies. These tools provide answers to specific problems and are typically developed for decisions that are made very routinely. When should we use a prescribed burn? What water level should we use for this wetland in the spring? How much water should be released from this dam to create fish spawning habitat downstream?

An expert system combines expertise from many people and sources into one system. The process uses a principle known as forward chaining, in which we start with current data and work forward through decision steps to arrive at a suggested management action. These systems are typically a series of "Yes/No" or "If/Then" inference rules. For a quick example of an expert system, look back to the figure at the start of this chapter on which decision process to use. Through a series of questions, the user is guided to an answer.

This process is used in artificial intelligence applications (Luger and Stubblefield 1990), and it is used by computer software to help users. Are you having trouble printing from your laptop? The help menu starts with a basic question: is your printer turned on? If no, the problem is solved. If yes, then you are asked if your printer is connected to your computer. Still not working? More questions appear, and you are guided to a solution.

Expert systems are most effective when there is very little uncertainty about any of the steps. Your computer software designer is 100% certain that if you do not have your printer turned on, it will not work. Of course, nature can be uncertain, but there are decision situations that occur in fairly predictable conditions.

Building an Expert System

There are three components needed to construct an expert system: knowledge base (facts), logical reasoning (steps), and a user interface (application). Experts provide the knowledge base, and the system builder creates the logical steps (Pivello and Norton 1996). The interface depends on how a manager will use the system. Do you want it to be on cards that a landowner can use in the field or should it be in the form of an app for use on a mobile device?

Using the PrOACT process, an expert system is developed to solve a problem identified by a user. The entire decision system is framed in the context of an objective. For example, Joubert et al. (2014) used an expert system to meet the objective to reduce *Acacia* density in grasslands of southern Africa as part of a regional effort to limit bush encroachment (Figure 3.7).

Step One: Following PrOACT, the next step is to consider alternatives. Listing alternatives provides all end-nodes in the expert system. Notice that Joubert et al. (2014) had six alternatives (gray boxes), including a do-nothing option.

Step Two: With end-nodes (alternative actions) chosen, the expert system must have the routes to the end-nodes designed. The first decision step is critical. Joubert et al. (2014) chose to ask farmers about rainfall, as the answer to that question would decide if the user needs to go through the rest of the system (if low rainfall, *Acacia* trees will not produce seeds, and bush encroachment will not be accelerated). In other scenarios, the first question could be used as a key distinction, after which there are two main paths to follow. For water level management in a wetland, the first question might

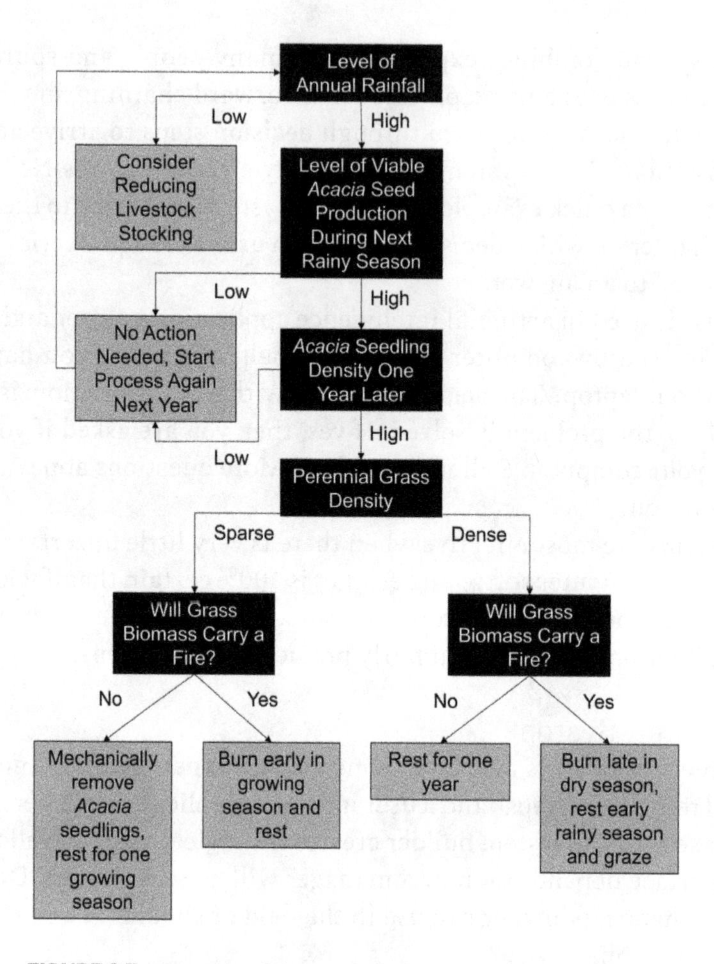

FIGURE 3.7 Example of the steps used in an expert system for natural resource management. Modified from Joubert et al. (2014) for management of *Acacia* density in southern Africa.

decipher if the user has access to an artificial water source (pumping) for the wetland. If there is, the user is taken one way through more questions. If there is not, the user may need to consider a completely different set of questions.

The expert system process combines the consequences and tradeoff steps in the PrOACT process. As the designer plans the route, the user is asked to consider current situations and guided to a next step based on tradeoffs or consequences.

Step Three: The order of the questions in an expert system is important, and the builder may need to experiment with different orders to see if the system can be made more efficient by modifying the order of questions. Joubert et al. (2014) used the natural sequence of seed production and seedling growth to guide the steps in the expert system.

Step Four: Once the expert system is developed, the designer should check it with a set of potential users. Field-testing the system will provide critical feedback. Are the questions and steps understood? Are the potential answers clear and easy to interpret?

QUICK COMPREHENSION CHECK

Describe how the expert system framework fits the PrOACT decision process.

Decision Tree Analysis for Non-Iterative Decisions

Wildlife managers encounter some decisions for which the system's responses to management are not completely clear. Under the expert system process, a management action assures success for the user. Life does not always line up perfectly, however.

Decision trees are a simple, yet effective process to describe decision contexts that include uncertainty (Gray et al. 2016, Figure 3.8). **The decision team is allowed to weigh their value for a potential decision outcome by the probability that the outcome will occur.**

Step One: A formal decision tree starts with a node that describes the decision (Figure 3.8), which corresponds with the statement of problem in the PrOACT model. To complete the decision tree framework, we need to consider the possible outcomes and what decisions are possible.

For exploration of the process, we will use an example of whether to remove introduced, invasive Burmese pythons from the Florida Everglades in an attempt to reduce their effect on birds, mammals and other reptiles (Snow et al. 2007, Figure 3.9). Pythons were originally released by former pet owners and have started to affect the ecosystem in the Everglades (Dorcas et al. 2012). Since 2002, more than 2000 pythons have been removed from the Everglades National Park and the surrounding areas, and that is considered only a fraction of the population. Although a decision tree was not been used formally by managers to solve this problem, the context makes an easy example for our introductory use.

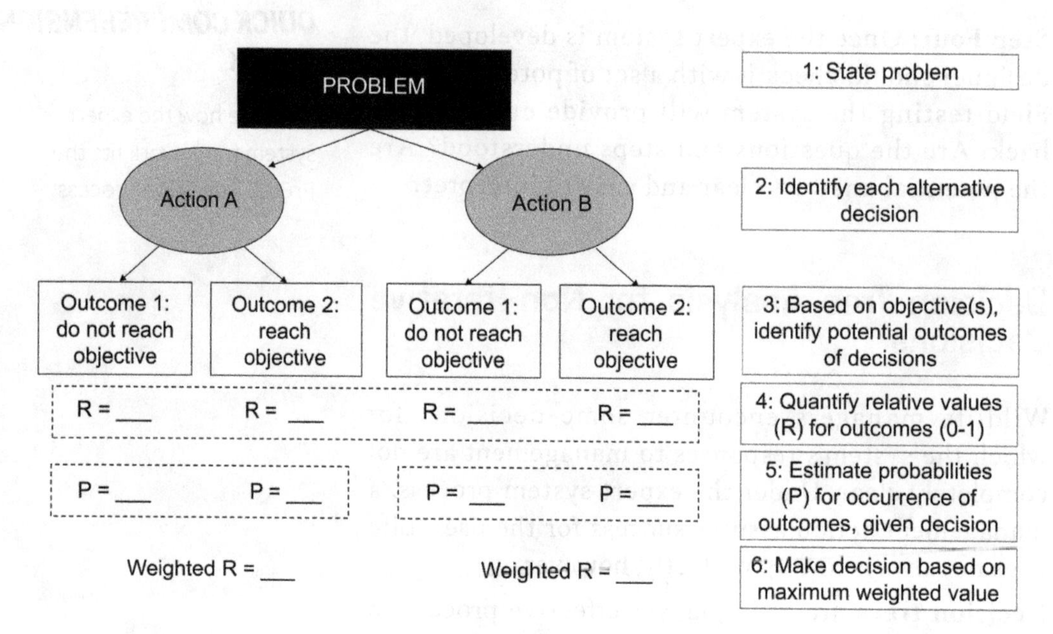

FIGURE 3.8 Process and function of a decision tree model for structured decision-making. User inputs include the relative values (R) for decision outcomes, and the probability (P) of occurrence of each outcome, given the decision. Weighted R values are calculated by multiplying R*P for each outcome and summing the R*P products under each action.

To refer back to our PrOACT process, our objective is to reduce the impact of python predation on birds, mammals, and reptiles. Therefore, we hope to increase their populations through a python removal program. We have defined our decision. Should we take action (spend money, time, and effort)? In the simplest two-branch decision tree, the alternatives are either to take action or not. Note that we could make our decision process more complicated with more decision nodes (e.g., no action, python removal by hand, use of poisoned carcasses for removal, etc.). The decision tree process would allow for expansion.

Step Two: We determine the possible outcomes, or consequences of the actions. In this case, small animal populations could increase (our objective) or our management action could have no effect on the small animal populations (we fail to meet our objective). Either outcome is possible, regardless of our decision to implement a removal program or not. Therefore, each outcome appears at the end of the branches under each decision.

Step Three: We derive **values** for each outcome. Here, we are using stakeholder input to explicitly assess tradeoffs. We do this by giving **utility scores** (R) in a range of 0 to 1, where 0 is the lowest value and 1 is the highest value. To decide which outcome to assign a value of 0, we need to think of the worst-case scenario. It would seem

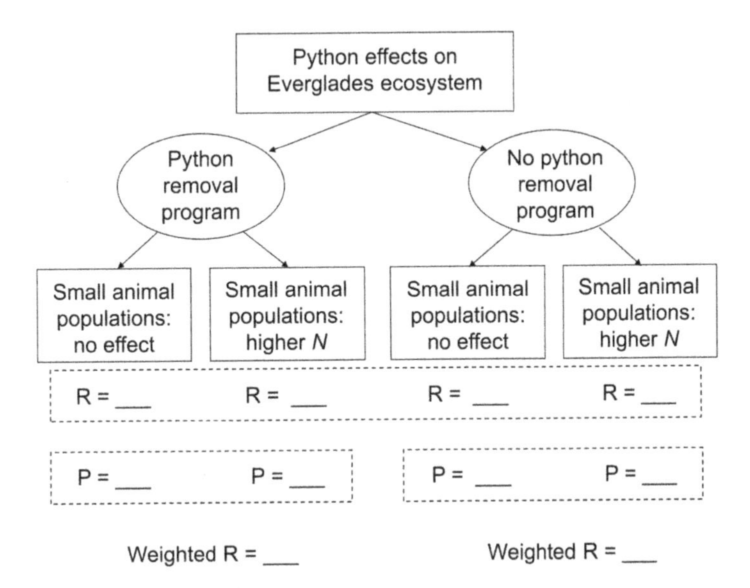

FIGURE 3.9 Decision tree structured-decision example for management of pythons in the Everglades ecosystem. Fill in the R, P, and Weighted R values by following the example in the text.

that taking action (spending money, using agency resources) and not accomplishing the goal would be the worst. So, we can place a 0 for that utility score. What is the best outcome? This may not be intuitive at first, but stakeholders might argue that not taking action (avoiding expense and time commitments) and accomplishing the goal would be the best. So, we place a utility value of 1 on that outcome. Now, the stakeholders must decide on values for the intermediate outcomes. How much do we value being successful, relative to the expenses involved and other tradeoffs? These outcomes would receive a decimal value between 0 and 1. For our example, we will use values of 0.8 for taking action and achieving the goal, and 0.1 for not taking action and not achieving the goal.

What if stakeholders don't agree on values? A simple way to negotiate a value, which you could use in a group exercise in class, is to take the average of values submitted by the group.

Step Four: We incorporate uncertainty surrounding our decision in this step. How probable is each of the outcomes? It is possible that the decision team has a large amount of data information to guide their answer, but often we have to use imperfect information—hence the uncertainty in our decision. In our Everglades example, how likely is it that mammal, bird, and reptile populations will benefit from a conservation action to remove pythons? At the beginning of the process, biologists really had no idea—this type of program had never been attempted.

How to estimate the level of uncertainty? The best way forward would be to construct a population model that could be used to predict the impact of a removal of a specified number of pythons on prey species. **Predictive models** are highly useful (Conroy 1993), and the construction of the model serves as an opportunity to engage stakeholders in framing the important features of the system for use in the model. Once constructed, the team can use the predictive model to simulate prey populations in a **stochastic** manner. The proportion of times that a removal resulted in achievement of the objective can be used for the values of P in our decision framework.

At the moment, we do not have a model, so we might be prone to simply pick a number as a rough estimate of the answer—such a process is referred to, in decision-making terms, as a **WAG**, a Wild-Ass Guess. Sometimes, that is all that is possible when a decision must be made, but it may still be useful as a starting place. Preferably, we would upgrade our description of uncertainty to a **SWAG**, a Scientific Wild-Ass Guess (a rough estimate made by an expert in the field) (Mehta and Desai 2014). Can a biologist who has worked in the system help estimate the likelihood of this management action's success?

Perhaps you know a little about pythons. Maybe you have been to the Everglades. You have taken ecology courses. That is good enough for expert status here! Pick some SWAG numbers that make sense to you—numbers that you could defend, generally. *The probabilities under each decision option should add up to 1.0.* For example, if we were to implement the conservation program, we might make a SWAG that there is a greater chance (say, 0.6) that we will have more small animals in the Everglades, and a lower chance that we will have fewer small animals (0.4; and 0.6 + 0.4 = 1.0).

We also might predict that if we were to do nothing, there is a greater probability that the small animal population will remain low (0.7) than the probability it will increase with no effort (0.3; 0.7 + 0.3 = 1.0).

Step Five: We have all decision components we need. It is time to grab a calculator and solve our decision problem by calculating weighted average utility values (weighted Rs) for each decision. We consider each decision (e.g., remove pythons) on its own. For each outcome of that decision, we multiply the utility value (R) by the probability of the outcome occurring. Think of this step as weighting the values by the likelihood of their occurrence. An outcome with a high value and a high probability will receive a high weighted value. Outcomes with low value and low likelihood of occurrence will receive a score close to 0.

We add the weighted values for each decision and then compare the weighted R values for each decision. The alternative with the higher weighted value (R) is the better choice, because it represents the decision with an outcome that (1) we value highly, and (2) has a high likelihood of occurring (we are more likely to reach our desired goal).

Adaptive Decisions: Learning about the System

Adaptive management is a formal decision process that provides opportunities for feedback, evaluation, and learning about the system over recurring decision opportunities. The US Fish and Wildlife Service defines adaptive management as:

> A deliberate, science-based process for decision-making in the face of uncertainty. This approach treats management actions as experiments, and uses the outcomes of those experiments to inform and improve future actions. Because it is based on a continual learning process, adaptive management improves long-term management outcomes.

The adaptive management process (Figure 3.10) allows managers to incorporate the knowledge gained from the experience of the previous decision into their next decision. Adaptive management is *not* simply *learning by doing.* The key elements needed for formal adaptive management are monitoring data, an evaluation process, and a formal way to integrate new information into the next SDM process.

In our python management decision in the previous section, we had uncertainties with regards to the effect of our python removal plan on the populations of small animals in the Everglades. After the experience of one year, our monitoring data may help us update the SWAGs to more informed SWAGs or even a model-estimated probability. Now, we can update our decision tree probabilities (P).

For example, suppose we find that our management option for removing pythons was very ineffective. We removed pythons, but we do not see a response in mammals. Based on the monitoring data and meetings with our biologists, we lower the probability for success under the python removal to 0.3 (it was 0.6 previously). Leaving the P's on the "no removal" side the same, now

QUICK COMPREHENSION CHECK

Use the numbers provided in the Decision Tree Analysis section to populate a decision tree for python removal (Figure 3.9). What decision do you reach? Hint: you should obtain weighted R values for python removal of 0.48 and for no action of 0.37.

What do the values (R) and the probability of success (P) represent? Explain the concept to a friend in your own words.

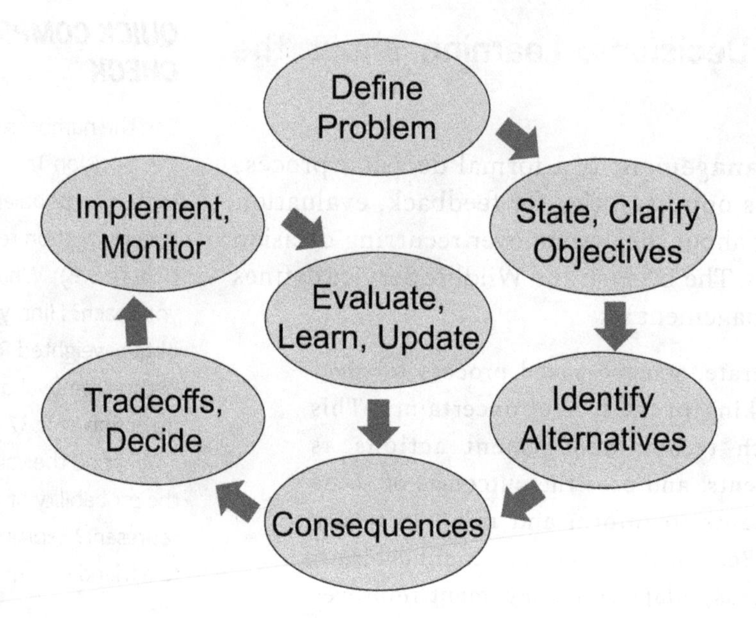

FIGURE 3.10 Modification of the PrOACT structured decision-making model to include the evaluation, learning, and updating features of adaptive resource management.

re-calculate the weighted R values and re-evaluate your decision. What do you decide to do now?

Our example of an adaptive management framework with a decision tree is just one way to implement adaptive management. Federal wildlife agencies have incorporated adaptive management processes, both formal and informal, into decision-making. For example, the US Fish and Wildlife Service (2011) states this vision for their National Wildlife Refuge System mission:

> We embrace a scientific, adaptive, landscape-level approach to conserving, managing and restoring refuge lands and waters, and work to project conservation benefits beyond our boundaries.

Experimentation: A Key Component to Adaptive Management

We noted that learning from prior management is critical in a formal adaptive management framework. How do we learn?

Experimentation provides for learning, and managers may experiment in various formats (Figure 3.11), depending on time, space, and funding constraints (Allen et al. 2011). For example, a loose type of adaptive management is **trial and error**, which might be especially useful in an emergency situation in which an approach must be selected quickly without time for listing all possible alternatives. A **step-wise** approach is similar but differs from trial and error in that a complete set of alternatives was

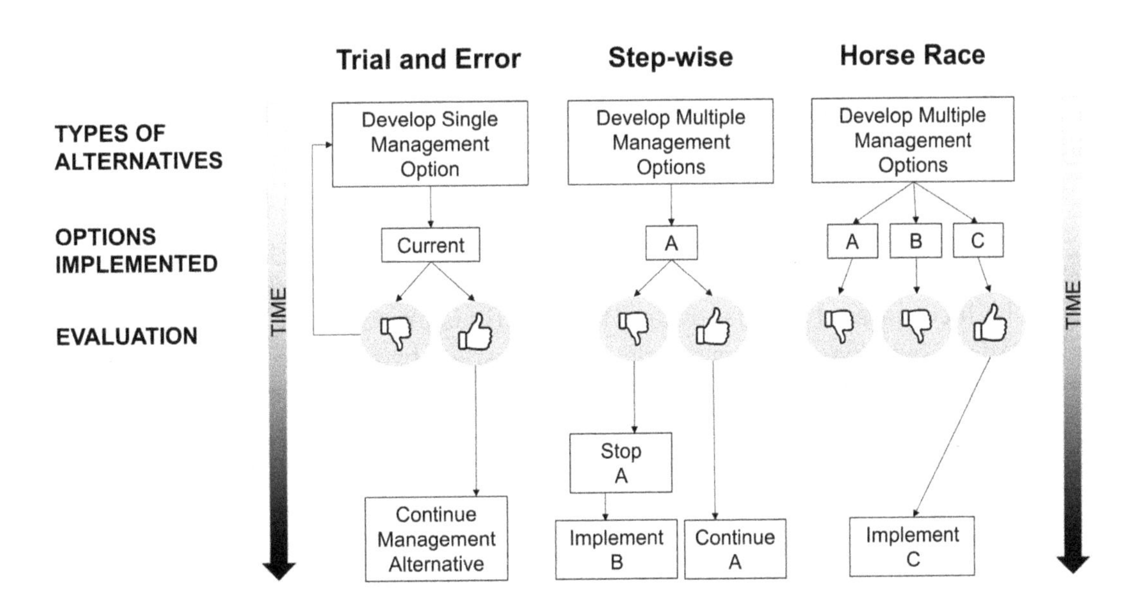

FIGURE 3.11 Comparison of three methods of implementation of adaptive resource management. Methods vary by the number of options implemented and the designation of alternatives prior to the beginning of the process. Modified from Allen et al. (2011).

developed initially. Step-wise may be useful if space does not permit a side-by-side comparison, which is characteristic of the **horse race** approach to experimentation.

Beyond the amount of time it takes to find the best management action, the three approaches to experimentation vary in the level of inference that they allow the decision team to draw from the experiment. The horse race allows the highest level of inference, as all management options are used at the same time, in the same place, as in a rigorous design for research with treatments and controls. For example, if a drought occurs, all treatments all experience the drought. If a drought occurs during the use of the step-wise approach, we may incorrectly infer that the method is not useful during a normal year.

In our Everglades example with python removal, a step-wise approach would involve trying various alternative methods for python removal over the entire national park in a series of years. Monitoring would suggest how each method of python removal affected populations of prey species. However, it may take five to six years to test all methods and the python population might grow even more numerous while we played with poor options. The horse race scenario would be deployed using different sections of the national park for different methods and comparing the results from monitoring each section. This type of experimentation may seem most effective, but it also takes time and effort to establish the logistics of the experiment throughout the park.

Although adaptive management sounds logical, full implementation of formal adaptive management processes in agencies remains relatively uncommon (Stankey et al. 2006). It is clear that your generation of biologists and managers will be involved in the development of new frameworks that will improve the use of formal decision-making in our agencies. Currently, barriers to implementation and success of adaptive management include:

- **Use of jargon to mislead:** Initial framing of adaptive management is often done by stating "we intend to learn adaptively as we move forward on this project" rather than formally setting up the mechanisms that will allow learning to be incorporated and denoting what exactly is uncertain at the current time. Adaptive management is not clearly understood by many managers, currently, and the use of the phrase may be enough to impress fellow team members as the team falls into a less-than-perfect decision process that, in reality, does not resemble adaptive management in the slightest.
- **Failing to monitor:** The collection of monitoring data costs money and time, and shortages of either may lead to lack of the critical element that would allow evaluation of the results in light of the objectives.
- **Monitoring, but not learning:** Decision teams may have monitoring information available but fail to implement adequate designs to facilitate and communicate learning. Perhaps the monitoring data is not shared with the entire team, or perhaps there is not framework to incorporate the monitoring data for comparison to the objectives.
- **Time lags:** In some cases, data and/or analyses resulting from last year's monitoring are not available before the next decision must be made.
- **Complex problems, complex mission:** We started the chapter by noting that structured decision-making was useful to solve complex problems. However, complexity breeds complexity—in a complex decision environment, communication is complex, team management is complex, monitoring is complex, and evaluation is complex. Simply put, implementing adaptive management is logistically difficult and requires unique leaders and communicators to facilitate the process.
- **Poor predictive models:** Decision teams underestimate the time and information needed for construction of a predictive model, or the system may be so complex that predictive models fail to make useful predictions.
- **Politics:** When we state that stakeholders must agree on objectives, we have invoked the description of a political situation. Social conflict may surround complex problems such as salmon fisheries, management of rangelands on public land, or harvest of forests used by commercial loggers. Ironically, many wildlife managers chose their occupation because they imagined working in remote environments with little contact with people. The lack of well-trained wildlife managers who can facilitate open conversations with stakeholders is a real problem in current efforts. Most failures of adaptive management can be

traced to conflicts among stakeholders regarding the tradeoffs between ecological and social values.

- **No lead employee:** The basic structure of wildlife agencies does not typically include facilitators who can spend time to develop networks for learning from management. Annual evaluations do not typically reward managers who spend the extra time to create new teams and management structures. For structured decision-making to be successful, organizational change will have to happen in our agencies during the coming decades.
- **Risk-averse organizations:** Wildlife agencies do not typically reward managers who try new things. Agencies will typically balk at redesigning surveys to improve monitoring.

In some cases, employees may see examples of colleagues who are sanctioned or penalized for trying something new that failed. We must remember that most upper-level managers in wildlife agencies started their careers using textbooks that did not include chapters on decision-making. Employees wishing to change the system may benefit from practical guidance with easy to follow scenarios that demonstrate the benefits of incorporating stakeholder views and allowing for transparency. The benefits of documenting decision steps to prepare for potential court challenges may be useful in making organization change.

In response to these problems, which are characteristic of complex, single- or multi-agency management processes, some agencies have begun to hire specialists to coordinate larger projects. In addition, **ecological consulting firms** and **NGOs** may fill a coordinating role with funds provided by the participating agencies (Hood 1998). Regional **associations of state fish and wildlife agencies** may also serve to coordinate efforts that involve multiple states. For example, the Western Association of Fish and Wildlife Agencies helps to coordinate a Sagebrush Ecosystem Initiative to support decisions made for sage-grouse and a Western Native Trout Initiative to support habitat protection for 21 fish species.

WRAPPING UP

In our problem case, Sara Whitefeather has to make a quick decision on how to remove feral hogs. What suggestions to optimize success of the decision would you have for her if you were on her quick response team?

Fill in the blank boxes in Figure 3.12. Without looking back to Figure 3.2, select the most appropriate situation to use the following decision processes: adaptive structured decision-making, intuitive process, one-off structured decision-making, quick thought process, expert system, and the satisficing process? Explain why each is best in the given circumstance.

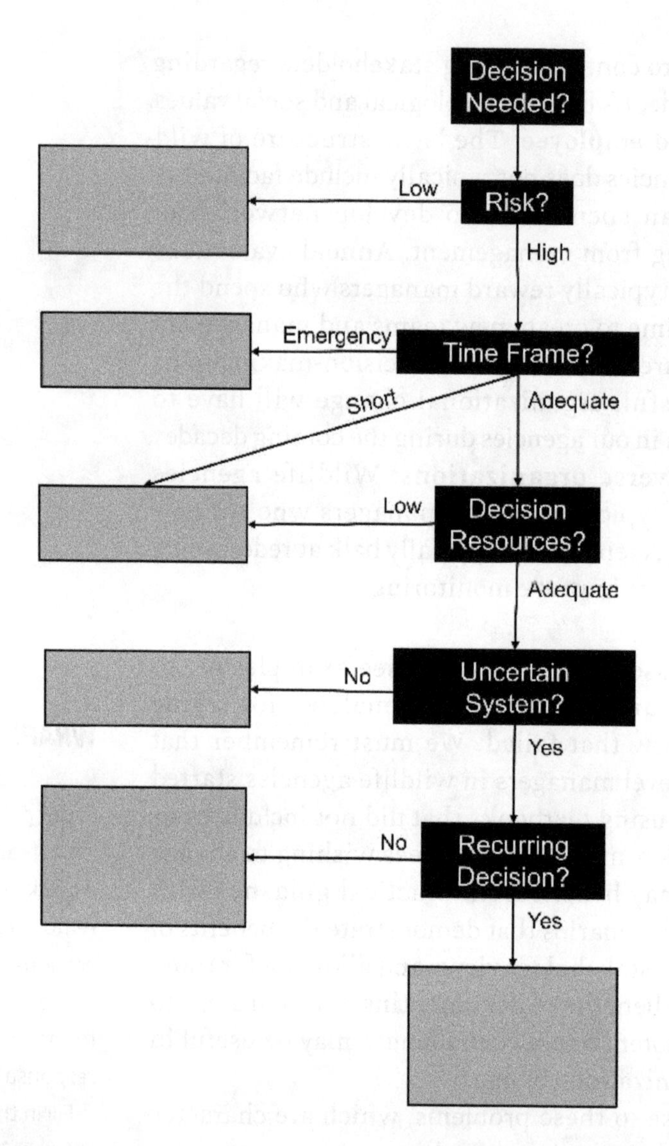

FIGURE 3.12 Blank decision tree for use in Wrapping Up.

Decision-Making on the Ground

1: Complex Management Teams, Adaptive Management, and Forest Habitat

The designation of northern spotted owls as a threatened species in 1990 started a firestorm of discussions in the Pacific Northwest, as the old growth forests that served as habitat for the owls did not fit with the traditional management of forest lands for commercial logging. Many efforts by federal forest managers affiliated with the US Forest Service, US Fish and Wildlife Service, and the Bureau of Land Management, in coordination with state wildlife agencies, were undertaken to support appropriate forest management for maintenance and restoration of species of concern.

Forest harvesting levels were reduced, which impacted rural communities, but the decline in habitat and species continued. The situation became a part of the 1992 presidential campaign, which led to the 1993 Forest Summit hosted by President Clinton in Portland, Oregon. The president asked agencies to create a team of experts to identify options that might break the paralyzed state of regional forest management.

The Forest Ecosystem Management Assessment Team (FEMAT) prepared a series of options, and developed a plan for a way forward, known as the Northwest Forest Plan. The plan included the use of monitoring and adaptive management as a key element (Stankey et al. 2006), and the plan's objectives included optimized sustainability of endangered species, old-growth forest, commodity production, and community resiliency.

Stankey et al. (2006) conducted an evaluation of the performance of the adaptive management program embedded in the plan. The document includes 50 interviews with resource managers and scientists involved with the plan's implementation and a survey of over 400 citizens in Oregon and Washington who participated in public involvement programs related to the adaptive management elements of the plan.

APPLICATION, ANALYSIS, SYNTHESIS, AND EVALUATION

Visit: https://www.fs.usda.gov/treesearch/pubs/24764 and review the summary, chapter 1, and chapter 7 of the evaluation document by Stankey et al. (2006). Can you find examples from the Northwest Pacific forest management experience that represent the potential pitfalls listed in this chapter that are inherent in complex problems and adaptive management?

After your review of the complexities of this large management process in the Pacific Northwest, consider the potential for an external (not an employee of federal or state agency) ecological consultant to act as a coordinator for the project. Why might the project benefit from an external consultant?

2: Expert System for Invasive Fisheries Management in Africa

Fryer (1960) stated:

> The suggestion that the fishery in Lake Victoria would benefit if the Nile perch were introduced into the lake is shown to be based on ignorance of several fundamental biological concepts. Both theoretical reasoning and practical experience

strongly suggest that such an introduction is not only undesirable but would jeopardize the existing commercial fishery.

Despite the warning, Nile perch (native to Ethiopia) were discovered to have been introduced into Lake Victoria in 1962. The Nile perch diet includes crustaceans, mollusks, insects, and fish (including its own species). The females produce over 15 million eggs at once, giving the species potential for invasive qualities. The size of prey increases with the size of the individual perch, and perch reach maximum lengths of nearly two meters (Ogutu-Ohwayo 1993).

APPLICATION, ANALYSIS, SYNTHESIS, AND EVALUATION

Investigate what is currently known about Nile perch in Lake Victoria and the effects of the fishes' introduction on the Lake Victoria ecosystem. Summarize those results and compare them to the predictions of Fryer (1960).

Woodford et al. (2017) published a general expert system (Figure 3.13) to assist managers in their initial assessment of reports of an invasive fish species in Africa and initial actions for management. Continue your investigations regarding Lake Victoria and Nile perch. Use the expert system to guide you to answer the question, "What approach should be taken with Nile perch in Lake Victoria?"

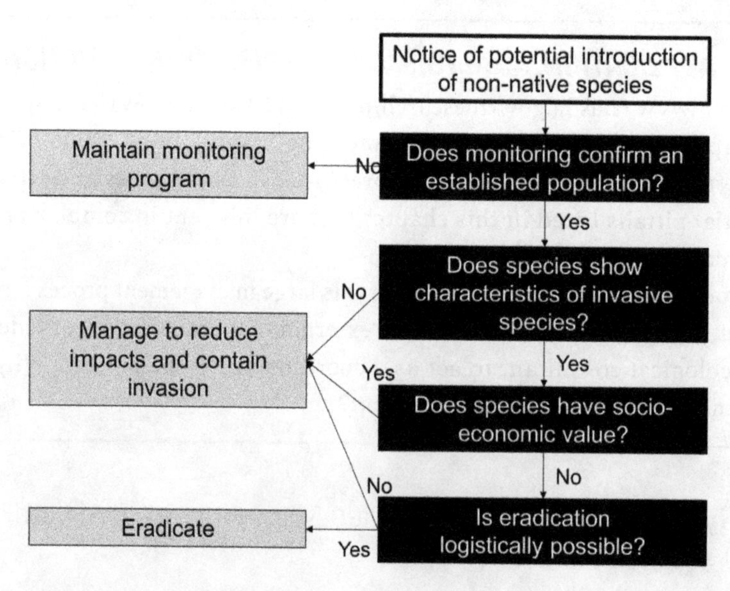

FIGURE 3.13 Depiction of an expert system used by Woodford et al. (2017) to assess response to an invasive fish.

Sources of Information and Further Reading

Allen, C. R., Fontaine, J. J., Pope, K. L., and Garmestani, A. S. "Adaptive management for a turbulent future." *Journal of environmental management* 92, no. 5 (2011): 1339–1345.

Conroy M. J. "The use of models in natural resource management: prediction, not prescription." *Transactions of the North American Wildife and Natural Resources Conference* 58 (1993): 509–519.

Conroy, M. J. and J. P. Carroll. *Quantitative conservation of vertebrates*. Oxford, UK: Wiley-Blackwell, 2009.

Dorcas, M .E., Willson, J. D., Reed, R. N., Snow, R. W., Rochford, M. R., Miller, M. A., Meshaka, W. E., Andreadis, P. T., Mazzotti, F. J., Romagosa, C. M. and Hart, K. M. "Severe mammal declines coincide with proliferation of invasive Burmese pythons in Everglades National Park." *Proceedings of the National Academy of Sciences* 109, no. 7 (2012): 2418–2422.

Eisenhardt, K. M. "Making Fast Strategic Decisions in High-Velocity Environments." *The Academy of Management Journal* 32 (1989): 543–576.

Franke, V. "Decision-making under uncertainty: using case studies for teaching strategy in complex environments." *Journal of Military and Strategic Studies* 13, no. 2 (2011): 1–21.

Fryer, G. "Concering the Proposed Introduction of Nile Perch Into Lake Victoria." *The East African Agricultural Journal* 25, no. 4 (1960): 267–270.

Gray, S., Paolisso, M. Jordan, R., and Gray, S. (eds.). *Environmental Modeling with Stakeholders: Theory, Methods, and Applications*. Springer, 2016.

Gregory, R. S. and R. L. Keeney. "Making smarter environmental management decisions." *Journal of the American Water Resources Association* 38 (2002): 1601–1612.

Hammond, J. S., Keeney, R. L., and Raiffa, H. *Smart choices: A practical guide to making better decisions*. Harvard Business Review Press, 2015.

Hood, L. C. *Frayed Safety Nets: conservation planning under the endangered species act*. Washington, DC: Defenders of Wildlife, 1998.

Jablonsky, D. "Why is Strategy Difficult?" In *U.S. Army War College Guide to Strategy*, 143–156. Carlisle, PA: Strategic Studies Institute, United States Army War College, 2001.

Johnson, B. L. "Introduction to the special issue: adaptive management—scientifically sound, socially challenged? *Conservation Ecology* 3, no. 1 (1999): 10.

Joubert, D., Zimmermann, I., Fendler, J., Winschiers-Theophilus, H., Graz, F. P., Smit, N., and Hoffman, M. T. "The development of an expert system for arid rangeland management in central Namibia with emphasis on bush thickening." *African journal of range and forage science* 31, no. 2 (2014): 161–172.

Keele, D. M., Malmsheimer, R. W., Floyd, D. W., and Perez, J. E. "Forest Service land management litigation 1989–2002." *Journal of Forestry* 104, no. 4 (2006): 196–202.

Keeney, R. L. "Making better decision makers." *Decision Analysis* 1, no. 4 (2004): 193–204.

Luger, G. F. and Stubblefield, W. A. *Artificial intelligence and the design of expert systems*. Benjamin-Cummings Publishing Co., Inc., 1990.

Lyons, J. E., Runge, M. C., Laskowski, H. P., and Kendall, W. L. "Monitoring in the context of structured decision-making and adaptive management." *Journal of Wildlife Management* 72, no. 8 (2008): 1683–1692.

Mehta, A. D. and Desai, D. A. "A Review of Industrial Engineering Technique: An Application and Future Scope of Work." *International Journal of Management* 2 (2014): 29–36.

Miller, A. *Environmental problem solving: psychosocial barriers to adaptive change*. New York: Springer-Verlag, 1999.

Nichols, J. D. and Williams, B. K. "Monitoring for conservation." *Trends in ecology and evolution* 21, no. 12 (2006): 668–673.

Noon, B. R. and Murphy, D. D. "Management of the spotted owl: the interaction of science, policy, politics, and litigation." In *Principles of Conservation Biology*, 2nd ed., 380–388. Sunderland, MA: C. R. Carroll. Sinauer Associates, 1997.

Nyhus, P., Fischer, H., Madden, F., and Osofsky, S. "Taking the bite out of wildlife damage the challenges of wildlife compensation schemes." *Conservation in Practice* 4, no. 2 (2003): 37–43.

Ogutu-Ohwayo, R. "The effects of predation by Nile perch, Lates niloticus L., on the fish of Lake Nabugabo, with suggestions for conservation of endangered endemic cichlids." *Conservation Biology* 7, no. 3 (1993): 701–711.

Paparone, C. R., Anderson, R. A., and McDaniel Jr, R. R. "Where military professionalism meets complexity science." *Armed Forces & Society* 34, no. 3 (2008): 433–449.

Pivello, V. R. and Norton, G. A. "FIRETOOL: an expert system for the use of prescribed fires in Brazilian savannas." *Journal of Applied Ecology* 33 *(1996):* 348–356.

Snow, R. W., Brien, M. L., Cherkiss, M. S., Wilkins, L., and Mazzotti, F. J. "Dietary habits of the Burmese python, Python molurus bivittatus, in Everglades National Park, Florida." *Herpetological Bulletin* 101 (2007): 5–7.

Stankey, George H., Clark, Roger N., Bormann, Bernard T. (eds.). *Learning to manage a complex ecosystem: adaptive management and the Northwest Forest Plan*. Res. Pap. PNW- RP-567. Portland, OR: US Department of Agriculture, Forest Service, Pacific Northwest Research Station, 2006.

Stewart, T. A. "How to think with your gut." *Business* 2, no. 3 (2002): 11.

US Fish and Wildlife Service. *Conserving the Future: Wildlife Refuges and the Next Generation*. The National Wildlife Refuge System, US Fish and Wildlife Service, Department of the Interior, 2011.

Williams, B. K., Nichols, J. D., and Conroy, M. J. *Analysis and management of animal populations*. Academic Press, 2002.

Woodford, D. J., Ivey, P., Jordaan, M. S., Kimberg, P. K., Zengeya, T., and Weyl, O. L. "Optimising invasive fish management in the context of invasive species legislation in South Africa." *Bothalia-African Biodiversity & Conservation* 47, no. 2 (2017): 1–9.

Image Credits

CHAPTER FOUR

Management Planning for Success

Learning Outcomes

After participating in learning experiences related to this chapter, students should be able to:

- Compare and contrast strategic, fundamental, process, and means objectives.
- Write a SMART means objective.
- Assess a management plan to determine if critical components are included.
- Describe the direct and byproduct functions of a management plan.
- Explain how the management planning process leads to development of a management plan.
- Evaluate a management planning process using a PrOACT decision framework.
- Compare a management plan to a simple business plan.
- Describe the relationship between a fundamental objective and a monitoring plan.

A One-Minute Summary

The wildlife management plan is the most basic tool used by our profession. The plan is a physical document that is produced by a multi-phase management planning process. Agencies and organizations use management plans to document decisions regarding habitat management, population management, harvest management, and endangered species recovery, at international, national, regional, and local scales.

The planning process involves several intentional steps that are centered upon the PrOACT decision-making process that we introduced in chapter 3. The activities surrounding development of the plan, including stakeholder development and discussions about issues, may eventually be just as important as the written management plan.

Planning involves the determination of a hierarchical set of objectives, starting with the acknowledgement of the strategic objectives of the organization, the fundamental objective to be achieved through the specific management effort, the process objectives for how the planning process will unfold, and the means objectives that describe in detail the actions that have been selected.

Monitoring is a critical part of the planning process and should be designed to directly evaluate the progress towards the fundamental objective. Monitoring prior to the implementation of management provides a baseline to compare following management, and subsequent monitoring should feed back into the organization to provide learning that will improve management decisions in the future.

Principles for Your Toolkit

Agency mission trumps all: The mandated or legal purpose(s) of the land or water body in question provides the foundation for the population and/or habitat goals, objectives, and management strategies. A management plan will not be approved if its proposals are in opposition to the agency's goals, and the flavor of management actions will represent the culture, history, and land ethics held by the agency that is responsible for the management plan (USFWS 2002).

Objectives drive the planning process: The decision-making process is often rushed, skipping the consideration of objectives, by those who assume everyone knows or agrees on the underpinning foundations of the decision process. Managers also may confuse the type of objectives, which range from strategic objectives of the agency or organization to fundamental objectives for a decision-specific situation to means objectives used to carry out the management action (Figure 4.1).

Monitor to inform your objectives: It may be easy to fall into a trap of setting up a monitoring program that attempts to monitor everything on a refuge or wildlife management area or reservoir, except for the single thing that would inform the progress towards meeting the fundamental objective. Once a manager has defined a fundamental objective that includes a target level for population size, habitat characteristic, or human use level, a monitoring program must be designed to provide a measure of that quantity. Ironically, blanket monitoring programs designed to record the status of a multitude of species may risk wasting staff time and energy (Nichols and Williams 2006).

A Problem: A Wetland Management Plan

A smile crept onto Mel Oto's face as he re-read the wetland management plan on his desk. Sometimes he felt like a watchmaker. Tinkering with natural systems could be rewarding, but it could be frustrating, too.

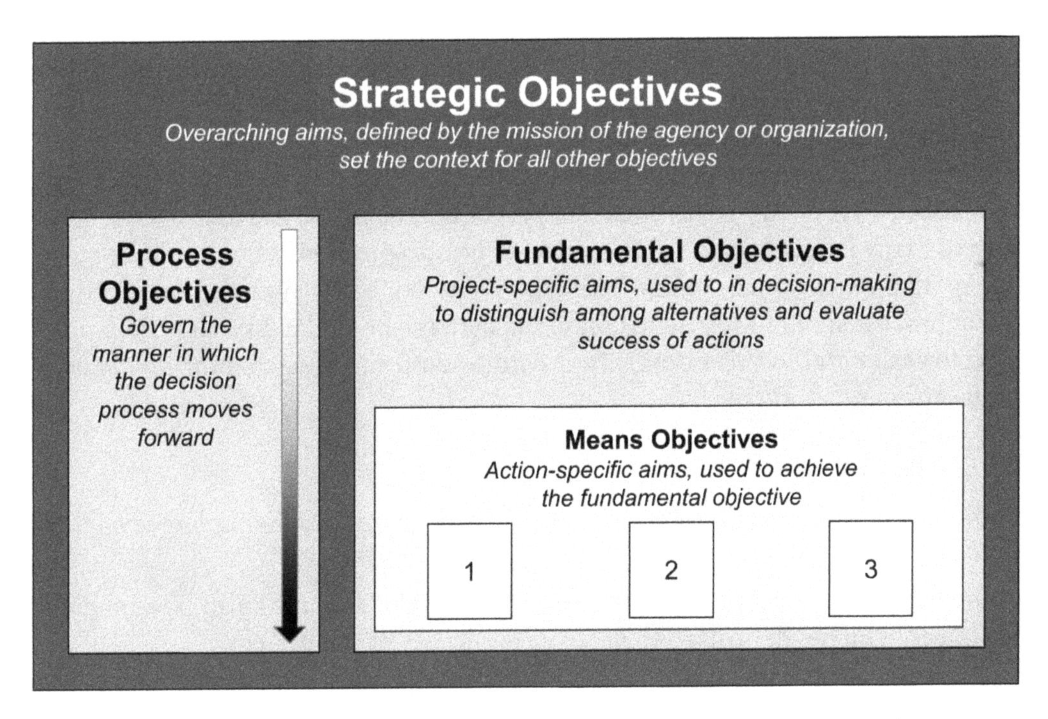

FIGURE 4.1 Relationship among four types of objectives involved in the management planning process: strategic, process, fundamental, and means objectives.

The management plan in his hands documented a decade of attempts to effectively manage habitat at the Clear Creek Wildlife Management Area (WMA). The WMA contained about 600 acres of land used for public hunting, and this area was particularly of interest to Mel. The wetlands in this area were filled with water in the fall with very large pumps. In the summer, the wetlands were drained to low levels to encourage annual plants to grow. Ducks loved seeds on annual smartweed, in particular. He had been charged with developing a management plan to provide habitat for migrating waterfowl and shorebirds, as well as breeding habitat for non- game birds and other wildlife.

"Hmmmm ..." Mel mused. "This soil data for Clear Creek WMA looks interesting—much of it is hydric. But the wetlands are so crowded with cattail and reed canary grass. Not a lot of open water for ducks. Should be a good place for a management project."

Recently, Mel's supervisor had asked him to produce the management plan quickly. Specifically, Mel had been asked to determine how to remove cattails and reed canary grass to create open water conditions that would be favorable to migrating ducks. Mel knew that some biologists in his agency favored prescribed grazing as a way to create openings in wetlands. Others argued that cattle took too much time to manage, and they favored herbicides. Pheasants Forever, a local conservation group, hoped that the agency could restore the site's upland areas with native grasses that would create dense cover for ring-necked pheasants, but the local Audubon chapter reminded him that shorebirds needed sparse vegetation surrounding mud flats for optimum habitat—it seemed pheasants and shorebirds might not be able to co-exist. Prescribed burns were feared by nearby farmers and ranchers, yet they could be used very effectively. For the past few years, dry conditions had prevented the use of burns.

With so many issues, how was Mel to decide how to proceed? How could he move forward with a management plan when there were so many ways this project might go? What process should Mel use to create the management plan? What do you need to know to assist Mel in this effort? By the time you finish this chapter, you should know the answer.

Terms and Definitions

Comprehensive Conservation Plan: A specific type of management plan developed by each national wildlife refuge.

Fundamental objective: The measurable, controllable, essential aim of a management project, which will be used to determine success of the project.

Means objective: An aim developed to accomplish the fundamental objective; an action, described in specific, measurable, achievable, results-oriented, and time-specific terms.

Monitor: To observe, check, or keep track of environmental conditions over the long-term.

Process objective: A description of the aim for how the management planning process will be carried out, typically a function of the strategic objectives of the organization.

Recovery Plan: A specific type of management plan developed for each species listed under the Endangered Species Act.

Species Survival Plan: A specific type of management plan developed to improve breeding activities, husbandry, and other decisions for species in captivity in zoos, aquaria, or other facilities.

Stakeholder (management): A party that has interest in a decision or process.

State Wildlife Action Plan: A specific type of management plan developed by state wildlife agencies to guide decisions for management of species of conservation concern.

Strategic objective: Over-arching aims of the organization or agency, determined by legal mandate and/or mission.

Wildlife management plan: A document used to capture the results of a management planning process intended to assist decision-making for wildlife, habitats, and related human activities.

The Wildlife Management Plan

A **wildlife management plan** is used to properly manage wildlife habitats, populations, and associated recreational activities. A stonemason uses a mallet and chisel to form stones. An auto mechanic relies on sockets and wrenches. An accountant would be lost without a calculator and pencil. Similarly, the management plan is the basic tool for a wildlife manager.

Although the management plan is a physical document, it represents a planning process that assesses goals and proposes a realistic set of actions to meet those goals. Historically, management plans focused on ensuring populations of fish and game to maximize recreational opportunities associated with these species. Modern management plans address threatened and endangered species and habitats, nongame species, habitats on private lands, and captive animal species in a variety of styles, depending on the agency, zoo or aquarium, NGO, private landowner, or organization writing the plan.

Types of Wildlife Management Plans

Management plans may focus on the management of a wildlife population of interest, such as a catfish population in a reservoir or the grizzly bear population in the Rocky Mountains. Agencies create harvest management plans for fish and wildlife, plans to guide the reintroduction or stocking of individuals, plans to reduce damage by wildlife, or plans to recover a species listed under the Endangered Species Act. Habitat management plans indirectly affect wildlife populations in an effort to increase or decrease the size of the population. Regardless of the context-specific unique qualities of each management plan, the planning process represents an application of the six-step PrOACT decision-making process, covered in chapter 3 (Figure 4.2).

Some management plans are created voluntarily by organizations or agencies to address concerns of a species of interest. Regional plans may be developed by a group of state agencies to address populations of concern that need collaboration among states. **Species Survival Plans** are coordinated by zoos and other facilities accredited by the Association of Zoos and Aquariums to better manage the breeding programs, husbandry, and management of critical species. However, law, regulation, or process mandates many types of management plans. For example, a harvest management plan may be required before a state commission or legislature approves new harvest regulations. Any species listed as threatened or endangered under the **Endangered Species Act** must have an approved **Recovery Plan**. National wildlife refuges are required to have a **Comprehensive Conservation Plan** to guide management, and state wildlife agencies are required to create a **State Wildlife Action Plan** before the state can receive funding to support the management of nongame species of conservation concern.

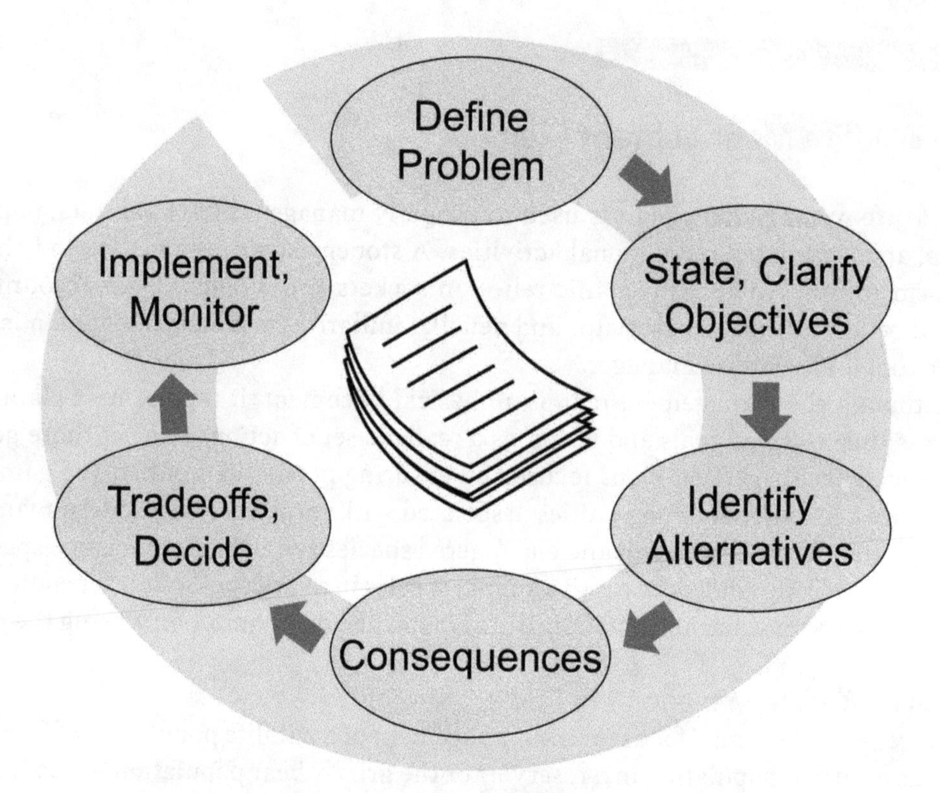

FIGURE 4.2 The management planning process is based on the PrOACT decision-making process introduced in chapter 3.

Byproduct Functions of a Management Plan

The primary reason for creating a management plan is to provide a **roadmap of actions** that are the result of formal management decisions. However, the **planning process** used to create the plan may result in byproducts that are more important than the words that a manager places on paper.

One common byproduct is the use of the management plan as a **communication tool**. The announcement of the planning process for some species may cause significant interest among stakeholders. For example, management planning for cougar populations in western states may result in opportunities for agencies and NGOs to provide information about ecosystem dynamics and predator-prey relationships. In addition, the final document will contain a significant amount of background information that may be useful to the public. For example, state wildlife agencies often place their State Wildlife Action Plan online, with supporting outreach materials, photos, and information.

Management plans require consensus on objectives from a variety of stakeholder groups, so the planning process automatically creates opportunities for **stakeholder engagement**. Although public meetings or working group meetings may be contentious in some circumstances, the opportunity for an agency or NGO to engage with

TABLE 4.1 *Representative wildlife management and conservation plans by scale (after Rupp et al. 2013).*

SCALE	EXAMPLE	DESCRIPTION
International	IUCN Species Action Plan	Compiled by IUCN specialist groups, contain an assessment of the conservation status of species and their habitats and outlines conservation priorities.
National	ESA Species Recovery Plan	Describe the current status, threats, and proposed methods for increasing species listed as threatened or endangered under the US Endangered Species Act of 1973.
Regional	Fisheries management plans	Developed by regional fishery management councils to establish fishing seasons, quotas, and closed areas for species needing coordinated efforts among agencies.
State	State wildlife action plans	Developed by states to receive federal funds provided through the Wildlife Conservation and Restoration Program and the State Wildlife Grants Program; plans are intended to conserve fish and wildlife (including habitat) in a proactive manner.
District or community	City wildlife damage management plans	Developed by natural resource districts, watershed management areas, and communities to respond to wildlife issues.
Private land owner	Farm bill-related land management plans	Developed by landowners in association with US Department of Agriculture biologists to meet requirements of federal programs designed to provide farm subsidy payments in return for conservation practices.

stakeholders who provide political and financial support should not be taken lightly. A wise management team will approach stakeholder engagement carefully and constructively rather than seeing the stakeholder process as something to get through as rapidly as possible.

Wildlife managers may also benefit from the approval of a carefully prepared management plan, as the plan serves as a **record of planning**. Supervisors of refuges or wildlife management divisions are bound to change over time, so a management plan can be a document to share with new employees who are responsible for management actions. It may be useful to write a management plan with the knowledge that some readers may access the plan at a point in the future without having participated in the planning process. A well-constructed management plan may be useful to show transparency in the decision process. Given controversies surrounding some management situations, court cases may occur. The plan may be critical documentation and evidence to of the measures taken for public input, the alternatives considered, and the process used to make the management decision.

Objectives Guide the Planning Process

The articulation of clear, meaningful objectives is critical during decision-making and the management planning process (Gregory and Keeney 2002). However, it is important for the wildlife manager to be able to distinguish between four different types of objectives (Keeney 2007; Figure 4.1).

Strategic Objectives

Strategic objectives relate to the legal mandates and/or mission statement of an agency or organization. During the management process, strategic objectives are of the widest scale, and therefore serve to guide the formation of all other objectives. Strategic objectives do not change from year to year. Here are mission statements of four federal land management agencies (see also Table 13.1):

> **The Bureau of Land Management:** "To sustain the health, diversity, and productivity of public lands for the use and enjoyment of present and future generations."
>
> **The US Fish and Wildlife Service:** "Working with others to conserve, protect, and enhance fish, wildlife, plants, and their habitats for the continuing benefit of the American people."
>
> **The US Forest Service:** "To sustain the health, diversity, and productivity of the Nation's forests and grasslands to meet the needs of present and future generations."
>
> **The National Park Service:** "Preserves unimpaired the natural and cultural resources and values of the National Park System for the enjoyment, education, and inspiration of this and future generations."

The US Fish and Wildlife Service's system of national wildlife refuges emphasizes the importance of strategic objectives in their hierarchical relationship (Adamcik et al. 2004) of the agency's mission to refuge-specific and project-specific objectives (Figure 4.3). Under this framework, a refuge would never develop goals in conflict with the agency's mission, and an individual project's objectives must work to accomplish the purpose of the refuge and the refuge system and the US Fish and Wildlife Service. Therefore, the strategic objectives of the agency set the context for all management within the agency.

Process Objectives

Process objectives are a product of the strategic objectives, the culture of the organization, and the type of planning being undertaken. These objectives dictate how the decision will be made (Keeney 2007). For example, in the Department of the Interior, the use of structured decision-making and adaptive management is strongly encouraged as a process to make decisions (Williams et al. 2009). State wildlife agencies commonly use public meetings as a process to gather feedback and elicit alternatives during management planning for harvest management. Thus, the process objectives for harvest management at a state agency are influenced by the political need to include stakeholders in the decision process.

Fundamental Objectives

The second step in a PrOACT decision process is to develop objectives. We refer to these project-specific or decision-specific objectives as **fundamental objectives.** As the decision process moves forward, the manager uses the fundamental objectives to help sort through alternatives. Which option will achieve the fundamental objective(s)?

Fundamental objectives must be measurable, and they must have the potential to be controlled by actions that will be considered. Further, as their name suggests, fundamental objectives should be essential, vital, and ultimate (all synonyms of "fundamental") descriptions of the reason for taking an action—these are the central aims for the project. Although fundamental objectives are usually stable in nature, these objectives have the potential to shift slightly from year to year, depending on the project (Figure 4.3).

Let us consider a draft proposal for a **fundamental objective** and the process to improve it:

> *"Use prescribed burning to improve 25,000 acres of ring-necked pheasant breeding habitat in eastern South Dakota during 2020."*

In truth, this is a fairly specific means objective, not a fundamental objective. The statement does not capture

QUICK COMPREHENSION CHECK

Revisit the mission statements for the four federal land management agencies. How do you think each agency might approach wildlife management from different perspectives? Which agency might be more likely to prioritize management for wildlife over recreational use of land or economic benefit from resources?

If the mission statement affects the strategic objectives of each federal land management agency, which agency do you think would be least likely to regularly use an active program of prescribed burning as a management tool for wildlife?

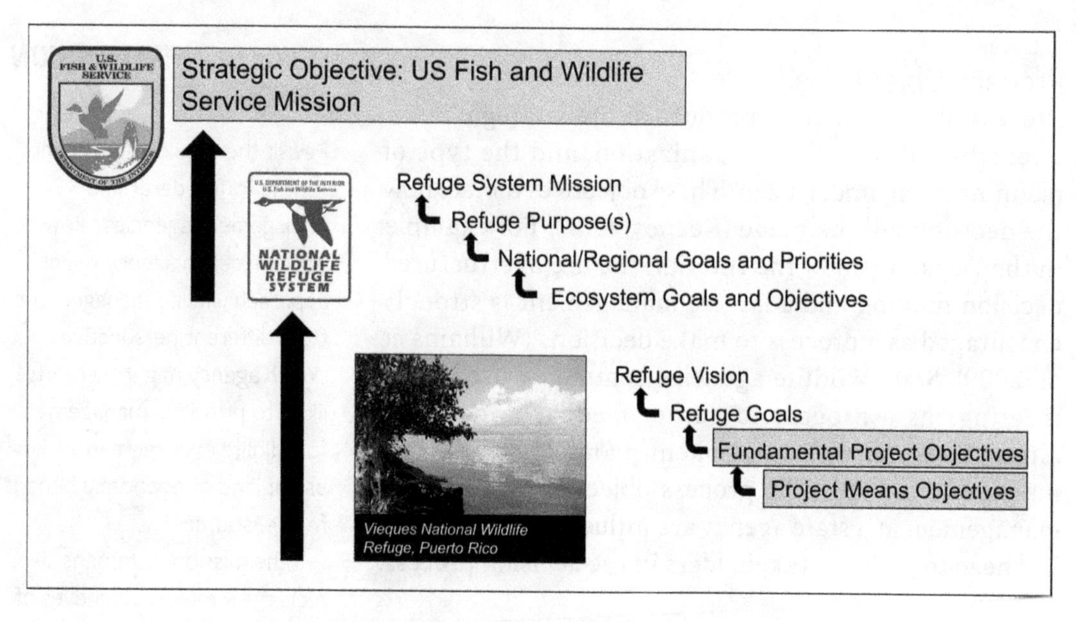

FIGURE 4.3 The hierarchy of objectives that guides decision-making within the US Fish and Wildlife Service and its National Wildlife Refuge System. In this example, the set of objectives used for planning at Vieques National Wildlife Refuge in Puerto Rico support the refuge system, which in turns supports the mission of the US Fish and Wildlife Service.

the essential reason that we are engaged in habitat management. To help reach the fundamental objective, we should ask, ***"Why is this important?"***

We might receive the reply, "Because it will increase pheasant numbers." "And, why is that important?"

Now, if we were to ask a hunter why it is important to increase pheasant numbers, they might reply, *"It will provide hunters with more opportunities to find game in the fall."*

A director of a state wildlife agency might respond in a different manner, as to why we want to increase pheasant numbers: *"We need income from pheasant hunters' license fees to finance the operations of the wildlife research staff."*

And, we ask one more time, "Why is that important?" Both individuals now reply, *"It just is."*

We now know we have reached the essential statements of fundamental objectives as viewed by a hunter and an agency director. It is critical to realize that there may be more than one functional objective for a management process. In this example, both "recreational opportunities" and "funding staff" could be captured in the final fundamental objectives for habitat management. If we modify both statements to include **measurable aspects** that can be **controlled by management**, we could state:

> *"To increase the estimated pheasant population on public hunting lands in the state to at least 2.5 million birds."*

PROJECT: The North American Waterfowl Management Plan

Fundamental Objectives

WILDLIFE	*Maintain long-term average populations of breeding ducks [1955 to 2014 in traditional survey area (TSA) and 1990 to 2014 in eastern survey area (ESA)] and periodically, 40 million or more total breeding ducks and 2.7 million or more breeding ducks in the TSA and ESA, respectively.*
PEOPLE	*Increase waterfowl conservation support among various constituencies to at least the levels experienced during the last two decades.*
HABITAT	*Conserve a habitat system with the capacity to maintain long-term average waterfowl population levels, to periodically support abundant populations, and to consistently support resource users at objective levels.*

FIGURE 4.4 The North American Waterfowl Management Plan has three fundamental objectives related to the size of duck populations, conservation engagement of citizens, and habitat status (US Fish and Wildlife Service 2014).

And:

"To maintain a pheasant hunting clientele of 175,000 licensed hunters."

Means Objectives

Means objectives are action-specific and will define the methods used to meet the fundamental objectives. It is common to confuse fundamental objectives with means objectives (Runge et al. 2013). If fundamental objectives are the end goals for our management, then means objectives are literally the means to that end. What specific actions will help achieve our fundamental aim? For example, under the umbrella of the fundamental habitat management objective of the North American Waterfowl Management Plan (Figure 4.4), a state might embark on a local project (one of many that will help accomplish the overall fundamental objective) to restore a wetland.

However, "restore a wetland" is not a well-stated means objective. To allow management teams to carry out actions effectively and efficiently means objectives need to be **s**pecific, **m**easurable, **a**chievable, **r**esults-oriented, and **t**ime-specific (SMART).

To make "restore wetland habitat" SMART, we could rewrite it as:

"Restore 750 acres of palustrine wetland habitat by working with willing landowners in Johnson County during 2025."

How do we get SMART means objectives (Adamcik et al. 2004)?

Specific. Word objectives clearly. Specify who will do the action, what will be done, when and where and why it will be accomplished.

Measurable. Monitoring will be meaningless without a measurable aim. We need a quantitative measure for success. How many? How dense? What level? To what degree?

Achievable. Check to be sure that the objective is realistic and achievable. There is no value in stating an objective that requires more from staff, the land, or wildlife than it can deliver in the time period provided.

Results-oriented. What is the desired end result? What habitat or population condition is envisioned?

Time-fixed. Include the time period during which the management aim is to be accomplished. Do you desire the result in one month, one year, or five years?

QUICK COMPREHENSION CHECK

What does the acronym SMART describe about a well-written means objective?

What components of SMART can you find in the rewritten means objective for wetland habitat?

An effective management planning process relies on careful objective statements and consideration of all four types of objectives. However, the two most important to the planning process are the fundamental objective(s), to serve as the litmus test to determine if the plan is successful, and the means objective(s), as the descriptions of the selected actions.

The Three-Phase Planning Process

A management plan is a document. The document is created through a detailed, step-by-step decision process, which allows a manager to break an assignment to make a tough decision into parts, each with separate functions and items for a to-do list. The process makes order from a process that might seem overwhelming. Planning processes vary slightly by agency and organization (Rupp et al. 2013), but they typically share the following three phases and steps, modified from the process used by the Natural Resources Conservation Service (2014).

First Phase

The first four steps are part of a preliminary process to **gather information to serve as a background** for later decision-making. These steps cover the problem, definition, and objectives parts of the PrOACT decision process. During the planning process, the team can begin to take notes and write introductory portions of the management plan.

Step One: Define Your Plan's Focus

Prior to writing the plan and launching into the public portion of the planning process, it is critical for the decision team to define the problem addressed by the plan. Where are you now with this issue? How does your agency or organization's mission interact with this management problem? Why are you writing the plan? Is it necessary to spend time and resources on this problem? Who are the stakeholders for this plan? Who will be reading it and participating in the planning process during at least one step? What time frame have you been given for the plan's implementation?

During this step, it is important for you and your decision team to develop a draft of the fundamental objective(s), which may change slightly or be fleshed out as the process moves forward. Nevertheless, it may help to define the problem clearly, if you think about the fundamental objective during this step.

This step also allows an opportunity to review your organization's process objectives. How will the decision be made? How will stakeholders be involved? What is expected of your decision team?

Step Two: Stakeholder/Client Input Regarding Problem

Your process objectives will guide how stakeholder input is included during this step. Perhaps you are required or encouraged to hold public meetings. Perhaps you need to gather a set of experts related to the issue to help further define the problem. The focus of the stakeholder input meetings should be to (1) discuss and clarify the problem, and (2) discuss your proposed fundamental objective(s) for the management action.

As you meet with stakeholders, listen to them and document their concerns. You may wish to record meetings using audio or video to revisit later, but at a minimum the discussions at input meetings should be recorded in detailed notes. The notes may be used to document who participated, what concerns they raised, and the general level of agreement with the fundamental objective(s). Does it appear stakeholders are supportive of your initial fundamental objective statement? This level of agreement may help you determine if a form of active conflict resolution or negotiation is needed before you continue (chapter 3, Figure 3.6)

A discussion of alternative management actions is not the primary purpose of initial stakeholder meetings, but it is likely that stakeholders may offer advice on management actions. These should be recorded for future use, as they may be quite helpful later in the decision process as alternatives are developed. However, the facilitator of the meeting should return the meeting's focus to discussion that helps define the problem from the perspective of the stakeholders.

As this step concludes, you should have a problem statement that is clearly defined by your organization and its stakeholders. In addition, you will have a revised statement of the fundamental objectives to use in the planning process. You may also have developed a valuable list of project collaborators who are willing to provide monetary or in-kind contributions of resources to assist with the management actions.

Step Three: Define Critical Constraints

Document the resources available to use in the management actions within your organization and from any collaborators. Given that list of resources, what limitations do you see? What other limiting factors are present? What is your budget? Does the time frame established in step one provide constraints to possible actions or allow for unique opportunities?

Perhaps you can already see some constraints on management actions. For example, an urban grassland may not be able to use prescribed burning as a potential management tool because of city regulations.

Step Four: Determine Current Resource Status

Your decision later in the process will most likely be a function of the current status of the target of your management. For example, if your fishery is currently at the goal for population level, then your decision for harvest may be more liberal than if the population size was below the goal.

Gather the available monitoring data or research information for the area and species in question. Perform an assessment so that you can describe where you are now, with regard to the fundamental objective that you have established. If this step is ignored, there will be no way to tell if your management changed the population or habitat.

Second Phase

With the management problem clearly defined, the next four steps guide the planning team through the **heart of the decision-making process**. In terms of the PrOACT process, this phase covers the alternatives, consequences, and tradeoffs steps.

Step Five: Agree on Decision Control Rules

In step one, you documented your organization's preferences for a decision process. It is now time to put this process to paper and describe it. If you are using a structured method that is quantitative, such as a decision tree, you must create the model so that your team and your supervisors approve of this process. If you are using an expert system to guide you, you need to distribute it to your decision team for evaluation. If you are using an intuitive process, you need to establish ground rules, describe the process that will be used, and define roles for members of your team.

You may wish to involve key stakeholders in this discussion. What process will be used to evaluate the alternatives?

Step Six: Formulate Management Action Alternatives

Of course, this step is the step that everyone has been waiting for. Often, participants want to skip directly to this step! As a good project manager, you may have been pushing back discussions of possible management actions during phase one. But the second phase of planning is the time for your team to openly discuss alternative actions (means objectives) that may potentially achieve the fundamental objective.

Your team should remember the three-legged stool principle for wildlife management (Figure 1.1) for complete consideration of alternatives that may be used to achieve objectives. Can you think of ways to directly manage the wildlife population, their habitat, or the people that interact with the species? Consider how your actions mimic the historic frequency and timing of processes such as flooding, fires, and grazing.

As you develop a list of possible strategies, consult with external partners. Perhaps your team is interacting with NGOs, local conservation organizations, other state or federal wildlife agencies, or tribal natural resource agencies. The use of peer review and input from stakeholders will provide more confidence to your team. Expert assessment is valuable to ensure that the plan will use appropriate techniques and protocols.

You may be able to find themes within all options placed on the table, so that you can refine the alternative list into a manageable list of realistic management alternatives. However, document all alternatives put forward.

Be sure that your list of alternatives includes a "do nothing" or "status quo" alternative. This is always appropriate as a comparison to other actions. Deciding to take no new action is a potential decision.

Step Seven: Evaluate Alternatives

Go back to your list of constraints to see if any apply to the actions on the table. Are any actions not worthy of further consideration because of constraints?

For the remaining alternative management actions, evaluate and describe the potential consequences. Describe their effect on the population or habitat. In some situations, this step involves the use of predictive models (Conroy 1993).

Following the evaluation of the consequences of each management action, compare your alternatives. Quantify, if possible, the tradeoffs. Perhaps one action is less expensive to implement, but it will increase nest survival of an endangered bird species by a lesser degree than a more expensive alternative. Your team may find it useful to develop utility values (chapter 3, Figure 3.8) for each of the potential outcomes from each action, and a process similar to a decision tree process may help you sort through complicated trade-offs.

If applicable, your team should also attempt to integrate uncertainties involved with each alternative with regard to the potential outcomes. What is the potential for each action to allow your team to reach the fundamental objective? All of these decision parameters (consequences, trade-offs/utilities, uncertainties) should be placed in the decision control process that you defined in step five.

Step Eight: Arrive at Decision

Use the decision control process that you selected in step five to integrate the trade-offs of each possible action to select a way forward.

There may be a set of actions prescribed as part of a general "action set" that is chosen. It is now time to develop the SMART means objectives to describe your proposed actions.

Third Phase

With a clearly defined problem and a decision for action based on a rigorous and clearly documented decision process, it is now time to **implement the decision and monitor the results**. In the PrOACT decision process, this represents the implementation, or "act" steps (chapter 3, Figure 3.1).

Step Nine: Implement the Decision

Use your SMART means objective statements as a basis to clearly define your action plan. Under each means objective statement, you may want to go into more detail. Which budget account will be used? Which vehicles are available? Which staff positions will be assigned to the task? Who will supervise a particular portion of the management action? When will the first step start?

Start the bulldozers, stock the fish, or enact new harvest regulations. Implementation may proceed!

Step Ten: Monitor and Evaluate Your Decision

Revisit the information you gathered to define the baseline conditions in step four. At an appropriate point (described in the implementation plan in step nine), gather updated monitoring information. Review and evaluate these new data to determine the level of your success at meeting your fundamental objective. As this occurs, remember to incorporate learning processes in your team and organization by providing proper feedback to your team and organization for possible revision or recurring planning.

QUICK COMPREHENSION CHECK

Map the three phases of development of a management plan to the steps in the PrOACT decision-making process.

The Management Plan Document

The management plan is the physical representation of the planning process. As planning moves through each step, the goal is to provide information needed to create the management plan, so there is a tight connection between the steps of the planning process and the sections of a management plan. We have noted that management plans are created in many contexts and for various purposes (Figure 4.5). However, most management plans have similar structures (Anderson et al. 2002, Hindson et al. 2005, US Fish and Wildlife Service 2002).

Section One: Introduction and Definition of Planning Context

- A statement of purpose that defines the management problem and its context
- Agency goals, the mission and strategic objective of the organization, and any guiding policies
- Any legal mandates that may have required the plan's existence or may affect its content
- A statement of rationale: what is reason for the plan?

Section Two: Background Information and Context

- A list of previous management plans, if any
- Description of the location, ecosystem and landscape, applicable history of land use patterns, climate, soils, and hydrology

FIGURE 4.5 A desert tortoise, a threatened species in the United States, hatches from its egg. Wildlife biologists conduct research on the tortoise to inform land use and conservation plans, while balancing the recovery of the species with other resource priorities in the Mojave Desert. Photo by K. Krtistina Drake, USGS.

- A map of the area of interest with appropriate details like land use patterns in the surrounding area, land cover distribution at the site, water points, water depth, etc.
- A discussion of future trends and needs
- A sub-section on the current status of the species or habitat in question, including historical trends in population size and distribution, as well as the latest monitoring information that will be used to compare with similar data after the management action is implemented
- A sub-section on potential constraints, including staffing, expertise, finances, and unique compliance requirements or legal constraints

Section Three: Goals and Objectives for the Project

- A simple section that states the aims for the project and the fundamental objective(s)

Section Four: List of Alternative Management Actions

- An annotated list of the management options that could potentially achieve the fundamental objective(s)
- A description of the predicted consequences of actions and tradeoffs among alternatives
- A description of the sources of uncertainties associated with outcomes
- A description and documentation of the process that will be used to make the decision

Section Five: The Management Decision

- A clear statement of the action or set of actions chosen and a justification for the decision
- An annotated list of the SMART means objectives with additional details needed by the action team
- A re-statement or more detailed description of consequences of the decision. What response to this management action is anticipated?

Section Six: Implementation Plan

- A detailed plan for the logistics of carrying out the management action(s) selected
- A timetable for implementation
- Staff assignments and leadership roles, including roles of external collaborators
- A list of resources needed: what is on hand, what will need to be purchased or contributed by collaborators?
- A list of compliance issues that must be followed during implementation
- By-products of the decision (law enforcement needed, public relations necessary, negative effects on other systems)
- A detailed budget and anticipated costs

Section Seven: Plan for Monitoring

- A plan for monitoring including staffing and timetables
- A description of methods used to incorporate monitoring information into a learning process. How will you know management is working? What performance measures relate to your fundamental objective?
- A description for the process used to update the management plan in the future and the connection to monitoring and learning in the next version of the plan

Section Eight: Appendices, Supporting Information

- Research summaries used to develop the plan
- Records of stakeholder interactions
- Legal assessments performed during the planning process
- References and sources for information
- Preliminary monitoring data used to support the decision
- Other information that should be recorded as part of the planning process

Developing Monitoring Schemes for Project Evaluation

It is clear from chapter 3 and the planning processes described in this chapter that monitoring is an integral part of management. However, a review of processes by NGOs, state wildlife agencies, and federal wildlife agencies will suggest that monitoring is often done off the cuff with little thought as to what is monitored and how it is monitored. Most critically, the failure of most monitoring schemes is to connect the monitoring plan to the learning plan that integrates monitoring data into a recurring decision.

Nichols and Williams (2006) describe the goals of monitoring as follows:

> Understanding the roles of monitoring in an informed conservation process helps to guide the design of monitoring programs. Monitoring data are not gathered with a vague hope that somehow they will prove useful for conservation. Instead, monitoring focuses on precisely the information needed to make conservation decisions.

The basic principle to follow in the design of a monitoring program is that monitoring should be carefully designed to allow assessment of the state of the management system in relation to the fundamental management objective. For example, federal biologists working for the North American Waterfowl Management Plan, described earlier in this chapter, must have monitoring systems in place to determine if harvest regulations and habitat management result in a population of at least 40 million total breeding ducks. Without appropriate monitoring programs, there is no way to determine if the management actions are successful.

It would be possible for example, to have cartloads of PhD dissertations completed on duck nesting success, gut parasite levels, behavioral dynamics, and taxonomic clarifications from genetics, but none of those types of information about ducks (although interesting in their own right) are useful to determine if the current management plans are effective in meeting the population goal. The question is not about the quality of the information collected, but rather the specific type of information collected.

The proper combination of planned management and monitoring is critical. In chapter 3, we described a range of approaches to the implementation of adaptive management, from trial and error to horse race designs. A robust monitoring program would include data from control areas to substantiate that the changes observed in forest structure, water clarity, or fish population size are due to the management actions and not the effects of drought or other environmental influences, as described in chapter 3. The horse race scenario (Figure 3.11), which allows simultaneous comparison between alternative management actions, provides high levels of inference and meets criteria for a rigorous experimental design (Nichols and Williams 2006).

Monitoring plans have the same logistical and monetary constraints as the management actions. Budgets are always tight, which underscores the need to purposefully design monitoring to collect information directly usable by the agency in the learning process. Cost-efficiency is an important consideration, and monitoring plans must be designed to survive through the ups and downs of state and federal budget cycles. The technique manuals produced by the American Fisheries Society and The Wildlife Society contain useful descriptions of survey methods for habitat and animal populations that can be adopted for monitoring plans.

Federal agencies such as the US Fish and Wildlife Service and the National Park Service require monitoring plans for lands under their management. The development of a robust monitoring plan for these federal agencies follows a simplified version of the management planning process described earlier in this chapter. Essentially, alternative methods of surveys and species to be monitored should be enumerated, and managers should assess the ability of each of the possible monitoring methods to provide information that is pertinent to evaluation of the fundamental objective for wildlife management.

WRAPPING UP

In our problem case, Mel is at a loss for how to begin to write a wetland habitat management plan. Can you describe the three phases of the development process to Mel? How might he incorporate the views of the various stakeholders who have interest in the project?

FIGURE 4.6 An intern at Piedmont National Wildlife Refuge near Macon, Georgia ignites the forest understory with a driptorch on a prescribed burn in 2014. Photo by Josh O'Connor, USFWS; public domain photo, Wikicommons.

Finally, it is critical to establish protocols for monitoring methods. The surveys should be repeatable, and a count or estimate should not be affected by the use of a new observer in a future year.

Decision-Making on the Ground

1: Piedmont National Wildlife Refuge: Comprehensive Conservation Plan

The Piedmont National Wildlife Refuge, north of Macon, Georgia, was established in 1939 to provide breeding ground for birds and other wildlife, a sanctuary for migratory birds, and to provide for land conservation and utilization. A series of economic hardships from the Civil War, to the depression of the 1880s, and the boll weevil's impact on the cotton industry, left almost 35% of the landscape abandoned prior to the establishment of the refuge. An early mission was to carry out a substantial erosion control program following degradation of the area farmland through intensive cotton farming.

The refuge is almost entirely forested (~75% pine, 25% hardwood), and the refuge is home to several colonies of the endangered red-cockaded woodpecker. Almost three-fourths of the loblolly pine forests are in mature size classes, which provides suitable nesting for the woodpeckers. However, the forest structure is not sustainable; as the current mature pine are harvested or die, young pines will not be able to grow into mature sizes fast enough to provide continual habitat for red-cockaded woodpeckers.

Each national wildlife refuge is required to constructed, and routinely update, a Comprehensive Conservation Plan. The plan for the Piedmont National Wildlife Refuge is intended to guide management policies for 15 years. You can access the plan online at:

https://catalog.data.gov/dataset/piedmont-national-wildlife-refuge- comprehensive-conservation-plan

APPLICATION, ANALYSIS, SYNTHESIS, AND EVALUATION

Scan the Piedmont NWR's document at the link above. Describe the area to be managed under the decisions found in this document. Where is the refuge located? What type of agency manages the refuge? What kind of habitats are involved? Are there any species of wildlife that have priority for management?

What is the purpose of this document? Who is the potential audience of the document?

Summarize the context of the management plan: Why was the document generated? What clues could you find as to the requirements to create such a document or why it was generated at the time it was generated?

This is a management plan, and all management plans should have goals. Can you find a goal statement(s) or objective statement(s) in the document? What four management alternatives were considered? Summarize each in one sentence. Which option was selected? What justifications where given? How did the refuge managers arrive at this decision?

Does the plan include proposed methods to monitor to see if the management is "working"? If so, what types of monitoring are proposed?

2: Urban Fisheries Management Planning

State wildlife agencies have been working to reverse trends in the number of fishing and hunting licenses sold in the United States. The number of hunting licenses sold peaked in the 1970s and early 1980s, while fishing licenses peaked in the mid-1980s (Figure 4.4). When we quantify the proportion of the public who purchases a hunting or fishing license, we see steep declines. Revenues collected by state agencies

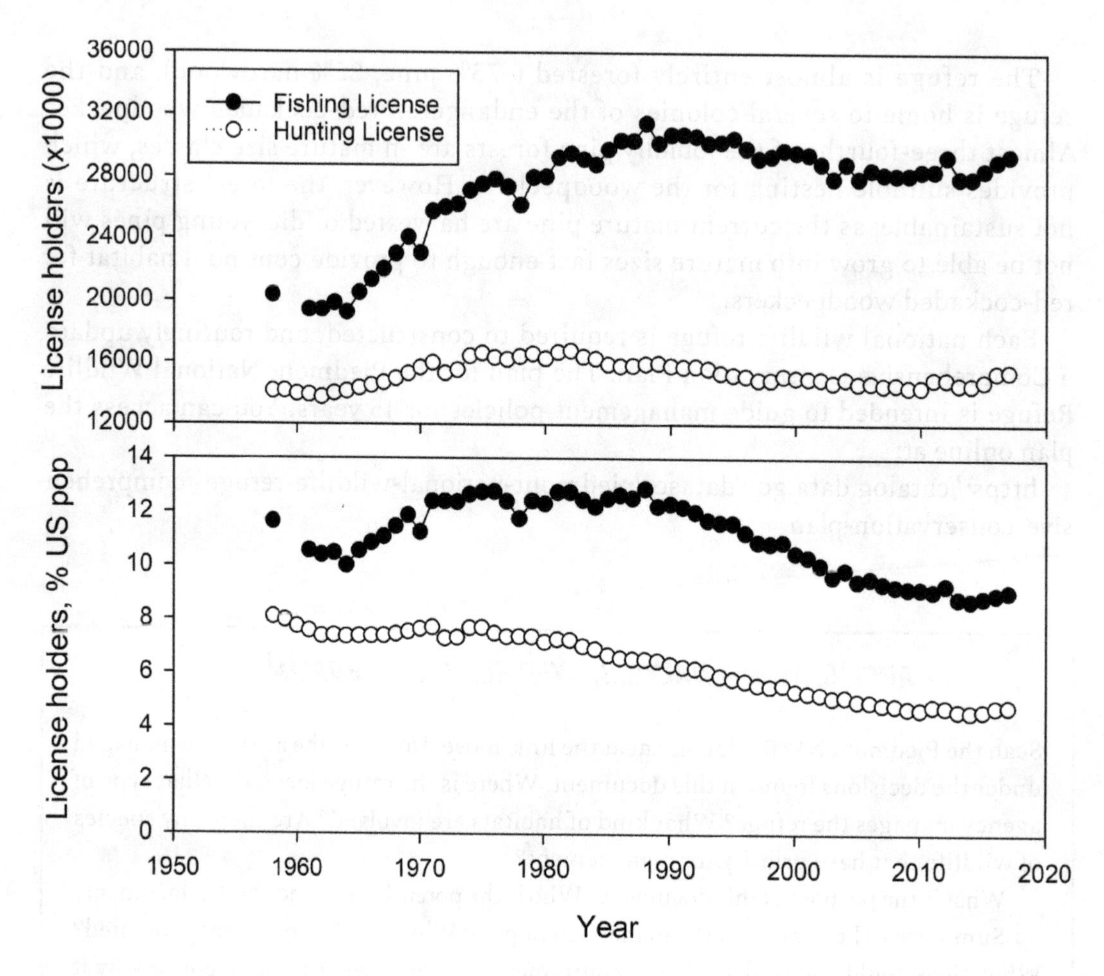

FIGURE 4.7 License holders of fishing and hunting licenses as (top) number of licenses sold and (bottom) percent of the US population. Summary figures shown here are from US Fish and Wildlife Service statistics, as cumulative totals of licenses sold in each state. A single angler who purchases a license in two states would show up as two licenses purchased in the summary, therefore the true percentage of the US population holding a license is slightly lower than the levels depicted.

from license sales has stagnated, and managers have begun to develop recruitment, retention, and reactivation (R3) programs. One potential cause for the decline in the proportion of the population purchasing licenses is the increasing urbanization of the United States. Thus, urban fisheries programs have focused on developing fish breeding habitat in city lakes, providing easy access, and fishing clinics.

APPLICATION, ANALYSIS, SYNTHESIS, AND EVALUATION

Consider a planning exercise starting in a state fisheries division to make improvements to an urban fishery with the fundamental objective to increase the number of anglers using the lakes by 30%. Who are the stakeholders you might invite to an initial meeting? Who might be interested in the management of an urban fishery? List at least three stakeholders under each category provided in the table below.

Potential Stakeholders In Urban Fisheries Management

INDIVIDUAL CITIZENS	SMALL BUSINESSES AND CORPORATIONS	NON-GOVERNMENTAL ORGANIZATIONS (NGOS)	GOVERNMENT AGENCIES

You have been given the initial means objective statement shown below, which you recognize does not meet the SMART criteria:

"Provide fishing jetties during the restoration of Copper Creek Lake."

Using the characteristics described in this chapter to create SMART means objectives, decide on ways that you might make the statement better. Of course, this is a hypothetical situation, so you may have leeway to be creative in the face of a lack of details.

Specific:

Measurable:

Achievable:

Results-oriented:

Time-fixed:

Now, write your final SMART means objective here by combining the characteristics listed above:

Consider the fundamental objective to increase the number of anglers using the lakes by 30%. What kind of monitoring program would provide information on the current status of the lake and the future status after the jetties are created?

Sources of Information and Further Reading

Adamcik, R. S., E. S. Bellantoni, D. C. DeLong Jr., J. H. Schomaker, D. B. Hamilton, M. K. Laubhan, and R. L. Schroeder. *Writing Refuge Management Goals and Objectives: A Handbook*. Washington, DC: US Fish and Wildlife Service, Department of the Interior, 2004.

Anderson, J. T., Forcey, G. M., Osbourne, J. D., and Spurgeon, A. B. "The importance and use of wildlife management plans: An example from the Camp Dawson Collective Training Area." *West Virginia Academy of Sciences* 74 (2002): 8–17.

City of Davis. *Wild Turkey Population Management Plan, City of Davis*. City of Davis, California, 2016.

Gregory, R. S., and R. L. Keeney. "Making smarter environmental management decisions." *Journal of the American Water Resources Association* 38 (2002): 1601–1612.

Hindson, J., D. D. Hoggarth, M.Krishna, C. C. Mees, and C. O'Neill. *How to manage a fishery: a simple guide to writing a fishery management plan*. London: Marine Resources Assessment Group, London Centre for Environmental Education, Ahmedabad, Scales Consulting, LTD., 2005.

IUCN Bangladesh. *Gharials of Bangladesh*. Bangladesh: IUCN, International Union for Conservation of Nature, Bangladesh Country Office, Dhaka, 2016.

Keeney, R. L. "Developing objectives and attributes." In *Advances in decision analysis: from foundations to applications*, 104–128. New York: Cambridge University Press, 2007.

Mid-Atlantic Fishery Management Council and Atlantic States Marine Fisheries Commission. *Fishery Management Plan for the Bluefish Fishery*. Mid-Atlantic Fishery Management Council and Atlantic States Marine Fisheries Commission, 1989.

National Marine Fisheries Service. *Final Recovery Plan for the North Pacific Right Whale* (Eubalaena japonica). Silver Spring, MD: National Marine Fisheries Service, Office of Protected Resources, 2013.

Natural Resources Conservation Service. *National Planning Procedures Handbook* (NPPH), 1st ed. Washington, DC: Natural Resources Conservation Service, US Department of Agriculture, 2014.

New Hampshire Fish and Game Department. *New Hampshire Wildlife Action Plan 2015*, Revised Edition. Concord, NH: New Hampshire Fish and Game Department, 2015.

Nichols, J. D., and Williams, B. K. "Monitoring for conservation." *Trends in Ecology & Evolution* 21, no. 12 (2006): 668–673.

Runge, M. C., J. B. Grand, and M. S. Mitchell. "Structured decision making." In *Wildlife management and conservation: contemporary principles and practices*, 51–72. Baltimore, MD: The John Hopkins Press, 2013.

Rupp, S. P., A. M. Muñoz, and R. R. Lopez. "Conservation planning for wildlife and wildlife habitat." In *Wildlife management and conservation: contemporary principles and practices*, 51–72. Baltimore, MD: The John Hopkins Press, 2013.

US Fish and Wildlife Service. *Habitat Management Plans, Part 620: Habitat Management Practices*. US Fish and Wildlife Service, US Department of the Interior, 2002. Accessed 2 March, 2018. https://www.fws.gov/policy/620fw1.html

US Fish and Wildlife Service. *Piedmont National Wildlife Refuge Comprehensive Conservation Plan*. US Fish and Wildlife Service (Southeast Region), US Department of the Interior, 2010.

US Fish and Wildlife Service. *Revised Objectives: An Addendum to the 2012 North American Waterfowl Management Plan*. US Fish and Wildlife Service, Department of the Interior, 2014.

Williams, B. K, R. C. Szaro, and C. D. Shapiro. *Adaptive management: The U.S. Department of the Interior technical guide*. Washington, DC: US Department of the Interior, 2009.

Zimmerer, T. W., Scarborough, N. M., and Wilson, D. *Essentials of entrepreneurship and small business management*. Upper Saddle River, NJ: Prentice Hall, 2005.

Image Credits

Fig. 4.2b: Source: https://www.clker.com/clipart-763502.html.
Fig. 4.3a: Source: https://www.fws.gov/refuge/Vieques/multimedia/generalPhotos.html#.
Fig. 4.3b: Source: https://www.fws.gov/refuge/Vieques/multimedia/generalPhotos.html#.
Fig. 4.3c: Source: https://www.fws.gov/refuge/Vieques/multimedia/generalPhotos.html#.
Fig. 4.4: Source: https://www.fws.gov/migratorybirds/pdf/management/AHM/HMWGReport2014.pdf.
Fig. 4.5: Source: https://www.flickr.com/photos/usgeologicalsurvey/16490346262/in/photolist-r8ckqS-246daN5-9kWy9e-oc5pqG-aetBkg-p4Z1qs-bYBwpQ-9kYoo6-nxsLKt-Rwi7g1-ejJ4M8-QRZGn4-pYF1xw-9m2ou5-99xYtf-nGaSVy-8rgSD3-UAvsF9-ntCBay-fKqYjD-ewx-v7Z-aBA6JJ-4DX1uB-pLQZjn-fm1DJb-dJQYk.
Fig. 4.6: Source: https://commons.wikimedia.org/wiki/File:Piedmont_C26_Prescribed_Fire_(13777123595).jpg.

CHAPTER FIVE

Values and Ethics in Wildlife Management

Learning Outcomes

After participating in learning experiences related to this chapter, students should be able to:

- Describe how values and attitudes influence human behavior.
- Explain why stakeholders vary in their attitudes and behaviors related to conservation and wildlife management.
- Contrast the utilitarian value orientation with the mutualistic value orientation with regard to views on wildlife.
- List ethical expectations of public workers based on agency or professional codes of ethics.
- Provide examples of pressures to violate codes of ethics for wildlife managers.
- Describe how ethical considerations may be included in the decision-making process.
- Evaluate ethical dilemmas to determine how contrasting value orientations or ethics are responsible for the dilemma.

A One-Minute Summary

People vary in their perspective on what is right and what is wrong. Differences between perspectives are a result of basic philosophical views and personal experiences, and the contrasts in views can be seen during public meetings on contentious issues in wildlife management, such as harvest management, human-wildlife conflict, or planning for habitat management.

Wildlife managers encounter a variety of situations in which ethics are important considerations. Professionally, there are standards known as ethical codes that describe proper actions of employees to ensure trust between the public and employees of agencies and companies. Employees should not accept gifts that influence decisions, they should not use their positions for personal gain, and their actions should be legal, honest, and in line with their obligations to stakeholders.

Ethical decisions range from decisions that involve legal questions or potential violations of codes of ethics to ethical dilemmas—situations in which two stakeholders may logically argue from an ethical position to support contrasting actions. Ethics can and should be incorporated into the PrOACT decision-making process, especially during discussion of objectives, evaluation of consequences, and examination of trade-offs. Discarding or ignoring ethical concerns from stakeholders may destroy the potential for success because of the emotional attachment to positions that arise when ethics are used to support a position.

Principles for Your Toolkit

Cognitive hierarchy of human behavior: The behaviors displayed by people, including on matters related to conservation and wildlife, may be explained or predicted by assessing their basic beliefs and attitudes (Figure 5.1). Thus, wildlife managers who are involved in a controversial decision-making process may benefit from evaluation

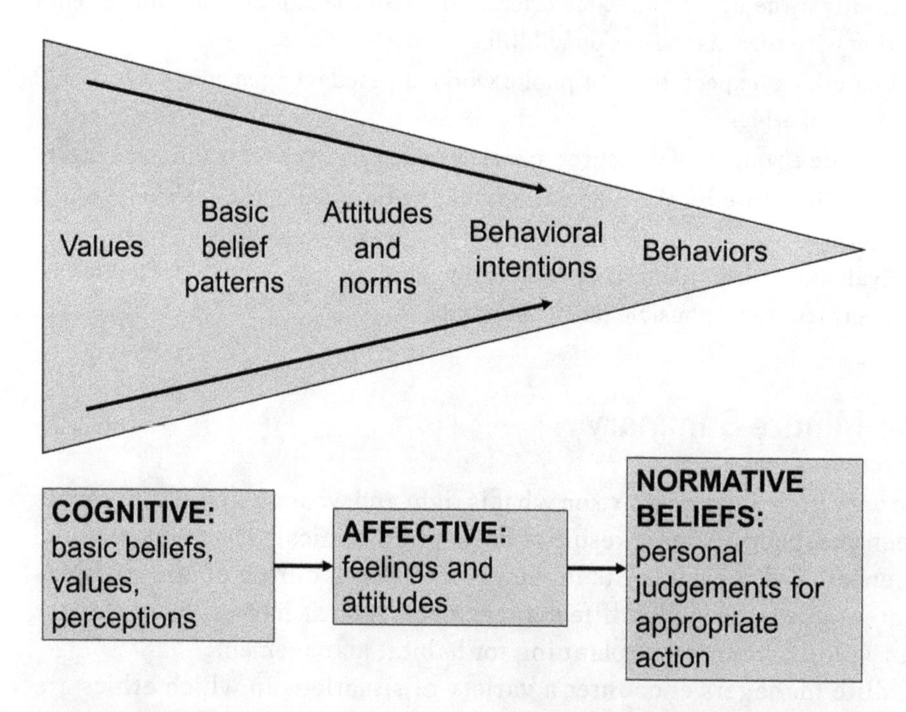

FIGURE 5.1 The cognitive hierarchy model of human behavior, modified from Fulton et al. (1996) and Vaske and Donnelly (1999). Behaviors result from values, beliefs, and attitudes. Variation in behaviors among subjects may be the result of different underlying cognitive or affective characteristics.

of the distribution of their stakeholders' basic beliefs (e.g., what proportion believe wildlife should benefit humans [utilitarian] and what proportion believe humans and wildlife should co-exist peacefully [mutualistic]) and their perceptions with regard to an issue (e.g., during a mountain lion reintroduction, how prevalent is the perception that mountain lions will kill large numbers of livestock or the perception that mountain lions will be good for ecosystem balance).

Value orientations: The philosophical perspectives of stakeholders can be evaluated with a series of questions that produce a metric corresponding to a specific axis of interest (e.g., utilitarianism, mutualism). Although it is difficult to extract and quantify raw information on philosophical perspectives, value orientations allow the description of those perspectives. For example, a person may score as highly utilitarian but as low mutualistic, which suggests they would support efforts to manage wildlife populations for the benefit of humans.

A Problem: A Rough Day at the Office for a Fisheries Biologist

Heather just finished a long, emotional day of public hearings. She was a fisheries biologist for a state wildlife agency, and one of her commissioners persuaded the fisheries division head to consider legalizing spear-fishing in one of the state's reservoirs. The commissioner was a scuba diver, and he enjoyed spear-fishing in the Caribbean. He and a handful of stakeholders wanted to be able to enjoy the activity in their home state.

The reservoir selected for the trial run was a favorite of traditional anglers as well, especially for those pursuing largemouth bass. The first public meeting, held today, attracted a large contingency from the local fishing club, as well as animal rights activists. The traditional anglers used their time to complain about potential effects of the divers staking out areas of the shoreline with their dive boats, which would make the area unusable by anglers. Further, the traditionalists worried about the effect of the spearfishers taking a disproportionately high number of trophy-sized fish, as their fishing would be more like hunting than fishing. The animal rights representatives presented videos of fish writhing underwater after being shot by a spear. The few supporters at the meeting argued that the number of spearfishers would be very low, and the new authorization would simply provide a new type of recreation in the state.

Heather's job at the meeting was to facilitate the conversations and to try to give everyone equal time to discuss their opinions on the record. But, now, she had a headache as she thought about the way forward. Luckily, she kept a fishing pole in the back of her state-issued truck, which had a large image of a bass wrapped along the side of the vehicle. She deviated a few miles from her way home to visit another small recreation area, and she sat on the dock and watched a bobber for an hour as she cleared her head.

What ethical considerations do you see imbedded in this story? What information do you need to learn how you might suggest alternate actions or ways forward for

Heather? What information would you need to help determine if spearfishing was acceptable from an ethical standpoint?

By the time you finish this chapter, you should be able to find the answer.

Terms and Definitions

Ethics (personal): Moral principles that govern a person's behavior or the conducting of an activity.

Ethics (professional): The moral correctness of specified conduct as evaluated by members of a professional society or body.

Values: Enduring beliefs about preferred modes of conduct or desired states of existence; guiding principles in life.

Values and Behaviors in Wildlife Management

A universal truth experienced by all wildlife managers is that it is rare for all stakeholders in a wildlife management decision to agree. Further, many stakeholders do not agree with natural resources professionals. The question of "What is right?" has the potential to disrupt management planning and decision-making. Public oversight of wildlife management brings the professional ethics of wildlife managers under a spotlight.

Laws are based on what society, at large, believes is correct and good, in terms of human actions, and we judge others based on ethical standards. Variation in wildlife laws from state to state in the US, as well as country to country around the world, emphasizes how different cultures and traditions may result in different ethical statements on topics ranging from whether hunting is allowed to the private ownership of wildlife.

Why doesn't everyone agree? Our experiences and basic beliefs and perceptions affect our attitudes, and our attitudes affect our actions. This relationship is known as the **cognitive hierarchy of human behavior** (Figure 5.1), which has been adapted by wildlife researchers to explain the variety of personal judgements that exist on critical wildlife issues (Vaske and Donnelly 1999, Glickman et al. 2012).

Values, in this context, might be defined as enduring beliefs about preferred modes of conduct or desired states of existence (Rokeach 1973). Therefore, values are goals that transcend situations, vary in importance, and serve as guiding principles to an individual (Schwartz 1992). Broadly, values are often shared by many members of a society (Figure 5.1). For example, most parents value a good future for their children, and many individuals share a common value for states of being such as safety, food security, and pleasant surroundings. Shared values, however, do not necessarily indicate similarities in behavior. For example, many people value the beauty of their neighborhood, but only a portion of these people recycle plastic or paper products. Similarly, the vast majority of farmers will express value for soil quality, but not all farmers engage in soil conservation measures.

The underlying reasons that humans (even those with shared values) exhibit different behaviors is related to personal experiences in life, which vary between individuals. Our unique experiences create distinct patterns of basic beliefs, which affect attitudes. Attitudes, in turn, affect behaviors.

Human dimensions scientists focus on understanding behaviors of people as they relate to wildlife, and cognitive hierarchy is one framework used to study human behaviors as they relate to wildlife. How supportive will the public be towards new regulations that allow limited harvest of mountain lions? Why do some anglers stop fishing? How might wildlife managers effectively engage farmers to provide habitat for northern bobwhites?

As Figure 5.1 suggests, one method to predict behaviors is to determine the feelings or attitudes of individuals toward a species of wildlife, and we might be able to predict attitudes towards wildlife if we know something about an individual's basic beliefs and values. As an example, Glickman et al. (2012) used the cognitive hierarchy framework to evaluate support for management alternatives for protection, selective killing, or hunting of wolves in a national park in Italy. A survey was used to assess perceptions and basic beliefs about the impact of wolves on other wildlife and livestock, and other questions were used to assess attitudes towards wolves. Those who believed that wolves had negative impacts on wildlife and livestock were less likely to have positive attitudes towards wolves and less likely to support protection of wolves.

Managers in this Italian wolf scenario confront the task of making decisions about wolves with a diverse group of stakeholders with contrasting beliefs and attitudes towards wolves, which leads to differing opinions about the best alternative. From an ethical perspective, stakeholders disagree, at least initially, on what is "right." One solution is to use formal decision-making processes, which will most likely begin with some conflict resolution discussions to establish objectives that are agreeable to all parties. Perhaps a population goal for wolves can be established that satisfies stakeholders who want to minimize harm to their livestock, while still providing for sustainable populations of wolves as a part of the ecosystem. The contrasting viewpoints and ethical stances must be addressed if the management actions are to be successful.

Establishing Value Orientations to Quantify Values

Although broad value statements may not be useful to understanding differences in human behavior, researchers have developed methods to delve deeper. These methods involve the use of scales for **value orientations** (Fulton et al. 1996). For example, many people may express a value for wildlife. But, people with a shared value for wildlife

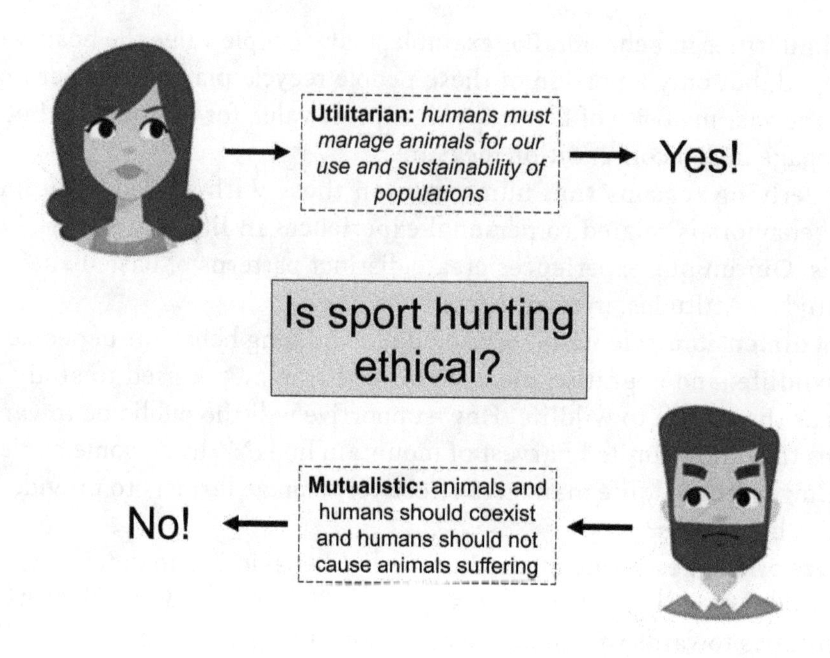
Utilitarian: humans must manage animals for our use and sustainability of populations
Yes!
Is sport hunting ethical?
Mutualistic: animals and humans should coexist and humans should not cause animals suffering
No!

FIGURE 5.2 Contrasting ethical responses to sport hunting, as explained by differing value orientations of utilitarian or mutualistic relationships with animals.

may respond very differently to a basic question about the ethics of sport hunting ("Is sport hunting ethical?", Figure 5.2).

To delve into the differences between those who support hunting and those who do not, surveys can be designed to pose a series of questions (e.g., "It important for humans to manage population of animals," "I object to hunting because it violates the rights of individual animals to exist," "Hunting for food is acceptable," "Catching fish for sport is cruel") that allow an individual to be scored along a gradient from **utilitarian** to **protectionist** based on their responses. In a 2003 survey of adults in six western states, 80% were scored as utilitarian and 7% were protectionist; others were neutral (Manfredo et al. 2003).

The utilitarian/protectionist framework can be expanded (Teel et al. 2005), with a slight modification of the use of "**mutualist**" (humans and wildlife live side by side without fear, no animal suffering, emotional bonding with animals) rather than "protectionist" to account for further distinctions between individuals. In the 19 western US states surveyed, 34% of respondents were utilitarian, 20% were pluralist, 33% were mutualist, and 13% were distanced. However, states in the survey varied highly as to the distribution of the orientation types among respondents. States with populations that had less education, were more rural, and had lower income were more likely to have higher proportions of utilitarian citizens, while states with higher

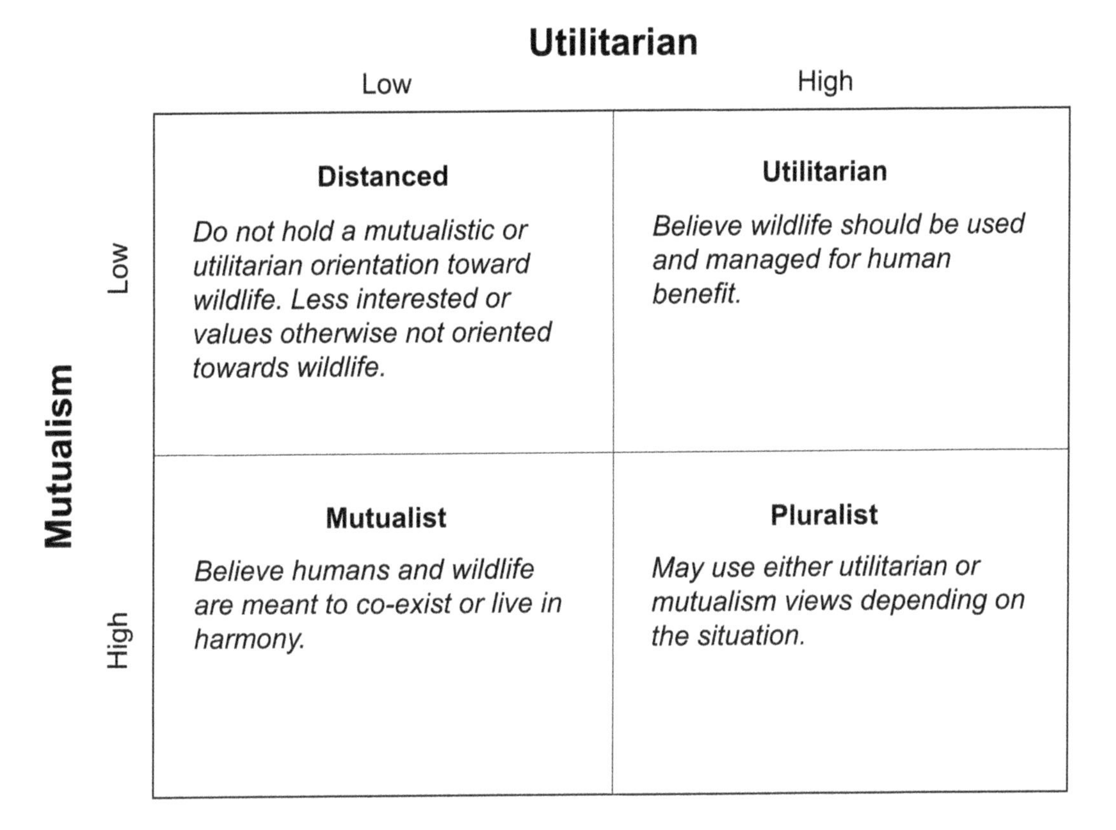

FIGURE 5.3 Gradients of mutualistic and utilitarian qualities provide for four general categories of people who may make similar decisions about wildlife (adapted from Teel et al. 2005).

levels of education, fewer rural residents, and higher income had higher percentages of mutualists.

These are two examples of value orientations used in our profession. People vary greatly in their value orientations, which affects their decisions, daily actions, and support for wildlife management proposals. Basic differences in philosophical approaches to ethics, determining right and wrong, are at the heart of the issue. A wildlife manager has personal biases, because we all have our own experiences and attitudes that affect how we operate. It is clear that a wildlife manager should realize that stakeholders for a management decision are most likely not of the same mind. If we act under the assumption of a variety of ethical perspectives, we are able to design more effective communication strategies, and we are able to design conflict resolution strategies to bring diverse groups together as they begin the decision-making process.

QUICK COMPREHENSION CHECK

Do you believe you would score as utilitarian, mutualist, pluralist, or distanced? Why?

How do you think people living in Russia, Japan, Botswana, Chile, or China might respond in the survey? Would the distribution be similar to the US or different? Why?

Why do you believe education and income levels play a large role in how individuals respond? Why are urban respondents less likely to be utilitarian?

If society is transitioning from a majority of people with utilitarian views to a majority of people with mutualistic views, what implications are in store for the wildlife management profession? Develop a list and discuss with your fellow students.

Ethics in Action: Professional Standards for Wildlife Managers

An individual's values affect their choices and the manner in which they operate. In similar fashion, organizations often establish statements that describe group values. The American Fisheries Society, the Wildlife Society, the Association of Zoos and Aquariums, the Society for Conservation Biology, and many other professional organizations related to wildlife management have codes of ethics. In fact, most professional fields, such as accounting, law, business, engineering, and waste management, have similar codes that describe what is acceptable and unacceptable for members of their profession.

Many practical applications of professional ethics for wildlife managers are spelled out in an executive order signed in 1989 by President George H. W. Bush that applies to all federal employees (Department of the Interior 2017):

EXECUTIVE ORDER #12674

Public service is public trust, requiring you to place loyalty to the Constitution, the law, and ethical principles above private gain.

- You shall not hold financial interests that conflict with the conscientious performance of duty.
- You shall not engage in financial transactions using non-public Government information or allow improper use of such information to further any private interest.
- You shall not, except pursuant to such reasonable exceptions as are provided by regulation, solicit or accept any gift or other item of monetary value from any person or entity seeking official action from, doing business with, or conducting activities regulated by your agency, or whose interests may be substantially affected by the performance or nonperformance of your duties.

- You shall make no unauthorized commitments or promise of any kind purported to bind the Government.
- You shall put forth honest effort in the performance of your duties.
- You shall not engage in outside employment or activities, including seeking or negotiating for employment, that conflict with your official Government duties and responsibilities.
- You shall disclose waste, fraud, abuse, and corruption to appropriate authorities.
- You shall satisfy in good faith your obligations as citizens, including all just financial obligations, especially those such as Federal, state, or local taxes that are imposed by law.
- You shall adhere to all laws and regulations that provide equal opportunities for all Americans regardless of race, color, religion, sex, age, or handicap.
- You shall not use your public office for private gain.
- You shall act impartially and not give preferential treatment to any private organization or individual.
- You shall protect and conserve Federal property and shall not use it for other than authorized activity.
- You shall endeavor to avoid any actions creating the appearance that you are violating the law, or (regulations that set standards for ethical conduct).

Although these standards are for federal employees, we can apply the concepts broadly to wildlife managers employed by states and to privately employed individuals. Violation of ethical standards may result in actions ranging from formal reprimands to dismissal from a position. The underlying justification for ethical standards for employees, whether in a corporation, a private business, or a government agency, is trust. Colleagues, clients, and stakeholders must be able to trust that an employee's actions and statements are not biased for personal gain in any way.

QUICK COMPREHENSION CHECK

A new federal wildlife biologist knows his salary is lower than many of his friends who work in finance. He has been issued boots and some tools by his agency, and he has heard that some colleagues request new boots and tools while selling their old equipment on Craigslist. What tenet of the Executive Order is he at risk of violating if he follows his colleagues' example?

Professional Standards: Case Studies

Because of the moral implications imbedded in ethics discussions, it is easy for professionals to view a statement for professional ethics, such as the Executive Order, and move forward in confidence that they would never violate any of the ethical statements. Many people have chosen the field of wildlife management to study because they feel a sense of moral obligation to the earth and its ecosystems, so we may be especially emboldened to think that we do not need to evaluate potential ethical violations. However, we know that ethical miscues often happen in all professions, and the wildlife management profession is not immune to cases of poor decision-making with regards to professional ethics.

One of the best ways to train our thinking processes to watch for situations when we may be close to an ethical violation is to evaluate known situations of ethical misconduct. Business and medical students use the same approach. The following cases are real situations, with the names protected, but each may be further researched for more information should you have interest. As you read each case involving professional standards, put yourself in the role of the protagonist, and evaluate how you might have responded in each situation. At what point, do you feel the professional made a poor decision related to professional ethics?

Professional Ethics Case One: Bird Biologist Poisons Feral Cats

The effects of feral cats preying on birds have been documented worldwide (Nogales et al. 2004), and domestic cats are considered by some to be one of the largest threats faced by songbirds. A research biologist with the Smithsonian National Zoo's Migratory Bird Center, Dr. D, lived in a neighborhood in Washington, DC. She observed her neighbors putting out food to feed feral cats. Dr. D's response to this situation was documented by another resident who noticed that a white powder appeared on the food that she put out for neighborhood cats. The neighbor used video cameras to capture images of Dr. D reaching into a bag and putting something on the food. The white powder was determined to be a poison.

Dr. D was charged with attempted animal cruelty, but she denied the charges. She claimed she was removing the food rather than placing a poison on the food. A judge found her guilty (Alexander 2011).

- *What ethical stance might have been used by Dr. D to decide to poison the feral cats' food?*
- *Is the action by Dr. D ethical?*
- *Compare the ethics of using poison to kill rats and cats. Both are considered pests.*
- *What should the employer's action (the Zoo) be, if anything?*

Professional Ethics Case Two: Administrator Approves Agreement that Benefits Family Member

Dr. R, the chief of the Division of International Conservation of the US Fish and Wildlife Service, faced an ethics complaint regarding his involvement in agency grants of over $100,000 for development of a training program from which a family member was paid about $5,600 as a trainer. A report found that, indeed, Dr. R had violated federal laws and regulations because neither Dr. R nor the family member disclosed their relationship in writing.

Dr. R had also approved a $30,000 modification to the award at a later date, although he initially said he was not involved in that review.

A supervisor of the employee knew about the family relationship and consulted with the agency's ethics office on behalf of Dr. R. However, the advice to have Dr. R draft a recusal memo for review by the ethics office was not followed by the supervisor. Other agency employees also knew about the potential conflict of interest but did not report it to anyone.

Dr. R had drafted a recusal memo, but only sent it to two people; the memo was incomplete and did not qualify as an official recusal. In addition, Dr. R did not actually recuse himself from the decision process. Evidence also was found that suggested Dr. R had been a decision maker on two other agency grants that involved the same family member (Bur 2018).

- *Which clause of the Executive Order of ethics for federal employees did Dr. R violate?*
- *An ethics board found ethical problems with Dr. R's behavior. How egregious was this violation?*
- *If you were the ethics board or Dr. R's supervisor, what would you recommend as a penalty?*
- *What should Dr. R have done to perform his job in an ethical manner?*

Professional Ethics Case Three: A Free Mountain Lion Hunt for a Commissioner

California residents voted to ban mountain lion hunting in 1990, but tensions remain high as mountain lion populations increase near urban areas. The state wildlife agency in California is administered by an appointed group of five commissioners. In 2012, newspapers reported that Mr. R, the President of the California Fish and Game Commission, shot a mountain lion in Idaho during a visit to a private ranch. Photos of Mr. R smiling over the body of a dead mountain lion lying in the snow activated anti-hunting groups in California who argued that it was poor judgement to leave the state to do something that was not legal in California.

A few days later, news broke that Mr. R, a Republican, had not paid for his mountain lion hunt, which typically costs $6,800. An ethics complaint filed by a former executive director of the California Democratic Party, accused the commissioner of violating state ethics rules, which limit gifts to elected officials and members of state commissions to $420. Gifts must be reported within 30 days, and Mr. R did not report the gift.

The commissioner went on local radio shows to argue that his hunt was legal in Idaho, and he suggested the Humane Society of the United States and other animal welfare and environmental groups had circulated the photo to arouse their members to call for his removal. Mr. R labeled the group "enviro-terrorists."

The hunting guide on the trip said that Mr. R had visited the ranch, initially, to hunt pheasants. The guide said that he had asked the commissioner to kill one of several mountain lions on the 5,000-acre hunting ranch, because the lions were killing deer that paying visitors could have hunted. The guide said Mr. R "killed the cat as a favor to me," and he did not charge the commissioner for the hunt.

Further political complication arose because the removal of the Republican would allow the Democratic governor to appoint a Democrat to the commission. Some suggested that one of the Democrats accusing Mr. R of ethics violations was interested in the legislator's father being appointed to replace Mr. R.

The President and CEO of the Humane Society of the United States weighed in on the issue by stating that their organization does not want to ban all hunting, but they do oppose "chasing mountain lions with packs of dogs and shooting them from trees."

Mr. R talked about eating portions of the mountain lion that he had shot while at the ranch. "It doesn't taste like chicken. It's like a pork loin," he said on the radio show. "It's white meat, and it is pretty good. In frontier times it was a delicacy" (Rogers 2012).

- *Make a list of all of the possible ethical dilemmas and problems associated with this case.*
- *Do you believe Mr. R is guilty of an ethics violation? If he were a federal employee, would he have violated any clauses of the Executive Order of ethics?*
- *Legislators or the commission could vote to remove the commissioner. If you do believe Mr. R is guilty of an ethics violation, is it egregious enough for legislators to vote for his removal?*
- *What should Mr. R have done to avoid any ethics questions and controversies?*

Professional Ethics Case Four: Research and Publication Ethics

Dr. O and Dr. P are Swedish scientists who gained worldwide recognition in 2016 with a paper they published in the journal *Science*. Their work suggested that tiny particles of plastic (microplastics) in the ocean harm fish. Dr. O and Dr. P reported that young fish that ingested microplastics had reduced effort to avoid predators, resulting in higher mortality rates.

However, other scientists began to ask questions about details of the experiments that were lacking, which eventually led a scientific review board in Sweden to conclude Dr. O and Dr. P were guilty of scientific misconduct. The researchers still maintained that their paper was sound, but they requested that *Science* retract it in light of the questions about their results (Lönnstedt and Eklöv 2016). Their university's vice-chancellor asked an in-house board for research conduct to investigate further.

The board found that one of the scientists, Dr. O, intentionally fabricated data and did not conduct experiments during the time described. The co-author, Dr. P, did not know that data had been fabricated, but Dr. P did not take due diligence to confirm that Dr. O carried out the research as she described. The board concluded that the scientists were guilty of scientific misconduct.

- *Why do you believe Dr. O might have decided to fabricate the data? What pressures might lead to such a poor decision?*
- *How do Dr. P's actions compare to Dr. O's?*
- *What professional repercussions do Dr. P and Dr. O face in the future, beyond any reprimands or actions with regard to their present employment?*

Professional Ethics Case Five: Research Permits

Over 100 million acres of federal, public lands in the United States are designated as wilderness areas, under the provisions of the 1964 Wilderness Act. Visitors to wilderness areas subscribe to ethical principles, such as the National Park Service's Leave No Trace philosophy: plan ahead and prepare, travel and camp on durable surfaces, dispose of waste properly, leave what you find, minimize campfire impacts, respect wildlife, and be considerate of other visitors.

Federal and state agencies are also required to abide by restrictions imposed by the wilderness designation. For example, researchers must obtain permits for their work, and research crews are typically required to travel on foot. Vehicles and aircraft—anything with engines—may only be used when special permission is granted.

In 2017, a US District Court judge heard testimony on a complaint that the US Forest Service violated the law when the agency allowed the Idaho Fish and Game Department to make helicopter landings for the purpose of placing radio collars on elk in the Frank Church River of No Return Wilderness. Previous court orders had directed the US Forest Service to publicize the special permit decisions to allow citizens or conservation organizations to challenge the decision, but in this incident the research operation started immediately after the special permit was issued.

During the three-day operation, the state wildlife agency had tagged 57 elk, but they also placed collars on four wolves that the US Forest Service did not authorize.

The judge ruled that the flights had violated the National Environmental Protection Act (NEPA) and the Wilderness Act of 1964, and he ordered the agencies to destroy all data from the research efforts (Landers 2017).

- *What ethical stance might have been used by the state agency to ignore the previous court order and immediately begin to put collars on animals? What pressures might lead to such a poor decision?*
- *Do you believe it is ethical to allow research in areas designated as wilderness? Why might someone else disagree with you?*
- *What repercussions do you believe the employee in charge of the Idaho Fish and Game's operation should receive for the violation and poor judgement?*

Professional Ethics Case Six: Whistleblowing

Mr. E was a 17-year employee with the US Fish and Wildlife Service in Florida and worked for a decade as part of the team that supported the recovery of the endangered Florida panther. Development in Florida was occurring at an astounding rate, shrinking the habitat used by the panthers, and Mr. E's job included evaluating commercial proposals for development in and near areas used by panthers (Fleshler 2005).

The Endangered Species Act status provides for protection of critical habitat, so biologists established a Panther Habitat Evaluation Model (PHEM) to support decisions as to what areas were priority for protection. Over several years, Mr. E noticed irregularities with the PHEM and its implementation. Generally, the PHEM classified critical habitats much more narrowly than available data supported, suggesting panthers kept to forest patches and would not cross 90-meter gaps between forest patches. Thus, development continued in areas that might have been used by panthers.

Several peer-reviewed papers were written by scientists involved with the project, which were used for policy implementation. Policy reports were written with statements with which Mr. E and others disagreed, based on their interpretation of the data that had been gathered. Even when reviewers of a report unanimously recommended revisions, the draft report without revisions continued to be circulated and used for decisions. So, in 2002, Mr. E started criticizing his agency for the lack of science used in policy guidelines and in that same year a scientific review team of four external scientists was established to review the science and policy decisions related to panthers in Florida.

The review team concluded their work with a report in 2003 (Beier et al. 2003) that supported the criticisms by Mr. E and others; the report was a devastating critique of misuse and misrepresentation of data by the panther recovery team (Beier et al. 2006, Conroy et al. 2006). Among the revelations was the decision to use radio-telemetry data gathered only during daylight hours to represent the movements and habitat use of a species known to be more active at night. A review team member commented, "A lot of land was developed that likely would not have been developed had these flawed inferences

FIGURE 5.4 A Florida panther in a region in which conservation easements were planned to allow for a proposed "panther corridor" to enable panthers to disperse more freely (U.S. Army Corps of Engineers photo).

not appeared in those publications, and they were calling this the 'best available science'" (Gross 2005). The review team's work was reviewed by six more external reviewers.

Eventually, in 2004, Mr. E reached out to PEER (Protecting Employees for Environmental Responsibility), a non-governmental organization set up to support government employees who had determined to blow the whistle on their agency's actions. Mr. E and PEER filed a complaint with the Department of the Interior and the US Fish and Wildlife Service as an accusation of violating the Data Quality Act of 2000. Perhaps Mr. E felt it was an official way to force the US Fish and Wildlife Service to accept the review team's findings and change their policies to better support the Florida panther. Throughout the process, Mr. E had spoken freely with the media about pressures he felt from superiors to approve housing developments and roads in areas that he felt were important to panthers.

Five months later, the US Fish and Wildlife Service fired Mr. E for failing to meet deadlines and "unprofessional exchanges with the public," among other charges.

- *Do you believe it was ethical for Mr. E to go to the media to bring his interpretations of misuse of scientific data to the public?*

QUICK COMPREHENSION CHECK

Review the professional ethics case studies. Can you place each case study into a category for type of decision in Table 5.1? What details of the case were most useful to categorize it?

- *Evaluate the ethical actions of the scientists involved with the misuse of data. What might cause a scientist and management team to selectively use data to support a certain agenda? After reading Conroy et al. (2006), what steps do you think are necessary to ensure better use of science in conservation policy and management?*
- *Should Mr. E have been fired by his agency? Why would they fire him when his arguments were supported by the review team's report?*
- *How do you think the story ends? Read Gross (2005) to find out.*

Ethical Dilemmas in Decision-Making

When Does a Decision Involve Ethics?

As employees of an agency, a company, or an organization, wildlife biologists and managers face daily choices that involve ethics on various levels. These challenges range from those with alternatives that have legal implications to those in which stakeholders voice ethical concerns (Table 5.1). Because ethics is defined as a framework by which we decide what is right and what is wrong, it is possible to see all decisions as having an ethical implication at some level.

Questions regarding legality are paramount, and prohibitory laws in functional democracies reflect society's agreed-upon ethical stances on what is wrong. But legal actions are not always ethical actions. Professional codes of ethics give us another rubric by which to judge actions that might be legal but might violate principles established by our profession and perhaps risk our future employment.

Therefore, two types of ethical decisions are easily dealt with—those that (1) involve a legal question or (2) violate professional codes of ethics. The proper course of action should be clear in these situations, even though circumstances may make it difficult to carry out. For example, perhaps a supervisor pressures you to take an action that borders on being

TABLE 5.1 *Toolbox for Ethical Decisions*

TYPE OF DECISION	DEFINITION	WAY FORWARD
A: Management or personal decision with legal implications	At least one alternative is not legal, or in which the legality is in question	Consult an attorney representing your organization or a personal attorney; document your communication, and follow their recommendations
B: Management or personal decision with ethical implications	Includes at least one alternative that violates, or may violate, a workplace ethics guideline or a professional code of ethics	Consult your organization's ethics council; document your communication, and follow their recommendations
C: Management decision that involves an ethical dilemma	More than one alternative exists, and logical ethical arguments are made by stakeholders to support more than one alternative	Follow formal decision-making processes (outlined in chapter 3) to consider the ethical perspectives of stakeholders and incorporate them into the decision process
D: Personal decision that involves an ethical dilemma	More than one alternative exists, and although no alternatives violate professional codes of ethics, you entertain doubts as to the personal ethics of at least one choice	Start with the gut check methods outlined in this chapter and in chapter 3; proceed to a more formal decision-making process if needed
E: Management decision with minimal voiced ethical implications	Ethics or references to ethics (e.g., "right thing to do") are not mentioned during the decision process, but stakeholders disagree on alternative courses of action based on their perspectives	Follow formal decision-making processes outlined in chapter 3 to address consequences of alternative actions with regard to objectives; evaluate stakeholder perspectives to determine if differences in ethical perspectives plays a role in their opinion on action

illegal or unethical based on company policies. In that case, you should immediately consult an attorney for guidance and document all interactions by saving emails and creating personal notes with times and dates. Government workers are often protected by whistleblower clauses in law, but you should confirm the proper action with an attorney.

Gut Checks for Personal Ethical Dilemmas

Ethical dilemmas involve situations that are not clearly illegal (Type A, Table 5.1) and do not violate professional codes of ethics (Type B). Instead, the decision-maker is faced with at least two alternatives, each of which has a logical ethical argument as to its "rightness" (Type C or D).

Ethical dilemmas, therefore, are decisions. In chapter 3, we covered a variety of ways to make difficult decisions, and we noted that many decisions can be made quickly with little need for any kind of formal decision-making process. Some decisions may be made based on gut reactions with some thought to consequences. The same is the case with ethical dilemmas.

For example, consider two common ethical dilemmas faced by college students:

> It is the night before the big exam, and a friend gives you a copy of last year's Biology II exam. "Everyone in the class has a copy of it," he says. "Just read it to see what kinds of questions Dr. Smith asks."
>
> or
>
> Your final paper is due in a week, and you find an online document that you could use for a source. Unfortunately, your grandmother passes away, and in the rush to get the paper completed before you go to the funeral, you consider copying several paragraphs from the document you found, rather than using it as a cited source for your ideas. "Prof. Heng doesn't use computer software to compare our papers with other works," you mutter.

Plagiarism has stiff consequences at most colleges and universities, ranging from failing an assignment to expulsion from the university depending on the situation. However, the temptation to stretch ethical boundaries may be mentally justified by the payoff of long-term academic success or the situation—such as "everyone else is doing it" or an unfair life event (the timing of your grandmother's death). How does a person navigate these conflicting ethical arguments?

One low-risk, quick method for addressing a personal ethical dilemma (Type D, Table 5.1) is to review the situation and consider the following questions (revised from Collins 2018):

- Is an action illegal? (If so, this is not an ethical dilemma, it is Type A, Table 5.1.)
- Does the action violate my profession's code of ethics? (If so, this is not an ethical dilemma, it is Type B, Table 5.1.)
- Is the action unfair or discriminatory to someone?
- Is this action something I would feel badly about?
- Will I be ashamed to tell my family, friends, coworkers, or boss about this decision?
- Will I be embarrassed if the newspaper or radio does a story on my decision?

The last four questions in this list are **gut checks**, or conscience-seeking questions that ask us to stop and think about our values that are a manifestation of our personal ethics. These questions ask us to remove ourselves from the immediate situation and think about how society might view our actions. It is worth noting that the answer may vary depending on culture and scenario. For example, the decision to go hunting or wear short pants to work might embarrass family and coworkers in some regions or countries, while being completely acceptable in others.

Addressing Difficult Ethical Dilemmas

Some ethical dilemmas cannot be solved with a simple gut check and basic soul-searching. In fact, as ethical dilemmas increase in their complexity, we may find ourselves conflicted with a personal choice (Type D, Table 5.1) that seems almost impossible to make. Examples of personal dilemmas may include the following trade-offs (Johnson 2017):

- **Truth telling vs. loyalty to others and institutions:** Both options are respected virtues, and whistleblowers often feel torn between saying something about an action in their organization they perceive to be wrong and staying loyal to their boss or organization.
- **Personal needs vs. the needs of the community:** Farmers balance the needs to feed their family versus the need to not pollute rivers with fertilizer for the benefit of those downstream. Taking sick leave or vacation time at work is a tough decision for some people, as they fear their work group will suffer without their presence.
- **Short-term benefits vs. long-term negative consequences:** Supervisors of employees struggle to balance short-term needs of employees (salary raise, more health benefits) with the long-term stability of the company (perhaps long-term stability is hindered by spending more money on employees now).
- **Justice vs. mercy:** A professor may realize how much a student worked on a paper on a subject that was difficult for them. Although the paper justifiably deserves a C grade relative to other students' work and the rubric for the assignment, a professor may feel like rewarding the student for their hard work with a B. Similarly, responding to a fellow employee who apologizes after being heard to bully a co-worker may cause a person to struggle with future distrust or the use of forgiveness.

Similarly, in a management situation (Type C, Table 5.1), we find a group of stakeholders in disagreement about what constitutes the "right" action—two or more sides may claim the ethical high ground because of contrasting value orientations. During a decision to allow a new harvest of mountain lions, the pro-harvest side may argue that their intended actions will be positive for the ecosystem to prevent an over-population of predators, while the anti-harvest side may use an argument that humans should not kill animals. Both submit two different views of what is right.

Even stakeholders who share similar philosophical viewpoints may come to disagreement in certain situations. For example, biologists and managers who share a vision of protecting rhinos from poaching disagree on the ethics of dehorning black and white rhinos. Proponents argue that dehorning greatly reduces the chances of a poacher killing a rhino, while opponents argue that dehorning is unethical as it may change the status of a rhino and leave it less able to defend itself against predators (Lindeque 1990).

In situations where stakeholder value orientations do not clearly provide an answer for "What is the most ethical action?" we need a way forward to solve the dilemma.

To improve **ethical decision-making** the following steps can be taken (after Kidder 1995, Markkula Center for Applied Ethics 2009, Johnson 2017):

- Recognize an ethical issue and define the actors, or stakeholders
- Get the relevant facts
- Evaluate alternative actions as to their rightness or wrongness from different ethical approaches
- Contrast the consequences and tradeoffs of each alternative for all stakeholders
- Make a decision
- Act and reflect on the outcome

Does the basic structure of these steps remind you of the PrOACT process? Indeed, the process above also involves clarifying the problem and alternatives, as well as evaluating the consequences of alternatives. Further, the ethical decision-making framework also allows for learning after each decision, which is similar to the process of adaptive management.

In chapter 3, we suggested that a logical decision process should lead to better decisions. In an ethical context, a well-structured decision-making process should also lead to decisions that are ethical as judged by our stakeholders, colleagues, and our profession.

Ethical Dilemmas in the Wildlife Profession: Case Studies

The wildlife profession is like all other professions in that ethical dilemmas and ethical considerations are common. The wildlife profession may be unique as we are managing other species of vertebrate animals, which leads to many ethical questions regarding the relationship between humans and animals and the welfare of animals. In addition, many of our decisions are made in the context of conservation, which is a "good" goal by most standards. However, the drive to be successful in conservation efforts may lead to ethical questions regarding some management alternatives, even though the action may result in accomplishment of conservation goals.

Ethical Dilemma Case One: Is it Ethical to use Contraception on Wildlife?

Hilton Head Island, off the coast of South Carolina, is just over 100 square km in size. Most of the 37,000 residents live in highly-developed, gated communities, and white-tailed deer have established high density populations on the island with few natural predators. Car collisions are the largest source of mortality for deer, which of course frustrates the residents. It is not legal to use a firearm on the island, so hunting or culling the population is not possible. Further, deer cannot be legally transported to the mainland. Translocations to more natural areas within the island were not successful, as many deer returned to their capture locations (Cromwell et al. 1999). As is common in many urban areas with high deer populations and few other management alternatives, some residents have encouraged the use of contraceptives to limit reproduction in deer.

When residents were asked whether contraception for deer was an ethical alternative, researchers received a variety of perspectives (Lauber et al. 2007). Supporters of the use of contraceptives felt it was much better than killing the deer as an alternative management action, while opponents of contraceptives saw killing deer as an effective, suitable alternative. Further, opponents pointed to killing as being more humane than the potential side effects of contraceptives, which may include a lengthened reproductive season during which female deer are harassed by males for long periods, weight gain, and effects on antler development in males. The "wildness" and natural state of the deer were important to opponents of fertility control, who viewed using lethal methods of removal as preferable to altering the appearance or behavior of individuals. In contrast, supporters of contraceptives viewed these side effects as much better than killing the animals. The fertility control supporters tended to give more weight to individual animals, while opponents were concerned more about the ecosystem and its balance than the rights of individual animals.

- *What do you believe about the ethics of using contraceptives for limiting populations of deer? Explain your views.*
- *How do you think your experiences in life contribute to your ethical stance on this issue? Does it matter if you were raised on a farm or in a city? Does it matter if you are a deer hunter or not? Does it matter if you have hand-raised an animal?*
- *In some locations, there is a choice between using lethal culling or contraceptives, but on Hilton Head Island contraceptives may be the only option. Would you support the use of fertility control on Hilton Head Island? Why?*

Ethical Dilemma Case Two: Introducing Non-Native Species in a Lake?

Fisheries biologists commonly stock fish in lakes and reservoirs to meet management objectives for the interest of anglers. Reservoirs, of course, are not natural lakes, so the fish community that exists after a reservoir is built is often a highly managed and prescribed community assemblage of stocked species. The question of "what is natural?" in a reservoir system is a question for debate and ethical discussion a well.

On a broader basis, commercial aquaculture may bring species from other countries to be raised in new, farmed environments—species such as tilapias, carp from China or India, and African sharptooth catfish. Subsequently, floods or inadequate housing facilities have resulted in unplanned releases of these non-native fish species, and many more, into new waterbodies throughout the world. Elsewhere, non-native species are purposefully introduced for economic or recreational reasons on water bodies that are commercially fished or used by sport anglers.

Two recent papers (Gozlan 2008, Vitule et al. 2009) debate whether introductions of non-native freshwater fish are bad. The issues can be boiled down to these arguments:

> *Non-native fish are everywhere.* Gozlan (2008) describes a world in which there are almost no natural fish communities—30% of the world's salmon production happens in Chile, and seven times more African tilapia are raised in Asia than in Africa. The author suggests that it is inherently impossible to stop new introductions of non-native fish, so a new attitude that admits the benefits of non-native introductions is necessary.
>
> *Economics.* Gozlan (2008) takes the most iconic example for invasive species caution—the case of Nile perch released in Lake Victoria—and suggests that the region may have benefited economically from the introduction. Other examples are given of non-native fish that supported economics for local people.
>
> *Pathogens.* Gozlan (2008) suggests the fear of introducing novel pathogens into systems with the stocking of non-native fish is largely a function of stocking practices; because disease can be introduced with native fish that are stocked, the author suggests it is not an argument to be made against stocking non-native fish.
>
> *Hybridization.* Gozlan (2008) acknowledges a few cases where hybridization between the introduced, non-native species and the native species have caused the degradation of the native fish genetic stock. However, the author suggests hybridization is a natural phenomenon.
>
> *Biodiversity.* Gozlan (2008) states that introductions of non-native fish to a system increase the diversity in a waterbody with the addition of a new species, and in some cases the introduction of rare or endangered species to new systems may benefit their long-term survival.
>
> *Ecological impact.* Gozlan (2008) argues the risk of ecological impact is rare (less than 15% of all introductions results in problems by his count), and the author

suggests that some ecological impacts may not be as bad as the dogma surrounding the fear of non-native introductions would suggest. Indeed, he writes, ecological impact may be worth the benefits to a local economy.

Vitule et al. (2009) provide a point-by-point counter-argument to each of the arguments made by Gozlan (2008). A description of a very different reality is presented, in which system stability, native ecosystems, and caution towards change are highly valued.

- *With some online research, can you come up with the arguments that you believe Vitule et al. (2009) might make to Gozlan's (2008) arguments?*
- *What differences in value orientation do you see in the two arguments?*
- *Do you believe non-native fish should be purposefully stocked into new water bodies? Why? If so, in what circumstances? Explain how your ethical philosophy and experiences affect your views.*
- *Which arguments above are the most convincing or bring out the largest response from you? Why?*

Ethical Dilemma Case Three: Restored Wetland Systems

The Wisconsin Assembly Majority Leader proposed and passed a bill in 2018 that rolls back state wetland protections to support economic development in the state (Lundstrom 2018). Following debate and modification, the permitting process to allow development in areas defined as wetlands was made substantially easier. Although many stakeholders supported the bill, many others argued against it.

Supporters argued that "draconian wetland permitting laws" hampered growth and business development in the state. However, a leader of a local conservation organization argued that wetlands were important, not just for wildlife and plant habitat, but for their flood control functions and water quality services in agricultural landscapes.

Wetlands have been greatly affected by agricultural and urban development throughout the world—not just in Wisconsin. Wetlands can be either drained, preserved/maintained, or restored/recreated, and ethical arguments can be made in support or against each proposal. The decision to remove wetlands may be supported, ethically, using utilitarian consequences such as using land for agriculture, reducing disease through drainage to reduce mosquitos or other vectors, or creating economic opportunities through urban development. The decision may be countered with utilitarian values of tourism benefits of wetlands for bird watching or economic benefits of water quality improvement by wetlands. Ethical arguments may also be based on systems consequences such as the value of wetlands in natural hydrology dynamics, sedimentation traps, or biodiversity support (Armstrong 2000).

Controversy over wetland management is complicated by the nature of wetlands—they are hard to define, compared to forests or grasslands for example. Where does a wetland begin? Is the presence of hydric soils enough to declare an area a wetland? Do wetlands have to have water year-round (Walker and Richardson 1991)?

Restoration ecology is an applied field for management of systems that have been degraded, which has gained attention and momentum especially over the last 40 years. The Society for Restoration Ecology was established in 1988, and its members are active in returning systems to a previous state. Society members often disagree as to the definition of "natural," relative to restoration goals, and there are frequent discussions as to the goals used for restoration projects. What previous time frame represents the "natural" system goal?

Some philosophers have forced the society to defend its actions by suggesting that restoration of a system will never be able to replace the intrinsic value of a natural system that has been degraded (Elliot 1982, 2008). Further, arguments could be made that a false sense of the future is presented when making a current decision to degrade a system, thinking that restoration is possible in the future. Supporters of this view argue that current decisions should give much more weight to the intrinsic value of a natural, intact system that will disappear forever once a wetland is drained, a forest is harvested, or a prairie is plowed.

- *Wildlife managers, by definition, manage systems, which means that we make decisions regarding the future state of systems and what manipulations may be done to systems. Are you comfortable with your future role in working through ethical dilemmas of management actions? What is most intimidating to you about this responsibility?*
- *Compared to forests and grasslands, wetlands seem to have gained a reputation for having more "public goods"—values that extend to society beyond the border of the type of land cover, such as the ability for wetlands to serve in flood control and water quality improvement. Is that comparison true? Do grasslands and forests have values to the public in the state as well? How does this reputation affect our ethical stance towards decisions made in each type of land cover?*
- *How do philosophical viewpoints with regard to wetland use (drain, protect, or restore) play out politically? Which viewpoint is easier to argue? Which viewpoint is currently shared by more members of legislative bodies? How can other viewpoints increase their traction with politicians?*

Ethical Dilemma Case Four: Hunting and Angling Technology

In 2017, the Nova Scotia Federation of Anglers and Hunters asked provincial authorities to restrict the use of drones during hunting, stating that their use crosses an ethical line. The president of the association stated, "It's pretty unethical to use a helicopter or a plane or a drone, in this case, to go after wildlife."

Current provincial law, the Wildlife Act, forbids hunters from using any type of aerial vehicle to hunt or chase wildlife. Drones are not specifically mentioned in the act, because of their recent surge in development and use.

FIGURE 5.5 A bighorn sheep is captured on a remote camera at Kofa National Wildlife Refuge in Arizona. The use of remote cameras is useful for research, but the technology is increasingly being used by hunters, prompting ethical dilemmas of fair chase (USFWS photo).

Hunters are using drones to pursue deer and moose, and the technology may save time for hunters who would normally have to walk through woodlands and fields to find tracks or other signs of animals. The federation also suggests that the availability of drones is hurting the guiding and outfitting business, as the drones can replace the human who has the training to assist hunters. "If someone can just take a drone and fly it around, there's really no need for us," said a local guide.

The federation president remarked that good hunters have to spend time preparing for hunts by scouting and checking where animals are active. Trail cameras, the president noted, are not as intrusive as drones. Hunters still need to set up the cameras in areas where animals are moving, and hunters must visit most types of cameras to retrieve images, although recent camera models can connect to mobile phones.

The president of the federation stated that trail camera technology doesn't bother him, because the hunter still has to be in the woods "doing legwork and looking for signs of animals," while a drone operator doesn't have to do that (Burke 2017).

"Put the technology away and just get out in the woods."

- *What ethical arguments can be used to suggest that drones are not ethical for hunting?*
- *Compare the ethics of the use of drones and trail cameras. Both could potentially affect the dynamics of "fair chase" in hunting. Explain any differences that you perceive in the ethics of their use.*

- *What other types of hunting technology affect fair chase? Consider the use of camouflage clothing, long-range optical sights for rifles, scent-reducing clothing, or the use of mobile phones during hunting.*
- *What kinds of technology might give an angler unfair advantage? In your opinion, is the use of a fish-finder scanner on a boat ethical?*

Ethical Dilemma Case Five: Trophy Hunting and Emotional Response

The 2015 killing of a 13-year-old male lion in Zimbabwe, nicknamed Cecil by researchers who had followed his movements for six years with a satellite transmitter, galvanized many people around the globe as to the ethics of trophy hunting of predators and its role in conservation. Some suggested that the outcry was the largest reaction to a wildlife conservation event in history, although the death of Cecil was not a unique event. Sixty-five other lions had been hunted in land surrounding a protected area and 45 of them were also wearing tracking devices. Two other lions killed by trophy hunters also bore nicknames from the research group (Macdonald et al. 2016).

Cecil was initially wounded at 10:00pm by an American bowhunter from Minnesota on a farm in the Gwaai Conservancy, which was next to Hwange National Park. The hunt may have been illegal, as no hunting quota had been issued for 2015 for the farm's owner or the professional hunting guide by Zimbabwe's National Parks and Wildlife Management Authority. The hunters tracked the wounded lion and, 11 hours later, killed it with a second arrow. Although initial reports suggested the lion was lured from the park, this was not the case. The lion was hunted on a bait in an area of its normal range. The research team believes the satellite transmitter was then destroyed by the hunters (Macdonald et al. 2016). As the story unfolded, the hunter was named by the media, and other international events including the unrelated death of a safari guide by a lion in the nearby park may have fueled interest in the story.

Some wildlife biologists took the opportunity of the attention on the topic to espouse the benefits of sport hunting for conservation (Nelson et al. 2016). Indeed, there are arguments to be made that the money obtained from hunts of predators can be used to manage their populations in countries where resources are otherwise unavailable to support conservation (Di Minin et al. 2016). Alternatively, there are arguments that suggest that trophy hunting is often not regulated to provide for sustainable local populations (Packer et al. 2011).

However, one of the most powerful legacies of the killing of Cecil the lion was the emotional outrage from those who considered the hunt unethical in any shape or form. Many wildlife biologists downplayed or even chastised those emotional responses, suggesting that we should not allow emotions to overtake decision-making (Nelson et al. 2016).

In contrast, Nelson et al. (2016) suggested that wildlife biologists, who often apply **consequentialist** tests to determine if an action has consequences ("Does trophy hunting benefit or harm a species or population?"), should not discount emotional responses to events like Cecil's killing:

The Cecil case highlights the underappreciated importance of the human dimensions of conservation, in particular those pertaining to ethics and psychology. Trophy hunting as a means of conserving species is vigorously defended by some conservationists who implicitly rely on consequentialist ethical arguments. More than a century of scholarship in the field of ethics reveals flaws with consequentialism, calling into question conservation actions that rely solely on consequentialist arguments. The idea that emotion is the antithesis of rationality is also centuries old and is employed as a means of dismissing people who display emotion in conservation debates. Yet, psychological research suggests emotional reactions to injustice are normal and healthy, and emotions can be critical for making "good" judgments and decisions.

These new perspectives need not paralyze conservationists. As seen above, a variety of practical tools are available for assisting conservationists in understanding the ethical underpinnings of their positions, and for addressing the proper role of emotions in decision-making.

- *Discuss the ethical implications of Cecil's death: what facts in the story are important to your ethical judgement?*
- *Nelson et al. (2016) refer to emotional responses that are different than utilitarian perspectives on trophy hunting. What value orientations do those with negative (and emotional) responses to Cecil's death bring to their framing of the incident? What framework are they using to decide between right and wrong?*
- *Do some research into the effect of trophy hunting and angling on ecological systems and conservation efforts. Develop a position on the use of trophy harvest.*

WRAPPING UP

Return to the problem case at the beginning of the chapter. What kind of ethical dilemmas were described in the public hearing facilitated by Heather? Can you find an example of a violation of professional ethics in the problem case?

What common themes do you see throughout the ethical dilemma problem cases?

Decision-Making on the Ground

1: Are Fish Lesser Vertebrates?

A 2010 workshop was held to address fish welfare and its moral implications (Meijboom and Bovenkerk 2013). At issue was whether fish have the moral position of other vertebrates (mammals, birds, reptiles, amphibians) or fish are considered somewhere between mammals and plants. Fish are typically invisible to us, live in a different type of environment, and lack visual similarities to humans, which may affect our concept of their moral rights.

Experts at the workshop discussed three basic questions that could affect the level of moral rights of fish:

- Can fish feel pain and suffer, or feel pleasure and enjoyment?
- Do fish have memory, and are they conscious in their actions?
- What does the public believe about the capacities and moral status of fish, and can science and morality influence these views?

The implications for how we perceive fish may affect standard research procedures, such as surgeries to implant radio telemetry devices (with or without anesthesia?), and day-to-day operations at aquaculture facilities. Fish are often housed and slaughtered using different standards than we have for other vertebrates.

APPLICATION, ANALYSIS, SYNTHESIS, AND EVALUATION

What information do you need to determine whether a fish has the same moral rights as other vertebrates?

Conduct a search for standard practices for research used by universities' institutional animal care and use committees for fish and other vertebrates. What differences do you find? Does this surprise you?

Develop a plan with a group of fellow students to investigate what is available in published papers to answer the three questions listed above. You may find especially relevant papers to use in the February 2013 issue of the Journal of Agricultural and Environmental Ethics (volume 26, issue 1). Discuss your findings and write a position paper using science to support your position.

2: Is Captive Breeding of Animals Ethical?

The Copenhagen Zoo, in Demark, made the decision to euthanize a healthy juvenile male reticulated giraffe in 2014 (Goldman 2014). Zoos and aquaria have limited capacity and limited funds that are largely obtained through memberships, donations, and visitor entrance fees. The zoo's reasoning for the decision was that the giraffe, named Marius, was already represented genetically in the giraffe population across the zoos in Europe. Marius' brother was at a zoo in England; therefore, Marius was a surplus animal relative to expenses for housing, feeding, and maintenance.

Scientists at the zoo performed live necropsy to a public crowd, and Marius was used to feed the zoo's lions, polar bears, and other carnivores.

Following Marius' death, there were global discussions of dilemmas facing zoo managers and the rights of animals housed in zoos.

Better husbandry in zoos has led to longer lives for animals in captivity, which exacerbates the number of dilemmas to be faced by zoo managers. Zoos have carrying capacities based on space and keeper time as well as available funds, and zoos have breeding plans designed to meet the goals for species recovery and enhancement. The general public sees a zoo as a chance to encounter unique and wondrous animals, but the zoo provides viewing opportunities in the context of highly managed species recovery programs that are coordinated with other zoos around the world. Species Survival Plans (chapter 9) are coordinated by the Association of Zoos and Aquariums for over 500 species of animals.

To prevent the production of individuals who are not needed for breeding recommendations, zoos may house animals in single-sex enclosures, use contraception, or use permanent sterilization techniques. If zoos allow for breeding of animals not used in global breeding pairings, they must decide how to maintain the animals and they must make future decisions when those animals reach the age of reproduction.

APPLICATION, ANALYSIS, SYNTHESIS, AND EVALUATION

Is it more ethical to sterilize a tiger that is not needed in a breeding program and then house it for the rest of its life or to euthanize that tiger so that animals needed in the breeding program will have space to be housed?

Is it more ethical to euthanize a white rhinoceros that is not needed for a breeding program or to send it to a facility that will keep it alive but may not be adequately equipped to provide the size of space or other measures of quality of life that would be desired for the animal? Is length of life more valued than quality of life?

Is it ethical to use contraception to prevent breeding if there is evidence that contraception may have health risks or cause "unnatural" behavior changes?

Is it ethical to return zoo animals to the wild? If so, under what circumstances?

What is your reaction to the euthanizing of the giraffe in the Copenhagen Zoo? What other alternative might you suggest?

3: Is Sport Hunting Ethical?

Protestors lined up along a highway in Canton, Massachusetts to show their dismay with a special deer hunt designed to decrease populations of deer in an area known as Blue Hills (Ornell 2016). The Friends of the Blue Hills Deer waved signs to passersby.

On four days in late November and early December, hunters may apply to harvest deer in 3500 acres of the 7000-acre Blue Hills Reservation using shotguns with "slug" ammunition or archery. The Department of Conservation and Recreation determined that deer overpopulation is damaging vegetation in the forest. The director of the "friends" organization for the reservation agreed: "The deer population needs to be brought down to a healthy level through a controlled hunt for the health of the forest, its inhabitants, and visitors."

However, opponents did not believe the hunt was necessary and disagreed with hunting in general. Members of the Friends of the Blue Hills Deer and the Massachusetts Animal Rights Coalition made the following statements:

- The hunt is "unnecessary, cruel, and costly"
- "This is a way of taxpayers subsidizing a hunter's playground."
- "They let people hike in that area. What if their luck runs out? Is everyone supposed to wear an orange vest?" Communication between the Department of Conservation and Recreation and Friends of the Blue Hills Deer has been unproductive, according to the group.
- "They (agency officials) are not listening to anyone. They don't debate us. It's barbaric."
- Bow hunting leaves animals "wounded and suffering."
- "What will be next? Poison? Guillotines? For 100 years this was a safe space for all the creatures. The deer are accustomed to people."

The ethics of hunting are often debated. Recreational hunting, distinguished from subsistence hunting where the hunter depends on hunting for their primary source of food, may be evaluated ethically from several angles. Vitali (1990) and Gilbert (2000) published a pair of papers debating the issue, which provide a succinct overview of common ethical arguments:

ARGUMENT	VITALI (1990)	GILBERT (2000)
Do animals have moral rights?	Because animals lack reflective intelligence and complex language, they do not have moral rights; intentional death of animal is different than intentional death of a human	Research has shown more evidence of reflective intelligence in animals; moral rights may also be ascribed to animals in other ways, such as the ability to feel pleasure and pain

Is the "natural evil" of hunting balanced by "natural goods"?	Hunting is an exercise of human skills (stalking, knowledge of nature), a sufficient good that balances the natural evil of the animal's death	Wounding animals by hunting or trapping contributes to natural evils without a balancing natural good; technology and use of dogs are not human skills, and not all hunters are ethical in their practices during hunting; not all hunters have adequate skills to limit chances of wounding animals
Does hunting contribute to the function of ecological systems?	Life and death are critical to ecosystem dynamics; hunters help to keep ecosystems in balance, which is a natural good that balances the natural evil of the animal's death	Predator control and prairie-dog shooting are examples of hunting that may contribute to ecosystem instability; trophy hunting has potential to remove best genes from population

APPLICATION, ANALYSIS, SYNTHESIS, AND EVALUATION

From your own experiences, complete this sentence: "A hunter is ..."

How do you evaluate the ethics of sport hunting? How do your experiences contribute to your perspectives and to your views on hunters?

Could you make a similar set of arguments for the ethics of angling?

In other countries, it is common for hunters to be tested on their shooting ability before issuing a hunting permit. Should the US adopt this policy? How would it affect the ethical arguments surrounding sport hunting?

What ethical arguments are being made by the anti-hunting group in Massachusetts?

Gilbert (2000) ends his manuscript, published in the Wildlife Society Bulletin, as follows: "My intent here has been to point out that wildlife managers do not occupy the moral high ground in the ethics debates related to hunting and trapping. Unless we are prepared to acknowledge that philosophical counterarguments have validity ... this is increasing likelihood that animal rights groups, as well as anti-hunting and anti-trapping interests, will convince the public and ultimately the politicians that sport hunting and trapping pose unacceptable ethical considerations and should not be allowed to continue." Discuss this statement in the context of changes in demography (urban/rural) in the US and shifting stakeholder views of hunting. Is there evidence that (almost two decades later) wildlife managers have failed to heed Gilbert's warning?

Sources of Information and Further Reading

Alexander, K. L. "National Zoo employee found guilty of attempted animal cruelty." Washington, DC: *Washington Post*, 2011.

Armstrong, A. "Ethical considerations in wetland management. Physics and Chemistry of the Earth, Part B: Hydrology." *Oceans and Atmosphere* 25, no. 7-8, (2000): 641–644.

Beier, P., Vaughan, M. R., Conroy, M. J., and Quigley, H. *An analysis of scientific literature related to the Florida panther.* Final report, Project NG01-105. Tallahassee, FL: Florida Fish and Wildlife Conservation Commission, 2003.

Beier, P., Vaughan, M. R., Conroy, M. J., and Quigley, H. "Evaluating scientific inferences about the Florida panther." *Journal of Wildlife Management* 70, no. 1 (2006): 236–245.

Bur, J. *Fish and Wildlife Service official reportedly violated conflict of interest* rules. Vienna, VA: Federal Times, 2018.

Burke, D. "'Unethical' high-tech hunters using drones to find prey." Toronto, ON: *CBC News*, 2017.

Collins, K. *Exploring Business, v. 2.0.* Flatworld, 2018. Accessed online 28 April 2018. https://scholar.flatworldknowledge.com/books/22211.

Conroy, M. J., Beier, P., Quigley, H., and Vaughan, M. R. "Improving the use of science in conservation: lessons from the Florida panther." *Journal of Wildlife Management* 70, no. 1 (2006): 1–7.

Cromwell, J. A., Warren, R. J., and Henderson, D. W. "Live-capture and small-scale relocation of urban deer on Hilton Head Island, South Carolina." *Wildlife Society Bulletin* 27 (1999): 1025–1031.

Department of the Interior. "Ethics guide for DOI employees." Washington, DC: Department of the Interior, 2017.

Di Minin, E., Leader-Williams, N., and Bradshaw, C. J. "Banning trophy hunting will exacerbate biodiversity loss." *Trends in Ecology & Evolution* 31, no. 2 (2016): 99–102.

Elliot, R. "Faking Nature." *Inquiry* 25, no. 38 (1982): 1–389.

Elliot, R. *Faking nature: the ethics of environmental restoration*. London: Routledge, 2008.

Fleshler, D. "U.S. Wildlife Biologist Who Was Fired Over Panther Data Wins Job Back." *Sun-Sentinel.* Deerfield Beach, FL: 2005.

Fulton, D. C., Manfredo, M. J., & Lipscomb, J. "Wildlife value orientations: A conceptual and measurement approach." *Human dimensions of wildlife* 1, no. 2 (1996): 24–47.

Gilbert, F. F. "Considerations in managing wildlife populations for sport." *Wildlife Society Bulletin* 28, no. 2 (2000): 459–463.

Glikman, J. A., Vaske, J. J., Bath, A. J., Ciucci, P., and Boitani, L. "Residents' support for wolf and bear conservation: The moderating influence of knowledge." *European Journal of Wildlife Research* 58 (2012): 295–302.

Goldman, J. G. "Ethics at the Zoo: The Case of Marius the Giraffe." *Scientific American*, 2014.

Gozlan, R.E. "Introduction of non-native freshwater fish: is it all bad?" *Fish and Fisheries* 9 (2008): 106–115.

Gross, L. "Why not the best? How science failed the Florida panther." *PLoS Biology* 3, no. 9 (2005): 333.

Hiller, A. "System Consequentialism." In *Consequentialism and Environmental Ethics*, edited by Hiller A., Ilea R., and Kahn L., 54–69. 2013.

Johnson, C. E. *Meeting the ethical challenges of leadership: Casting light or shadow.* Thousand Oaks, CA: Sage Publications, 2017.

Kidder, R. M. *How good people make tough choices: Resolving the dilemmas of ethical living.* New York: Fireside, 1995.

Landers, R. "Court: Forest Service illegally allowed helicopter in wilderness for wolf collaring." *The Spokesman-Review.* 2017.

Lauber, B., T., Knuth, B. A., Tantillo, J. A., and Curtis, P. D. "The role of ethical judgments related to wildlife fertility control." *Society & Natural Resources* 20, no. 2 (2007): 119–133.

Leopold, A. *A Sand County Almanac, and Sketches Here and There.* New York: Oxford University Press, 1949.

Lindeque, M. "The case for dehorning the black rhinoceros in Namibia." *South African Journal of Science* 86, no. 5–6 (1990): 226.

Lönnstedt, O. and Eklöv, P. *Science* 352, 1213–1216 (2016); retraction 356, 812 (2017).

Lundstrom, J. "Wetlands Fill-in Bill Passes Legislature." *Peninsula Pulse*. Baileys Harbor, WI: 2018.

Macdonald, D. W., Jacobsen, K. S., Burnham, D., Johnson, P. J., and Loveridge, A. J. "Cecil: a moment or a movement? Analysis of media coverage of the death of a lion, Panthera leo." *Animals* 6, no. 5 (2016): 26.

Manfredo, M., Teel, T., and Bright, A. "Why are public values toward wildlife changing?" *Human Dimensions of Wildlife* 8, no. 4 (2003): 287–306.

Markkula Center for Applied Ethics. "A Framework for Ethical Decision Making." Santa Clara, CA: Santa Clara University, 2009. Accessed 30 April 2018. https://www.scu.edu/ethics/ethics- resources/ethical-decision-making/a-framework-for-ethical-decision-making/

Meijboom, F. L. B., and Bovenkerk, B. "Fish welfare: Challenge for science and ethics—Why fish makes the difference." *Journal of Agricultural and Environmental Ethics* 26, no. 1 (2013): 1–6.

Nelson, M. P., Bruskotter, J. T., Vucetich, J. A., and Chapron, G. "Emotions and the ethics of consequence in conservation decisions: Lessons from Cecil the Lion." *Conservation Letters* 9, no. 4 (2016): 302–306.

Nogales, M., A. Martín, B. Tershy, C. J. Donlan, D. Veitch, N. Puerta, B. Wood, and J. Alsonso. "A review of feral cat eradication on islands." *Conservation Biology* 18 (2004): 310–319.

Ornell, N. "Protesters in Canton condemn second Blue Hills deer hunt." *Patriot Ledger*. Quincy, MA: 2016

Packer, C., Brink, H., Kissui, B. M., Maliti, H., Kushnir, H., and Caro, T. "Effects of trophy hunting on lion and leopard populations in Tanzania." *Conservation Biology* 25, no. 1 (2011): 142–153.

Roemer, G. W., Donlan, C. J., and Courchamp, F. "Golden eagles, feral pigs, and insular carnivores: how exotic species turn native predators into prey." *Proceedings of the National Academy of Sciences* 99, no. 2 (2002): 791–796.

Rogers, P. "Ethics complaint filed against wildlife official who shot mountain lion." *The Mercury News*. San Jose, CA: Bay Area News Group, 2012.

Rokeach, M. *The nature of human values*. New York: Free Press, 1973.

Sandler, R. L. *Character and environment: A virtue-oriented approach to environmental ethics*. Columbia University Press, 2009.

Schwartz, S. H. "Universals in the content and structure of values: Theoretical advances and empirical tests in 20 countries." *Advances in Experimental Social Psychology* 25 (1992): 1–65.

Smith, G. P. "Environmental Hedonism or, Securing the Environment Through the Common Law." *Wm. & Mary Envtl. L. & Pol'y Rev.* 40 (2015): 65.

Sonner, S. "Nevada biologist sues bear activists for defamation." *The Associated Press*, 2017.

Spash, C. L. "Ethics and environmental attitudes with implications for economic valuation." *Journal of Environmental Management* 50, no. 4 (1997): 403–416.

State of Nevada. *Deferral Agreement: Ethics Complaint Case No. 17-27C*. Nevada Commission on Ethics, 2017.

Teel, T. L., Dayer, A., Manfredo, M. J., and Bright, A. D. *Regional Results from the Research Project Entitled Wildlife Values in the West*. Colorado State University, Human Dimensions in Natural Resources Unit, 2005.

Vaske, J. J. and Donnelly, M. P. "A value-attitude-behavior model predicting wildland preservation voting intentions." *Society & Natural Resources* 12 (1999): 523–537.

Vitali, T. R. "Sport hunting: Moral or immoral?" *Environmental Ethics* 12, no. 1 (1990): 69–82.

Vitule, J. R. S., Freire, C. A., and Simberloff, D. "Introduction of non-native freshwater fish can certainly be bad." *Fish and Fisheries* 10, no. 1 (2009): 98–108.

Walker, W. R., & Richardson, S. C. *The federal wetlands manual: swamped by controversy*. Special Report No. 24, Virginia Water Resources Research Center. Blacksburg, VA: Virginia Polytechnic Institute and State University, 1991.

Image Credits

Fig. 5.2: Copyright © 2016 Depositphotos/adekvat.
Fig. 5.4: Source: https://commons.wikimedia.org/wiki/File:Puma_concolor_coryi_Florida_panther.jpg.
Fig. 5.5: Source: https://www.fws.gov/refuges/features/Wildlife_Selfies.html.

SECTION III

Population Management

SECTION III

Population Management

CHAPTER SIX

Biology of Wildlife Populations

Learning Outcomes

After participating in learning experiences related to this chapter, students should be able to:

- Create a conceptual diagram showing BIDE dynamics for a species, including density-dependent and density-independent effects.
- Compare and contrast exponential and logistic models for population growth.
- Identify differences between limiting and regulatory effects on populations.
- Evaluate the regulatory potential of competition and predation for a given population of interest.
- Develop management actions for scenarios that account for the potential effects of competition and predation.
- Use an age- and stage-structured population model to evaluate differences in the contribution of various age and stage classes to population growth.

A One-Minute Summary

The framework for population growth is simple: populations can only increase through birth and immigration, and populations can only decrease through death and emigration. However, predicting the dynamics of populations is complex. Wildlife biologists observe exponential growth in populations during restorations of native species or during invasions by alien species. However, we know that populations eventually reach a point at which they can no longer sustain constant growth. What factors are responsible for these limits, and how should we model their effects?

Populations are limited, or reduced in size, by a range of factors. Freezing spells and droughts, for example, may cause drops in the size of a population, but these factors are not predictable, and they are density independent as they may occur at any population density. Regulatory factors are a type of limiting factor that is density-dependent. As density increases, competition for resources may increase, causing lower birth rates and higher mortality. Similarly, predators may respond in density-dependent fashion to prey populations. Prey populations, therefore, can be evaluated to determine if the prey is regulating itself through competition or if the prey population is being regulated by predators.

Management of both prey and predators, therefore, can be complex because of (1) uncertainties of what dynamics will occur to regulate a population, (2) the lack of predictability of limiting factors such as weather, and (3) the unequal contributions to population growth by members of different ages or age-based stages in a population. Such complexity reinforces the need for conceptual and mathematical models of population dynamics to predict outcomes under various management options.

Principles for Your Toolkit

BIDE: The simplest conceptual model for population growth states that a population can only grow through **b**irths and **i**mmigration, while it can only decrease through **d**eaths and **e**migration. All other population models, both conceptual and mathematical, are variations on the basic structure of the BIDE model (Figure 6.1).

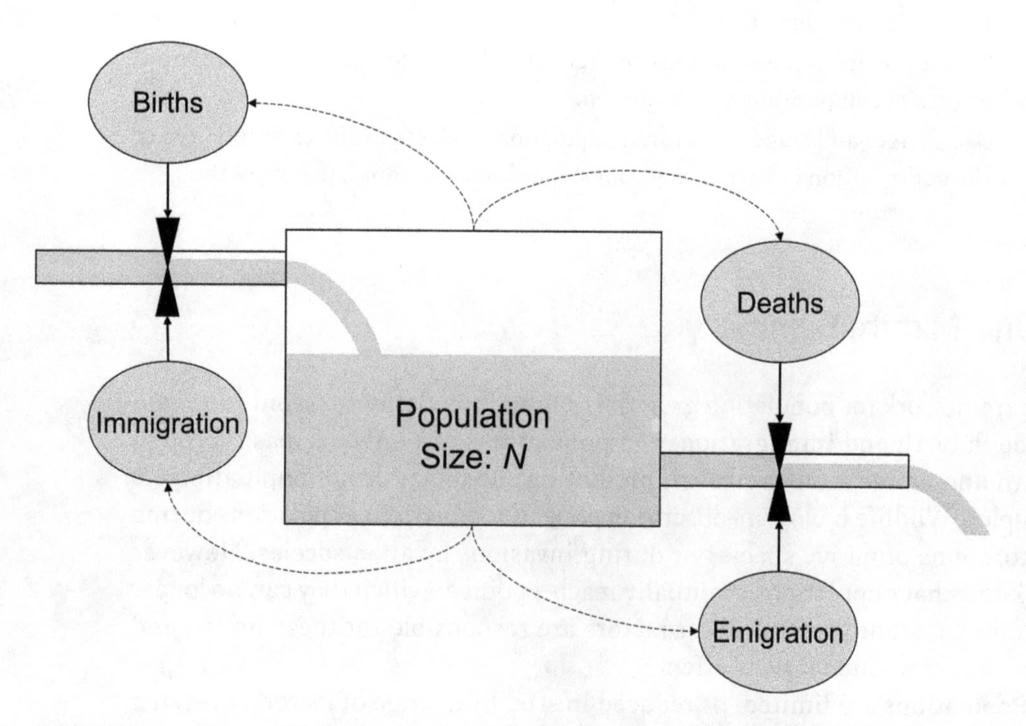

FIGURE 6.1 The BIDE conceptual model of population growth. Births and immigrants add to the population, while deaths and emigrants subtract from the size of the population (N).

Exponential growth potential: A population has the potential to grow in an exponential fashion. The principle becomes very important to managers during restoration projects for native species that have become extirpated from a given location and during biological invasions of alien species. Under ideal conditions, growth rates in both circumstances can be large, which may pose challenges to management.

Density dependence: Birth, death, and movement rates change as populations increase in density. This principle is used by harvest managers who assess the potential for a population to respond to decreases in density after hunting or angling. Managers of captive populations are aware that disease transmission is higher when animals are kept at high densities and close quarters in zoos, aquaria, and breeding facilities. Conservation planners use the principle of density dependence to predict the results of reintroductions of native species. The use of supplemental feeding is designed to alleviate a limited resource and delay the effects of density-dependent competition. As such, this principle may be one of the most important for wildlife managers to retain in their toolkit.

Competitive Exclusion Principle: Hardin (1960) proposed that "complete competitors cannot co-exist." This ecological and evolutionary principle suggests that if two species occupy exactly the same niche in the same location, one species will eventually exclude the other through competition if resources are limiting. Wildlife managers must be aware of the implications of this principle when managing ecosystems and communities of multiple species that may depend on a limited resource.

Age-structured populations: All individuals within a population are not equal, with regard to their contributions to population growth. Age classes within populations often have different survival probabilities and levels of fecundity of females, and age-specific patterns often vary for mammals, fish, amphibians, reptiles, and birds. Generally, survival is lowest for early and late age classes and fecundity is lower for females in early age classes. Managers who want to support population growth may, therefore, focus on actions designed to increase fecundity, especially for the age classes that contribute most to recruitment, and actions may also be taken to increase survival to allow more individuals to reach the more fecund age classes. In contrast, if population reduction is desired, actions may be taken to produce the opposite results.

A Problem: Wolves and Elk in Yellowstone

Anne Archer sat at her desk. A tingle ran up her spine as she looked out her window over the Yellowstone National Park in Wyoming. As a summer research technician, this was her dream come true: a summer job in Yellowstone working with elk and gray wolves.

On her desk was a paper written by Christianson and Creel (2014) that her new boss, Dr. Jennifer Youngson, had given her to look at before the first meeting of the summer research team. The paper led with a figure describing the pattern of elk

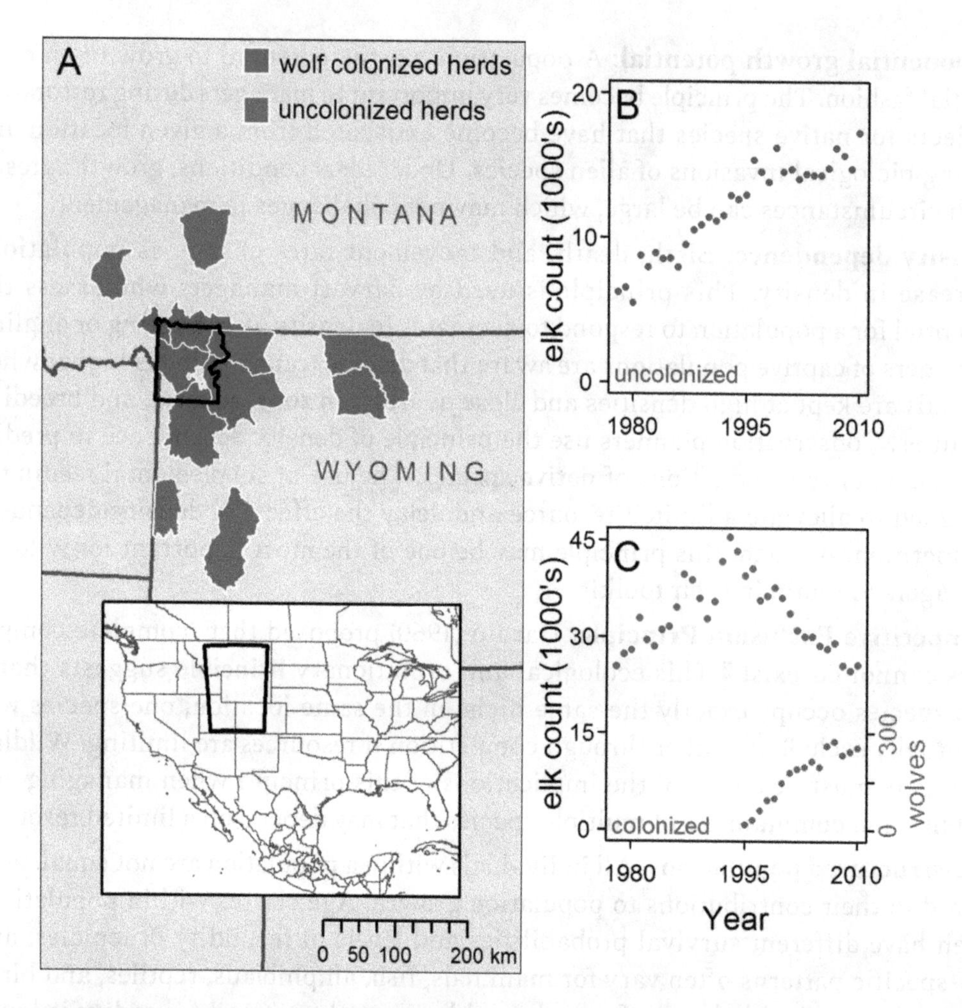

FIGURE 6.2 Population trends and distributions of 12 elk herds in the Greater Yellowstone Ecosystem. (A) Annual ranges of six central (red polygons) Yellowstone elk herds colonized by wolves after wolf reintroduction to Yellowstone National Park (YNP, black polygon) in 1995 and 1996 and six outlying elk herds (blue) that were not known to be recolonized by wolves before 2010. (B) Counts of elk summed across uncolonized herds from 1978–2010. (C) Counts of elk summed across herds colonized by wolves from 1978–2010, which represent the majority of the Greater Yellowstone Ecosystem elk population. Reprinted from Christianson and Creel (2014); Open Access publication.

population counts before and after the infamous reintroduction of wolves to the Greater Yellowstone Ecosystem (Figure 6.2).

Anne read:

> Prior to the reintroduction of wolves to the Greater Yellowstone Ecosystem in 1995 and 1996, over five decades of research and monitoring of Yellowstone elk dynamics consistently found that (1) variation in juvenile recruitment explained

most of the annual variation in elk population growth and that (2) negative density dependence and winter severity were the strongest drivers of annual variation in recruitment.

As Anne continued through the paper, she found the results intriguing: wolf predation of young elk was substantial but not enough to cause such a large decline in the herd sizes at the wolf introduction sites. Instead, the authors suggested that lower than expected pregnancy rates of female elk could be caused by enhanced perception of the risk of predation.

Dr. Youngson called Anne and her fellow researchers into the conference room for their discussion of the paper. Anne asked the first question: "If elk have such a negative response of productivity to higher densities, then why are the herd sizes in the control areas of the study still increasing steadily? Shouldn't the density-dependent factors begin to regulate the population?"

What information do you need to learn to contribute to this research discussion? What does Anne mean by population regulation? How might you answer Anne's question? Can you think of other possible factors that might play a role in elk population dynamics? By the time you finish this chapter, you should be able to find the answer.

Terms and Definitions

Age structure: For populations, the number of individuals alive at a given time in each of the population's age classes.

Birth rate, per capita: The number of offspring produced by a population in a given time period (usually a year), per the number of adults in the population.

Carrying capacity: Dynamic, but the maximum population size of a species that can be sustained by the food, habitat, water, and other limiting resources in the environment at a given place and time.

Competition: Interaction between organisms within and between species in which a limited resource affects rates of birth, individual growth, and/or mortality.

Conspecifics: Members of the same species.

Death, or mortality rate: The per capita number of animals in a population that die during a specified period of time.

Density-dependent factor: For populations, a factor that effects population size that changes in strength, either positively or negatively, as the population density changes.

Density independent factor: For populations, a factor that effects population size that is not affected by changes in the density of the population.

Exploitation competition: A mechanism for competitive effects between individuals or species in which an individual uses resources, which removes them from availability for other individuals.

Fecundity: For population biology and population modeling, synonymous with "recruitment," the per capita rate of offspring production, which is a function of birth, or natality rate and survival of young to the end of the time period; genetically, fecundity may be used to describe the actual reproductive rate of an organism or population measured by the number of gametes produced (a lack of fecundity in this use is sterility).

Functional response by predators: A change in the kill rate (prey eaten per time period) by predators in response to changes in prey density.

Interference competition: A mechanism for competitive effects between individuals or species in which an individual removes resources from use by other individuals by preventing access to the resource.

Natality rate: The per capita number of individuals born or hatched successfully in a population; often used synonymously with "birth rate," but to be distinguished from "recruitment rate."

Numerical response by predators: A change in the number of predators in a given location at a specified time in response to changes in prey density.

Population: Demographically, the members of a given species at a specified time and place; genetically, populations extend in space as far as individuals among proximate locations interbreed. Biologists often use *Nt* to denote the size of a population at a given time, *t*.

Recruitment: The per capita number of offspring born or hatched in a given year that survive to be incorporated into a specific age class at a specified time (e.g., often measured for at the end of the breeding season, often measured for fish at the beginning of the next breeding season).

Satiation: For predation or herbivory, for the digestive system of the predator or herbivore to be filled to capacity with food.

Stage structure: For populations, the number of individuals alive at a given time in each of the population's age-defined stages; often used for long-lived species to lump age classes into categories such as juvenile, pre-reproductive, reproductive, and post-reproductive.

Stock: For fisheries management, either the act of introducing hatchery-reared fish to another water body, or the population level reference to an identifiable management unit within a fish species (e.g., the Mississippi River walleye stock).

Switching: The dynamic of a predator changing its search image to focus on a different prey species as available prey species change in density.

Population Dynamics 101

The wildlife manager relies on conceptual models of population growth, as well as mathematical models that predict the results of management actions on a species of management concern.

The fundamental conceptual model of population growth[1] is the **BIDE** model, which describes population growth (ΔN) as a function of the number of **births** (*B*), **deaths** (*D*), **immigrants** (*I*), and **emigrants** (*E*):

$$\Delta N = B - D + I - E$$

The BIDE model captures the simple principle that only these four dynamics cause changes to population size over time. For simplicity in some circumstances, ecologists ignore the "movement" parameters and focus simply on births and deaths.

We can extend the basic BIDE model to predict population size in the next time step (time $t+1$). Typically, in wildlife management, our monitoring cycles conveniently allow us to use discrete, one-year time steps. The population size at the next time step, N_{t+1}, is a function of the current population, N_t, and the finite rate of growth, lambda (λ):

$$N_{t+1} = \lambda N_t$$

If our population is growing, $\lambda > 1$, and if the population is declining, $\lambda < 1$. Lambda may be calculated from annual monitoring data for our population as:

$$\lambda = \frac{N_{t+1}}{N_t}$$

Population biology is the study of changes in numbers of organisms in populations and the dynamics that influence those changes. Terrestrial wildlife biologists usually focus on predicting numbers of individuals, but fisheries biologists often tweak the basic definition to include the study of **biomass** of organisms in

QUICK COMPREHENSION CHECK

Start with a population of 1000 individuals (N_t). Now, pick a population size for N_{t+1}. Calculate the rate of growth, λ. Try scenarios of stable, growing, and declining populations. What is the value for λ in a stable population? What range of values for λ are possible for declining populations and growing populations?

---

[1] We approach this applied unit on population biology with the assumption that wildlife management students have completed theoretical coursework on populations in a general ecology course. For review of detailed theory, consult an ecology textbook and the sources provided in this chapter.

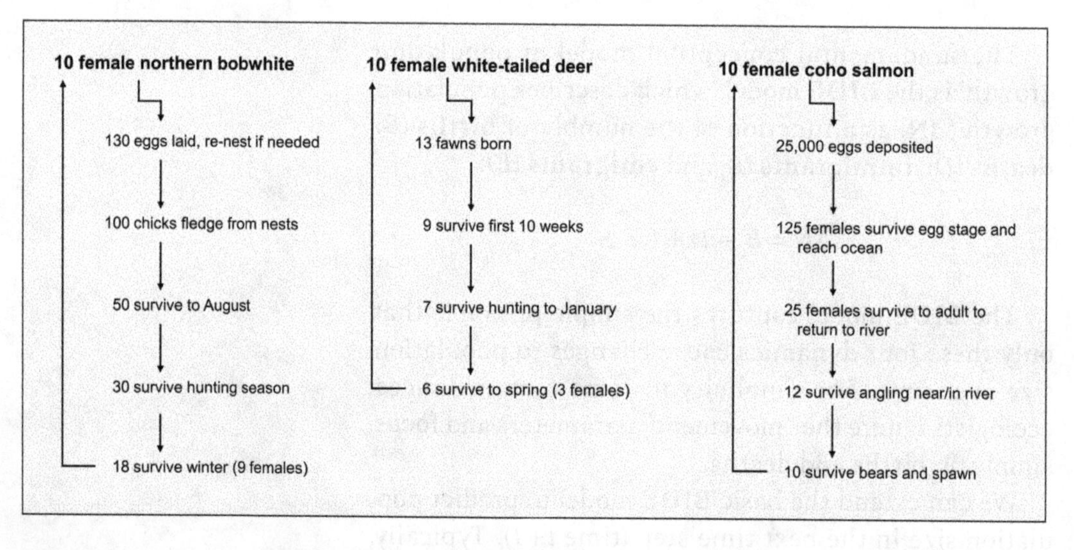

FIGURE 6.3 Patterns of production and survival of offspring for northern bobwhite, white-tailed deer, and coho salmon. After conceptual diagram for red grouse in Redpath and Thirgood 1997.

populations. Why? Fish may be measured in tons during commercial harvest, rather than counting individuals.

As biologists consider the group of individuals that are living (breeding and surviving) in a given area of interest, they use the term **population** ("Colorado's elk population" or the "Atlantic leatherback turtle population"). However, fisheries biologists may use the term **stock** to refer to an identifiable unit within a species that might be managed, such as the "Missouri River flathead catfish stock" or the "Lake Wanahoo walleye stock."

Biologists define the **birth rate** for populations or stocks in two ways. First, the number of individuals born or hatched within a specified time, such as a year, is termed the **natality rate.** Some terrestrial wildlife and fisheries biologists also consider **recruitment**—the number, or proportion, of individuals that survive to a certain stage (e.g., one-year-old fish or a pheasant chick that survives the breeding season to be present at the time of hunting). Recruitment may be more relevant for species in which a large number of eggs are produced, and a low proportion of individuals survive to reproduce again, such as northern bobwhite (Burger et al. 1995, Suchy and Munkel 2000, Rader et al. 2007) and coho salmon (Sandercock 1991). However, white-tailed deer have higher annual survival rates, so females have more reproductive seasons to attempt to replace themselves (Vreeland et al. 2004, Figure 6.3).

We will discuss population biology in the applied context of management issues in this chapter. How might management influence reproduction or survival of individuals in a population? We will consider both harvest mortality (e.g., hunting, angling, commercial fishing, trapping) and non-harvest mortality (e.g., disease, predation). **Demography** is a key interest to biologists who manage populations, especially when attempting to manage an invasive species, support an endangered species, or set harvest regulations.

Regulation and Limitation of Populations

Most populations of wildlife show constancy in numbers over time, despite their potential to over-produce. That is, the sizes of their population are not skyrocketing. Something appears to be keeping the population in check.

Charles Darwin pointed out this fact and suggested that even a single pair of elephants (with very low reproductive potentials because of long generation intervals and one offspring/birth event) had potential to blanket the earth with their population within 500 years:

> There is no exception to the rule that every organic being naturally increase at so high a rate that if not destroyed, the earth would soon be covered by the progeny of a single pair ...
>
> The Elephant is reckoned to be the slowest breeder of all known animals, and I have taken some pains to estimate its probable minimum rate of natural increase: it will be under the mark to assume that it breeds when thirty years old, and goes on breeding till ninety years old, bringing forth three pairs of young in this interval; if this be so, at the end of the fifth century there would be alive fifteen million elephants, descended from the first pair (Darwin 1859, p. 64).

Aldo Leopold's Welfare and Decimating Factors

In his first wildlife management textbook, *Game Management*, Aldo Leopold echoed Darwin's statement on population potential. Leopold (1933) wrote:

> We may conceive, therefore, of population as a flexible curved steel spring which, by its inherent force of natural increase, is constantly striving (so to speak) to bend upward toward the theoretical maximum, but which the various factors are at the same time constantly striving to pull down.

To describe the dynamics that brought populations into check, Leopold referred to **welfare and decimating**

QUICK COMPREHENSION CHECK

What dynamics keep animal populations bounded in population size? Why do they fail to realize their potential to cover the earth, as Darwin describes?

Refer to Figure 6.1. Do you see any hints in the conceptual BIDE model that might suggest ways in which an animal's population size is used as a feedback to alter key demographic rates of change?

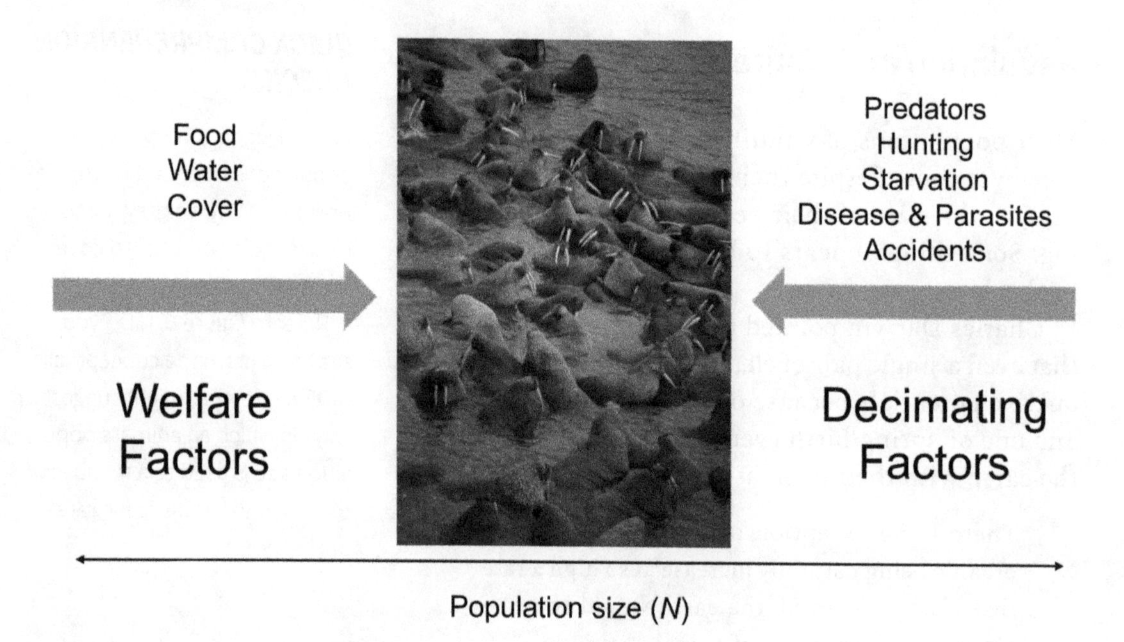

FIGURE 6.4 Competing forces of welfare and decimating factors (terms after Leopold 1933) that shape size of a population (depicted here, walrus, USFWS public domain photo).

factors (Figure 6.4). It is the values, or strengths, of each factor that management seeks to control, Leopold noted. Using this framework, one may erroneously see the wildlife manager as an expert puppeteer, pulling strings to effect an ecosystem. Unfortunately, it is usually not clear which string to pull or how much to pull it. Leopold explains (emphases are his):

> What we have called removals is ... the sum of the toll taken by hunters, predators, starvation and drouth [sic], diseases and parasites, and mechanical accidents. These we call decimating factors because <u>they kill directly</u>. The other class of factors ... includes non-lethal deficiencies of food, water, and coverts, and of certain special requirements such as salt ..., which we call welfare factors, reduce productivity not directly by decimation, but <u>indirectly by decreasing the breeding rate and by weakening the defense against the decimating factors.</u>

Taken in sum, both Leopold and Darwin described a key biological principle: **a population has the potential to grow in an exponential fashion.**

For a population monitored over any length of time period (Δt), we can further describe the change in population size (ΔN) in terms of the geometric rate of growth, r:

$$\frac{\Delta N}{\Delta t} = rN$$

For a population with a per capita birth rate, b (number of births per individual), and per capita death rate, d (number of deaths per individual):

$$r = b - d$$

A model of **exponential growth** describes the potential for a population to grow at the same rate of growth, r, over time, which results in a J-shaped curve for population size. The growth of the population compounds like a constant-rate interest in a bank account, as more and more mothers are added to the population, the population size begins to skyrocket **exponentially**. For a one-year monitoring period, we can write:

$$N_{t+1} = N_t + rN_t$$

We often describe exponential growth as a theoretical description of a population's biotic potential. However, wildlife managers may encounter real-life situations of exponential growth for limited time periods like the re-introduction of a species, such as black-footed ferrets (Grenier et al. 2007), into an area from which they were previously extirpated. Another example is the growth of a guanaco population on a ranch on the island of Tierra del Feugo, Chile (Zubillaga et al. 2014, Figure 6.5). Following several years of heavy hunting and removal of animals for domestication to the US, biologists followed the growth of the population, which grew at a steady rate initially.

Similarly, the initial rapid growth of an invasive fish species, such as lionfish (Green et al. 2012) in reef systems, clearly exemplifies exponential growth (Figure 6.6). Lionfish are predators and have spread rapidly in the Western Atlantic, Caribbean, and Gulf of Mexico. The invasive fish have strong effects on native reef fish communities, and such rapid growth makes containment or eradication efforts difficult.

Following rapid, exponential growth, the lionfish and guanaco populations eventually slowed in their growth and reached a point of apparent **carrying capacity.** What dynamics kept them from reaching their biotic

QUICK COMPREHENSION CHECK

Use a starting population size of 50 individuals, and a positive growth rate of $r = 0.32$. What is the growth of the population in the first year?

Add the growth to the initial population to obtain the new population size, and carry out the population growth for ten years, step by step. How large is the population after ten years?

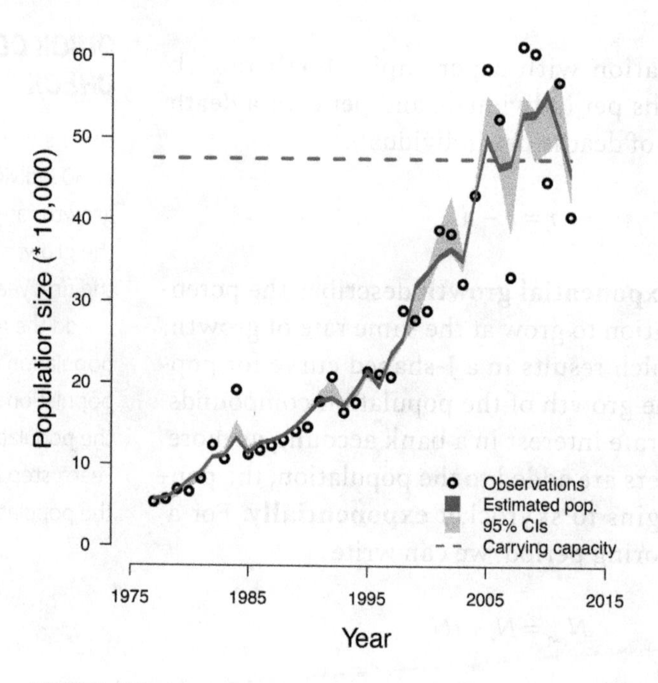

FIGURE 6.5 Observed population size and predicted trends for a guanaco population on Tierra del Feugo, Chile following several years of heavy hunting and removal of animals. Initial population growth was exponential in nature. Reprinted from Zubillaga et al. 2014, Open Access publication.

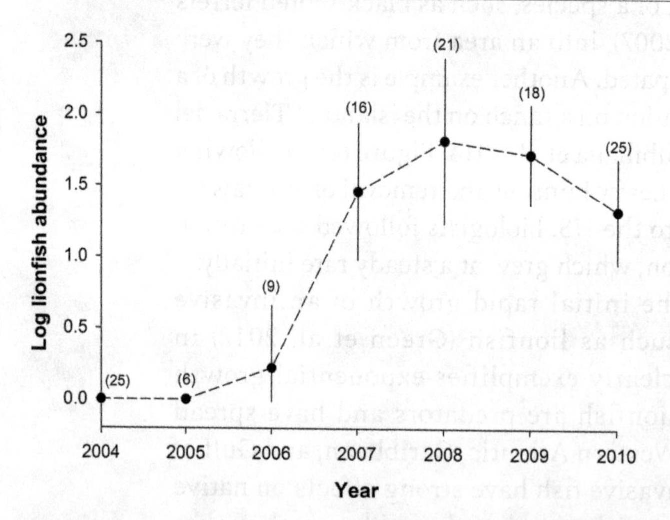

FIGURE 6.6 The abundance of Indo-Pacific lionfish (*Pterois volitans* and *P. miles*) on coral reefs off southwest New Providence, Bahamas. Abundance is the number of lionfish sighted during each roving survey (95% confidence intervals shown, with annual number of surveys in parentheses). Reprinted from Green et al. 2012, Open Access publication.

potential? We could surmise that a lack of welfare factors might have been responsible for slowing productivity or increasing the mortality rate. Welfare factors, such as water, support population growth when they are present. However, animals may die of the effects of dehydration during droughts when water is absent or rare. During hard winters, when food is scarce, animals may die of the effects of malnutrition as they compete for resources with other animals. The lack of these important factors increases the mortality rate and may decrease the birth rate to pull the population down to the present carrying capacity, a population level that can be supported by the currently available resources.

Thomas Malthus may have been the first to hint at some limit for population growth when he suggested late in the 18th century that there were checks on the growth of human populations (Malthus 1798):

> The power of population is so superior to the power of the earth to produce subsistence for man, that premature death must in some shape or other visit the human race. The vices of mankind are active and able ministers of depopulation. They are the precursors in the great army of destruction, and often finish the dreadful work themselves. But should they fail in this war of extermination, sickly seasons, epidemics, pestilence, and plague advance in terrific array, and sweep off their thousands and tens of thousands. Should success be still incomplete, gigantic inevitable famine stalks in the rear, and with one mighty blow levels the population with the food of the world.

After reading Malthus' essay, Pierre Francoi Verhulst, so the story goes, was inspired to develop a simple model of **logistic growth.** We still use this concept today, and the full time series for the lionfish and guanaco data exemplify the model of logistic growth behind the dynamics embedded in Malthus' "power of the population" concept and Leopold's welfare concept: quick initial growth that then slows as the population reaches **carrying capacity,** K. The key concept here will be important to the rest of this unit: **density dependence**, the response of population dynamics to the population density (numbers of animals per area). As density changes, the rate of growth is modified and eventually becomes equal to zero as the carrying capacity is reached. Here, notice that the population's intrinsic rate of growth, r, remains in the equation for logistic growth. However, growth is modified by the last component of the question, which measures how close the population is to the carrying capacity:

$$\Delta N = rN\left(\frac{K-N}{K}\right)$$

For amphibians, the presence of water is a critical welfare factor, and the population size of lowland leopard frogs in intermittent mountain streams in the Sonoran

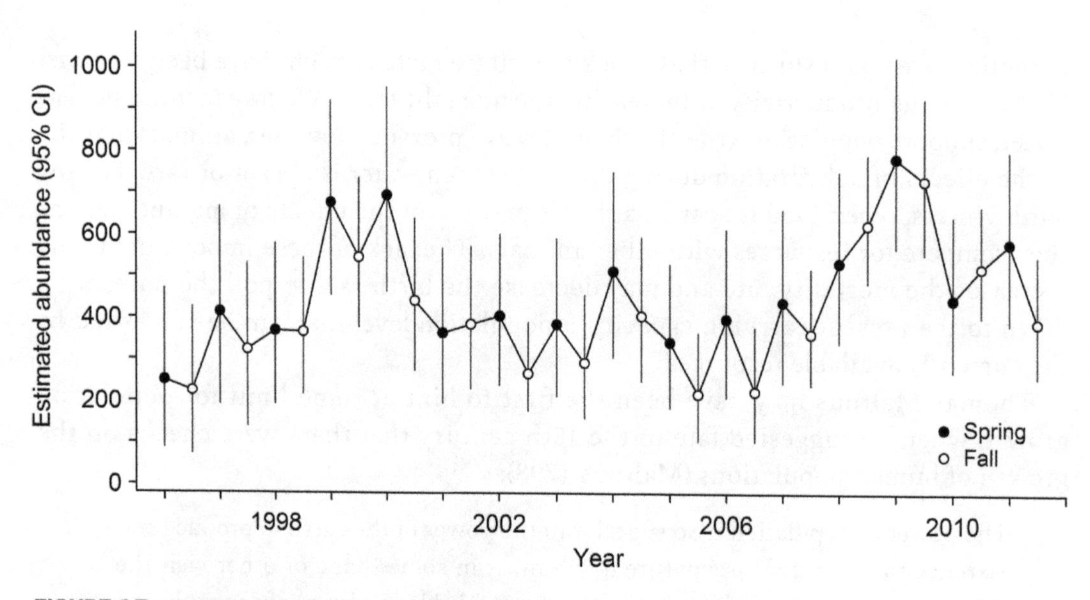

FIGURE 6.7 Estimated abundance (95% confidence intervals) of adult lowland leopard frogs in the Rincon Mountains, Arizona, USA between 1996 and 2011. Population size varied by proportion of pools at site with water. Reprinted from Zylstra et al. (2015), Open Access publication.

Desert is highly variable. The size of the population is driven by the proportion of pools that have water (Zylstra et al. 2015). Annual survival increases with available surface water, so a welfare-driven mechanism is responsible for changes in population growth of leopard frogs (Figure 6.7).

Resources (welfare factors) are important to support populations, but Leopold also suggested that **decimating factors** are responsible for bringing a population down from its biotic potential. Predation, disease, parasites, and human predation (hunting or angling) are factors that cause mortality. When disease is less common, survival rates go up, and a population may increase. Leopold's visual image of welfare and decimating factors is a useful place to start, as we envision factors that make populations go up and down. However, there is a bit more complexity in real life.

Regulation versus Limitation

Populations are reduced in size by **limiting factors** and **regulatory factors**, and the contrast is critical to the study of populations. By definition, all factors that cause a population's growth to slow, even temporarily, are limiting factors. But not all limiting factors are regulatory. Regulatory factors are density-dependent, and therefore will always cause a population to slow in growth when density increases.

We might use the temperature in a house as an example. The thermostat regulates the temperature. When the temperature rises, the thermostat eventually turns off the furnace, and when the temperature falls to a set point, the thermostat will turn on the furnace. Unless your thermostat is broken, you can count on the thermostat to regulate the temperature at the level you have set. The thermostat is a regulatory mechanism built into your house's temperature control system.

However, there are other methods to raise or lower the temperature in your house. The body heat created by a large group of people in the house for a holiday dinner will raise the temperature in the room. Likewise, if you are cooking, the stove will raise the temperature. Opening a door or a window, in the wintertime, will lower the temperature. So, you can limit the temperature in the room by opening a window. However, the window does not regulate the temperature, as it will not automatically open when the temperature gets high. It has no feedback mechanism in the system.

Similarly, a wildlife population may be affected by factors that limit or regulate the population. The Oklahoma Department of Wildlife Conservation, the state wildlife agency, has collected and published an annual population index (counts per standardized survey route performed during August and October) for northern bobwhite in Oklahoma over a span of almost two decades. We can see variability in the counts. The population has apparently risen and fallen over time (Figure 6.8). Why?

Quail biologists know that cold, icy winters may cause severe population declines in bobwhites, and wet, cold weather during the time when chicks leave the nest may result in high chick mortality. Droughts and high temperatures during June also cause high mortality because of lower insect availability and lack of cover to enhance survival of chicks. All of these factors make it difficult to predict the limiting effects of weather on bobwhites (Lusk et al. 2002). Life for bobwhites seems to consist of a long list of abiotic and biotic hazards to avoid. In this time series, we can see the limiting effects of a prolonged drought between 2006 and 2013 as well as the effects of cold brood-rearing periods and cold winters.

We can also see a relative long-term maximum for the count index, approximately ten quail/route, a level to which the population seems to recover after each limiting period. Perhaps this represents a general level of carrying capacity in a normal year. However, defining a normal year, with regards to weather, is quite difficult. Perhaps food resources create competition for food or predators begin to focus on quail when populations are high. At high densities of northern bobwhite in Iowa, winter losses (mortality) in population size were higher and summer gains (productivity) in population were lower (Errington 1945). We can infer similar mechanisms as potential drivers of population dynamics for bobwhite in Oklahoma, and the result is that population growth slows and the population levels off as it recovers. This is a real-life example of logistic growth, and the mechanism that slows the population growth is density-dependent. That is, as the density increases, reproduction decreases or mortality increases. At these points in the cycle, the quail population was regulated and did not increase beyond the carrying capacity.

Is climate a regulating factor? It certainly causes the population to decrease, rather than increase. But, can we count on severe droughts to occur every time the population grows to a certain level? No. Therefore, mortality associated with

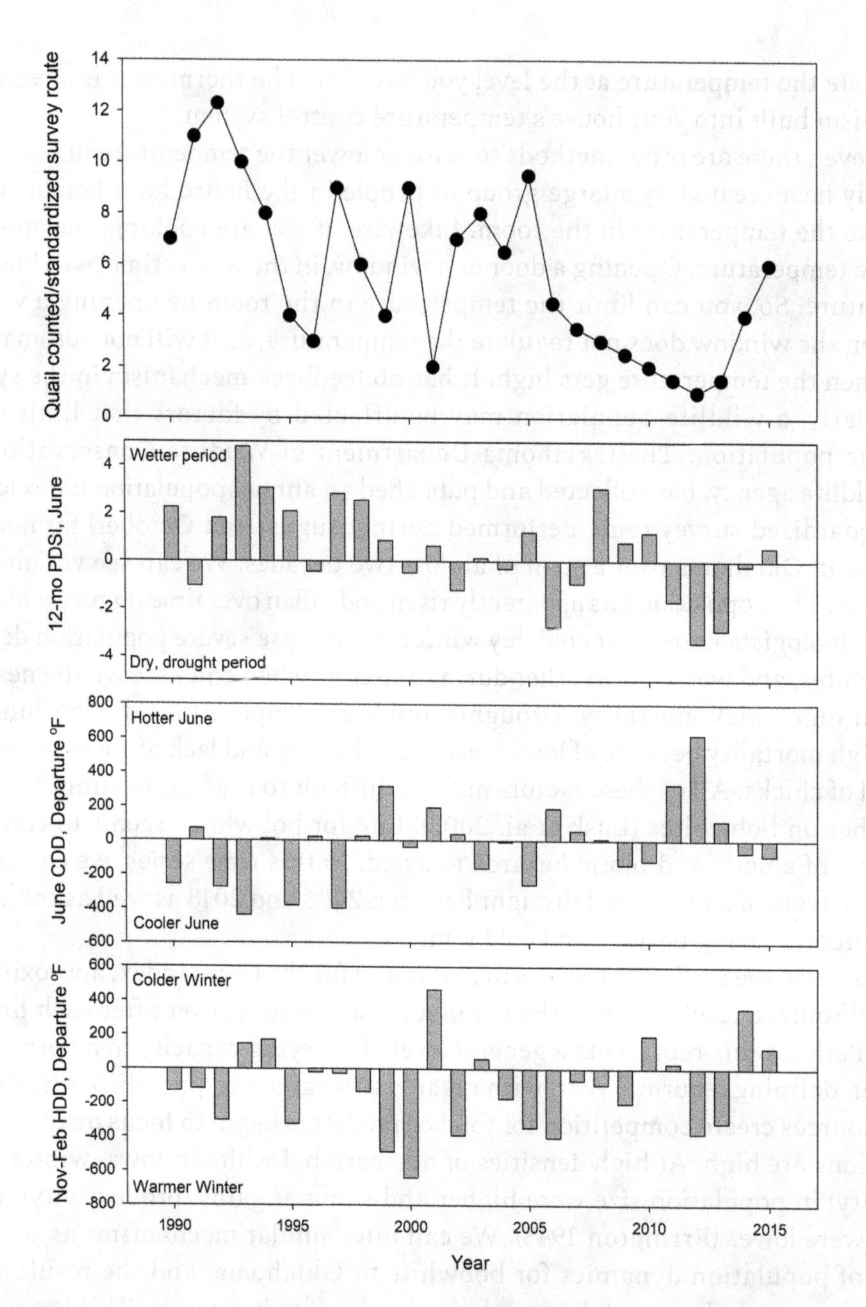

FIGURE 6.8 Annual population index (counts per survey route) of northern bobwhite (quail) in Oklahoma, shown with corresponding weather information: Palmer Drought Severity Index (PDSI) 12 months prior to June, June cooling degree days (CDD: sum of daily average temperatures above 65 degrees F), departure from average, and November-February heating degree days (HDD: sum of daily average temperatures below 65 degrees F), departure from average. Bobwhite data from public domain report of the Oklahoma Department of Wildlife Conservation; weather data from National Weather Service.

droughts and cold breeding periods is **density independent.** Severe weather does not automatically occur when the quail population size grows to a large number. Climate is a limiting factor, but climate is not a regulating factor.

Intraspecific Competition

The dynamic of individuals of a species competing with **conspecifics** is known as **intraspecific competition.** Competition may lead to population regulation if competition for resources increases with density. Such competition can take two forms: **exploitation competition** and **interference competition.** Exploitation refers to one individual removing a resource, through use, so that the resource is no longer available. Eating a food item or using a nesting cavity are examples of exploitation. Interference refers to keeping other individuals from using a resource, even if the resource is not used. Territorial animals might keep other individuals from eating berries on a tree, simply because the tree is in their territory.

So, how is competition regulatory? Consider an example of muskrats in a complex of marshes in Canada (Clark and Kroeker 1993). In many ways, marshes are habitat islands. Movement may be constrained to the marsh, and resources must come from the marsh or nearby. Muskrats need submerged vegetation for winter food and cover, and they build their homes using vegetation. At high densities, muskrats may have a devastating impact on marsh vegetation, which is a concern for managers of waterfowl populations that use the same marsh for foraging habitat. Annual survival of muskrats varies between 5–15%, and muskrats often have an average of about two litters (but as many as four) per year with seven young per litter (Clay and Clark 1985). Therefore, muskrat populations have high potential for growth, and populations fluctuate with weather, water level, and vegetation conditions. Scientists have followed this muskrat population and estimated recruitment (a measure of

QUICK COMPREHENSION CHECK

Are there ways that managers can use the concept of population regulation? Imagine a population of sea turtles that nest along the Florida coast. The nests are often preyed upon by raccoons and other mammalian predators. As the nesting density of sea turtles increases, predators respond in density-dependent fashion by regulating the turtles through higher rates of nest predation. What might we expect to happen to the sea turtle population if a manager artificially reduced the effect of raccoons by erecting barriers around each sea turtle nest?

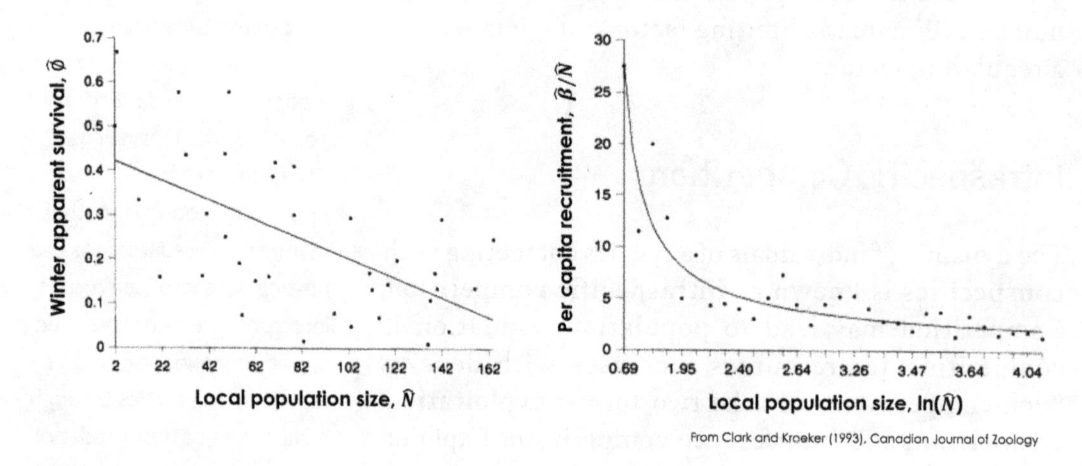

FIGURE 6.9 Density-dependent winter survival (left) and per capita recruitment (right) for a population of muskrats at Delta Marsh, Manitoba, Canada. Data from Clark and Kroeker (1993), reprinted with permission of Canadian Journal of Zoology.

the number of new individuals in the population, as a function of immigration and births between May and October) and survival of marked animals in the population (Figure 6.9).

Biologists found that the density of muskrats in a given marsh had a profound impact on the muskrat population. First, we can look at recruitment. Biologists documented little movement between marshes, so recruitment is primarily a measure of birth rate in this study. Populations at the lowest densities added 10–20 new individuals per individual in the population. Conversely, recruitment of muskrats is lowest at high population levels, adding less than 3–4 individuals per capita between May and October. Therefore, reproduction is density-dependent in this population.

What is the implication? Intraspecific competition may regulate the population by causing productivity to decrease. The mechanism is just like a thermostat, and the population may never increase beyond a given level. As the number of muskrats climbs, the females reproduce at lower rates, thereby slowing and eventually lowering the population size.

But, there are more dynamics at play. Survival of muskrats during winter (October to May) is also density-dependent in this population. Winter survival for a population in a given marsh varied tremendously in this study, from as high as 68% to less than 1%. And, density was one factor that caused the variation in survival: muskrats survive at higher levels during the winter when the muskrat population is low. So, intraspecific competition also causes survival to be density-dependent.

The overall effect is that as the population grows, survival and reproduction decrease. The growth rate of the population slows as more muskrats die, and fewer muskrat young are produced. We can infer that high densities cause resources to be limited, suggesting that competition has regulated the population. To support this conclusion, biologists reported that mass change in adults and juveniles during the winter was negatively related to population density, suggesting that it became problematic for individuals to obtain food to build body mass at high muskrat densities. In addition, populations from marshes with higher mass gain had higher winter survival.

What specifically causes survival and recruitment to be lower at high muskrat densities? Biologists suggested that increases in density resulted in less emergent vegetation and poor habitat conditions that created higher energetic demands on muskrats. As food sources declined, perhaps muskrats were faced with increased energetic costs of foraging farther and across open water, which could lead to predation. The lack of building material for shelters or lack of access to food that becomes frozen to the marsh bottom may lead to lower survival and poor body condition for survivors who then reproduce at lower rates. In this manner, the demography of the muskrat population is dependent on the size of the local muskrat population, leading to regulatory dynamics.

QUICK COMPREHENSION CHECK

Compare the potential population dynamics of muskrats, given the description of demographic rates, to the dynamics of northern bobwhite described earlier. What similarities and differences can you see?

Interspecific Competition and Niches

Interspecific competition is much harder to study, because we need to look at all of the interactions between different species. We know from the principle of logistic growth that a species may be regulated by competition with its own species (intraspecific competition), and now we consider the possibility that another species may cause additional exploitive or interference competition to occur (interspecific).

For a simple two-species competitive interaction, we can modify the logistic growth equation to include effects of interspecific competition:

$$\Delta N_1 = r_1 N_1 \left(\frac{K_1 - (N_1 + \beta_{12} N_2)}{K_1} \right)$$

and

$$\Delta N_2 = r_2 N_2 \left(\frac{K_2 - (N_2 + \beta_{21} N_1)}{K_2} \right)$$

Using this model to describe effects of competition, we propose that the growth of a population is affected by two forces: intraspecific and interspecific competition. First, the growth of the population continues to be dependent on how close the population is to its carrying capacity, as a function of intraspecific competition. In addition, we now add a component, $\beta_{ij} N_j$, which describes the effect of a competitor, species *j*, on species *i*. The competition coefficient, β, describes the relative effect of the competitor species.

We can note that if $\beta_{12} = 1.0$, the population size of the competitor, species two is added in complete fashion to the population size of species one. Therefore, the competitor will reduce the population growth by filling in the gap between the current population size of species one and its carrying capacity—essentially acting as just another individual in the population. However, if β_{12} is < 1.0, the effect is to add only a portion of the size of the competitor species' population as we evaluate how close species one is to its carrying capacity. Likewise, if $\beta_{12} > 1.0$, the competitive effect is that species one perceives an individual of species two to be more competitive than a conspecific. For example, if $\beta_{12} = 1.5$, species one feels the effect of one individual of species two as 1.5 individuals of species one.

In practice, estimation of a competition coefficient for a competitor is extremely difficult, because (1) carrying capacity is not steady in most populations, (2) discrete two-competitor situations are rare, (3) critical resources are not always limited in abundance, and (4) the estimation of relative resource use by two species is not straightforward. **Competition can only occur if resources are limited.**

Therefore, wildlife biologists tend to use the concepts found in these equations to focus on relevant factors for two species with potential for competition, such as the overlap in diet or habitat components as they make decisions regarding management of habitats. Have European starlings taken over nesting cavities for native species (Koenig 2003)? Are there enough winter food resources for migrating elk and domestic cattle sharing the same range (Hansen and Reid 1975)? Do enough food resources exist for native frog larval forms in the presence of invasive American bullfrogs (Kupferberg 1997)? How does competition between fish species affect the community assemblage in a lake (Larkin 1956)?

The **competitive exclusion principle** states "complete competitors cannot co-exist" (Hardin 1960). That is, if two species occupy exactly the same niche in the same location, one species will eventually exclude the other through competition. A **niche,** the role of a species in an ecosystem, may be defined by a multitude of dimensions such as trophic level, size of prey items, habitat use, or activity time of day. For example, in a Brazilian floodplain system, four common, medium-sized carnivore species exhibit dietary (Bianchi et al. 2014), spatial, and temporal partitioning of niche space (de Cassia Bianchi et al. 2016). Crab-eating foxes and brown-nosed coati overlap in their diets of arthropods, fruits, and vertebrates (Figure 6.10), while ocelots were specialized and strictly carnivorous (rodents and snakes). Little is known about the diet of crab-eating raccoons, but they are hypothesized to be generalists that compete for food and habitat with crab-eating foxes. Ocelots and coati were generalist habitat users, while crab-eating foxes preferred savanna habitats. The biologists found that foxes showed crepuscular-nocturnal activity with little daytime activity. Coatis were diurnal with few night records, and ocelots and raccoons were more active at night. Ocelots and raccoons had the highest overlap in their activity patterns, while ocelots and coati overlapped the least in activity pattern. Thus, diet and habitat segregation were not as important to the reduction of potential competition as temporal segregation. The two species with the largest overlap in activity pattern had different diets. Thus, niche partitioning allows these similarly-sized predators to be sympatric throughout most of their ranges.

Can a competitor limit a wildlife population? Wildlife biologists must consider potential competitive effects during management planning, and scenarios involving invasive species are a prime example.

As bighead and silver carp, two species of Asian carp, invaded the Mississippi River system in the 1980s, biologists became concerned that the invasive carp, which are phytoplankton and zooplankton filter feeders, would outcompete native filter feeders. Sampson et al. (2009)

QUICK COMPREHENSION CHECK

Ocelots are often poached for their uniquely marked skins. If ocelots were to be removed from a system, which of the other three mesopredators would benefit the most, given the information in Figure 6.10?

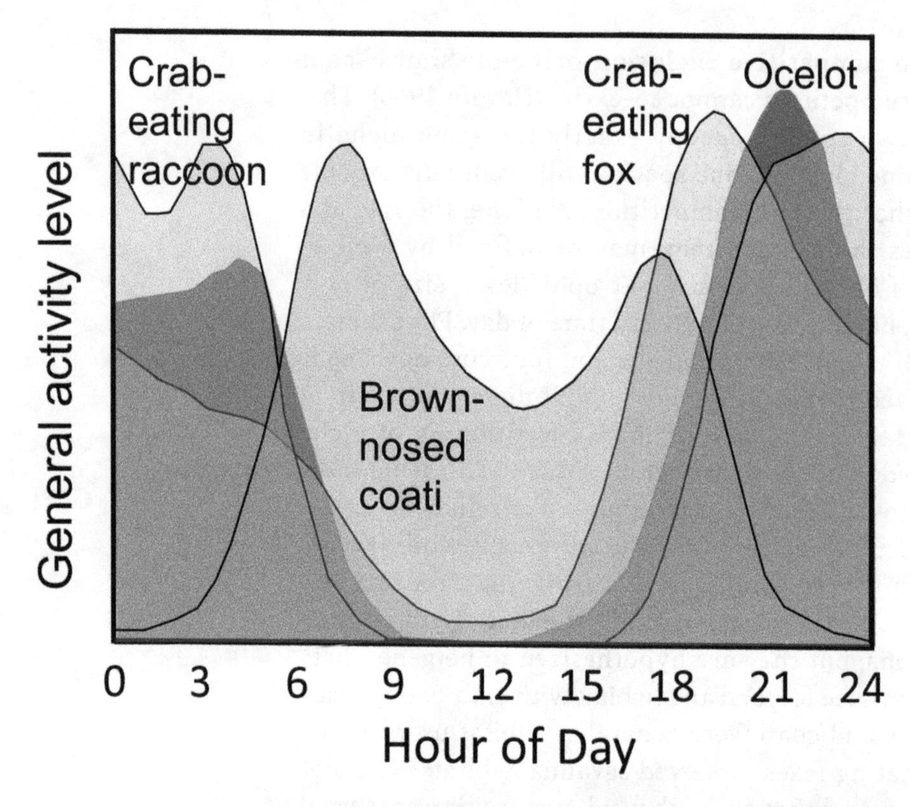

FIGURE 6.10 Overlap of active period among carnivore species: ocelot, crab-eating fox, brown-nosed coati, and crab-eating raccoon in a Brazilian wetland. Overlaps indicate potential temporal competition. Figure modified from de Cassia Bianchi et al. (2016), Open Access publication.

found that rotifers, small zooplankton, were the predominant diet item of Asian carp, which overlapped with the diet of American gizzard shad, whereas crustacean zooplankton were the preferred prey of American paddlefish. The bigmouth buffalo had a broad diet, so the authors suggested that gizzard shad would be the most likely species to encounter competition should food resources be limiting. However, the authors suggested that the highly productive waters of the Mississippi River most likely forestalled the effects of competition—in less productive aquatic systems, Asian carp would be expected to compete with gizzard shad and possibly bigmouth buffalo.

In the United Kingdom, native red squirrels have been on the losing side of a dramatic example on pathogen-mediated apparent competition with non-native, invasive Eastern gray squirrels (Sheehy et al. 2018). Red squirrels are replaced by gray squirrels in an expedited fashion in the presence of squirrelpox virus, a disease that is typically lethal to red squirrels. However, gray squirrels do not respond to the disease, although they act as a reservoir and may spread the disease. However, both squirrels share a native predator, the European pine marten, which has recently recovered from historical persecution. In landscapes that pine martins use more intensely, gray squirrels

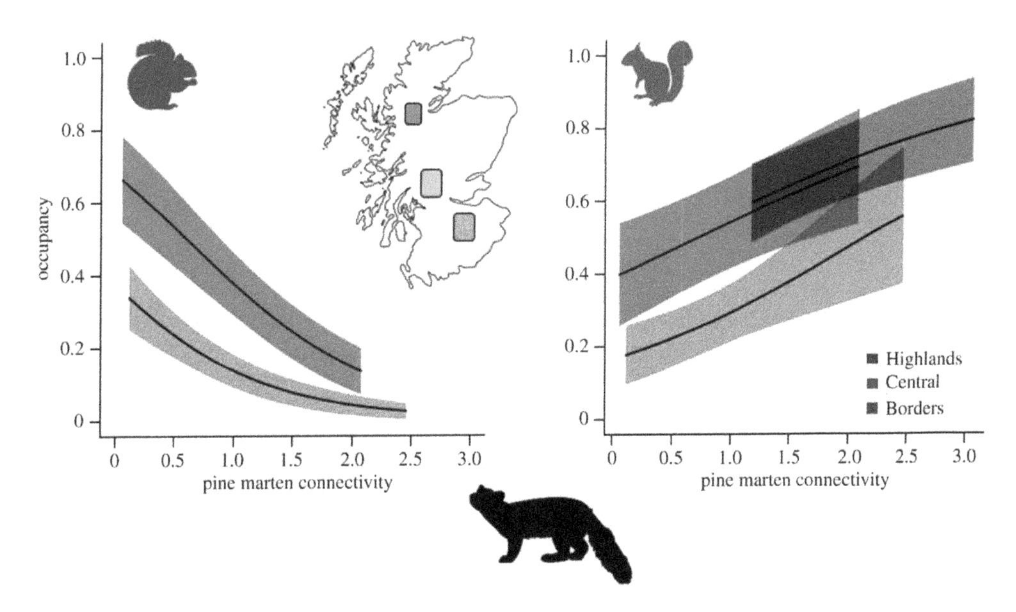

FIGURE 6.11 Relationships between occupancy of eastern gray squirrels (left) and red squirrels (right) and pine marten density weighted connectivity in the Borders, Central, and Highland regions of Scotland. Reprinted from Sheehy et al. (2018), Open Access publication under Creative Commons Attribution License.

are less likely to be present, while red squirrels are more likely to be present. This correlational pattern suggests that pine martens may prey on gray squirrels more than red squirrels, which may have begun to release red squirrels from apparent competition with gray squirrels.

Community interactions between species are complicated, but wildlife managers must consider potential interactions as they make decisions. Uncertainties in interspecies dynamics may be accounted for in decision-making approaches.

Predation

Predation, the killing of prey by a predator, is a force that will, by definition, limit populations of a prey species. But, can predators regulate prey populations? Not always. In what conditions can predators regulate populations of prey animals?

Based on our definition of regulation, we would expect predation to be regulatory when predators respond to prey in a density-dependent fashion. An initial assessment of the time series data for rock ptarmigans and gyrfalcons in Iceland shows the ptarmigan population increasing and the gyrfalcon population responding with a lagged increase, known as a **numerical response.** As the number of prey increases, the number of predators also increases. The predator response may occur

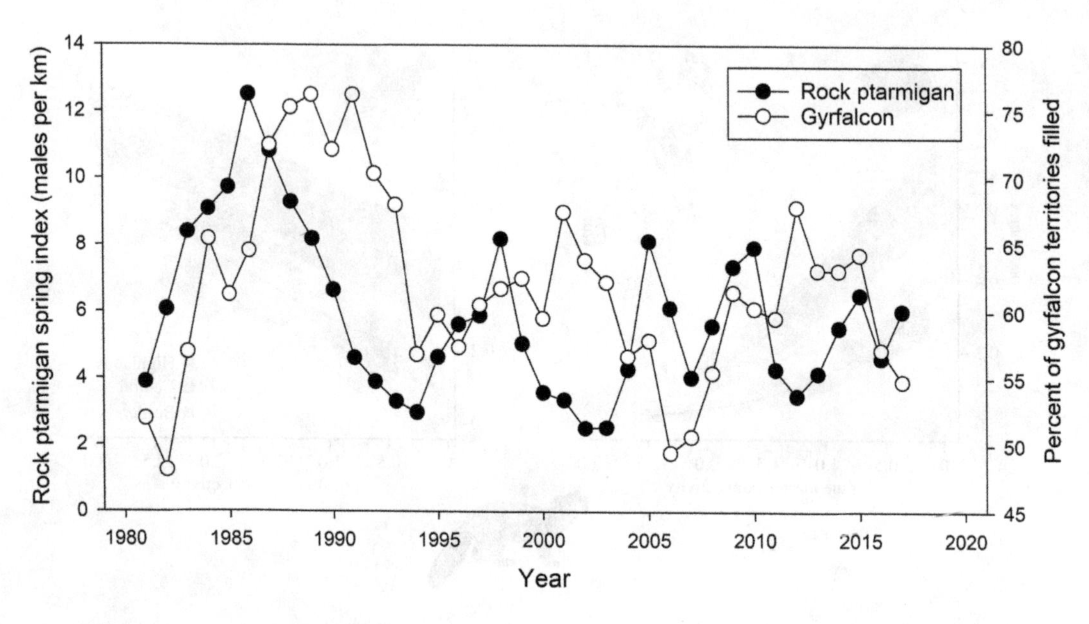

FIGURE 6.12 Cycles in population sizes of rock ptarmigan (males per km) and gyrfalcon (percent of territories filled) in Iceland. Data collected by Ólafur Nielson, used with permission.

from additional gyrfalcons immigrating to nest sites in areas with high ptarmigan densities, or the increase in gyrfalcons might be a result of higher productivity or survival of gyrfalcons at the site (Nielsen 2011).

As we look further along the time series, we see ptarmigan numbers decreasing after their peak. Did the numerical response by gyrfalcons regulate the ptarmigan population? Not necessarily. Each gyrfalcon also preys on more ptarmigan per breeding season as ptarmigan densities increase (Nielsen 2011), which we define as the **functional response.**

The classical interpretation of a predator prey cycle, such as the cycles shown for ptarmigans and gyfalcons, is to infer that the predator regulated the prey, and that the prey's falling population then regulates the predator because of a lack of food. Similar cycles have been observed in Canada lynx and showshoe hares in Canada (Elton and Nicholson 1942), mustelids and rodents in Europe (Hanski et al. 1991), moose and wolves on Isle Royale in the United States (Vucetich and Peterson 2004). and piscivore and planktavore fishes in the northern United States (Carpenter and Kitchell 1988). However, the reason for the cycles is complicated in each example and may not always exemplify a tight top-down regulatory relationship between the predator and prey. Regardless, the cycles are incredibly interesting to study and discuss to learn more about predator-prey interactions.

For example, gamekeepers and biologists in the UK have observed four- to five-year cycles in the size of populations of red grouse for over 100 years. Although it might be logical to look for regulating effects of a linked species of predator, red grouse have

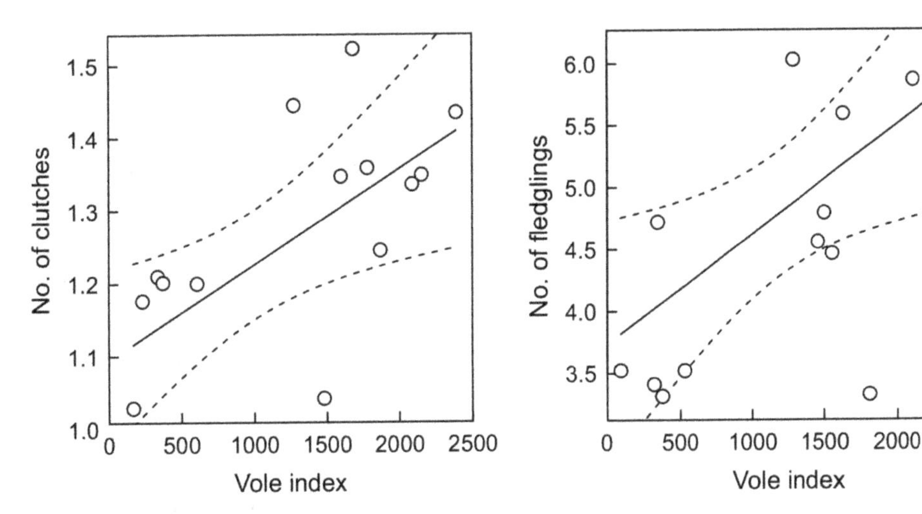

FIGURE 6.13 The relationship between barn owl productivity responses (left: number of clutches, right: number of fledglings) and autumn vole index over time in the Czech Republic. Dashed lines indicate 95% confidence intervals for the regression line. Modified from Pavluvčík et al. (2015), Open Access publication.

multiple predators. Farmers and gamekeepers became convinced early on that a parasitic "worm" was responsible for "grouse disease" that caused declines in red grouse (Cobbald 1873). Later, the Committee of Inquiry on Grouse Disease (1911) concluded that, indeed, a small nematode parasite, *Trichostrongylus tenuis*, was responsible for the cycling. As red grouse populations increased, the transmission of the parasite was more likely. The parasite caused chick and adult mortality, which led the populations to plummet. At certain times and locations, predators such as red foxes and northern harriers show initial numerical response to higher red grouse populations, and they often show local declines due to emigration or lower survival when grouse populations decline.

But predators do not regulate red grouse, despite the fact that their populations often track the population sizes of the grouse.

More broadly, wildlife biologists should note that the potential for parasites and other disease vectors to respond in density-dependent fashion as a population increases is an important consideration for managers who are involved with aquaculture, fish or game rearing, zoo and aquarium animal care, or other attempts to confine wildlife at higher densities than they experience in the wild. As in the farming of domestic livestock, disease transmission becomes a concern for wildlife kept in close proximity and at high densities.

Numerical Response

As seen previously in many predator-prey cycles, such as the Icelandic ptarmigan and gyrfalcons, the predator responds with higher numbers as the prey increases. Scientists in Iceland quantified predator population levels as the proportion of possible gyrfalcon nest sites that were occupied during a season.

One mechanism for a numerical response is increased body condition of females, which leads to higher levels of reproduction. For example, biologists assessed a predator-prey system in the Czech Republic in which barn owls feed almost exclusively on common voles. When vole numbers increase, barn owls are more likely to re-nest within a season and they produce more fledglings (Pavluvčík et al. 2015). Of course, the increased productivity represents a numerical response to an increasing prey population.

The numerical response of predators rarely regulates prey populations alone. In concept, prey populations rapidly rise to high levels when predator numbers are low, after which the predator numbers start to increase. But, by the time the predator has responded through births or immigration, the prey species begins to experience intraspecific competition, which regulates the prey due to limited food or other resource. Following a decline in prey, the predators may also experience a population decline. Eventually, the prey rebounds, because their low populations have enough food and few predators, and the cycle begins again. In this scenario, the prey is self-regulating, and the prey are regulating the predator. Thus, a simple glance at a numerical response of predators does not suffice to show regulation by predators.

QUICK COMPREHENSION CHECK

Consider a large recruitment event for juvenile fish from a coral reef system using a mangrove edge on the coast of Puerto Rico as a nursery. A biologist notes a numerical response within a month by predators in the zone around the mangroves. What mechanism resulted in more predators in response to the prey?

Functional Response

An individual predator's rate of killing prey may increase with density of prey. Conceptually, this is logical. It is easier for a predator to find and kill prey when the prey are present in higher numbers. Predators have lower **search times**, because there are more prey individuals to find. Such an increase in predation rate is shown as the increase in prey items eaten per day for two species of crayfish (one native, another introduced) in the United Kingdom (Haddaway et al. 2012, Figure 6.14).

A generalist predator may have more than one prey option, and predators may **switch** to a different prey species when the density of that prey species increases to a certain level that makes foraging more efficient for the predator. In Scotland, hen harriers feed on chicks

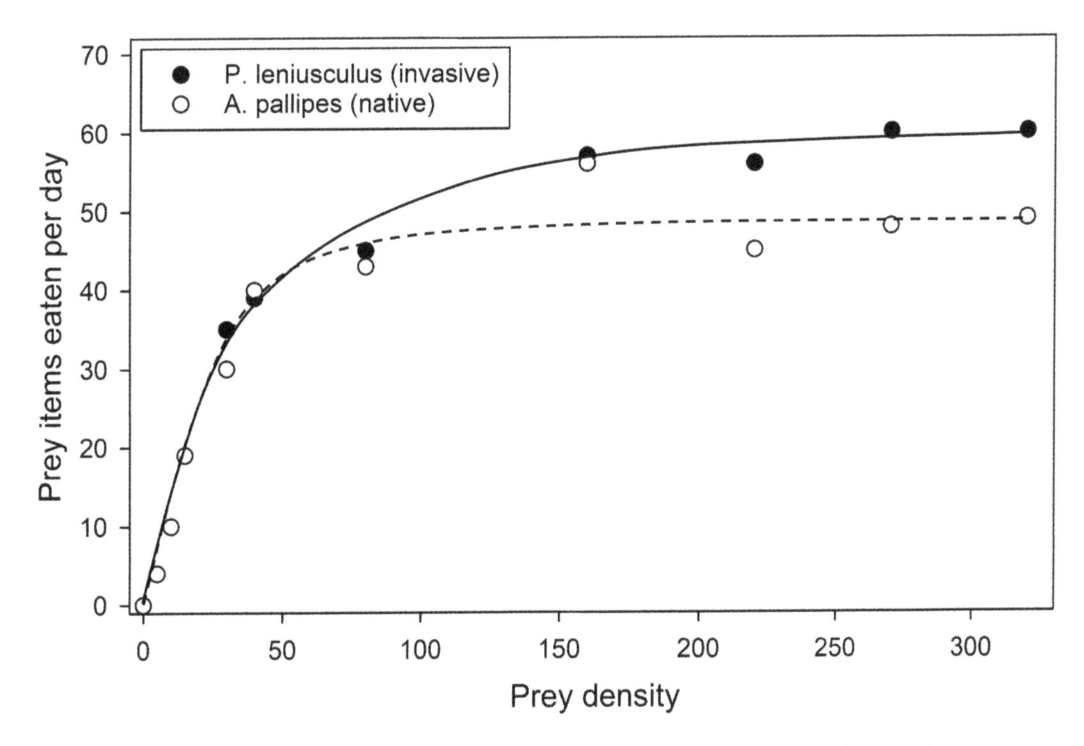

FIGURE 6.14 Functional response curves for prey items eaten per day for two crayfish species in a range of densities of prey (Gammarus pulex) in streams in the UK. Modified from Haddaway et al. (2012), Open Access publication.

of red grouse, meadow pipits, and field voles. The harriers switch to red grouse when grouse are at lower densities only when alternative prey are scarce (Figure 6.15), and the consumption rate of grouse is predicted to reach the same level when grouse are abundant, regardless of the availability of other (smaller) prey items (Smout et al. 2010).

You will notice in both of the examples above that the consumption rate for the predator eventually slows and stabilizes. The figures suggest that hen harriers cannot consume more than 0.45 grouse chicks per hour and crayfish cannot consume more than 60 prey items per day. Why?

At high prey densities, predators eventually become **satiated** and are not able to keep up their kill rate. Satiation is a function of hunting and **handling time** and the physical capacity of the predator's digestive system to contain food material. The shape of functional responses can be important for management. In the example of the invasive and native crayfish species in the UK, the satiation point for the invasive crayfish is greater than for the native crayfish. Thus, the invasive crayfish has the potential to outcompete the native crayfish for food.

Consider your own food consumption functional abilities. How many hot dogs can you eat per day? There is a limit. Even the world champion hot dog eater

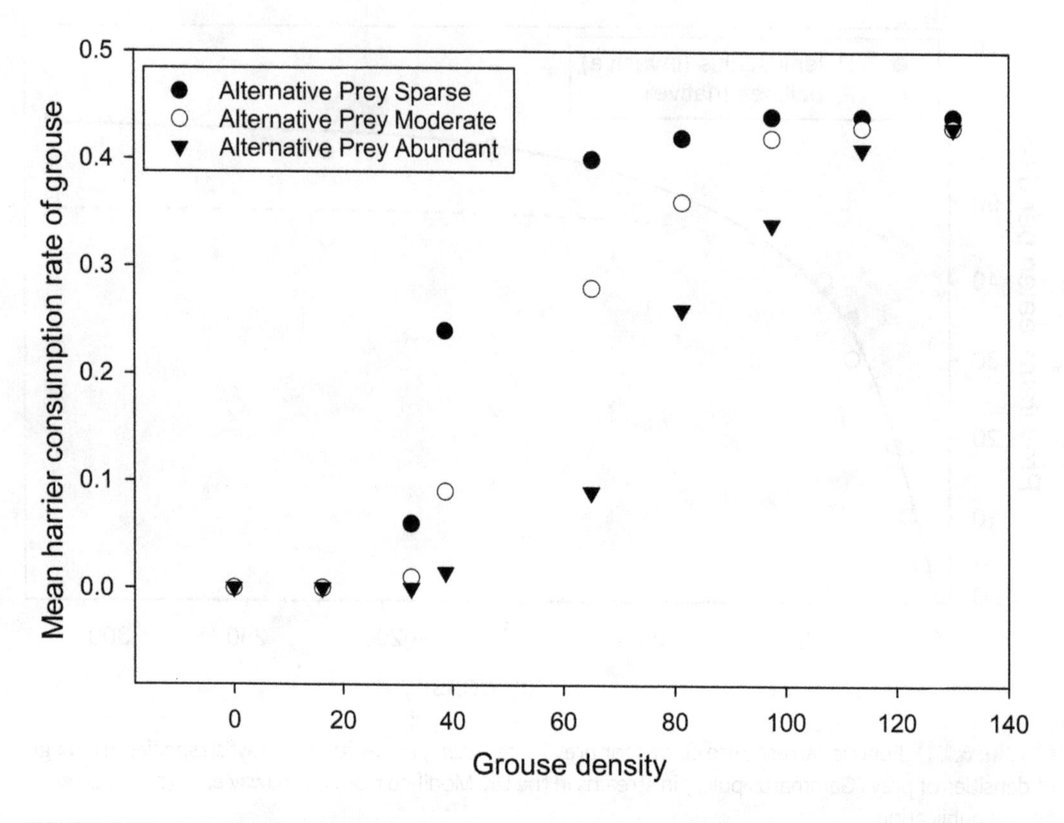

FIGURE 6.15 Estimated consumption rate of grouse chicks by hen harrier in the UK as a function of grouse density when alternative prey (meadow pipits and field voles) were sparse, moderate, or abundant. Per capita grouse chick mortality was calculated as hourly consumption rate per grouse chick density. Modified from Smout et al. (2010), Open Access publication.

(Nathan's Hot Dog Eating champion from 2017 was Joey Chestnut with 72 hot dogs and buns in ten minutes), with the prey stacked neatly on a tray in front of them, eventually reaches capacity. Using data from three hot dog contestants from the 2017 Las Vegas qualifying competition, we can see the worst contestant's consumption rate slowing tremendously during the competition (Figure 6.16). The winner of the competition maintained a steady rate, coming from behind to beat the second-place contestant, who appears to have begun to satiate in the last four minutes of the competition.

A Regulatory Predation Response

We would then conclude that a prey population can be regulated by predators if the predators can increase numerically and if the functional response of predators to prey changes. The functional response, or the predation rate (number of prey killed per time period), eventually slows as the predator becomes satiated or as handling time constrains the predator. However, more predators eating more prey per predator has

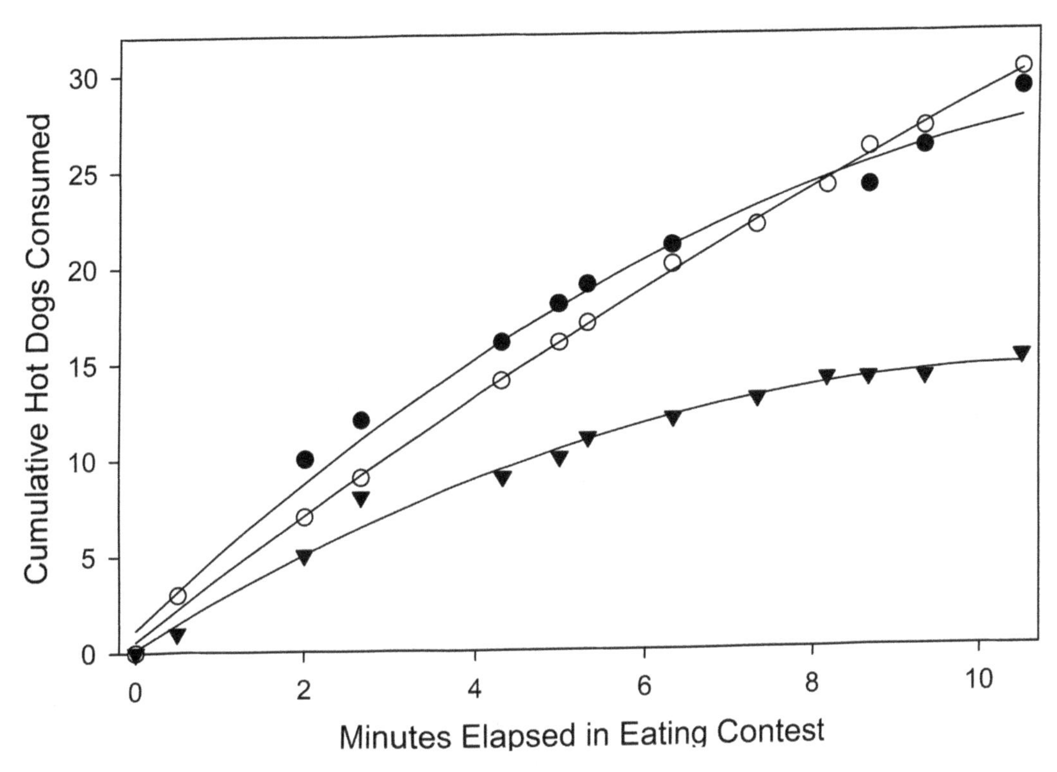

FIGURE 6.16 Satiation curves for three competitors in a regional qualifying competition in 2017 in Las Vegas, Nevada for Nathan's Hog Dog Eating Contest. Data collected from public domain video.

potential to cause the prey's survival to change in a density-dependent fashion until the prey population is no longer increasing in size. However, for predators to claim the status of regulators of the prey, the predators have to regulate the prey before the prey species regulates itself through intraspecific competition. As the prey population is increasing in size, competition may also start to increase, so predation does not happen in a vacuum. Other processes, such as competition and disease dynamics, happen concurrently.

As Darwin and Leopold suggested, population regulation is a dependable feature of population dynamics; without regulation, populations would increase in an exponential fashion (Figure 6.17A). For effective decision-making, a wildlife manager needs to determine which forces operate on populations of interest. For example, if forces "below" a species in the food web hierarchy are more impactful in regulation, such as food sources and resulting competition, we refer to regulation as **bottom-up.** The manager knows that the population may be manipulated (changing the dynamic equilibrium point) by focusing on those supporting resources. However, if a species is regulated by predators (forces "above" it), we refer to regulation as **top-down.** The manager knows that manipulation of the predator-prey dynamic may also affect the target species (Figure 6.17 B and C). It

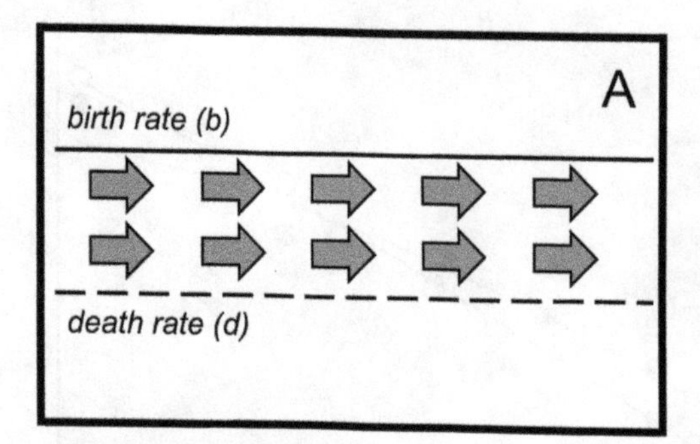

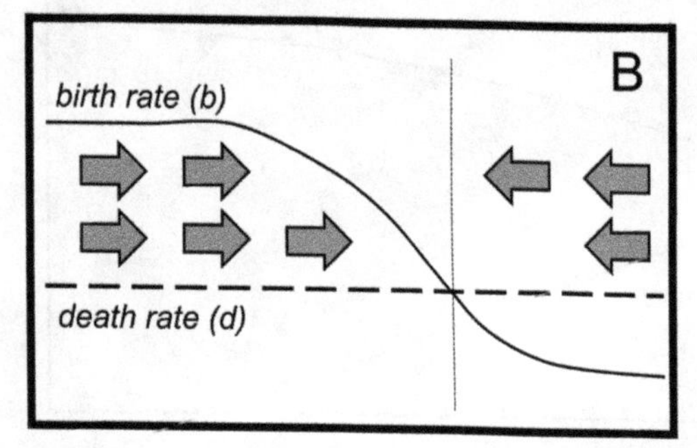

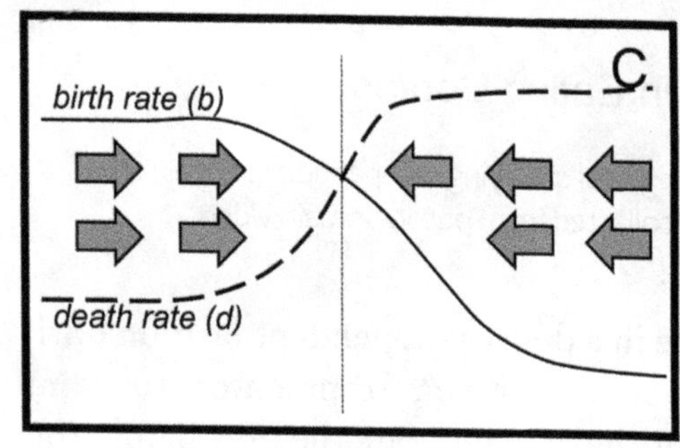

Population size (*N*)

FIGURE 6.17 Forces influencing the growth and/or regulation of a prey species: A) absence of regulating force results in continual growth, B and C) variation in strength of regulating force from above creates variation in the temporary equilibrium point for the prey.

is logical to assume that both top-down and bottom-up types of forces operate on a prey species, which makes management of populations complicated. The use of alternative (PrOACT, chapter 3) top-down and bottom-up models in an adaptive management process may be a useful way to learn about predator-prey dynamics during a management program.

Complexity of population dynamics, along with a species' intrinsic growth potential and the effect of predators, competition, parasites, disease, and human-induced dynamics, creates opportunity for mismanagement. Predator management has been especially difficult throughout the history of wildlife management. Biologists have often made decisions to cull predators to benefit prey. For example, gamekeepers in the UK remove some predators to support local grouse populations, and wolves are culled at some locations in Alaska to maintain moose, elk, and deer populations for hunters). Historically, social pressure for livestock and human protection resulted in the extirpation of most large predators from a large portion of the United States in the 19th and 20th centuries, and predators are now expanding back into many of these systems.

Biologists have sometimes used introductions of predators to attempt to regulate nuisance prey species. One such misguided effort was the introduction of the small Indian mongoose to Hawaii to control non-native brown rats in sugar plantations in the late 1800s. Unfortunately, the mongoose decided that nests of native birds, such as the endemic Hawaiian goose, the Nene, were much easier prey items. Today, the Nene is listed as an endangered species. It is clear that consideration of trade-offs and consequences (PrOACT, chapter 3) of potential management alternatives is critical.

Age and Stage Structures in Populations

To this point, all of our models for population growth have considered populations as one entity, but we know that populations are structured by **age**, the time since birth. Biologists sometimes use **stage structure** instead of **age structure** to define groups of individuals within a population of similar ages. Stages are most often used for species with long life spans. For example, a painted turtle may have a hatchling stage, a pre-reproductive stage, and a reproductive stage, and each stage may have more than one year class as members.

Why is it important to consider age or stage in our population assessments? Not all age or stage classes can reproduce, and those classes that do reproduce may produce at different levels of success. It is also common for survival to vary among age or stage classes. That seems important if we want to make a robust prediction of the population size in the next time period, but how might we incorporate this variation into our models?

We may start to envision the roles of age classes within a population with a simple two-age model for discrete population growth, λ, which is a function of annual adult survival, S_a, juvenile survival from end of breeding season to start of next breeding season, S_j, and productivity, P (per capita birth rate, alive at end of breeding season; Pulliam 1988):

$$\lambda = S_a + PS_j$$

This description of population processes shows that, for a stable population, the production of juveniles that survive to the next breeding season must balance the proportion of the adult population that dies during the year. If production does not replace dead adults, the population will have $\lambda < 1$, and if the production more than replaces dead adults, $\lambda > 1$.

Some avian, mammalian, and herpetological species are difficult to age beyond two age categories, or stages: juvenile (< 1 yr) and adult (≥ 1 yr), so the two-age model for population growth is commonly used by biologists. However, biologists can create multiple, well-defined

QUICK COMPREHENSION CHECK

In a simple age-structured population, if $S_a = 0.6$, what proportion of the adult population must be replaced each year to maintain a stable population size (hint: stable population is when $\lambda = 1$)?

age or size (stage) categories for fish and other terrestrial wildlife species. The most common method to organize demographic data and predict population growth is with a mathematical device known as the Leslie matrix. Patrick Leslie was an ecologist at Oxford University when he proposed the use of this system for population projection over time (Leslie 1945). The matrix is assembled using age-specific **fecundity** values (F_i) and probabilities of survival from one age to the next (S_i):

$$M = \begin{bmatrix} F_1 & F_2 & F_3 \\ S_1 & 0 & 0 \\ 0 & S_2 & 0 \end{bmatrix}$$

The matrix, M, is referred to as a **transition matrix**, because it literally defines the manner in which the population transitions from age to age and the rate at which new members of the first age class are added. For fathead minnows, a three-age class Leslie matrix was derived using age-specific survival (S) and productivity (F) data from field studies (Miller and Ankley 2004):

$$M = \begin{bmatrix} 0.75 & 1.50 & 3.00 \\ 0.39 & 0 & 0 \\ 0 & 0.39 & 0 \end{bmatrix}$$

The vector, N_i, containing the current number of minnows in each of the three age classes at time i is defined as follows, with example numbers for each age class:

$$N_i = \begin{bmatrix} n_{1,i} \\ n_{2,i} \\ n_{3,i} \end{bmatrix} = \begin{bmatrix} 4178 \\ 1163 \\ 324 \end{bmatrix}$$

To obtain the population size and structure at time $i+1$, we multiply the vector N_i by the transition matrix, M:

$$N_{i+1} = MN_i$$

Operationally, this results in the following calculations as you transpose the N_i vector and multiply its members by each row of the matrix, M:

$$n_{1,i+1} = M_{1,1}n_{1,i} + M_{1,2}n_{2,i} + M_{1,3}n_{3,i}$$
$$n_{2,i+1} = M_{2,1}n_{2,i} + M_{2,2}n_{2,i} + M_{2,3}n_{3,i}$$
$$n_{3,i+1} = M_{3,1}n_{1,i} + M_{3,2}n_{2,i} + M_{3,3}n_{3,i}$$

And

$$n_{1,i+1} = (0.75*4178) + (1.5*1163) + (3.00*324) = 3133.5 + 1744.5 + 972.0$$
$$n_{2,i+1} = (0.39*4178) + (0*1163) + (0*324) = 1629.4 + 0 + 0$$
$$n_{3,i+1} = (0*4178) + (0.39*1163) + (0*324) = 0+453.6 + 0$$

We then obtain a new age-structured population of minnows:

$$N_{i+1} = \begin{bmatrix} n_{1,i+1} \\ n_{2,i+1} \\ n_{3,i+1} \end{bmatrix} = \begin{bmatrix} 5850 \\ 1629 \\ 454 \end{bmatrix}$$

Notice that the design of the Leslie matrix results in new age-one individuals in year i + 1 by multiplying the age-specific fecundity rates (F_i) by the size of the age class. Next, age-two individuals are provided in the next time period by multiplying the original number of age-one individuals by their survival probability, S_1. The survivors then become age-two individuals. Finally, age-two individuals during time i survive (at a probability of S_2) to become age-three individuals. The Leslie transition matrix, M, has zeros in specific locations on purpose—in this three-age system, there is no way for an age-two individual to remain age-two in the next time step, so $M_{2,2} = 0$. Similarly, an age-three individual cannot become an age-two individual in the next time step, so $M_{3,3} = 0$. Age-one individuals cannot become age-three, and age-three individuals cannot remain in age-three (they all die), so $M_{3,1} = 0$ and $M_{3,3} = 0$.

The prediction for discrete population growth then, is

$$\lambda = \frac{N_{t+1}}{N_t} = \frac{7933}{5665} = 1.40$$

Conclusion

Populations are complex, and a wildlife manager must account for many dynamics. A wildlife biologist must be able to predict the potential limiting and regulatory factors to be able to construct a working model of population growth. In the context of managing populations, the PrOACT process allows the use of models to

QUICK COMPREHENSION CHECK

Is $\lambda = 1.4$ indicative of a growing, declining, or stable population?

Which age class of fathead minnows produced the most offspring (total production of the age class) in the example? Is it the same age class as the class with the highest value for F?

WRAPPING UP

Can you help Anne, in our Yellowstone problem case, understand why density-dependent reproduction is not observed in the control areas without wolves? Under what conditions might you expect to see effects of elk density on elk reproduction in areas without wolves?

estimate the consequences of alternative management actions (including doing nothing) for a population. What will happen if we enhance habitat in a certain manner? How might the population respond to a translocation? What is the predicted effect of the invasive competitor on our species of interest? How might harvest impact the population? Although systems are complex, the process of creating relatively simple models for population growth allows a management team to discuss and learn about their population while making predictions for the future under a variety of scenarios.

Decision-Making on the Ground

1: Regulating Reindeer

Assume that biologists have gathered the following data from several wild herds of reindeer in Norway (scenario based on a study by Skogland 1985). Birth rate is presented as recruitment rate (female calves produced per female that survive the first winter). Plot the data on the blank figure opposite, using the y-axis for the birth and death rates as shown in Figure 6.17.

SAMPLE	A	B	C	D	E	F	G
POPULATION DENSITY (N/KM²)	2	16	28	20	10	4	30
BIRTH RATE (FEMALE PER FEMALE)	0.35	0.22	0.11	0.24	0.26	0.32	0.09
DEATH RATE (ADULT)	0.03	0.02	0.08	0.03	0.04	0.10	0.06

APPLICATION, ANALYSIS, SYNTHESIS, AND EVALUATION

Is this hypothetical reindeer population regulated? If so, which demographic rate appears to provide the regulating dynamic?

What is the approximate equilibrium point, or carrying capacity for this population?

The densities provided are estimated from herds that use areas of 500–8000 km². If the average area per herd is 3000 km², what is the average population size of the herds in the study?

If you were managing the population represented by these herds, would you feel justified to raise the number of hunting permits? If so, under what conditions? Why or why not?

2: Sea Turtles in the Matrix

The following information for fecundity (females per female) and the annual probability of survival is available from field studies to create a stage-based model for long-lived logger-head sea turtles, based on data from Crouse et al. (1987):

AGE CLASSES:	ANNUAL SURVIVAL	ANNUAL FECUNDITY
1. EGGS, HATCHLINGS (<1 YEAR)	0.67	0
2. JUVENILES (1–15 YEARS OLD)	0.73	0
3. SUBADULT (16–21 YEARS OLD)	0.74	0
4. ADULTS (22–54 YEARS OLD)	0.81	100

We can create the following stage-based projection matrix, M, which includes the traditional stage-specific fecundity, F_i, from the Leslie matrix format. However, the stage-based modeling with multiple age classes requires two additional stage-specific parameters. G_i and P_i. P_i describes the proportion of individuals in a stage that (1) survives the year, and (2) remains in the stage-class, while G_i describes the proportion of individuals in a stage-class that (1) survives the year, and (2) transitions to the next stage-class (e.g., in a 15-year stage, 1/15th or 6.67% of the individuals age into the next stage, assuming an even distribution of ages within the stage).

These demographic parameters, patterns, and assumptions result in the following stage-based projection matrix for loggerhead sea turtles:

$$\begin{bmatrix} P_1 & F_2 & F_3 & F_4 \\ G_1 & P_2 & 0 & 0 \\ 0 & G_2 & P_3 & 0 \\ 0 & 0 & G_3 & G_4 \end{bmatrix} = M = \begin{bmatrix} 0 & 0 & 0 & 100 \\ 0.6700 & 0.7276 & 0 & 0 \\ 0 & 0.0024 & 0.6889 & 0 \\ 0 & 0 & 0.0511 & 0.8098 \end{bmatrix}$$

The current population structure, at time t, is:

$$N_t = \begin{bmatrix} 2065 \\ 7830 \\ 66 \\ 25 \end{bmatrix}$$

APPLICATION, ANALYSIS, SYNTHESIS, AND EVALUATION

How many subadults are there in the population at time t?

Can you evaluate the values for Pi and Gi in M? Can you see how they are calculated from the survival probabilities and proportion of ages that mature into the next stage-class? (Hint: for stage-class one, 100% of the individuals will mature into the second stage as the first stage is only one year in length, and survival of that stage class is 0.67.)

Given the vector Nt and the projection matrix M, what is the predicted population structure at time t + 2? (Hint: first find the population structure at time t + 1.) Now, how many subadults are there at time S_{t+2}?

How many total individuals are in the population at time t + 2? Is the population growing or declining?

Conservation biologists are concerned about loggerhead turtles and need to know where to spend their money on conservation efforts. Biologists could potentially spend money/effort to increase egg/hatchling survival, or they could spend the same amount of money/effort to reduce illegal harvest of adults (raising adult survival rates). Create a new projection matrix, M_j, that includes a new egg/hatchling survival probability of 0.90. Create a second new projection matrix, M_a, in which adult survival increases to 0.90. (Hint: remember that survival will affect the calculations for G4.) Which method (the use of M_j or M_a) results in a higher population in two years (t + 2)? Which management option would you choose? Can you find an easy way to carry out the calculations for 50 years? Does the same relative comparison hold after 50 years? If there are differences, can you explain them?

Where does the use of a population model to predict the population under two competing management options fit into the PrOACT decision-making process covered in chapter 3?

3: Let Us Prey? Restoring a Stunted Fish Population in a Reservoir

Fish species in lakes and reservoirs exist in quasi-closed systems, which provides an opportunity to see the effects of competition within and between species, as well as the effects of predation. Fisheries biologists often manage the community of fish in a lake or reservoir to maximize angling opportunities and sustain populations of fish species of interest. The goal may often be described as maintaining a "balanced community," which has consistent recruitment of both predator and prey species, diverse size distributions within each species, fast growth of individuals, and consistent production of harvestable-sized fish (Flickinger et al. 1999).

One signifier for an unbalanced community is the presence of a **stunted** fish population. Stunting can be defined as a fish population comprised of individuals with drastically reduced growth rates and a non-genetic reduction in maximum potential size as depicted for stunted and non-stunted populations of white perch (Gosch et al. 2010).

Individuals of stunted populations usually mature and begin to reproduce at earlier ages than non-stunted populations, which creates a high-density population of slow-growing individuals. As fish densities increase, intraspecific competition begins to take place, causing the reduction of growth. Stunting may be more prone to happen when species of predatory fish cannot respond quickly enough to regulate the prey population.

The stunted population is not desirable by anglers and indicates an ecosystem out of balance. Therefore, fisheries biologists have considered several approaches to restore normal growth of stunted fish:

- Stocking or otherwise increasing populations of predatory fish to thin the prey population
- Mechanical removal (nets) of specific size classes of stunted fish
- Water-level manipulation to interrupt a breeding cycle by exposing eggs deposited in shallow areas
- Chemical removal of the entire population of stunted fish and other species to restock the lake or reservoir with a new fish community

Gosch et al. (2010) reported that white perch were a frequent prey item for seven species of predatory fish in two Nebraska reservoirs. In the reservoir with nonstunted white perch, predators only preyed upon the smallest lengths of white perch, while in the reservoir with stunted white perch, predators preyed upon all sizes of white perch including the largest perch (Figure 6.18).

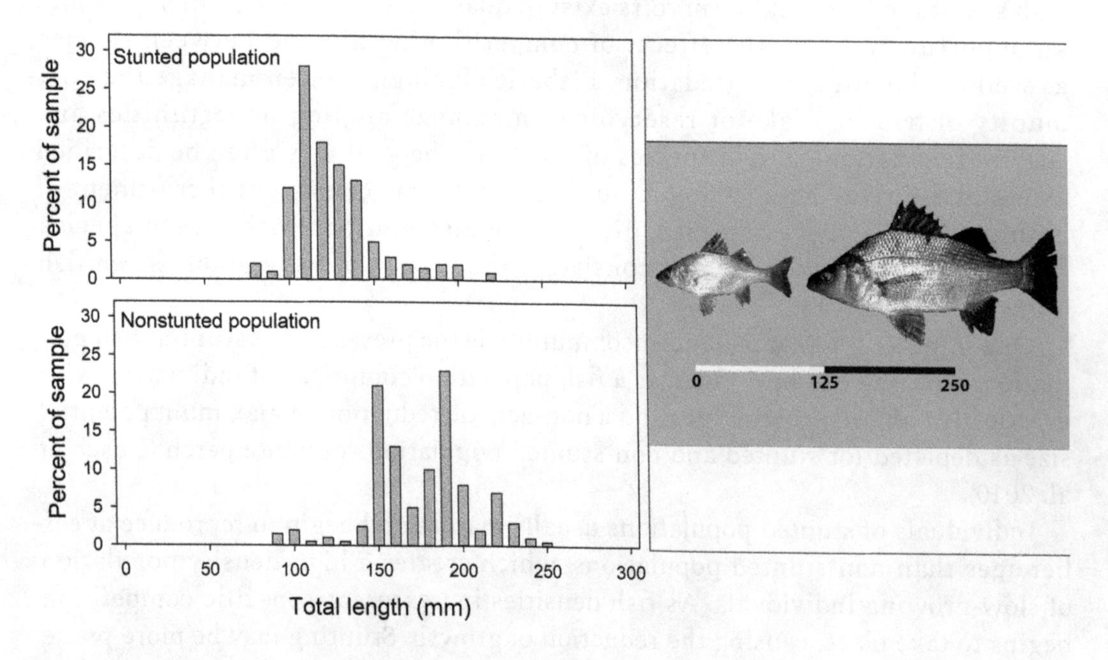

FIGURE 6.18 Comparison of frequency distributions for length of white perch in two reservoirs in eastern Nebraska. White perch in Branch Oak Lake were stunted (top), relative to Pawnee Lake (bottom). Representative male, three-year-old white perch from each reservoir are shown at right. Figure created with data from Gosch et al. (2010), public domain publication; photo provided by authors and used with permission.

APPLICATION, ANALYSIS, SYNTHESIS, AND EVALUATION

Consider the list of management options for the reversal of stunting in a fish population. How would each action affect either competition or predation dynamics in the lake? Why might biologists believe the action would result in a smaller population, free of the density-dependent effect of slow growth that leads to stunting? For further review of stunting, see Gosch et al. (2010).

Consider a conceptual age-specific model for stunted white perch. If predatory fish caused high mortality on the smallest age classes, how might this lead to a lower perch population than if the predatory fish preyed upon all age classes equally?

If, as Gosch et al. (2010) suggested, current predation is not addressing the stunting problem for perch effectively, what management actions might fisheries biologists use next to solve this problem?

Sources of Information and Further Reading

Bianchi R, Campos R, Xavier N, Olifiers N, Gompper M, and Mourao G. "Intraspecific, interspecific, and seasonal differences in the diet of three mid-sized carnivores in a large neotropical wetland." *Acta Theriologica* 59, no. 1 (2014): 13–23.

Burger Jr, L. W., Dailey, T. V., Kurzejeski, E. W., and Ryan, M. R. "Survival and cause-specific mortality of northern bobwhite in Missouri." *The Journal of Wildlife Management* 59 (1995): 401–410.

Carpenter, S. R. and Kitchell, J. F. "Consumer control of lake productivity." *BioScience* 38, no. 11 (1988): 764–769.

Christianson, D. and Creel, S. "Ecosystem scale declines in elk recruitment and population growth with wolf colonization: a before-after-control-impact approach." *PloS ONE* 9, no. 7 (2014): e102330.

Clark, W. R., and Kroeker, D. W. "Population dynamics of muskrats in experimental marshes at Delta, Manitoba." *Canadian Journal of Zoology* 71, no. 8 (1993): 1620–1628.

Clay, R. T. and Clark, W. R. "Demography of muskrats on the Upper Mississippi River." *The Journal of Wildlife Management* 49 (1985): 883–890.

Cobbald, T. S. "Contributions to our knowledge of grouse disease." *The Veterinarian* 46 (1873): 161–172.

Committee of Inquiry on Grouse Disease. *The grouse in health and in disease*, vols. 1 and 2. London: Smith, Elder and Co., 1911.

Crouse, D. T., L. B. Crowder, and H. Caswell. "A stage-based model for loggerhead sea- turtles and implications for conservation." *Ecology* 68 (1987): 1412–1423.

de Cassia Bianchi, R., Olifiers, N., Gompper, M. E., and Mourão, G. "Niche partitioning among meso-carnivores in a Brazilian wetland." *PloS one* 11, no. 9 (2016): e0162893.

Elton, C. and Nicholson, M. "The ten-year cycle in numbers of the lynx in Canada." *The Journal of Animal Ecology* 11 (1942): 215–244.

Errington, P. L. "Some Contributions of a Fifteen-Year Local Study of the Northern Bobwhite to a Knowledge of Population Phenomena." *Ecological Monographs* 15, no. 1 (1945): 1–34.

Flickinger, S.A., Bulow, F.J. and Willis, D.W. "Small impoundments." In *Inland fisheries management in North America*, 2nd ed., edited by Kohler, C.C. and Hubert, W.A., 561–587. Bethesda, MD: American Fisheries Society, 1999.

Gosch, N. J., Pierce, L. L., and Pope, K. L. "The effect of predation on stunted and nonstunted white perch." *Ecology of Freshwater Fish* 19, no. 3 (2010):401–407.

Green, S. J., Akins, J. L., Maljković, A., and Côté, I. M. "Invasive lionfish drive Atlantic coral reef fish declines." *PloS One* 7, no. 3 (2012): e32596.

Grenier, M. B., McDonald, D. B., ad Buskirk, S. W. "Rapid population growth of a critically endangered carnivore." *Science* 317, no. 5839 (2007): 779–779.

Haddaway, N. R., Wilcox, R. H., Heptonstall, R. E., Griffiths, H. M., Mortimer, R. J., Christmas, M., and Dunn, A. M. "Predatory functional response and prey choice identify predation differences between native/invasive and parasitised/unparasitised crayfish." *PloS one* 7, no. 2 (2012): e32229.

Hansen, R. M. and Reid, L. D. "Diet overlap of deer, elk, and cattle in southern Colorado." *Journal of Range Management* 28 (1975): 43–47.

Hanski, I., Hansson, L., and Henttonen, H. "Specialist predators, generalist predators, and the microtine rodent cycle." *The Journal of Animal Ecology* 60 (1991): 353–367.

Hardin, G. "The competitive exclusion principle." *Science* 131, no. 3409 (1960): 1292–1297.

Koenig, W. D. "European Starlings and Their Effect on Native Cavity-Nesting Birds." *Conservation Biology*, 17, no. 4 (2003): 1134–1140.

Kupferberg, S. J. "Bullfrog (Rana catesbeiana) invasion of a California river: the role of larval competition." *Ecology* 78, no. 6 (1997): 1736–1751.

Larkin, P. A. "Interspecific competition and population control in freshwater fish." *Journal of the Fisheries Board of Canada* 13, no. 3 (1956): 327–342.

Leslie, P. H. "On the use of matrices in certain population athematics." *Biometrika* 33, no. 3 (1945): 183–212.

Leopold, A. *Game management*. New York: Charles Scribner's Sons, 1933.

Lusk, J. J., Guthery, F. S., George, R. R., Peterson, M. J., and DeMaso, S. J. "Relative abundance of bobwhites in relation to weather and land use." *The Journal of wildlife management* 66 (2002): 1040–1051.

Miller, D. H. and Ankley, G. T. "Modeling impacts on populations: fathead minnow (Pimephales promelas) exposure to the endocrine disruptor 17β-trenbolone as a case study." *Ecotoxicology and environmental safety* 59, no. 1 (2004): 1–9.

Nielsen, Ó. K. "Gyrfalcon population and reproduction in relation to Rock Ptarmigan numbers in Iceland." In *Gyrfalcons and Ptarmigan in a Changing World*, vol. 2, edited by R. T. Watson, T. J. Cade, M. Fuller, G. Hunt, and E. Potapov, 21–48. Boise, ID: The Peregrine Fund, 2011.

Pardieck, K. L., D. J. Ziolkowski Jr., M. Lutmerding, K. Campbell and M. A. R. Hudson. *North American Breeding Bird Survey Dataset 1966–2016*, version 2016.0. U.S. Geological Survey, Patuxent Wildlife Research Center, 2017. <www.pwrc.usgs.gov/BBS/RawData/>; doi:10.5066/F7W0944J.

Pavluvčík, P., Poprach, K., Machar, I., Losík, J., Gouveia, A., and Tkadlec, E. "Barn Owl productivity response to variability of vole populations." *PloS one* 10, no. 12 (2015): e0145851.

Pulliam, H. R. "Sources, sinks, and population regulation." *The American Naturalist* 132, no. 5 (1988): 652–661.

Rader, M. J., Brennan, L. A., Herna ˇNdez, F., Silvy, N. J., and Wu, B. "Nest-site selection and nest survival of northern bobwhite in southern Texas." *The Wilson Journal of Ornithology* 119, no. 3 (2007): 392–399.

Redpath, S. M. and Thirgood, S. J. "Birds of prey and red grouse." London: Stationery Office.

Sampson, S. J., Chick, J. H., and Pegg, M. A. "Diet overlap among two Asian carp and three native fishes in backwater lakes on the Illinois and Mississippi rivers." *Biological Invasions* 11, no. 3 (2009): 483–496.

Sandercock, F. K. "Life history of coho salmon (Oncorhynchus kisutch)." In *Pacific Salmon Life Histories*, edited by C. Groot and L. Margolis, 395–445. UBC Press, 1991.

Sauer, J. R., D. K. Niven, J. E. Hines, D. J. Ziolkowski, Jr, K. L. Pardieck, J. E. Fallon, and W. A. Link. *The North American Breeding Bird Survey, Results and Analysis 1966–2015*. Version 2.07.2017. Laurel, MD: USGS Patuxent Wildlife Research Center, 2017.

Sheehy, E., Sutherland, C., O'Reilly, C., and Lambin, X. "The enemy of my enemy is my friend: native pine marten recovery reverses the decline of the red squirrel by suppressing grey squirrel populations." *Proc. R. Soc. B 285*, no. 1874 (2018): 20172603.

Skogland, T. "The effects of density-dependent resource limitations on the demography of wild reindeer." *Journal of Animal Ecology* 54 (1985): 359–374.

Smout, S., Asseburg, C., Matthiopoulos, J., Fernández, C., Redpath, S., Thirgood, S., and Harwood, J. "The functional response of a generalist predator." *PloS one* 5, no. 5 (2010): e10761.

Suchy, W. J. and Munkel, R. J. "Survival rates of northern bobwhite chicks in south-central Iowa." In *National Quail Symposium Proceedings Vol.* 4, 82–84. 1997.

Vreeland, J. K., Diefenbach, D. R., and Wallingford, B. D. "Survival rates, mortality causes, and habitats of Pennsylvania white-tailed deer fawns." *Wildlife Society Bulletin* 32, no. 2 (2014): 542–553.

Vucetich, J. A. and Peterson, R. O. "The influence of top-down, bottom-up and abiotic factors on the moose (Alces alces) population of Isle Royale." *Proceedings of the Royal Society of London B: Biological Sciences* 271, no. 1535 (2004): 183–189.

Zubillaga, M., Skewes, O., Soto, N., Rabinovich, J. E., and Colchero, F. "Bayesian inference on the effect of density dependence and weather on a guanaco population from Chile." *PloS One* 9, no. 12 (2004): e115307.

Zylstra E. R., Steidl R. J., Swann D. E., and K. Ratzlaff. "Hydrologic Variability Governs Population Dynamics of a Vulnerable Amphibian in an Arid Environment." *PLoS ONE* 10, no. 6 (2015): e0125670. doi:10.1371/journal.pone.0125670

Image Credits

Fig. 6.2: Source: https://journals.plos.org/plosone/article?id=10.1371/journal.pone.0102330.
Fig. 6.4b: Source: https://commons.wikimedia.org/wiki/File:Walrus_herd_swimming.jpg.
Fig. 6.5: Source: https://journals.plos.org/plosone/article?id=10.1371/journal.pone.0115307.
Fig. 6.6: Source: https://journals.plos.org/plosone/article?id=10.1371/journal.pone.0032596.
Fig. 6.7: Source: https://journals.plos.org/plosone/article?id=10.1371/journal.pone.0125670.
Fig. 6.9: Source: http://www.nrcresearchpress.com/doi/abs/10.1139/z93-228#.W8qUMktKjIU.
Fig. 6.10: Source: https://journals.plos.org/plosone/article?id=10.1371/journal.pone.0162893.
Fig. 6.11: Copyright © Emma Sheehy, Chris Sutherland, Catherine O'Reilly, and Xavier Lambin (CC by 4.0) at https://www.ncbi.nlm.nih.gov/pmc/articles/PMC5879625/.
Fig. 6.13: Source: https://journals.plos.org/plosone/article?id=10.1371/journal.pone.0145851.
Fig. 6.14: Source: https://journals.plos.org/plosone/article?id=10.1371/journal.pone.0032229.
Fig. 6.15: Source: https://journals.plos.org/plosone/article?id=10.1371/journal.pone.0010761.
Fig. 6.16: Source: https://www.youtube.com/watch?v=aUbpERtM8rs.
Fig. 6.18: Gosch, et al., "The effect of predation on stunted and nonstunted white perch," https://onlinelibrary.wiley.com/doi/full/10.1111/j.1600-0633.2010.00423.x. Copyright © 2010 by John Wiley & Sons, Inc.. Reprinted with permission of the authors.

CHAPTER SEVEN

Harvest Management Decisions

Learning Outcomes

After participating in learning experiences related to this chapter, students should be able to:

- Describe the types of decisions involved in setting harvest regulations.
- Describe how the PrOACT decision-making process can be applied to harvest management.
- Compare and contrast potential effects on harvested populations from three types of regulations: basic rules for hunting and angling, legal methods of take, and regulations defining limits, restrictions, and season length.
- Discuss the application of the concept of density dependence to the management of harvest of wildlife populations.
- Describe why the "doomed surplus" model for harvest management did not apply to all game species.
- Provide evidence for the failures of the concept of Maximum Sustainable Yield for marine fisheries.
- Provide conceptual predictions for a harvested population under alternative hypotheses of harvest mortality: additive and compensatory.

A One-Minute Summary

A relatively small percentage of the US public engages in hunting and fishing, but harvest management is a visible part of the wildlife management profession, in part because of complex and sometimes controversial decisions with regard to harvest of wildlife species. Harvest managers must decide if a harvest is justified, and, if so, the methods of harvest, the bag or creel limits, the lengths of seasons, and potential age/size/sex restrictions.

Modern harvest management often follows a structured decision-making process, especially when risks of the harvest decision are great. Alternative regulation sets are constructed, and managers may use conceptual or mathematical models to predict consequences of the alternative regulation sets. Once a decision has been made, monitoring is critical to confirm the predicted effects of the harvest action, and adaptive management may be used to incorporate learning to improve future decisions.

Biologists have struggled, with a century of experience setting harvest regulations, to determine the effects of harvest on wildlife populations. A theory described as "doomed surplus" was proposed in the 1940s to describe high population sizes of many species in the fall, which would decrease in a density-dependent fashion during the winter. Mathematical attempts to support harvest management began with the concept of Maximum Sustainable Yield (MSY), which suggested that a population should be lowered to one-half of its carrying capacity, following assumptions of the logistic growth model, to produce the greatest yield. However, marine fisheries managed under MSY were often overfished because of the interaction between politics and biology that characterized international, commercial fishing agreements. Modern attempts to account for uncertain effects of harvest on populations of fish and wildlife often compare alternative models for harvest mortality, additive and compensatory, during a decision-making process that aims to select the most appropriate harvest regulations, given what is known about the effect of harvest and the goals for harvest management.

Principles for Your Toolkit

Three types of harvest regulations: Harvest regulations are complex and include three levels of regulations. First, basic rules are established that largely ensure the safety of hunters and anglers and support fair-chase, or an ethical approach to hunting. Second, the methods of harvest determine what type of weapon may be legally used to harvest a game species. And third, managers set regulations that govern the bag or creel limit, season length, and any age, size, or sex restrictions.

Density-dependent response: The response of populations of game species that are harvested may include density-dependent dynamics. Harvest directly lowers the size of a population during the hunting or angling season. Some species (r-selected species) have the potential to respond with higher productivity at low densities to rebound after harvest, while other species (K-selected species) do not have the same potential for a density-dependent response. For a century, managers of harvests have used concepts of density dependence as they tried to appropriately predict the influence of harvest of wildlife populations. These dynamics were at the heart of Errington's description of "surplus" animals in the fall, the concept of Maximum Sustainable Yield, and modern alternative hypotheses of additive and compensatory harvest mortality.

Social expectations: The job of a harvest manager includes biological theory and calculations, but it also involves human dimensions. The manager must be aware of perceptions and expectations of hunters and anglers, as well as the general public. Harvest management decisions are often made in conservative, incremental steps to avoid announcing large changes in restrictions of harvest. Such an approach is based on a principle proposed by Hilborn and Walters (1992), who stated, "The hardest thing to do in fisheries management is reduce fishing pressure."

A Problem: Sandhill Crane Harvest

Bill and Jim eagerly placed their order at Mabel's Rib Shack in Minot, North Dakota, and sat down next to a rather large man with a walrus mustache, named Jack Coffee. Jack was a wildlife biologist, according to his cap.

Bill remarked that he and Jim had been out hunting sandhill cranes that morning, and the two hunters discovered that Jack used radio telemetry to study the movements of sandhill cranes during migration. He was following the cranes southward as they soared towards their wintering grounds.

"I really enjoy the miles I put on my truck during fall migration," grinned Jack, who was amused that he had encountered two crane hunters. Most people didn't even know you could hunt sandhill cranes.

"Folks are a little worried about the drought on the Plains this year," Jack informed his lunch friends. "If they don't find enough food as they come south, it's possible that harvest bag limits will be lower next year."

"That's not what I want to hear," Bill muttered. "There are over 400,000 cranes in the flyway. How could a few folks like us put any kind of dent in the population?"

"Actually, you'd be surprised," replied Jack. "Our harvest surveys show that hunters take 3–5% of the sandhill crane population. Biologists are concerned that harvest mortality may be additive to overall mortality in sandhill cranes. If that's the case, we have to be quite careful in our harvest regulations when the population is low. In the past, it seemed that harvest mortality was compensatory for this species, but recent habitat losses have been reducing reproductive efforts. Some states are reporting a leveling off in the population, and we monitor to make sure it doesn't go below the population objective set by the Flyway Council. That's why I'm out here—to monitor the harvest and the migration."

And with that, Jack bid the hunters a good day, and headed out to continue radio tracking his birds.

What information do you need to learn to contribute to this discussion? What information would you need to help determine if a reduction in bag limit was warranted for sandhill cranes? What is meant by compensatory harvest mortality? By the time you finish this chapter, you should be able to find the answer.

Terms and Definitions

Additive harvest mortality: A hypothesis describing the effect of harvest on wildlife populations in which there is a positive, linear relationship between hunting and overall mortality rate.

Bag limit: A regulation imposed on hunters that restricts the number of animals within a species or group of species that they may harvest and keep during a certain time period. See *creel limit* for anglers.

Compensatory harvest mortality: A hypothesis describing the effects of harvest on a wildlife population in which hunting mortality, for a certain range of hunting mortality rates, is compensated by changes in non-hunting mortality such that overall mortality remains unchanged.

Creel limit: A regulation imposed on anglers that restricts the number of animals within a species or group of species that they may harvest and keep during a certain time period. Term refers to the traditional wicker basket used to carry fish by anglers. See *bag limit* for hunters.

Effort, hunting or angling: The number of days or hours spent in the field by hunters and anglers.

Fair chase: A description of ethical hunting practices that limits the advantage of the hunter; the concept typically includes that animals in a harvested population should be wild, free-ranging, and not confined by artificial barriers. The use of technology, spot-lighting, and dogs to assist in hunting are often discussed in light of concepts of fair chase.

Maximum Sustained Yield: A concept based on assumptions of the logistic growth model that optimizes the largest yield that can be taken from a population over an indefinite period.

Regulation sets: Groups of harvest regulations that describe season length, bag or creel limits, and age/sex/size restrictions and are intended to produce alternate levels of harvest rates in a population, often referred to as restrictive, moderate, and liberal in nature.

The Context for Harvest Management

In 2016, 35.8 million (14%) Americans went fishing, while 11.5 million (5%) hunted (USFWS 2017a). The decisions related to harvest regulations are some of the most visible job responsibilities for wildlife biologists. These decisions are complex, as they consist of multiple decision options:

- Should we harvest this species?
- What methods of harvest will be legal?

- What is the length of the hunting or angling season?
- How many of this species can a person take per day?
- Should we place limits on age/size/sex of harvested individuals?

The proportion of a population harvested by hunters is referred to as the **harvest rate** or the **hunting mortality rate** (Caughley 1985). Fisheries biologists use **yield** or **fishing mortality rate** (Ricker 1975) to refer to the same concept.

In addition, harvest management consists of subjective values that influence management decisions. In some situations, harvest is used to lower the size of a nuisance species or population that is deemed to be too abundant (e.g. white-tailed deer, snow geese). In other situations, biologists work to ensure that a population of high value is not overharvested.

Further, wildlife managers face risks and uncertainties associated with outcomes. The potential density-dependent dynamics by which the population responds to reductions in density from harvest may not be known, so predicting future population size under a specific regulation set may be difficult. Harvest managers do not have complete control over harvest, as a manager may only establish a regulation set that they believe will result in a certain harvest rate. However, the weather and other factors may result in more or fewer hunters or anglers going afield than anticipated. Thus, the final harvest rate is uncertain.

Harvest managers use principles of population biology to support decisions. Therefore, it is important to know the biology of the populations under management, as harvest may affect each species differently.

The British poet, Alfred, Lord Tennyson, referred to nature as "red in tooth and claw" in his poem *In Memoriam* in 1849, in which he was distressed by the sudden death of a close friend. By definition, harvest management includes death. As humans, we fear death. We do not want to die, so it is understandable when people place that expectation on the animal kingdom, at large. One only has to view the comments on social media platforms that broadcast web cams of eagle nests or zoo animals giving birth to realize that a large portion of the public has unreasonable expectations regarding animal mortality.

In fact, animals have high natural mortality levels:

- 72% of coyotes survive one year (Grinder and Krausman 2001)
- 60–70% of adult mallards survive one year (Powell et al. 1995)
- 31% of white-tailed deer fawns survive their first year (Nelson and Mech 1986)
- 69% of mature channel catfish survive one year (Elrod 1974)
- 63% of ruffed grouse nests produce at least one chick (Tirpak et al. 2006)

These mortalities all represent energy flow to the next trophic level of the ecosystem, and reproductive strategies should result in general balance of mortalities.

Less than 15% of the wildlife species in North American are legally hunted. For example, 7% of the 836 avian species in the US are legally hunted (National Conservation Training Center 2014), and approximately 5% of inland, freshwater fish species are considered sport or game fish (Helfrich and Neves 2009). Although we may typically think of hunting birds and mammals and angling for fish, state laws also allow harvest of some amphibians and reptiles. **Non-game species** are either protected from harvest by law because of conservation status or they have not become **game species** because they do not provide large amounts of meat or fur or another product that is consumable.

Applying PrOACT to Harvest Management

The structured decision-making process, PrOACT (chapter 3), may be applied to harvest management decisions. In fact, decision makers who led the process for waterfowl management at the continental level in North America were among the first to formally embrace an adaptive management process (Nichols et al. 1995). Therefore, we will use waterfowl harvest management to illustrate the structured steps for harvest management:

Step One: Clarify the Problem and the Decision Context

What is the problem and who will make the decision? For harvest management, the problem is typically defined as determining (1) whether to harvest and (2) what regulations to adopt in a given year. Therefore, the managers' task will be to propose, approve, and implement a set of harvest regulations for a species.

The decision-making group varies by species. In the United States, the evolution of our Public Trust Doctrine has given the federal government responsibility for migratory birds and endangered species. Harvest is prohibited for endangered species, and that prohibition comes from the federal level. Migratory birds are managed from the federal level, but in coordination with the states. North America is divided in four management units, labeled **flyways** because the management units were designated based on the movement of birds during migration (Figure 7.1). Managers at the state level meet annually with managers at the federal level to discuss harvest regulations in a Flyway Council.

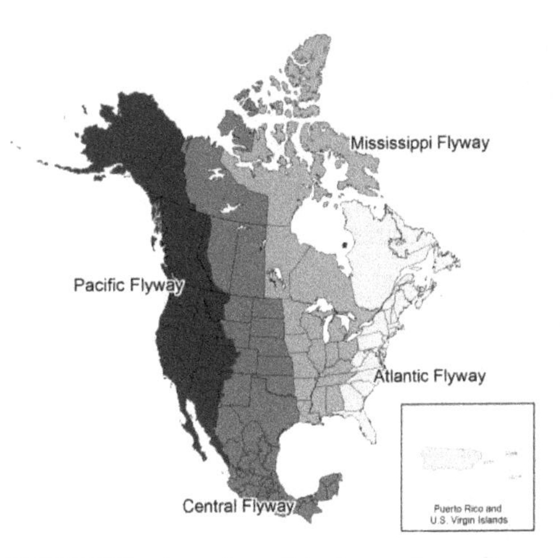

FIGURE 7.1 Location of the four primary flyways used to manage migratory birds in North America (USFWS public domain image).

Big game (a category of game animals usually applied to large mammals), small game (small mammals and non-migratory game birds), and fish harvest regulations are typically set at the state level. Angling regulations are often set at a lower spatial level for lakes and reservoirs, which may have specific regulations based on unique fish communities and goals for the individual water body. Rivers pose an interesting dilemma as they often form the boundaries between states. Although management of stocking and monitoring may be coordinated between states, angling regulations are rarely coordinated, leading to some situations where a species is completely protected from angling from one bank of the river, with legal angling occurring from the opposite bank. For these reasons, biologists have proposed implementing a "swimways" approach to improve harvest management of fish in rivers (Pracheil et al. 2012).

Step Two: Define Objectives

What are the objectives for the harvest? The objectives for populations under consideration for harvest typically have two components that are meant to work in tandem, which demonstrate potentially competing values that must be optimized by managers in their role as public trustees of the resource. First, there is a desire to maintain a population at a certain size (or in some cases to purposefully reduce numbers of an overabundant population). Second, there is a desire to provide a harvest opportunity for citizens. The trick for harvest managers is to maximize the second objective (opportunity to harvest) while also maximizing the probability of maintaining the population at the desired level.

We should also note that objectives for a harvest management problem will often lead to consideration of management actions that go beyond the simple harvest regulation decisions. For example, an agency can work to ensure population levels remain high through complementary habitat management actions. In some harvest management plans, those auxiliary actions are included, while other planning processes use parallel habitat management plans to consider those action in a separate, but related, decision process.

As an example of objectives for harvest management, we can evaluate the fundamental goals that were approved as part of the 2012 North American Waterfowl Management Plan (NAWMP).

QUICK COMPREHENSION CHECK

Can you find language in the three goals that fit the general "maintain populations while providing harvest opportunity" harvest goals?

In chapter 1, we described the three-legged stool principle for wildlife management. Review the principle. Can you find an objective that fits each of the three potential targets for wildlife management?

Goal Three was added to the NAWMP in 2012. Given how wildlife management is funded in the United States (chapter 2), why do you think the third goal is important for managers to include with the other two objectives?

Goal One: Abundant and resilient waterfowl populations to support hunting and other uses without imperiling habitat.

Goal Two: Wetlands and related habitats sufficient to sustain waterfowl populations at desired levels, while providing places to recreate and ecological services that benefit society.

Goal Three: Growing numbers of waterfowl hunters, other conservationists, and citizens who enjoy and actively support waterfowl and wetlands conservation.

Step Three: Develop a Set of Alternatives

What management options do we have to accomplish our objective? Harvest regulations have the potential to directly impact levels of annual mortality and thus may play a role in population dynamics. Therefore, it is necessary to develop a set of alternative harvest strategies, comprised of a range of season lengths, bag limits, and sex, age, or length restrictions. As such, this decision step is a multifaceted decision, and it may seem near impossible to use some kind of formal or informal optimization analysis to find an effective regulation package.

Because of the complexity of predicting outcomes of harvest from a large number of combinations of regulatory factors (bag limits, seasons lengths, and restrictions), managers have developed a framework for decision-making that limits the decision to a choice between three to four **regulation sets**, or **regulatory alternatives**. These alternatives are developed using an expert-based decision process that results in the proposal of a regulation set intended to result in different levels of harvest.

For example, the US Fish and Wildlife Service proposed the following regulatory alternatives for the 2017–2018 duck hunting season for the Mississippi Flyway (Table 7.1, USFWS 2017b). All three regulation sets proposed an opening shooting time of half an hour before sunrise and an ending shooting time of sunset. Within a regulation alternative, a state in the Mississippi Flyway could decide to set their 30-, 45-, or 60-day season to open and close on any dates within the date restrictions for that alternative, which allows states to adjust season timing to anticipated migratory arrival of waterfowl. The daily bag of three or six could be a mix of duck species with specific requirements that protected mallard females (only one or two in the daily bag).

TABLE 7.1 *Examples of three types of regulation sets for ducks in the Mississippi Flyway. Restrictive set is designed to produce the lowest harvest rates while the liberal set is designed to produce the highest harvest rates.*

REGULATION	RESTRICTIVE	MODERATE	LIBERAL
OPENING DATE	Saturday nearest October1	Saturday nearest September 24	Saturday nearest September 24
CLOSING DATE	Sunday nearest January 20	Last Sunday in January	Last Sunday in January
SEASON LENGTH (DAYS)	30	45	60
DAILY BAG	3	6	6
MALLARD (TOTAL/FEMALES)	2/1	4/1	4/2

Waterfowl regulatory sets have become well-known because of the federal support of the North American Waterfowl Management Plan, but similar sets of regulations may be established for any species by managers (Scrogin et al. 2004, Cornicelli et al. 2011). Throughout annual decision processes, these regulation sets serve as the alternative management options that are considered, with regard to consequences and tradeoffs.

Step Four: Estimate Consequences

What is the effect of harvest mortality on the population? This step is an analytical exercise in which the outcome of each alternative is predicted and considered. Biologists can use population models to account for the differential effects of the regulatory alternatives and predict next year's population size under the assumed harvest rates from each alternative.

For this step to be effective, biologists must determine four key factors (Williams et al. 2002, 2009):

- *Current population size:* To predict a future population size, biologists must know the current population size or have a dependable index to population size. Therefore, a monitoring system is required and must be in place prior to the harvest decision. Sampling errors are an intrinsic part of monitoring methods because of incomplete detection of individuals being counted (Pollack and

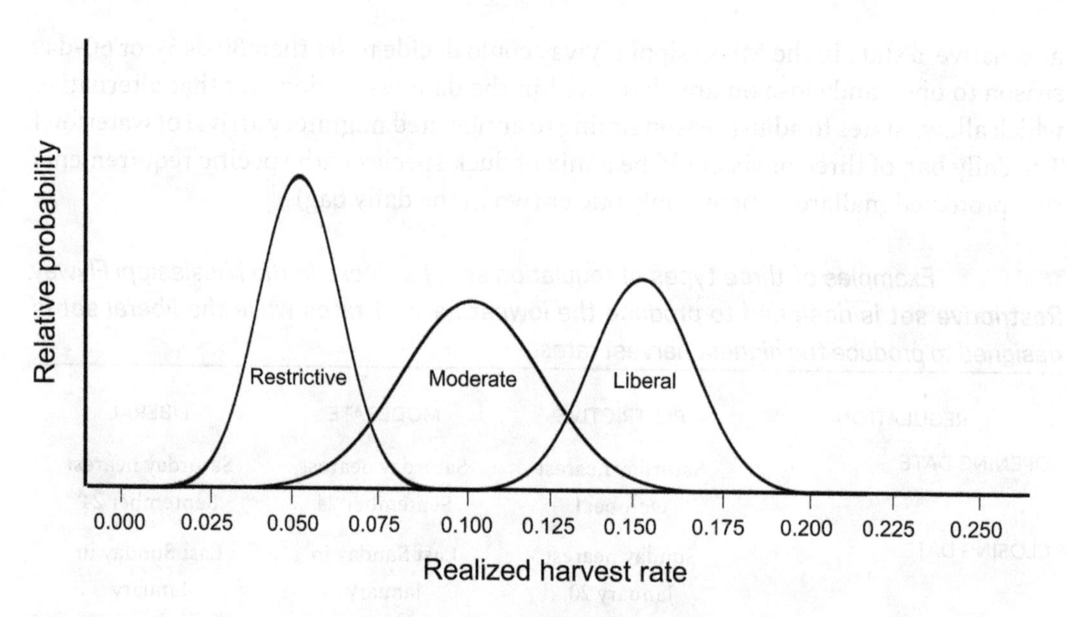

FIGURE 7.2 Theorized variation in realized harvest rate as a function of regulation sets (restrictive, moderate, or liberal in nature) used to manage a game species. Modified from Williams et al. (2002).

Kendall 1987, Thompson 2002), and the decision process must account for this error, or **partial observability**.

- *Effect of regulations on harvest rate:* Biologists need to be able to predict the effects of the regulatory alternatives. Of course, it is inherently impossible for biologists to control harvest rates (Post et al. 2003), and this management dynamics is referred to as **incomplete control**. That is, managers can approve a specific harvest regulation, but the hunters or anglers must go out and implement the harvest. Managers cannot control hunter and angler **effort**. A cold, icy fall may result in a below average harvest rate for deer, as some hunters may stay home. An unexpected, delayed migration of ducks may cause a mismatch in the season dates in a given state, resulting in fewer days when hunters may legally hunt while birds are migrating through their state, lowering the harvest rate. Of course, a perfect match of season dates and waterfowl migration may cause above average harvest rates. Further, individual hunters and anglers vary in their success and effort (Haugen et al. 2015). Incomplete control of harvest and angling rates must be considered in the decision-making process (Artelle et al. 2013).
- *The effect of harvest on the population:* Given an anticipated harvest rate, biologists need to understand the demographic dynamics for a harvested species to predict future population size. Will harvest be completely **additive** to natural mortality, thereby lowering the population size proportional to the rate of harvest? Or, does the species have the capacity to **compensate**, or respond

in density-dependent fashion to either reproduce at higher levels or survive at higher levels than if harvest had not occurred (Baranov 1927, as cited in Ricker 1975)? Certainly, different answers to these questions would cause managers to select different alternatives for harvest. **System uncertainty** must be reduced over time to make effective harvest decisions.

- *Environmental conditions between time of decision and harvest:* Managers typically make the decisions for harvest levels in late-spring or early-summer so that regulations can be printed, posted, and distributed to hunters in anticipation of the fall hunting seasons in North America. Therefore, the population model must account for productivity of the harvested species, which occurs after the time that harvest regulations have been announced. A mid-summer drought may cause lower than anticipated waterfowl populations and higher than anticipated harvest rates. A late-season disease outbreak may lower deer populations prior to harvest, increasing overall mortality significantly. Managers must account for **environmental uncertainty** as they set harvest regulations.

The consequence step of the decision process must account for the current status of the population and potential factors that will affect reproduction and survival of the population during the year. This particular step in harvest management has seen the largest advances over time, and we will discuss models for predicting population growth of harvested populations in more detail later in this chapter.

Step Five: Evaluate Tradeoffs and Select Action

What are the risks and uncertainties of each proposed option? Harvest management carries some logistical considerations that other types of management do not, namely the need for law enforcement to support the regulation choice. Will we be able to enforce such a regulation? Managers must address these concerns during the decision process.

More importantly, however, managers must combine the projected consequences of the harvest on the population with the values that have been determined for potential outcomes. Assume that a species is predicted to slightly decline in number after a harvest. This may have a positive value if the species is considered too abundant at present, while it may have a negative value if biologists would rather the species stay at its current level.

Values for different harvest outcomes may be incorporated in quantitative ways directly into the decision process using the range of population levels set in the objective statements (NAWMP 2012, Williams et al. 2002, Powell et al. 2011). For example, let us assume an objective has been set for northern bobwhite populations in northern Florida such that counts from the annual **Breeding Bird Surveys** along roads (Brennan et al. 2000) result in hearing an average of 20 males per route (Figure 7.3). We will also assume 15 males per route is a minimum limit as an index (I) to acceptable quail populations in this hypothetical situation. Such an objective can

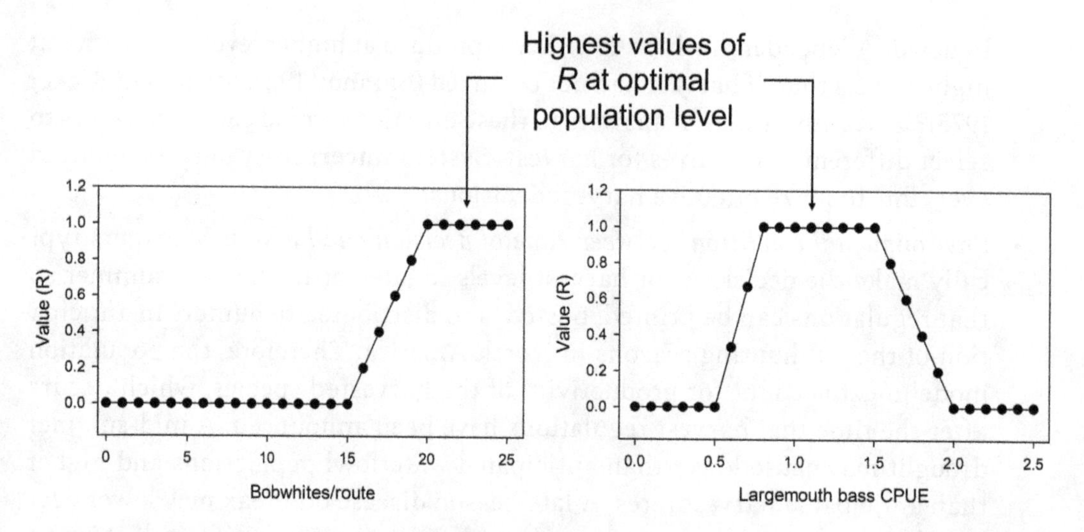

FIGURE 7.3 Changes in utility values (R) for northern bobwhites (left) and largemouth bass (right) as a function of relative population size. Objectives for populations guide utility values. Bobwhite populations are desired to be large, while largemouth bass populations are valued most at intermediary levels in these hypothetical scenarios.

be captured by the following value index (R), where $R = 1$ when $I \geq 20$, $R = 0$ when $I \leq 15$, and $0 < R < 1$ when I is within the goal of 15–20 males per route (Figure 7.3) such that:

$$R = \frac{I - Min}{Goal - Min}$$

$$R = \frac{I - 15}{20 - 15}$$

A manager can then work with a population biologist to predict the future population under two harvest alternatives. The set of harvest regulations that is predicted to result in a population that produces the highest value for R would be considered optimal for the population goal. If two harvest alternatives result in equal values for R, the manager may use other objectives such as the alternative predicted level of stakeholder opportunities to participate in hunting as a decision guide.

Of course, other formulations for values are possible depending on goals of a harvest. For one alternative, let us assume that managers have set goals for largemouth bass populations in a reservoir such that angling regulations result in large (reproductively mature or trophy) fish (Wilde 1997). In this hypothetical case (Figure 7.3), managers will use a catch-per-unit-effort (CPUE) index that could be obtained from electro-fishing samples taken along shorelines and calculated as the number of bass with length ≥15 inches per sample site. Fisheries managers believe a suitable population size would be indexed as a range of mean CPUE of 0.8–1.5 large-length bass captured during monitoring. Biologists state that they would be concerned if CPUE is below 0.5. Also, the biologists believe that if CPUE exceeds 1.5 (noting especially it CPUE exceeds 2.0), the number of large-length bass might indicate an unbalanced fish community that may be prone to over-predation by the large number of bass.

This situation is a bit more complicated than the bobwhite scenario, but, with some logic, managers could capture the values (R) stated in their objectives where $R = 0$ when CPUE is less than 0.5 or higher than 2.0, and $R = 1$ when $0.8 \leq$ CPUE $\leq$ 1.5. When the CPUE is in the transition levels between "desired level" and "level of concern," that is when $0.5 \leq$ CPUE < 0.8 and $1.5 <$ CPUE ≤ 2.0, R is calculated as follows:

$$R_{belowgoal} = \frac{CPUE - 0.5}{0.8 - 0.5}$$

$$R_{abovegoal} = \frac{CPUE - 1.5}{2.0 - 1.5}$$

Once the values for different predicted outcomes have been established, managers may use a variety of methods to select a harvest regulation set that will balance the tradeoffs and optimize harvest opportunity and population goals. These decisions may be made formally with adaptive harvest management (NAWMP 2012), but more often at state levels. The decisions are made using strategies similar to those discussed in chapter 3 for non-linear decision processes. Adaptive harvest management has the benefit of formally incorporating uncertainties inherent in the decision, which we will discuss later in this chapter.

Step Six: Implement and Monitor

The last step in the decision process is to implement the decision made in step five. Effective harvest decisions may only be made if there are feedbacks that provide timely information to managers on changes in population size and structure that may result from the implemented harvest (Reynolds et al. 2011).

In chapter 4, we discussed the goal for monitoring programs to focus directly on the type of measure needed to inform the decision process (Nichols and Williams 2006). Examples of monitoring used by state and federal agencies to provide feedback for harvest management include:

- Breeding Bird Survey (BBS): Annual survey of the bird community including game birds administered by the US Geological Survey. Surveys are conducted along secondary roads during the peak of the nesting season. Routes are 39.4 km in length with 50 stops located at 805 m intervals along the route. Surveyors count all birds seen or heard for three minutes at each stop (Sauer et al. 2017).

- Rural mail carrier surveys (Nebraska Game and Parks Commission): Rural mail carriers are given a postage-paid postcard three to four times per year to record the counts of ring-necked pheasants and other priority wildlife species during four to five consecutive days on their pre-established US Postal Service route. Results are reported in numbers on individuals per distance driven (Hiller et al. 2015).
- Tail/wing collection (Oregon Department of Fish and Wildlife): Hunters of ruffed grouse provide wings from harvested birds on a voluntary basis using paper collection bags and a depository at main road junctions in a priority area. Experienced biologists determine sex and age from the feather patterns of the wings (Hansen et al. 2015).
- Helicopter surveys (Wyoming Game and Fish Department): Biologists conduct aerial surveys in mid-winter following the harvest to classify individuals in herds of moose by sex and age class (Monteith et al. 2015).
- Fixed-wing pair surveys (US and Canadian Fish and Wildlife Service): Since 1955, mallard counts have been obtained from transect surveys that coincide with peak mallard breeding abundance in May. Mallards are recorded as single males, pairs, and groups (Janke et al. 2017).
- Catch-per-unit-effort (Ohio Division of Wildlife): Biologists conduct annual assessments of reservoir populations of largemouth bass by shoreline boat electrofishing during spring, an approach that generally follows accepted standard methods (see also Miranda and Boxrucker 2009; Pope et al. 2009). Fish are reported as total count, as well as segmented into size and sex classes. The catch-per-unit-effort index (CPUE) is reported as the number of fish captured per hour or by km of transect (Tyszko et al. 2017).
- Length-at-age data (Wisconsin Department of Natural Resources): Walleye are sampled annually with fyke nets to determine size structure of populations in lakes. Fish are measured for total length, and age is determined using operculum age rings for a subsample of fish in each size category (Pedersen et al. 2017).

Ask any state wildlife biologist to provide a time-series of wildlife population data for your state and you will find that structured monitoring programs started in the middle of the 20th century. The oldest time series tend to start in the 1950s. Leopold (1933) listed monitoring as the first step in his four-step framework for management of game animals, so we can surmise that state agencies were assessing stocks of fish and wildlife with some types of local surveys in the 1920s. However, lacking a formal example of a set of time trend data from a state agency, Leopold provides data from his personal notes on "ducks seen and killed" in New Mexico to illustrate how time trend data may be used to establish changes in population size. Thus, harvest regulations were set using anecdotal reports from biologists or informed persons in

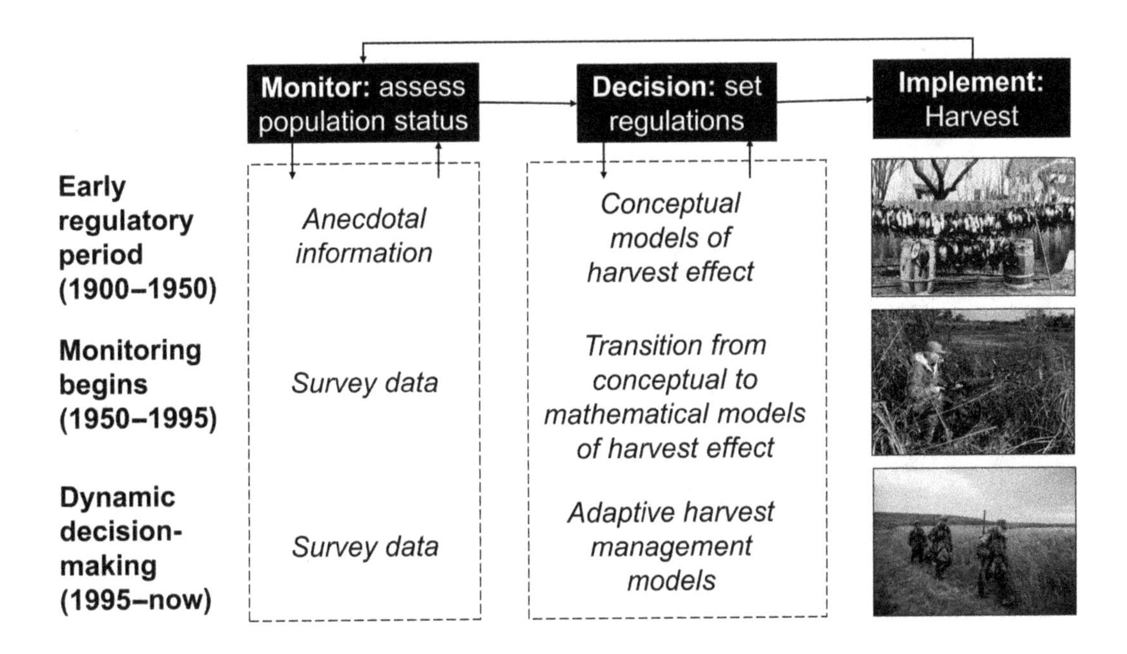

FIGURE 7.4 Comparisons of monitoring systems and decision processes for waterfowl harvest regulations among time periods in harvest management in North America. Photos in public domain (top: USFWS, middle/bottom: Wikicommons).

the field who may have had some survey or observational data to contribute to the discussion (Figure 7.4).

Before the turn of the 20th century, overexploitation was rarely considered (Conroy 2015), which was a result of the presence of robust, large populations and relatively few hunters. In situations like this, the additional mortality from hunting may have little influence on the population as harvest rates are low. A current example of a species with large populations is the eared dove in Argentina, which has responded to agricultural crops, especially sorghum and sunflowers, in the region in the last half of the 20th century. Hunting lodges host hunting parties that may legally shoot over 1,000 birds in a day as there are no bag limits. Still, the harvest rate on the entire population is very light, as international hunters are typically the only people who shoot doves in the region. Doves nest throughout the year, up to four to five times, and nest density has been recorded to reach an average of 1,000–2,000 nests per hectare (Bucher and Ranvaud 2006).

Of course, students of history will be reminded of cautionary tales in North America of large populations that have been hunted to extinction or near extinction, such as American bison and passenger pigeons (Figure 7.5). Both species were exploited when regulations were rarely enforced, when present, but each story's lesson is more complex than simple overharvest. Recent evidence suggests that human exploitation most likely interacted with natural booms and busts in populations of passenger

FIGURE 7.5 Depiction of shooting passenger pigeons in Iowa from Frank Leslie's Illustrated News, 1867. Public domain image, Wikicommons.

pigeons (Hung et al. 2014). Therefore, harvest may have been sustainable in good years of productivity for pigeons, but overharvest may have occurred during certain years in which the absence of monitoring and any regulatory feedback prevented harvest restrictions. Bison were exploited to provide leather and bison robes, as newly built railroads provided a transport system that made exploitation more efficient in a short period of time. The disappearance of bison was decried by many, but the absence of bison was supportive, whether purposeful or not, of the policy to remove native peoples from the plains (Wishart 1995). In this situation, political goals (now seen as unfathomable) allowed overharvest to continue in the face of calls for protection of bison.

A similarly complex story of a failure for fisheries management can be told for North Atlantic cod, a victim of the international common resource that was once seen as robust to a local fishery. Advancements in technology allowed the use of larger nets, and refrigerated processing ships allowed international boats to add to the pressure. The fishery collapsed during the 1960s and 1970s and further collapsed in the 1990s, and only recently have started to show signs of recovery (Rose and Rowe 2015). These cautionary tales serve a purpose to suggest that a combination of enforceable regulations and monitoring tied to a transparent process for decision-making is critical to avoid overharvesting.

Types of Harvest Regulations

Earlier in this chapter, we discussed the formation of alternative regulatory sets for bag limits, season lengths, and age, sex, or length restrictions, which is one of three types of regulatory decisions to be made by managers.

First, all states set **basic rules for hunting and angling** (Table 7.2) that govern considerations such as use of dogs for hunting, use of unattended lines for angling, legal hours for hunting and angling, use of hunter orange clothing, and party hunting rules. These regulations may vary by state and are developed to set the hunting environment for safety, **fair chase**, and protection of property rights.

Second, states set legal methods of take, including weapon and ammunition requirements (Table 7.2). Some states now allow the use of primitive spears, or atlatl, for hunting and spear-fishing for angling, while others do not. Most weapon and ammunition requirements for hunting are based on assuring a high probability of mortality, while requirements of barbless hooks for angling are meant to maximize survival during catch and release fishing.

The third type of regulations, detailed earlier, governs the daily **bag limits** or **creel limits** and possession limits, season length, and age-, size-, or sex-specific restrictions. While basic rules and legal methods of take do not tend to change from year to year, managers have annual decisions to make on the bag limits and season lengths in response to population levels. Larger bag limits and longer seasons would generally be predicted to increase harvest. Allowing harvest of younger individuals and females would generally be predicted to decrease the productivity potential of the population in the future, so protection of these age and sex classes is used to increase populations and vice versa. For angling, protection of large size classes protects the most fecund females and encourages reproduction and growth of population. **Slot limits** protect a specific range of sizes of fish (e.g., protection of largemouth bass between 12 and 16 inches), often intended to allow harvest of some trophy-sized fish that are above the slot range while protecting a significant proportion of the large, fecund females to encourage reproduction.

As managers consider sex-, age-, or length-specific regulations, it is necessary to determine if such regulations are reasonable and enforceable by law enforcement. For example, ring-necked pheasants are sexually dimorphic, and harvest regulations typically protect the females by only allowing take of males. Ducks are distinguishable by sex as well, and harvest regulations protect females. Similarly, deer regulations distinguish between antlered and antlerless deer. However, northern bobwhite and species of prairie grouse such as sharp-tailed grouse or greater prairie chicken cannot be distinguished in flight; therefore, harvest regulations allow the take of females and regulations are set with the knowledge that females will be taken. In similar fashion, anglers cannot be expected to differentiate between male and female fish, so there are rarely sex-specific regulations for fish.

TABLE 7.2 *Regulations affecting hunters of deer with firearms[1] in Alabama*

General rules for deer hunters using firearms:	
Required hunter education course for hunters 16 or older born after August 1, 1977.	Hunters cannot use fire or smoke to aid the hunt.
Legal hunting hours are daylight hours (30 minutes before sunrise until 30 minutes after sunset).	No hunting or discharging of a firearm from within 50 yards of public road, highway, or railroad.
Hunters must wear outer garment above the waist with a minimum of 144 square inches of hunter orange or either a full-size hunter orange hat or cap.	Hunters cannot cast artificial light away from the road from a motor vehicle at night.
Dogs may be used to run deer only in specific locations and during specific time periods.	Hunters may not concentrate, drive, rally, molest, hunt, take, capture or kill animal from or by the aid of any automobile, ATV, airplane, train, motor boat, sailboat or any other type mechanically propelled device.
Hunters may not sell any part of a taken deer except deer hides and hooves.	Hunters must not take or attempt to take or have in possession more than their daily bag limit.
Hunters utilizing a tree stand on public wildlife management areas must wear a body harness.	Except for legally blind hunters, hunters may not use laser sights to project beams from guns.
Hunters must have the appropriate permit for deer taken, and they must report all deer harvested using an appropriate form and in a Game Check.	Hunters may not hunt or take wildlife using poison, explosives, or chemicals including deer blocks, molasses blocks, mineral blocks, chemical licks, and similar products. Deer may be hunted over plain salt licks containing no other minerals or chemicals.
Hunters must not hunt deer under conditions where animals do not have opportunity for escape.	Hunters must have permission to enter any property including trailing wounded game.
Hunters may only hunt any area where baiting/feeding has occurred after bait/feed has been removed for ten days.	No hunting within 100 yards of any dwelling without the permission of the owner or lessee.
No deer may be taken while in a water body.	
Legal methods of taking deer in Alabama:	
Rifles using centerfire, mushrooming ammunition.	Long bows, compound bows, or crossbows in conformance with 220-2-.03.
Shotguns, ten gauge or smaller using buckshot, slugs, or single round ball.	Handguns or pistols using centerfire, mushrooming ammunition.
Air powered guns: .30 caliber or larger.	Hand thrown spear with sharpened blade in conformance with the standards for broadheads in paragraph 2(b) of 220-2-.03.
Muzzle-loaders and black powder handguns: .40 caliber or larger.	

[1] This list of regulations has been reworded for brevity from the regulation statements in the Alabama Department of Conservation and Natural Resources' published regulations. Other regulations cover use of archery equipment and harvest of species other than deer.

TABLE 7.3 *Daily and season bag limits for deer in Alabama under two types of licenses:*

GENERAL PERMIT TYPES	BAG LIMIT	RESTRICTIONS ON TAKE
White-tailed antlered buck	One per day, for a maximum of three during all combined seasons.	One of the three must have at least four antler points one inch or longer on one antler (except for Barbour County).
White-tailed unantlered deer	One per day may be taken in addition to one antlered buck per day during the unantlered deer seasons (gun, special muzzleloader and air rifle, bow and arrow/spear, and youth).	

Note: In Alabama, antlered bucks are defined as those deer with bare antlers visible above natural hairline. Unantlered deer are defined as all deer without bony antlers visible above the natural hairline.

TABLE 7.4 *Season dates in 2017 for Alabama deer hunting spatial zones:*

PERMIT TYPE	ZONE A (CENTRAL)	ZONE B (SOUTH)	ZONE C (NORTH)
Bow and arrow and spear-stalk hunting	Oct. 14 to Feb. 10*	Oct. 14-Oct. 23** Oct. 24-Feb. 10*	Oct. 14-Feb. 10*
Gun deer-stalk hunting, private and leased land	Nov. 18-Feb. 10*	Nov. 18-Feb. 10*	Nov. 18-Feb. 10** Nov. 18-Nov. 27* Nov. 22-Jan. 1*
Gun deer-stalk hunting, open permit-public land	Nov. 18-Feb. 10** Dec. 15-Jan. 1*	Nov. 18-Feb. 10** Dec. 15-Jan. 1*	Nov. 18-Feb. 10** Dec. 22-Jan. 1*
Dog deer hunting (where allowed)	Nov. 18-Jan. 15*	Nov. 18-Jan. 15*	Nov. 18-Jan. 15** Dec. 22-Jan. 1*
Special muzzleloader and air rifle season	Nov. 13-Nov. 17*	Nov. 13-Nov. 17*	Nov. 13-Nov. 17*

*either sex

**antlered bucks only

Predicting Consequences of Alternative Actions

Effective decisions on harvest regulations depend on several factors, as we discussed earlier in this chapter. However, one factor is more important than all others—*what effect will harvest have on the population?*

Biologists are unable to predict the consequences of their harvest decisions if they do not understand how harvest will affect the population. Here, we review the history of how biologists have grown to understand the dynamics of harvested populations.

The Theory of a "Doomed Surplus"

The earliest recorded use of a human weapon to kill animals for food is from modern-day Germany, where 400,000-year-old spears have been found together with the remains of horses (Thieme 1997). Evidence exists for ambush hunting in modern-day Kenya by hominids up to 1.2 million years ago (Kübler et al. 2015).

Over 1,300 years ago, there is evidence of early decisions made to limit harvest to protect populations. In chapter 1, we noted the importance of St. Hubert's vision of the white stag that led him to suggest that hunters should act to protect young and healthy deer to sustain a population in the late 600s. During the eighth century, Charlemagne, king of modern-day France, instituted game laws to limit harvest. Genghis Khan, the first Great Khan of the Mongol Empire in the 13th century, restricted harvest to the four winter months (Caughley 1985).

Early harvest restrictions were based on anecdotal information (Figure 7.4), in an attempt to sustain the use of populations of wildlife for food. But it would be several more centuries until ecologists began to construct basic models for populations that the first conceptual models for harvest impact would arise.

Paul Errington, of Iowa State University, was one of the first to document density dependence in game animals. Errington studied muskrats (Errington 1945) and northern bobwhites (Errington 1946). He observed that both populations typically entered the fall with a high population level, which then fell during the winter to its lowest levels in the spring. Then, reproduction brought the population back to high levels by the next fall. Errington's observations were pivotal. He showed that productivity during the summer was density dependent: females in low-density populations produced more young per capita than females in high-density populations. And, winter survival was also density dependent: animals in high-density populations had lower survival rates than animals in low-density populations.

Errington became engrossed with a concept that he termed "population surpluses," referring to the large stock of animals present in the fall. Errington also conceptualized the idea of a "threshold of security," representing the potential of winter habitat to protect a given number of the population over the winter. By putting the two concepts together, Errington inferred that the surplus of animals available in fall, would decline to the threshold level. Non-human predators could cause the decline, or human hunters could contribute to the decline:

> Modern man, with the advantage given him by his equipment, has unique potentialities for depleting or directly exterminating certain wild species, but others are rather well able to take human hunting "in stride." Shooting and trapping, in moderation and directed mainly against surpluses, has about the same population role as ordinary predation by native enemies, acting as a substitute for part of the predation more than as a superimposed pressure. The facility with which common game learns of weapons also helps to keep the biological impacts of human predation more comparable to the subhuman (Errington 1946).

Thus, Errington framed a concept suggesting that, at some minimum level, hunting might actually not contribute to additional mortality in game animals with traits similar to the muskrats and bobwhites that he studied. Although Errington never used the term in his original papers, the concept of population surpluses that decline until a threshold of protection is reached has become known as the **doomed surplus hypothesis**.

The idea of a **winter threshold** and its management implications for harvest was described by Wagner (1969):

> [The threshold hypothesis] visualizes game populations occupying environments with limited and generally well-fixed capacity to protect animals during the winter season. Each year the reproductive season produces a number in excess of the winter threshold. This annual surplus inevitably disappears through predation, weather, or emigration because of the animals' intolerance to crowding into the limited habitat niches. The animals living within the security threshold experience little if any losses, barring catastrophic weather incidents.
>
> If pitched so as to remove no more than a number equivalent to the annual surplus, hunting may take a portion of animals without increasing the fall-spring mortality rate or affecting the population level.

A few years earlier, Lauckhart and McKean (1956) stated an apt metaphor, relating the winter threshold for stocked pheasants to a bucket of water:

> To plant birds in an already "full" habitat is like pouring water into a full bucket ... If hens are going to die down to a certain capacity number, it should be possible to allow the hunter to take some ...

Wildlife biologists used tenants of the doomed surplus concept to manage game species for the next three to four decades. Unfortunately, the concept still exists in the minds of many biologists. History has refined the hypothesis. Errington serendipitously studied species (muskrats, bobwhite, and pheasant) that were unique in their ability to respond to population declines with high productivity. The three species

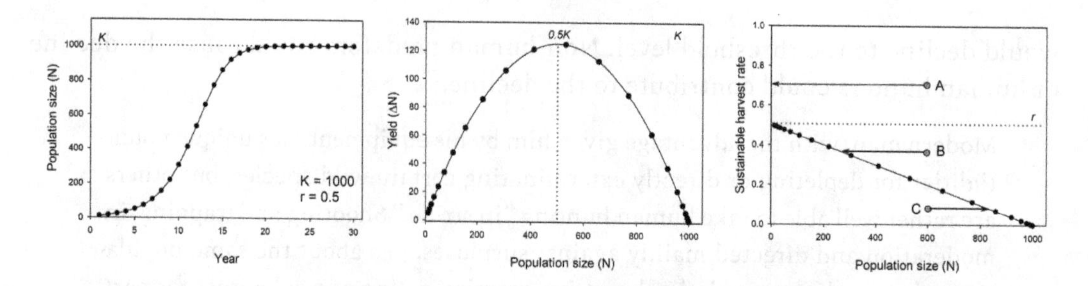

FIGURE 7.6 Dynamics of a population growing to carrying capacity following logistic growth curve (left), with yield during each time period maximizing at one-half of carrying capacity (middle). At right, the sustainable proportion of the population that may be harvested with respect to population size when $r = 0.5$ and $K = 1000$. Three hypothetical harvest rates (A, B, and C) at a population size of $N = 600$ are shown at right, with resulting population trajectories. Population declines to extinction (A), declines to equilibrium (B), or increases to equilibrium (C).

also exhibited high winter mortality, but many other game species do not share these trends. Decades of research have shown that hunters and predators are not sharing the "surplus" produced during the breeding season by game species.

Fisheries biologists did not start with a doomed surplus model, but they also recognized the power of density dependent reproduction. A Russian fisheries biologist explained the idea (Baranov 1927):

> *"A fishery, by thinning out a fish population, itself creates the production by which it is maintained."*

The conceptual models promoted by Errington and Baranov were the seeds to future models of harvest compensation by populations (Conroy 2015). Their observations that harvest did not necessarily result in long-term declines of populations was important, and they based their inferences on mathematically-derived descriptions of mechanisms of density dependence.

The Theory of Maximum Sustainable Yield

Concepts of density-dependent population growth were formulated by Verhulst (1845), and we referred to these, in chapter 6, as logistic growth models. It was natural, especially given that Errington's conceptual models of surplus populations were based on populations that exhibited density-dependent reproduction and survival, for wildlife managers to turn to this simple model of population growth to guide harvest regulations.

We can add a harvest component to the logistic growth model (see chapter 6) to predict population growth given a number of animals' harvest, H_t:

$$\Delta N = rN\left(\frac{K-N}{K}\right) - H_t$$

From this equation, we can calculate a sustainable annual level of harvest, assuming $\Delta N = 0$ (stable population) as:

$$H_t = rN\left(\frac{K-N}{K}\right)$$

You may notice that the sustainable level of harvest is simply the growth of the population, and of course, that is the trick—you may never harvest more of a population than it is predicted to grow in a given year if sustainability is the goal. For managers trying to maximize potential harvest in a sustainable manner, we can look to Figure 7.6 and determine that the maximum growth, or yield, of a population occurs at $K/2$ or $0.5K$. This concept is known as **Maximum Sustainable Yield**: if a population is lowered to one-half of the carrying capacity, it will yield the maximum amount on an annual basis.

Under the assumptions of logistic growth, the MSY concept is valid, although it may seem paradoxical at first glance. To allow maximum harvest, the population must be reduced to one-half the carrying capacity. At this level of population size, there is an optimal combination of low levels of competition and a population size that is high enough to result in maximum level of productivity. However, the concept depends on knowing the carrying capacity of the population, which (as we discussed in chapter 5) often varies from year to year as resources vary in availability. Consider, for example, the cautionary example we have from the passenger pigeon in North America.

What proportion of the population should be harvested? Figure 7.6 shows that the sustainable harvest rate of the population also mirrors the growth rate of the population. At low population levels, competition is almost nonexistent, and the realized population growth rate is very close to the intrinsic rate of growth for the population, *r*. In the example, that means that a harvest rate of close to 50% is sustainable when populations are low (although remember the population is very low, so the corresponding number of animals harvested, the

QUICK COMPREHENSION CHECK

Can you describe why, biologically, a population's growth rate is predicted to change when density changes? Propose potential mechanisms to explain the change. If necessary, refer back to chapter 6.

yield, is very small as shown in the yield figure). As the population grows towards carrying capacity, the growth rate slows and eventually becomes zero; thus, to support a stable population when a population is at carrying capacity, harvest rate must equal zero.

The model would predict that if a harvest rate was permanently set above the intrinsic growth rate of the population, r ($r = 0.5$ in Figure 7.6, right panel, and assumed constant), the population will decline to extinction (scenario A). If the harvest rate is permanently set below r but above the sustainable harvest rate for a given population size ($N = 600$, scenario B), then the population will decline until the harvest rate matches the sustainable harvest rate for a population. Theory predicts that the population will then be in equilibrium at that population size. Similarly, if the harvest rate is set below the sustainable harvest rate for a given population size ($N = 600$, scenario C), the population will increase to an equilibrium point at which the harvest rate is sustainable for the population size.

Maximum Sustainable Yield (MSY) was adopted widely in fisheries harvest management, especially for multi-nation agreements for commercial harvest of marine fish stocks. The political context, combined with the theoretical concept of MSY, usually resulted in annual quotas for tonnage of fish or numbers of fish to be taken (Finley and Oreskes 2013). You may be able to predict the fundamental problem with the use of MSY for harvest decisions: Commercial harvest contexts will most likely result in pressure to take the maximum harvest possible, compared to recreational angling or hunting in which more conservative harvest levels may be acceptable by the public. In the commercial context, if the population was mistakenly lowered below one-half of the carrying capacity, then there were fewer breeders, and the population responded with lower growth than originally anticipated. The harvest quota of harvest would again be applied, and the population would move even lower. If a population was not carefully monitored, a downward cycle in population size could result.

QUICK COMPREHENSION CHECK

The MSY theory of sustainable harvest is based on the logistic growth model, which assumes a constant carrying capacity (K) and a constant intrinsic rate of growth for the population (r). Is this realistic for wildlife populations?

What problems can you predict for managers trying to use MSY to set either sustainable harvest levels (quotas of numbers of animals removed) or sustainable harvest rates (proportion of the population to be harvested)?

Indeed, quotas may be hard to change once they are established. Hilborn and Walters (1992) stated this management principle:

> *"The hardest thing to do in fisheries management is reduce fishing pressure."*

The use of MSY was a step forward in harvest management as it integrated the use of formal, mathematical theory into harvest decisions. Further, MSY carried important ideas into the decision-making process, such as the notion of sustainability as a formal goal for harvest management and the idea of an optimal harvest level that could be calculated (Conroy 2015).

However, MSY did indeed have some problems. In addition to the potential political problems that are inherent in changing quotas once they are established, MSY assumes that a carrying capacity can be established for a population. MSY also assumes the carrying capacity stays constant. A century of ecological research in North America (and around the globe) suggests that resources vary dramatically over time. Estimation of carrying capacity has been attempted, but typically researchers only focus on a single factor such as habitat availability or food abundance. MSY also assumes that a population has a constant intrinsic rate of growth (r). However, we know that nature seldom is stationary. Droughts, food shortages, changes in predator or competitor abundance, and cold or hot spells happen, and each of these events may affect populations. A reduction of growth rate (r) may leave a population with a lower response than predicted, which leads to overharvest. It is fair to say that MSY, especially when applied in commercial situations for fisheries, often resulted in overharvests that dramatically affected fish populations.

Within two decades, biologists stated the following epitaph for MSY (Larkin 1977):

> *Here lies the concept, MSY.*
>
> *It advocated yields too high,*
>
> *And didn't spell out how to slice the pie.*
>
> *We bury it with the best of wishes,*
>
> *Especially on behalf of fishes.*
>
> *We don't know yet what will take its place,*
>
> *But hope it's as good for the human race.*

Yet, MSY continued to be used (Barber 1988, Finley 2011). MSY was an aggressive model for harvest that attempted to maximize the number of animals harvested. It seems clear that the prudent decision, instead, should be more conservative, to avoid overharvest. And, it also seems clear from examples of marine fisheries that annual harvest decisions need to be tied to annual monitoring programs.

A series of harvest management schemes were adopted to modify MSY. **Optimal Sustainable Yield** (OSY) posits that a social carrying capacity of a wildlife species may be different than the biological carrying capacity. That is, OSY incorporates stakeholder viewpoints on population size. Typically, OSY is more conservative than MSY. To avoid overharvesting, a target harvest rate of 5–15% of the population may be common. However, it should be noted that the use of OSY may lead to higher harvest rates if stakeholders perceive populations to be too high (e.g., white-tailed deer or Canada geese).

Quality harvest management is a form of OSY. In contrast to MSY, which assumes the goal is maximum number of animals or biomass of fish, the goal may be to harvest large animals (e.g., deer with large antlers and body size, large fish). Using MSY, very few animals are going to grow to large size. Quality harvest management may place restrictions on the size of deer or fish to be taken, to increase the chances of hunters and anglers encountering animals fitting their size preferences. In this manner, fewer animals are harvested, but the quality of animals harvested is higher.

It should be noted that both OSY and quality harvest management depend on some form of decision-making to determine what level of harvest to select. The initial benefits of MSY seemed to be an ideal "optimal" calculation of harvest level. Discarding the MSY required more complicated approaches, which often included age- or size-specific considerations.

Modern Harvest Management: Assessing Uncertainties in Response of Harvested Populations

The recent advance in harvest management, especially for populations for which the harvest decision of fish or terrestrial wildlife carries larger risk (see chapter 3), has been to place the decision in a structured decision framework (Nichols et al. 1995, Irwin et al. 2011). The use of SDM makes use of monitoring programs by state and federal agencies and integrates stakeholder considerations with regard to objectives, which were loosely considered in OSY frameworks. SDM also incorporates uncertainties with regard to annual weather and habitat conditions and incomplete controllability of harvest rate.

The effect of harvest on the population remains a challenge, almost a century after Errington and Baranov proposed how populations might respond to harvest. In the 1970s, a process of deductive comparison of possible harvest mortality models was formally introduced by Anderson and Burnham (1976). They focused on North American populations of mallard ducks and proposed two alternative, competing harvest models (Figure 7.7). The model descriptions were stated as hypotheses (Nichols et al. 1995):

Additive harvest mortality: Positive, linear relationship between hunting and overall mortality rate.

Compensatory harvest mortality: For a certain range of hunting mortality rates, changes in hunting mortality were compensated by changes in non-hunting mortality such that overall mortality remained unchanged.

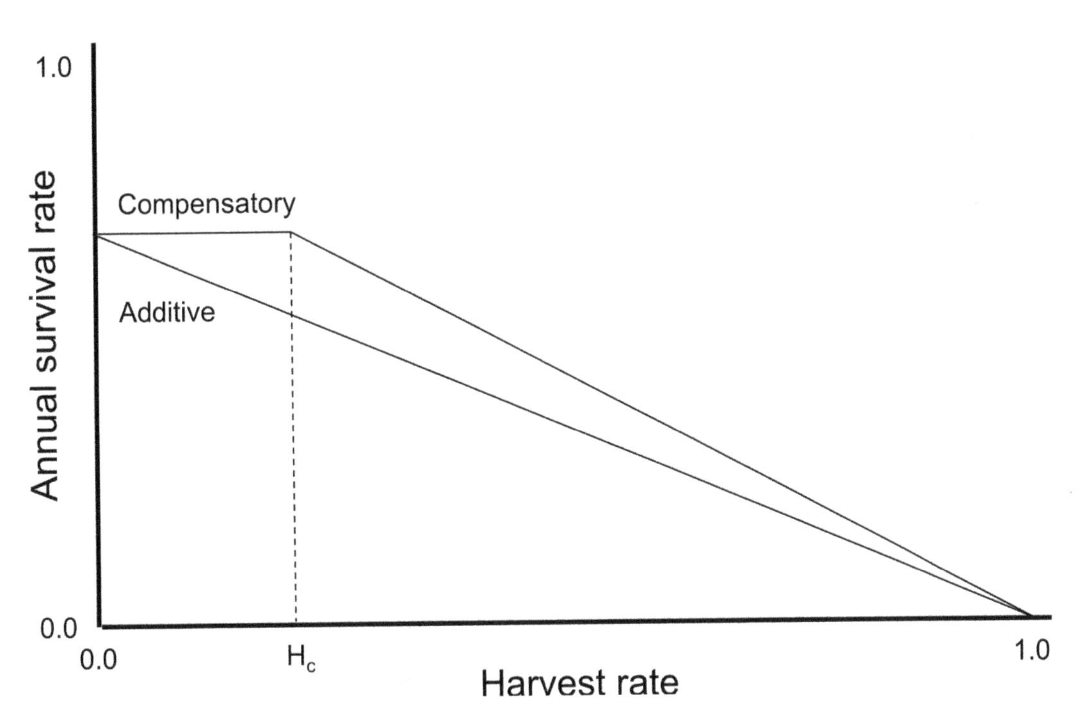

FIGURE 7.7 Comparison of realized annual survival rates under a range of harvest rates and alternative assumptions of compensatory or additive harvest mortality. Hc is the point at which harvest becomes additive under the compensatory harvest mortality model.

Rather than assuming a species could compensate for harvest, which was the assumption made by Errington and Baranov as they described density-dependent responses that led to the doomed surplus theory, Anderson and Burnham (1976) suggested the use of harvest information and monitoring to determine which model was more appropriate to consider. Of course, once more weight was placed on one model or the other, harvest management decisions could be made more effectively—uncertainty about the biological system would be reduced.

To distinguish the two models, as shown in Figure 7.7, the additive model predicts that when we have a harvest rate (proportion of population taken in harvest) of 0%, the annual survival rate is the intrinsic survival rate for the species (approximately 0.7 in Figure 7.7). As soon as the decision is made to harvest at any rate, the species survival is directly affected, even at low harvest rates of 0.01 or 0.05. Harvest mortality subtracts from the annual survival.

In contrast, the compensatory harvest mortality hypothesis predicts that when we harvest at low levels, such as 0.01 or 0.05, the population's overall survival is not affected. In fact, this dynamic occurs up to a point at which harvest becomes additive to the population (H_c). The species is no longer able to compensate for harvest. When $H > H_c$, harvest mortality is additive (Figure 7.7).

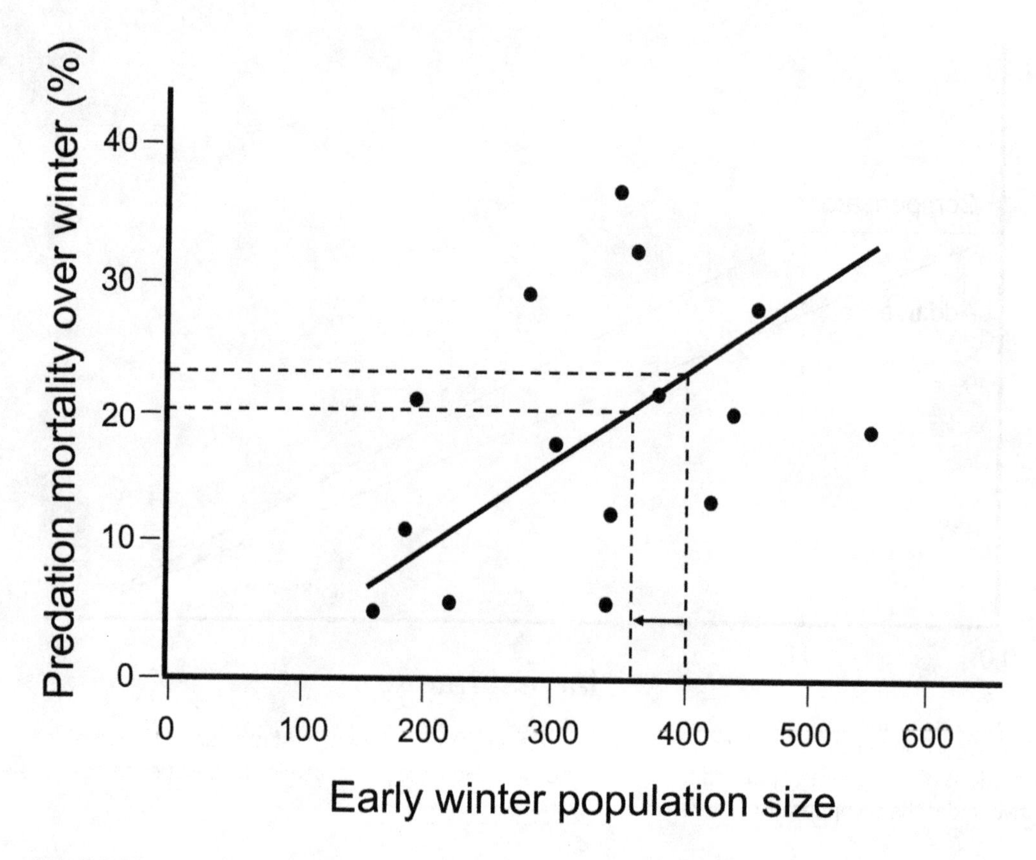

FIGURE 7.8 Density-dependent winter mortality for a species at a range of winter population sizes. Figure based loosely on data for northern bobwhites from Errington (1945). Dotted lines indicate mortality at two different winter population sizes, N = 360 and N = 400.

What is the mechanism for the compensatory harvest mortality hypothesis? Simply, the mechanism is density-dependent responses following a reduction in the population during harvest. To be clear, harvest reduces the population by the number of individuals harvested. However, harvest is often confined to the fall and early winter period, leaving a three- to five-month period of time until breeding begins in the spring. ***The focus of the question is how many animals will be present in the spring, and how did harvest affect the spring population?***

In chapter 6, we introduced the concept of density-dependent demographic rates. Here, we will use a hypothetical example of winter survival for a harvested species that is based loosely on data provided for northern bobwhite by Errington (1945, Figure 7.8). In our example, at a population of $N = 400$ individuals, the mortality rate, attributed to predators, over the winter is 23%. Therefore, 92 individuals (400*0.23 = 92) are killed by predators, leaving 308 alive in the spring.

To compare the additive and compensatory harvest mortality models, let us assume that 10% of the population was harvested in the fall, leaving us with 360 individuals, rather than 400. In the additive model, the population could not respond in a density-dependent fashion, and we would predict that mortality would be 23% over winter, regardless of population size. Therefore, after the harvest of 40 individuals, 23% of the remaining 360 individuals would be killed (0.23*360 = 83) by predators before the next spring, leaving 277 alive in the spring. In contrast, the compensatory model predicts that the survival of the remaining 360 animals is higher, because of density-dependent predation during the winter. The prediction of spring population under the compensatory harvest mortality model would predict that only 20% (Figure 7.8) of the remaining 360 animals, following harvest, would be taken by predators (0.20*360 = 72), leaving 288 animals from the original 400 in the spring.

No harvest:	Spring $N = 308$
10% harvest, additive harvest mortality:	Spring $N = 277$
10% harvest, compensatory harvest mortality:	Spring $N = 288$

In this example based on Errington's bobwhite data, the density-dependent response in survival following a 10% reduction in population size by harvest is only 3% (Figure 7.8), and the compensatory model only predicts 11 more birds alive in the spring relative to the additive model. Further, the increase in survival is not enough to fully compensate for the 10% harvest rate. A harvest manager would have to determine if the projected spring population size meets current objectives for the bobwhite population (e.g., Figure 7.3).

We should also note that populations may potentially compensate for harvest through density-dependent reproduction during the following summer, which may provide an additional, potential compensation mechanism, especially for *r*-selected species. However, a range of harvest contexts exist. We have focused on marine fisheries and waterfowl, and both of these scenarios include a stakeholder desire to maintain the population

QUICK COMPREHENSION CHECK

Explain the hypothesis of compensatory harvest mortality in your own words.

for long-term, sustainable use. However, biologists may often desire to use harvest to lower or even eradicate a population, such as an invasive feral pig population. Certainly, biologists are hoping to set regulations to result in harvest rates that are additive to the species' natural mortality levels, to allow confinement and eradication of the invasive species.

Reflections from History

Harvest management has been a critical part of the fisheries and wildlife profession since its beginning. We have reviewed some of the changes in approach to harvest management in this chapter. In 1985, Graeme Caughley (1937–1994), a leading population ecologist and conservation biologist from New Zealand, wrote comments on improvements to harvest management (Caughley 1985). Caughley's statements were written prior to the development of structured decision processes in our field:

> Wildlife harvest management today, in practice as against theory, differs little from what it was in 1900. The major advance is a relaxation of strictures against hunting on Sundays. There is now, however, a much wider gap between what is said and what is done. The wildlife management agencies of all countries claim that the hunting regulations that they so earnestly enforce are based on sound scientific principles and intricate mathematical calculations. In fact, current deliberations leading to harvesting regulations seldom differ in kind from those of the hunting subcommittee of the Mongol Supreme Command in the Thirteenth Century. Decisions on hunting seasons and bag limits are about as arbitrary now as they were then. Research findings contribute little to their formulation. The advice of practicing biologists, if it is sought at all, is largely ignored.
>
> This may seem a harsh judgment and, if true, a scandal. I view it differently. The regulations may appear arbitrary, but in most cases, they err on the side of caution. They may not have much scientific basis, but they have an ethical one underpinned by common sense. A cautious control of offtake, combined with a careful monitoring of indices, may not provide the best of yields; however, it seldom yields catastrophes.
>
> Wildlife biologists may claim that, with few exceptions, wildlife stocks are in as good a shape now as they were 30 years ago. Whaling and fisheries biologists cannot make the same claim. But over that period, wildlife biologists did not make the big decisions on wildlife harvesting. They were made by committees typically including a politician, an industrialist, a government administrator, an ex officio lawyer, and the president of the local hunting club. They served us well. We have been luckier than we deserve.

> Against that, consider what might have happened if 30 years ago wildlife biologists were solely responsible for setting offtake quotas. They would have accepted the challenge with the certainty that their skill and knowledge were equal to the task, they would have aimed not for safety but for a maximum sustainable yield, and they would have used models of population dynamics which, although accepted then, are now viewed as highly dubious. A number of populations would have been overharvested severely before the biologists learned that they did not know as much as they thought they did.

QUICK COMPREHENSION CHECK

Does Caughley's description fit the description of the history of approaches to waterfowl harvest management described in this chapter?

Does your state wildlife agency use a "commission" or appointed or elected officials, whose membership might mirror Caughley's description, to approve hunting and angling regulations? What affect does that have on the success of harvest regulations?

Caughley suggests that biologists might not be all-knowing individuals. How does that idea match with the use of a decision-making process by managers, rather than a single person making decisions without input from others?

The Future

Harvest management will continue to evolve as hunters and decision-making processes change. Globally, urbanization of society is increasing, making connections between people and nature more distant, which affects hunter participation and effort around the world (Hansen et al. 2012). For example, 50% of hunters in the Central Flyway hunted ducks for four days or less in a single season, regardless of types of regulations (Haugen et al. 2015). Recent surveys of waterfowl hunters suggested that hunters were more concerned about quality of experience, such as ease of access to hunting locations, proximity of hunting to their homes, and low competition for hunting spots than they were concerned about quantity of ducks shot per hunt (Slagle and Dietsch 2018).

Harvest management, in the past, has focused on the wildlife population. The recent decline in hunters and anglers (see chapter 2) creates an even more complex decision for agencies. In the future, harvest management will include more consideration of human dimensions, hunter and angler behavior, hunter and angler preferences, and non-hunting/angling viewpoints (Conroy 2015). The majority of a sample of the American public recently reported that they viewed hunting as an unpleasant experience (Wilkins and Miller 2018), which will add further complexity to stakeholder-based harvest management decisions in the future. In the past two decades, the public has voiced concern on management of wildlife through hunting (Minnis 1998) or angling (Arlinghouse et al. 2012), including the use of ballot initiatives to directly modify state regulations by restricting certain techniques such as fur trapping (Vantassel et al. 2010). The movement mirrors a similar increase in the use of ballot initiatives for a multitude of political issues, but the trend has caused some to question if the ballot initiatives represent a failure of the wildlife management profession to work with its stakeholders in a positive, constructive manner (Beck 1998, van Eeden et al. 2017).

A backlash to the anti-hunting and anti-angling movement has resulted in hunter- and angler-led ballot initiatives or legislation to confirm the right for citizens to fish and hunt (Manfredo et al. 2017). Agencies are genuinely concerned about the predicted loss of revenue from angling and hunting licenses that are the primary support for habitat management (Vrtiska et al. 2013). Students graduating during this decade will have a key role in the movement to broaden the conservation agenda in state and federal wildlife agencies. However, this progress may not be easy, because institutions faced with conflict tend to retract and appeal to traditional stakeholders rather than move to adjust to constructively address the conflict (Manfredo et al. 2017).

In chapter 2, we discussed and evaluated the concept of the "North American Model," which emerged as a popular phrase when hunting and angling participation started to decline in the US. Certainly, the messages in the hunter and angler recruitment campaigns using the ideals and emotions inherent in the North American Model were developed to appeal to traditional stakeholders. Recent success to propose alternative funding (H.R. 4647, Recovering America's Wildlife Act) for wildlife of conservation concern shows signs that agencies can reimagine and broaden their mission, financial support, and stakeholder base. In many ways, then, the future of harvest management hinges on the management successes of non-harvested species.

WRAPPING UP

In our problem case, Jack describes uncertainty related to whether harvest mortality for sandhill cranes was additive or compensatory. Can you explain why this is important for biologists to understand?

How might the success of wildlife management agencies to develop funding to support management for non-game species improve the public's perception of hunting and angling?

After reviewing the information in this chapter, list two facts that the general public may not understand about harvest management.

What do you believe is the most complicated part of harvest management?

How does a structured decision process enable biologists to defend harvest management decisions?

Decision-Making on the Ground

1: The Texas Deer Experiment

During 1991–2001, biologists at the Texas Parks and Wildlife agency collected data on the age structure of male white-tailed deer in a six-county area in eastern Texas. Hunters were not happy with the age distribution (Figure 7.9, left panel), as deer with larger antlers were desired by hunters. Many mid-aged deer (two and a half years old, with decent antlers, but not trophy size) were being taken in large numbers. Thus, male deer were not reaching three and a half or four and a half years old, so bucks with large antlers were not common (note that four-and-a-half-year-old bucks made up only 4% of the harvest, Texas Parks and Wildlife 2006).

The goal for the age distribution of the harvest is shown in Figure 7.9, compared to the 1991–2001 harvest age structure.

Bucks grow new antlers each year and drop them before growing their next set the following year, and antler size is affected by nutrition and other factors, in addition to age. However, generally, antler size increases with age. Logistically, there are three ages (or better, stages) of deer that hunters might be expected to recognize in the field, as distinguished by antler size. First, one-and-a-half-year-old bucks often are called "spike bucks" and have single spike antlers or perhaps small forked antlers. Second, two-and-a-half to three-and-a-half-year-old deer often have antlers with an inside spread (the distance between the main beams of the antlers) that is smaller than their "alert status"

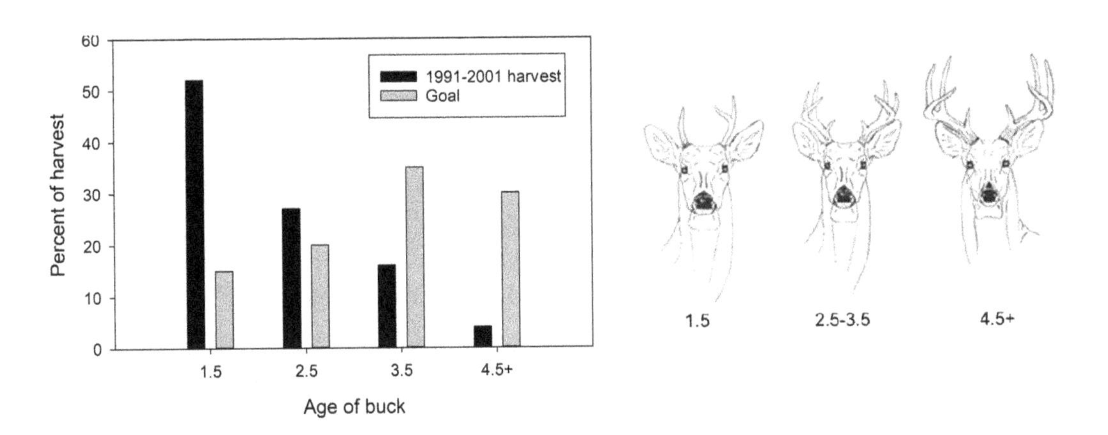

FIGURE 7.9 Comparison of observed age distribution in the harvest in a six-county area in eastern Texas during 1991–2001 with the goal for the harvest age distribution. Depictions of antler sizes used in experimental regulations are shown at right for three age classes: one and a half, two and a half to three and a half, and four and a half+. Data and public domain images from Texas Parks and Wildlife (2006).

ear span. And, third, deer with an inside antler spread greater than the span of their ears are typically four and a half years old or older (Figure 7.9, right panel).

APPLICATION, ANALYSIS, SYNTHESIS, AND EVALUATION

Assume each hunter can take two bucks in a season. Describe a set of regulations, based on age of deer, which might change the age structure of the harvest from the 1991–2001 structure to the desired goal. Describe biologically how such a regulation would work.

Large bucks are not common in the field, and hunters will be upset if they cannot harvest a deer. Does your set of regulations allow hunters to harvest deer, even if they do not see a buck in the largest category? If necessary, adjust your regulations to account for this hunter feedback.

Visit the website in the citation for Texas Parks and Wildlife (2006) to discover the regulations used in the six-county region by the biologists. How closely does it match the regulations you proposed? What are the differences? Did the regulations work in their experiment?

2: Effect of Harvest on Fish Population Structure

Angling regulations are complex because the size of females in the population has a direct relationship with recruitment. Large females produce more offspring than small, younger females. Research on anglers has shown that anglers prefer larger fish, regardless of species (Chizinski et al. 2014), because larger fish have more meat for use. Given a creel limit, a limit of how many fish may be harvested per day, anglers will return small captured fish and keep larger captured fish. Therefore, anglers can be expected to be biased in their harvest of fish by age/size, which may affect the population structure, and removal of large females is predicted to reduce productivity of the population of fish.

Three regulatory approaches are typically used to protect large females in a population in which harvest of fish is allowed. First, minimum size limits could be used to protect small fish to ensure they grow to a certain size before harvest is allowed (all fish smaller than the minimum limit must be returned, alive, to the water body). Second, a protected "harvest-slot limit" may be used to protect fish in a certain range of length, typically a range of lengths in which females are considered to be highly productive. Fish smaller or larger than the slot may be harvested. The use of the slot allows anglers to take a restricted number of large, trophy fish, which may serve to attract anglers and maintain angler interest in a water body. The third regulation is a maximum size limit, in which fish larger than a certain size are protected from harvest (Isermann and Paukert 2010).

APPLICATION, ANALYSIS, SYNTHESIS, AND EVALUATION

Review the data from Chizinski et al. (2014) in Figure 7.10. Water bodies in this study had a creel limit of a certain number of fish for each species taken per day, but no length limits. What patterns do you see? How does angler behavior play a role in the size of fish kept?

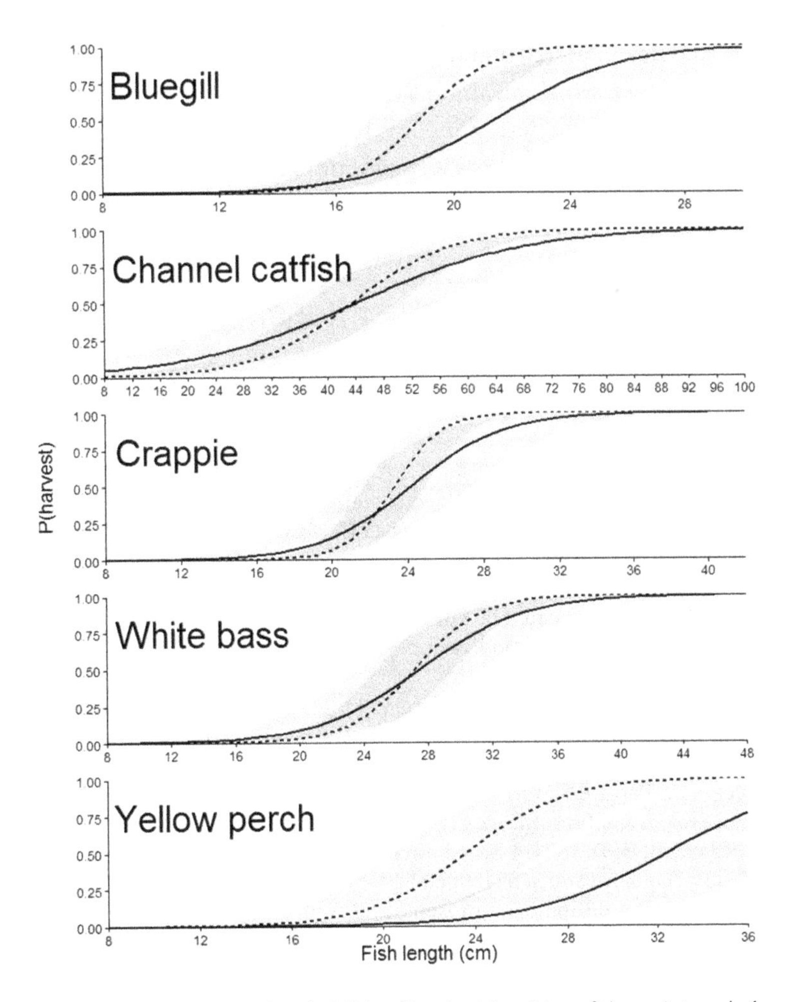

FIGURE 7.10 Predicted probabilities (lines) with 95% confidence intervals (gray ribbons) that bluegill, channel catfish, crappie (black crappie and white crappie combined), white bass, and yellow perch captured by anglers of different lengths were harvested during 2010 (solid lines) and 2011 (dashed lines) in six reservoirs throughout Nebraska. Figure from Chizinski et al. (2014), image in the public domain.

In a hypothetical scenario, assume that populations of each fish species begin to decline, and fish harvest managers decide some kind of size restriction for harvest is necessary to improve productivity and limit harvest. Of the three options described above, which would you select? What minimum or maximum size or protected slot would you select? Why?

How might concepts described in age-structured population models in chapter 5 assist predictions for future populations under the three harvest scenarios?

Sánchez-Hernández et al. (2016) faced a similar situation to the hypothetical scenario described above, in which minimum size limits were in place for brown trout in Spain. Review their paper and determine if minimum size limits are useful to protect large, productive females from harvest. Revise your management proposal, if necessary.

Sources of Information and Further Reading

Anderson, D. R. and K. P. Burnham. "VI. The effect of exploitation on survival." *Population ecology of the mallard.* US Department of the Interior, Fish and Wildlife Service Resource Publication 128, 1976.

Arlinghaus, R., Schwab, A., Riepe, C., and Teel, T. "A primer on anti-angling philosophy and its relevance for recreational fisheries in urbanized societies." *Fisheries* 37, no. 4 (2012): 153–164.

Artelle K. A., Anderson S. C., Cooper A. B., Paquet P. C., Reynolds J. D., and Darimont C. T. "Confronting Uncertainty in Wildlife Management: Performance of Grizzly Bear Management." *PLoS ONE* 8, no. 11 (2013): e78041. https://doi.org/10.1371/journal.pone.0078041

Baranov, F. I. "More about the poor catch of Volba." *Byull. Rybn. Khoz.* 1927.

Barber, W. E. "Maximum sustainable yield lives on." *North American Journal of Fisheries Management* 8, no. 2 (1988): 153–157.

Beck, T. D. "Citizen ballot initiatives: a failure of the wildlife management profession." *Human Dimensions of Wildlife* 3, no. 2 (1998): 21–28.

Brennan, L. A., Lee, J. M., and Fuller, R. S. "Long-Term Trends of Northern Bobwhite Populations and Hunting Success on Private Shooting Plantations in Northern Florida and Southern Georgia," *National Quail Symposium Proceedings* 4 (2000): 75–77.

Bucher, E. H. and Ranvaud, R. D. "S31-4 Eared dove outbreaks in South America: patterns and characteristics." *Acta Zoologica Sinica* 52 (2006): 564–567.

Caughley, G. "Harvesting of wildlife: past, present, and future." In *Game harvest management: a proceedings of the Third International Symposium of the Caesar Kleberg Wildlife Research Institute, 1983,* edited by Beasom, S. L. and Roberson, S. F, 3–14. Kingsville, TX: Caesar Kleberg Wildlife Research Institute, 1985.

Chizinski, C. J., Martin, D. R., Hurley, K. L., and Pope, K. L. "Self-imposed length limits in recreational fisheries." *Fisheries Research* 155 (2014): 83–89.

Conroy, M. J. *A brief history of harvest.* Annapolis, MD: J. D. Nichols Honor Symposium, 2015.

Cornicelli, L., Fulton, D. C., Grund, M. D., and Fieberg, J. "Hunter perceptions and acceptance of alternative deer management regulations." *Wildlife Society Bulletin* 35, no. 3 (2011): 323–329.

Elrod, J. H. "Abundance, growth, survival, and maturation of channel catfish in Lake Sharpe, South Dakota." *Transactions of the American Fisheries Society* 103, no. 1 (1974): 53–58.

Finley, C. *All the fish in the sea: maximum sustainable yield and the failure of fisheries management.* University of Chicago Press, 2011.

Finley, C. and Oreskes, N. "Maximum sustained yield: a policy disguised as science." *ICES Journal of Marine Science* 70 (2013): 245–250.

Grinder, M. and Krausman, P. R. "Morbidity—mortality factors and survival of an urban coyote population in Arizona." *Journal of Wildlife Diseases* 37, no. 2 (2001): 312–317.

Hansen, M. C., Hagen, C. A., Budeau, D. A., Coggins, V. L., and Reishus, B. S. "Comparison of 3 surveys for estimating forest grouse population trends." *Wildlife Society Bulletin* 39, no. 1 (2015): 197–202.

Hansen, H. P., Peterson, M. N., and Jensen, C. "Demographic transition among hunters: a temporal analysis of hunter recruitment dedication and motives in Denmark." *Wildlife Research* 39, no. 5 (2012): 446–451.

Haugen, M. T., Powell, L. A., Vrtiska, M. P., and Pope, K. L. "The Effects of Harvest Regulations on Behaviors of Duck Hunters." *Human dimensions of wildlife* 20, no. 1 (2015): 15–29.

Helfrich, L. A., and R. J. Neves. *Sustaining America's Aquatic Biodiversity: Freshwater Fish Biodiversity and Conservation.* Virginia Cooperative Extension, Publication 420-525. Virginia Polytechnic Institute and State University, 2009.

Hiller, T. L., Taylor, J. S., Lusk, J. J., Powell, L. A., and Tyre, A. J. "Evidence that the conservation reserve program slowed population declines of pheasants on a changing landscape in Nebraska, USA." *Wildlife Society Bulletin* 39, no. 3 (2015): 529–535.

Hung, C. M., Shaner, P. J. L., Zink, R. M., Liu, W. C., Chu, T. C., Huang, W. S., and Li, S. H. "Drastic population fluctuations explain the rapid extinction of the passenger pigeon." *Proceedings of the National Academy of Sciences* 111, no. 29 (2014): 10636–10641.

Irwin, B. J., Wilberg, M. J., Jones, M. L., and Bence, J. R. "Applying structured decision making to recreational fisheries management." *Fisheries* 36, no. 3 (2011): 113–122.

Isermann, D. A. and C. P. Paukert. "Regulating harvest." In *Inland fisheries management in North America*, 3rd ed., edited by W. A. Hubert and M. C. Quist, 185–212. Bethesda, MD: American Fisheries Society, 2010.

Janke, A. K., Anteau, M. J., and Stafford, J. D. "Long-term spatial heterogeneity in mallard distribution in the Prairie pothole region." *Wildlife Society Bulletin* 41, no. 1 (2017): 116–124.

Kübler, S., Owenga, P., Reynolds, S. C., Rucina, S. M., and King, G. C. "Animal movements in the Kenya Rift and evidence for the earliest ambush hunting by hominins." *Scientific Reports* 5 (2015): 14011.

Larkin, P. A. "An epitaph for the concept of maximum sustained yield." *Transactions of the American Fisheries Society* 106 (1977): 1–11.

Lauckhart, J. B. and J. W. Mckean. "Chinese pheasants in the Northwest." In *Pheasants in North America, edited by* D. L. Allen, 43–89. Harrisburg, PA: The Stackpole Co., 1956.

Manfredo, M. J., Teel, T. L., Sullivan, L., and Dietsch, A. M. "Values, trust, and cultural backlash in conservation governance: The case of wildlife management in the United States." *Biological Conservation* 214 (2017): 303–311.

Minnis, D. L. "Wildlife policy-making by the electorate: an overview of citizen-sponsored ballot measures on hunting and trapping." *Wildlife Society Bulletin (1973–2006)* 26, no.1 (1998): 75–83.

Monteith, K. L., Klaver, R. W., Hersey, K. R., Holland, A. A., Thomas, T. P., and Kauffman, M. J. "Effects of climate and plant phenology on recruitment of moose at the southern extent of their range." *Oecologia,* 178, no.4 (2015): 1137–1148.

National Conservation Training Center. *Strategies for conservation of avian diversity in North America.* US Fish and Wildlife Service, National Conservation Training Center, 2014. Accessed 16 April 2018. https://nctc.fws.gov/resources/knowledge-resources/bird-publications/strategies-avian-diversity.html

Nelson, M. E. and Mech, L. D. "Mortality of white-tailed deer in northeastern Minnesota." *The Journal of wildlife management* (1986): 691–698.

Nichols, J. D., Johnson, F. A., and Williams, B. K. "Managing North American waterfowl in the face of uncertainty." *Annual review of ecology and systematics* 26, no. 1 (1995): 177–199.

Nichols, J. D. and Williams, B. K. "Monitoring for conservation." *Trends in Ecology & Evolution* 21, no. 12 (2006): 668–673.

North American Waterfowl Management Plan Committee. *North American Waterfowl Management Plan 2012: people conserving waterfowl and wetlands.* Washington, DC: US Department of the Interior, US Fish and Wildlife Service. Ottawa, ON: Environment Canada, Canadian Wildlife Service. Mexico City: Secretaria de Medio Ambiente y Recursos Naturales, 2012.

Pedersen, E. J., Goto, D., Gaeta, J. W., Hansen G. J. A., Sass, G. G., Zanden, M. J. V., Cichosz T. A., and Rypel A. L. "Long-term growth trends in northern Wisconsin walleye populations under changing biotic and abiotic conditions." *Canadian Journal of Fisheries and Aquatic Sciences* 999 (2017): 1–13.

Pollock, K. H. and W. L. Kendall. "Visibility in aerial surveys: A review of estimation procedures." *Journal of Wildlife Management* 51 (1987): 502–510.

Post, J. R., Mushens, C., Paul, A., and Sullivan, M. "Assessment of alternative harvest regulations for sustaining recreational fisheries: model development and application to bull trout." *North American Journal of Fisheries Management* 23, no. 1 (2003): 22–34.

Powell, L. A., Clark, W. R., and Klaas, E. E. "Using post-release stratification to detect heterogeneity in mallard survival." *The Journal of wildlife management* 59 (1995): 683–690.

Powell, L. A., Taylor, J. S., Lusk, J. J., and Matthews, T. W. "Adaptive harvest management and harvest mortality of greater prairie-chickens." *Ecology, conservation, and management of grouse. Studies in Avian Biology,* 39 (2011): 329–339.

Pracheil, B. M., Pegg, M. A., Powell, L. A., and Mestl, G. E. "Swimways: Protecting Paddlefish through Movement-centered Management." *Fisheries* 37, no. 10 (2012): 449–457.

Reynolds, J. H., Thompson, W. L., and Russell, B. "Planning for success: identifying effective and efficient survey designs for monitoring." *Biological Conservation* 144, no. 5 (2011): 1278–1284.

Ricker, W. F. "Computation and interpretation of biological statistics of fish populations." *Bulletin of the Fisheries Research Board of Canada* 191 (1975): 382.

Rose, G. A. and Rowe, S. "Northern cod comeback." *Canadian Journal of Fisheries and Aquatic Sciences* 72, no. 12 (2015): 1789–1798.

Sánchez-Hernández, J., Shaw, S. L., Cobo, F., and Allen, M. S. "Influence of a Minimum-Length Limit Regulation on Wild Brown Trout: An Example of Recruitment and Growth Overfishing." *North American Journal of Fisheries Management* 36, no. 5 (2016): 1024–1035.

Sauer, J. R., Pardieck, K. L., Ziolkowski Jr, D. J., Smith, A. C., Hudson, M. A. R., Rodriguez, V., Berlanga, H., Niven, D. K. and Link, W. A. "The first 50 years of the North American Breeding Bird Survey." *The Condor* 119, no. 3 (2017): 576–593.

Scrogin, D., Boyle, K., Parsons, G., and Plantinga, A. J. "Effects of regulations on expected catch, expected harvest, and site choice of recreational anglers." *American Journal of Agricultural Economics* 86, no. 4 (2004): 963–974.

Slagle, K. and Dietsch A. *National Survey of Waterfowl Hunters: Summary Report Mississippi Flyway.* Report to the National Flyway Council from the Minnesota Cooperative Fish and Wildlife Research Unit. St. Paul, MN: University of Minnesota and The Ohio State University, 2018.

Texas Parks and Wildlife. *Antler Restrictions: Potential Antler-Restriction Regulation.* 2006. Accessed online 15 April 2018. https://tpwd.texas.gov/landwater/land/wildlife_management/deer/antler_restrictions/

Thieme, H. "Lower Palaeolithic hunting spears from Germany." *Nature* 385, no. 6619 (1997): 807.

Thompson, W. L. "Towards reliable bird surveys: accounting for individuals present but not detected." *The Auk* 119, *no.* 1 (2002): 18–25.

Tirpak, J. M., Giuliano, W. M., Miller, C. A., Allen, T. J., Bittner, S., Edwards, J. W., and Norman, G. W. Ruffed grouse nest success and habitat selection in the central and southern Appalachians. *Journal of Wildlife management* 70, no. 1 (2006): 138–144.

Tyszko, S. M., Hangsleben, M. A., Zweifel, R. D., Pritt, J. J., & Conroy, J. D. "Assessing Reservoir Largemouth Bass Standardized Boat Electrofishing: Effect of Catchability on Density and Size Structure Indices." *North American Journal of Fisheries Management* 37, no. 3 (2017): 587–598.

US Fish & Wildlife Service. *2016 National Survey of Fishing, Hunting, and Wildlife-Associated Recreation*, National Overview. Washington, DC: Department of the Interior, USFWS, 2017.

US Fish and Wildlife Service. "Migratory Bird Hunting; Proposed 2018-19 Migratory Game Bird Hunting Regulations (Preliminary) With Requests for Indian Tribal Proposals; Notice of Meetings." *Federal Register* 82, *no. 36308* (2017): 36308–36317.

van Eeden, L. M., Dickman, C. R., Ritchie, E. G., and Newsome, T. M. "Shifting public values and what they mean for increasing democracy in wildlife management decisions." *Biodiversity and Conservation* 26, no. 11 (2017): 2759–2763.

Vantassel, S. M., Hiller, T. L., Powell, K. D., and Hygnstrom, S. E. "Using advancements in cable-trapping to overcome barriers to furbearer management in the United States." *Journal of Wildlife Management* 74, no. 5 (2010): 934–939.

Verhulst, Pierre-François "Recherches mathématiques sur la loi d'accroissement de la population" [Mathematical Researches into the Law of Population Growth Increase]. *Nouveaux Mémoires de l'Académie Royale des Sciences et Belles-Lettres de Bruxelles* 18 (1845): 1–42.

Vrtiska, M. P., Gammonley, J. H., Naylor, L. W., and Raedeke, A. H. "Economic and conservation ramifications from the decline of waterfowl hunters." *Wildlife Society Bulletin* 37, no. 2 (2013): 380–388.

Wagner, F. H. "Ecosystem concepts in fish and game management." In *The ecosystem concept in natural resource management, edited by* G. M. Van Dyne, 259–307. New York, N.Y: Academic Press, 1969.

Wilde, G. R. "Largemouth bass fishery responses to length limits." *Fisheries* 22, no. 6 (1997): 14–23.

Williams, B. K., Nichols, J. D., and Conroy, M. J. *Analysis and management of animal populations.* Academic Press, 2002.

Williams, B. K., R. C. Szaro, and C. D. Shapiro. *Adaptive Management: The U.S. Department of the Interior Technical Guide.* Washington, DC: Adaptive Management Working Group, US Department of the Interior, 2009.

Wilkins, E. J. and Miller, H. M. *Public views of wetlands and waterfowl conservation in the United States—Results of a survey to inform the 2018 update of the North American Waterfowl Management Plan: U.S. Geological Survey Open-File Report 2017.* 2018.

Wishart, D. J. *An unspeakable sadness: the dispossession of the Nebraska Indians.* University of Nebraska Press, 1995.

Image Credits

Fig. 7.1: Source: https://www.fws.gov/birdhabitat/img/management/stateandprovinceflyway-map501x457.jpg.

Fig. 7.4b: Source: https://commons.wikimedia.org/wiki/File:Conservation_of_fish,_birds_and_game_(1916)_(14752119271).jpg.

Fig. 7.4c: Source: https://commons.wikimedia.org/wiki/File:Former_professional_baseball_player_Dazzy_Vance_duck_hunting_in_Crystal_River_(15245079568).jpg.

Fig. 7.4d: Source: https://commons.wikimedia.org/wiki/File:Group_of_duck_hunters_on_lake.jpg.

Fig. 7.5: Source: https://commons.wikimedia.org/wiki/File:Passenger_pigeon_shooting_in_Iowa.jpg.

Fig. 7.9: Source: https://tpwd.texas.gov/landwater/land/wildlife_management/deer/antler_restrictions/.

Fig. 7.10: Source: Chizinki et al.

SECTION IV

Threatened and Endangered Species Recovery

CHAPTER EIGHT

Small Population Problems

Learning Outcomes

After participating in learning experiences related to this chapter, students should be able to:

- Describe external factors that lead species to have low population size.
- Describe traits of species that increase the risk of extinction.
- Quantify the level of genetic variability within a population.
- Compare dynamics that cause genetic variability to increase or decrease in a population.
- Describe potential effects of inbreeding depression on species of wildlife.
- Describe sources of certainty among biologists regarding the level of heterozygosity at which a conservation planner should be concerned about increased risk of extinction for a species.

A One-Minute Summary

Wildlife species face a variety of threats such as overharvest, introduction of competitors or predators, and habitat loss. Worldwide, the proportion of species threatened with extinction ranges from 13% for birds to 41% for amphibians. Species with large body size, specialized habitat needs, and poor ability to disperse may be especially at risk to population size reduction and eventual extinction.

Small populations may lose genetic variability because of inbreeding, genetic drift, and lack of gene flow, especially if isolated. Biologists measure genetic variability by estimating the mean level of heterozygosity of a population for a set of given traits, and modern genetic methods allow complete sampling of the genome in species for which the entire genome has been sequenced.

Genetic sameness among individuals in a population may lead to inbreeding depression, which may manifest as low birth weight, low productivity and survival, or high risk of disease susceptibility or other environmental risks. Thus, small populations have the potential to be caught in an extinction vortex, in which reduction in size leads to loss of genetic variability which leads to even fewer individuals in the population. Given the potential for a lack of genetic variability to impact demographic success of a population, conservation planners should incorporate strategies that have the potential to increase gene flow as planners seek to support populations of threatened and endangered species.

Principles for Your Toolkit

Relative genetic variability is predictable: The Hardy-Weinberg principle states that the genetic structure of a large population (allele or genotype frequencies) will remain constant over time unless influenced by evolutionary forces. In contrast, conservation geneticists work with small populations that are often affected by these "exceptions" to the Hardy-Weinberg assumptions. We know from theory and empirical research that isolation from gene flow, inbreeding, and genetic drift may cause reductions in genetic variability in small populations of wildlife species.

Extinction vortex: Small populations are at higher risk of extinction than large populations as a result of random occurrences such as storms and extended droughts. However, small populations also have increased probability of loss of genetic variation, which may further decrease survival and productivity, and exacerbate the situation by lowering population size and continuing to increase the risk of extinction.

Inbreeding depression: Inbreeding occurs when closely related individuals mate, increasing the chance that the mates share similar genetic material. Inbreeding has the potential to increase the frequency of deleterious alleles that will cause a reduction in fitness. The effects of inbreeding depression in wildlife may include smaller birth weight, increased risk of environmental stress and predation, and reduction of survival, reproduction, and resistance to disease. Management strategies designed to improve genetic variability for animals in the wild or in zoos typically attempt to reduce the chances of related individuals mating.

A Problem: The Stranded Iguanas of Isla Magueyes

Luis sat in the shade, watching the behaviors of a group of 14 Cuban rock iguanas that were gathered on the sidewalk of a marine biological research station on Isla Magueyes, just a couple hundred meters off the southwest coast of Puerto Rico. In the 1960s, a handful of the iguanas escaped from a zoo and became established on the island. Now, the population (ironically listed in other locations as threatened by the US Fish and Wildlife Service) has grown to over 500 individuals on the 7-ha island, and biologists at the field station complained about feces on the sidewalks and frequent biting incidents.

Luis was a student at the University of Puerto Rico in nearby Mayaguez. He was starting a graduate program in conservation genetics, and this isolated, yet large, population intrigued him. The potential for inbreeding seemed high, given a small number of founding individuals that resembled similar conditions to a population bottleneck. Indeed, it was possible that all iguanas on the island were related. Luis had found some research from the 1980s that used allozyme analyses to assess the genetic structure of green iguanas. However, Luis' new graduate advisor had laughed when he suggested following the same techniques, and she guided him towards papers using microsatellite methods to estimate mean heterozygosity and inbreeding coefficients in isolated lizard populations.

Approximately 250 of the current population of iguanas at Isla Magueyes has been captured to mark them with colorful beads to allow individual identification. Luis mulled the possibility of using DNA samples from scat rather than embark on a capture program to obtain his genetic samples. Either way, he also needed to visit a few locations where Cuban rock iguanas lived in smaller numbers to provide comparison groups. A recent paper on greater sage-grouse genetics seemed to provide a model for comparison of isolated populations, and Luis was certain that levels of gene flow were much lower for rock iguanas on islands than for birds in sage dominated grasslands on the continent. Could he compare his estimates of heterozygosity for iguanas with the levels found in sage-grouse? Perhaps he would ask his advisor when he summoned the courage.

How might Luis best determine levels of heterozygosity for his population of interest? How comparable are levels of heterozygosity for grouse and iguanas? How would he know if levels of heterozygosity are low enough to be a concern? By the time you finish this chapter, you should be able to find the answer.

Terms and Definitions

Allele: One of two or more alternative forms of a gene that arise by mutation and are found at the same place on a chromosome. Often, different alleles may result in different observable phenotypic traits.

Chromosome: A threadlike assembly of nucleic acids and protein carrying genetic information in the form of genes, found in the nucleus of most cells of wildlife species.

Dominant allele: A result of the relationship between alleles of one gene, in which the effect on the phenotype of one allele masks the contribution of another allele (recessive allele) at the same locus.

Gene: A distinct sequence of nucleotides forming part of a chromosome, that allows for synthesis of a molecule that has a specific function.

Genotype: The genetic constitution of an individual organism, usually referring to the allelic structure of a specific gene.

Heterozygous: A condition within an individual organism's genetic structure in which a particular gene has different alleles on the two homologous chromosomes. In notation, we often refer to the condition with one uppercase and one lowercase letter (e.g., Aa) representing the dominant trait (A) and the recessive trait (a).

Homozygous: A condition within an individual organism's genetic structure in which a particular gene has identical alleles on both homologous chromosomes. In notation, we often refer to the condition with two uppercase letters (e.g., AA) for a dominant trait and two lowercase letters (aa) for a recessive trait.

Locus: The location of a gene on a chromosome (plural: loci).

Phenotype: The set of observable characteristics of an individual resulting from the interaction of its genotype with the environment.

Polymorphism: The presence of genetic variation for a trait in a population, typically measured by the presence of at least two or more forms of an allele at a given locus.

Recessive allele: A result of the relationship between alleles of one gene, in which the effect on phenotype of one allele is masked by the contribution of another allele (dominant allele) at the same locus.

The Path to Small Populations

Wildlife populations have potential for exponential growth (chapter 6). However, growth is usually regulated by ecological dynamics such as competition and predation limit populations. Although the majority of species of wildlife are not in danger of becoming too small (Table 8.1), the International Union for Conservation of Nature (IUCN) considers 25% of species of mammals, 13% of birds, 22% of reptiles, 41% of amphibians, and 18% of bony fishes to be threatened (either vulnerable, endangered, or critically endangered by IUCN standards). The IUCN uses probabilistic terms to define **vulnerable** (≥10% chance of extinction in the wild in the next 100 years), **endangered** (≥20% chance of extinction in the next 20 years or 5 generations, whichever is longer), and **critically endangered** (≥50% chance of extinction in the next 10 years or 3 generations, whichever is longer). Species in these categories are showing downward trends in the size of their population that worry scientists, or the species exist in populations with sizes deemed to be too small (e.g., <50 for status of critically endangered; IUCN 2018).

How does a species transition from having a large-sized population to a size small enough to merit conservation concern? The IUCN lists five factors that may lead to small population size, and four of the factors are human-caused (Fisher et al. 1969, Figure 8.1):

***TABLE 8.1** Summary of conservation status of species of vertebrate animals worldwide. Data from 2018 International Union for Conservation of Nature Red List. Percentages in each status category are for species with enough data to make a determination.*

Conservation status / level of concern

TAXONOMIC GROUP	TOTAL SPECIES	DATA DEFICIENT	LEAST CONCERN	NEAR THREATENED	VULNERABLE	ENDANGERED	CRITICALLY ENDANGERED	EXTINCT IN THE WILD	EXTINCT
Mammals	5,677	14%	66%	7%	11%	10%	4%	<0.1%	1.7%
Birds	11,122	1%	76%	9%	7%	4%	2%	<0.1%	1.4%
Reptiles	6,669	15%	70%	7%	8%	9%	5%	<0.1%	0.5%
Amphibians	6,682	22%	52%	7%	13%	17%	11%	<0.1%	0.6%
Bony Fishes	15,199	19%	78%	23%	9%	5%	4%	<0.1%	0.5%

- **Natural causes:** A quick look at the evolutionary history of life on earth will confirm that species of animals have appeared and disappeared throughout the fossil record. Extinction events are more likely to occur with rapid changes in climate or after a large-scale geologic event such as a volcanic eruption. Approximately one of every four extinctions of mammals and birds since 1600 CE are attributed to natural causes.
- **Unwise and unregulated hunting and fishing:** Species of wildlife may be directly affected by hunting or fishing mortality that exceeds the species' ability to recover (chapter 7). These losses may be driven by economic or consumptive value to humans of the animals killed, but species with little or no economic value may often die as non-target species during hunting or trapping activities or by-catch during commercial fishing activities. Black rhinos and green sea turtles are threatened by poaching, and green sea turtles have an additional risk of loss as by-catch in fishing nets. North Atlantic right whales were overexploited by the international whaling industry, and entanglement in fishing nets continues to pose a risk today.
- **Introduction of predators:** Humans have purposefully or accidently introduced predators to ecosystems, especially islands, which may lead to additional predation risk for prey animals and cause quick reduction in size of prey populations

FIGURE 8.1 Examples of species threatened with endangerment: A) green sea turtle (photo by Dominic Scaglioni), B) black rhino (photo by Roman Boed), C) Yellowstone cutthroat trout (photo by Jacob Frank, National Park Service), D) Yosemite toad (photo by Rob Grasso, National Park Service), E) Hawaiian goose (nene, photo by Gary Kramer, USFWS), and F) North Atlantic right whale (photo by NOAA). All photos public domain, Creative Commons license.

(chapter 6). The Hawaiian goose, or nene, has been at risk from an introduced predator, the small Indian mongoose, meant to control rats on the islands.

- **Other species introductions:** The introduction of non-predator species by humans may lead to heightened levels of competition or the spread of disease, and the presence of the exotic species may lead to lower levels of populations of native species (chapter 10). Yellowstone cutthroat trout are currently at risk because of introduced, non-native competitor species of fish: brown, brook, and rainbow trout. Rainbow trout also threaten cutthroats because of the risk of crossbreeding.
- **Habitat loss or modification:** Local loss of individuals in a species may occur when critical habitat, the resources available to a species in a given area, is lost or modified beyond its useful condition to the species (chapters 12 and 13). Resource extraction (mining or logging) as well as conversion of forests, wetlands, or grasslands to agricultural uses and urban development by humans are common reasons for global habitat loss. Habitat quality may also be affected by forces such as pollution or climate change so that once-usable habitat becomes unusable. Green sea turtles are dependent on beaches for nesting, which are often threatened by coastal development. Yosemite toads have a limited range, and habitat in available breeding meadows has been lost to development.

Our management of species of conservation concern can be more effective if we can detect patterns among the large number of species of wildlife that exist on the earth. What types of species tend to become endangered? What biological traits of species may predict endangerment? In the last 300–400 years, we have often seen that species with large body size, high trophic level (i.e., predators), specialized habitat needs, and poor dispersal rank among those most in danger of becoming threatened (Table 8.2). Of course, these are the species that have been most at risk from recent human exploitation and the IUCN's list of threats.

Development and habitat conversion are occurring at increasing rates because the human population continues to grow. The pressure on wildlife species to adapt to the changing world around them is increasing (Table 8.2), and we know that some species will be not meet that challenge. For example, with a changing climate, species with narrow temperature range requirements may be at risk, especially if they cannot move to areas with acceptable temperatures. Species that occur at naturally low population levels may be at risk from random events such as severe storms or volcanic disturbances. Species' ability to disperse may become especially important as our landscapes become further fragmented (Urban 2015).

By definition, small populations are threatened demographically. Random occurrences, such as a protracted drought or a severe storm are a greater risk for a species that exists with only 80 individuals in a single location than if the species had 10,000 individuals scattered about a large region. Basic BIDE models (chapter 6) tell us that the only two ways for a world-wide species' population to become extinct are lower survival or reproduction.

We also have good evidence that small populations encounter risks because of dynamics that lead small populations to lose genetic variability (Table 8.3), which may negatively affect their ability to respond to environmental challenges (Zink 2014). The dynamics facing small populations may create an **extinction vortex**, in which one risk factor leads to another and then another. For this reason, we must explore the biology of conservation

QUICK COMPREHENSION CHECK

The well-known conservation biologist E. O. Wilson reorganized the IUCN's list to describe the threats to species with the acronym HIPPO: Habitat destruction, Invasive species, Pollution, human over-Population, Overharvesting by hunting and fishing. Compare and contrast the two approaches to forming the lists.

Scientists working with threatened species label their field conservation biology. The Society for Conservation Biology, the professional organization for conservation biologists, expresses their mission as advancing the science and practice of conserving Earth's biological diversity. Wildlife ecology and management overlaps with conservation biology when the species in question is a vertebrate, but conservation biologists also work with invertebrate species of animals and plants.

TABLE 8.2 ***Traits that biologists believe to increase risk of extinction for modern species and species in the fossil record (modified from McKinney 1997). Evidence for traits is expressed as strong, moderate, or lacking based on number of supporting studies.***

TRAIT CATEGORY	SPECIFIC TRAIT	MODERN SPECIES	FOSSIL SPECIES
Specialization	Narrow temperature range	Strong	Strong
	Specialized diet	Strong	Strong
	High trophic level	Strong	Strong
	Symbiotic	Strong	Moderate
	Large body size	Strong	Strong
	Low fecundity	Strong	Moderate
	Long-lived	Strong	Moderate
	Slow growth/development	Strong	Moderate
	Limited mobility	Strong	Lacking
	Migratory	Strong	Lacking
Abundance	Localized range or low density	Strong	Strong
	High abundance variation	Strong	Moderate
	Seasonal aggregations	Strong	Lacking
Genetic structure	Low genetic variation	Strong	Lacking

genetics and its connections to population growth rates for small populations. Management strategies to support species of conservation concern may be designed to meet these challenges (chapter 9) once we have a clear understanding of the biology of small populations.

Population Genetics 101

Population genetics is the study of the variation and change of genetic structure within a population. The level of genetic variability in a population can be described in many ways. For example, at the most basic level, we may inquire whether a population has more than one **allele** present at a given **locus** in the genome, and we refer to this condition as **polymorphism** (many forms). A population for which only one allele is present is monomorphic for that trait, and all individuals would be homozygous for the same allele (typically symbolized by A for the dominant allele and a for the recessive allele).

Polymorphism is not incredibly descriptive of genetic variability, as a population can be polymorphic for a trait if there is just one heterozygous (Aa) individual to provide the genetic variability. **Heterozygosity,** the proportion of the population that is heterozygous at a given locus, is more specific and is commonly used to quantify genetic variation. Of course, an individual can be **heterozygous** for one trait and **homozygous** for another, so biologists often report a mean heterozygosity across several loci. **Heterozygotes** (heterozygous individuals for a given locus) are important when populations are small, as that individual carries all of the genetic information for a trait for a two-allele gene (remember some genes have more than two forms of an allele).

A central tenet of population genetics is that a handful of critical factors influence how genetic variability changes in a population over time, and thus we can predict if a species might be expected to lose or gain genetic variability in a specific situation. Lower than average levels of genetic variability are often regarded to have resulted from a decrease in the size of a population, and this is the connection between conservation biology and population genetics.

QUICK COMPREHENSION CHECK

Propose an example of an at-risk wildlife species for each category of species traits in Table 8.2. Use a different species for each category. Compare your list with a classmate and discuss your examples.

What species on your list could double- or triple-count as an example in other categories? Does this increase or decrease that species' chances of becoming endangered?

Approaches to Sampling Genetic Variability

The methods used by population geneticists to examine variation of a population's genetic structure have changed dramatically over the past three decades and will continue to change as you begin your career. Because the different techniques take very different approaches to sampling the genome of an individual, it is impossible to compare estimates of heterozygosity for a species derived from different methods. You should always try to determine the methods used as you read the literature of population genetics. In the selection of methods featured here, we start with the most recent analyses and move to the oldest analyses.

Nuclear DNA Sequencing

DNA sequencing refers to a variety of methods used to determine the exact order of the four nucleotide bases (adenine, guanine, cytosine, and thymine) in a strand of DNA. When an entire genome is sequenced, it allows deep investigations into variation of genetic structure, in contrast to earlier methods in which a portion of the genome (a limited number of loci) was assessed. In 2003, sequencing of the human genome was completed, and new methods for sequencing are increasing the efficiency of sequencing efforts. With each passing month, new wildlife species of management interest or conservation concern, such as the cheetah, are added to the list of species with whole-genome information available for analysis.

Nuclear DNA Microsatellites

A microsatellite is typically a specific, non-coding region of the genome that can be identified by the repetition of nucleotides. Microsatellite regions of the genome encounter greater mutation rates than other sites. Analysis of individuals through comparison of microsatellites is very useful to identify the matching individual to forensic material found at a crime scene or for paternity testing or other tests of relatedness. Conservation geneticists have extended microsatellite analyses to assessments of variability in the genetic structure of individuals in small populations. However, the loci chosen for analysis are not random samples of the genome. Instead, those loci were chosen because they were highly variable for a given taxonomic group, which makes them useful in relatedness tests. But this feature introduces bias to estimates of mean heterozygosity, which is typically much higher at microsatellites than heterozygosity in the genome at large. Different microsatellite regions are used for different species and taxonomic groups, so cross-species or cross-taxa comparisons may also be biased.

Allozymes

Before scientists had the ability to sequence the genome or target individual regions of the chromosome, they used the presence of forms of enzymes (proteins) produced in the cells to indicate the presence of different alleles. Because messenger-RNA transcribes DNA to produce proteins, evaluation of the alloenzymes, or allozymes, was assumed to indirectly sample the genome at various loci. However, these assumptions do not always hold, and allozyme-generated levels of mean heterozygosity across loci are typically lower than estimates from other methods. Allozyme analyses are not used in modern population genetics, given the presence of methods that can directly sample DNA.

Morphology Asymmetry

Asymmetry of a bilateral, morphometric trait occurs when the right and left sides of the body do not match. For over four decades, scientists have focused on the possible correlations of **fluctuating asymmetry** (in which the right or left sides are randomly asymmetrical, compared to **directional asymmetry** in which differences between the right and left sides are biased towards one side of the body) with levels of heterozygosity. Under the hypothesis that the body's development may be affected by environmental stresses (Beasley et al. 2013), some research has indicated that individuals with higher levels of heterozygosity seemed able to better buffer against environmental stresses on development. Heterozygous individuals, for a given trait, tended to be more symmetrical with regard to that trait's physical measurement (Parker and Strobeck 1986). A body of literature has used fluctuating asymmetry to infer genetic issues with species (e.g., cheetah, O'Brien 1994; elephant seal, Hoelzel et al. 2002; rainbow trout, Leary et al. 1983). Fluctuating asymmetry was seen to have potential use when genetic analyses were prohibitively expensive. However, inconsistencies in connections between asymmetry and heterogeneity (Vøllestad et al. 1999) have tended to lead scientists to discard this method in favor of more direct measures of the genetic code.

Heterogeneity under Hardy-Weinberg

The first step towards the ability to predict changes in genetic variability for populations of conservation concern is to consider the dynamics of large populations mating under assumed conditions. You may remember from Biology I or a Genetics course that biologists can use the **Hardy-Weinberg** equations to calculate the expected level of heterozygosity given an initial distribution of alleles in the population. However, we have to remember the following assumptions for Hardy-Weinberg dynamics, which describe a situation that rarely, if ever, occurs in nature: (1) a very large population, (2) completely random mating, (3) no natural selection, (4) no mutation of the genetic code, and (5) no gene flow derived from new individuals from nearby populations.

Genetic information is housed within individuals, but because we assume a large population and random mating for these calculations, we can consider the population's genetic code to be like a large vat of alleles that have been contributed by males and females. The alleles are about to be combined in random matches, very similar to drawing random numbers from a hat.

For a given locus in the genome, we can define p, the proportion of dominant alleles, A, in the population and q, the proportion of recessive alleles, a, in the population. Note that $q = 1\text{-}p$.

Consider a population that has had a complete genetic analysis completed for a single locus, so that we know the number of individuals with the following genotypes:

GENOTYPE	NO. OF INDIVIDUALS (%)	TOTAL A ALLELES	TOTAL A ALLELES
AA	1000 (26%)	2000	0
Aa	2200 (58%)	2200	2200
aa	600 (16%)	0	1200
Total:	3800 (100%)	4200	3400

For this population, the proportion of A alleles, $p = 4200/7600 = 0.55$. And the proportion of a alleles, $q = 3400/7600 = 0.45$.

What happens if these individuals randomly mate according to the expectations of Hardy- Weinberg (H-W)? We can use the following table to derive our expected proportion of offspring with each genotype:

GENOTYPE	H-W EQUATION	PROPORTION OF OFFSPRING	%
AA	$p2$	= (0.55)2 = 0.3025	30%
Aa	2pq	= 2(0.55)(0.45) = 0.4950	50%
aa	$q2$	= (0.45)2 = 0.2025	20%

To check the logic of the H-W equations in the table, consider standing near a big vat containing all alleles for a single trait in the population. What is the probability of creating an AA individual by drawing out two A's? For our population, the probability of drawing out one A is the same as the proportion of A's in the vat, 0.55 or 55%. Once we have drawn out one allele, the probability hasn't changed much because H-W assumes a very large population. Even with the loss of the allele that has just been drawn, the probability of drawing a second A is also 0.55 or 55%. We calculate the probability of drawing two A's as the product of the individual probabilities: $p^*p = (0.55)(0.55) = 0.3025$. We can simplify p^*p as p^2. We use the same logic to arrive as q^2 as the probability of drawing two a alleles: $q^*q = (0.45)(0.45) = 0.2025$.

The last equation to check is the calculation of the number of heterozygotes (Aa) in the population. Again, standing next to our vat of alleles, we draw an A allele with the probability of p (0.55 in our example) and an a allele with the probability of q (0.45 in our example). So, the probability of drawing an Aa is p*q. However, we can't stop there, as we can also get a heterozygote by creating an aA individual (although we always notate heterozygotes as Aa, either Aa or aA give us a heterozygote). Because there are two ways to get a heterozygote, the complete probability is written as $p^*q + q^*p$, which we can simplify as $2pq$.

Now, we have a way to quantify the expected proportion of heterozygotes at a given locus i, which we refer to as heterozygosity, hi:

$$h_i = 2pq$$

If, instead of calculating expected heterozygosity, we were able to measure known heterozygosity from genetic samples analyzed in the lab that provided genotypes at each loci, including the number of heterozygotes, $nhet$, in the sample of n individuals, then we could then estimate hi as:

$$h_i = \frac{n_{het}}{n}$$

A measure of heterozygosity from a single locus for a population of individuals may be informative for some questions, but we may wish to obtain a more representative description of a population's genetic variability. To do this, we would sample multiple loci to calculate a mean heterozygosity, H. If the number of loci examined is L:

$$H = \frac{1}{L}\sum_{i=1}^{L} h$$

A gene is a sequence of nucleotides at the molecular level, and modern population genetics is able to harness the power of whole-genome sequencing to assess molecular-level variation within the DNA. Nucleotide diversity, π, is the average proportion of nucleotides that differ between any randomly sampled pair of sequences within the genome. Although π is measured at a finer molecular scale than H, both describe the level of variation present in the genetic structure of a population.

QUICK COMPREHENSION CHECK

Compare and contrast two measures of heterozygosity, ***h*** and ***H***.

Why are conservation biologists interested in levels of heterozygosity in small populations?

Compare the information used to calculate nucleotide diversity, π, and mean heterozygosity, ***H***.

Into the Real World of Conservation Genetics

Heterozygosity varies among species and among populations within a species. To determine why we observe differences in heterozygosity, we should examine the dynamics inherent in populations, including the ways in which real species living in real situations violate the Hardy-Weinberg assumptions (Table 8.4).

Mutation

The rate of mutation at a given locus varies among species, but it is a relatively rare occurrence. Mutation is seen as a positive force for genetic variability because it is the source of new alleles.

Franklin (1980) and Soulé (1980) used the rate of mutation to estimate the oft-cited minimum viable population size of 50 for small populations, above which mutation counterbalances and minimizes the negative effects of genetic drift. To retain evolutionary potential, a larger minimum size of 500 was suggested by Franklin (1980). However, Lande (1995) argued that some

TABLE 8.4 *Factors that affect level of heterozygosity in a population.*

FACTOR	EFFECT ON HETEROZYGOSITY	BECOMES A PROBLEM AS POPULATIONS SHRINK IN SIZE?
Mutation	Increases	No
Gene flow	Increases	Yes
Negative assortative mating	Increases	No
Positive assortative mating	Decreases	No
Inbreeding	Decreases	Yes
Genetic drift	Decreases	Yes
Selection	Depends	Depends

mutations have an immediately negative effect on an individual, as a deleterious or fatal condition may result from a homozygous condition. Thus, a mutation to a homozygote may do more than simply lower the level of heterozygosity, *h*, at a specific trait. Lande (1995) suggested that the minimum population size to absorb the negative effects of fitness-degrading mutations and genetic drift should be closer to 5,000 than 500 or 50.

This argument highlights the important role of mutations in considerations of genetic effects on populations. Further, resolving the issue is critical to recovery efforts and policy, as many species are not listed as threatened or endangered in the US until their populations fall well below the 5,000 mark. Approximately two-thirds of species managed by zoos with goals of species preservation and maintenance of genetic diversity have populations of less than 100 animals (Baker 2007). Internationally, the IUCN uses a threshold of 10,000 wild individuals, combined with other factors, to identify a species as vulnerable and 2,500 for endangered (IUCN 2012).

Gene Flow

Gene flow is critical to the definition of a population, defined as a group of individuals of the same species that interacts in a given area. Immigration of individuals brings new genetic material to a population, which may be especially important when a species exists at a low population size. Conversely, segregation, or a lack of mixing, of individuals within a regionally distributed species may lead to reduced genetic variability. When a population is divided for breeding purposes into subpopulations, the effective heterozygosity of each subpopulation is lower than would be expected for the entire population. We refer to this as the **Wahlund effect**.

Taken to its extreme, we know that isolation of populations of a species over space and time may result in differentiation of genetic structure to the point where new morphological features, such as fur color, or behaviors, such as bird song, can be identified, which may eventually result in speciation. However, even short-term reductions in genetic flow can be important for species with small population sizes.

Take the example of several species of Pacific salmon, which return to their natal coastal river to breed and deposit eggs after spending from two to eight years, depending on the species, in the ocean. A few months after hatching, the young salmon migrate to the ocean, where they mix with other salmon. As salmon grow in the ocean, they are vulnerable to fishing, and the size of the ocean-based population is used to set regulations on harvest. As Pacific salmon numbers have dropped, biologists have considered the genetic structure during conservation planning exercises. Waples (1990) noted that the fidelity to natal areas served to functionally divide populations of species of Pacific salmon. In simulation modeling, heterozygosity of salmon showed expected declines under small population scenarios, and the predicted level of heterozygosity was even lower when accounting for lack of gene flow among the sub-sections of the population using different rivers for breeding.

Biologists using microsatellite analyses have compared genetic variability between species of fish and found that freshwater fish had lower genetic variability ($H = 0.54$), compared to anadromous fish that spend part of their life cycle in freshwater and a portion in the ocean ($H = 0.68$) and marine fish ($H = 0.77$). Marine fish likely have higher genetic variability because of larger effective population sizes and a more continuous spatial environment. Freshwater fish, in contrast, are often confined to specific lake or river drainage systems with smaller population sizes than marine fish, on average (DeWoody and Avise 2000). Again, we see that measures of heterozygosity must be interpreted in context.

Zoos implement plans to mix genetic material among facilities holding captive individuals in isolation to increase genetic variability. Some breeding stock can be moved between facilities to encounter new mates, or staff may use transfers of semen with artificial insemination. Similarly, conservation efforts in the field may rely on translocation of breeding individuals from one isolated population to another to bolster genetic variability (chapter 9).

Assortative Mating

Biologists have observed trends in some species of animals to either mate with similar individuals (**positive assortative mating**) or dissimilar individuals (**negative assortative mating**). These dynamics typically involve a single trait, such as body size in fish or plumage characteristics in birds.

If these traits are controlled by set of alleles with incomplete dominance (e.g., AA codes for a large individual, Aa for moderate size, and aa for small size), the offspring of homozygous parents will always be a heterozygote with negative assortative mating (AA with aa), or a homozygote with positive assortative mating (AA with AA or aa with aa). Theoretically, negative assortative mating increases heterozygosity, but such a trend in mating is rarely found in animals. Positive assortative mating tends to reduce the potential for heterozygosity, and it is much more common among vertebrates (Jiang et al. 2013).

A unique example of positive assortative mating occurs in snow geese, which have two color phases, white and blue. Early experiments showed the individuals raised by white parents were more likely to mate with white mates and vice versa, regardless of the individual's color. Before genetic analyses were available, biologists hypothesized that color morph was controlled by a single locus, and that the white color was the recessive trait (Cooke and Cooch 1968). Although recessive, white is the most common color morph of snow geese, and the phenotype is kept at high levels by familial positive assortative mating.

Inbreeding

When mating occurs between individuals that are closely related, there is a higher potential for mates to share similar genetic material. Similar to positive assortative mating, which typically involves a mate choice based on a single trait, inbreeding has potential to reduce heterozygosity throughout the genome of offspring. Typically, species of wildlife have behavioral traits, such as dispersal or kin recognition, that

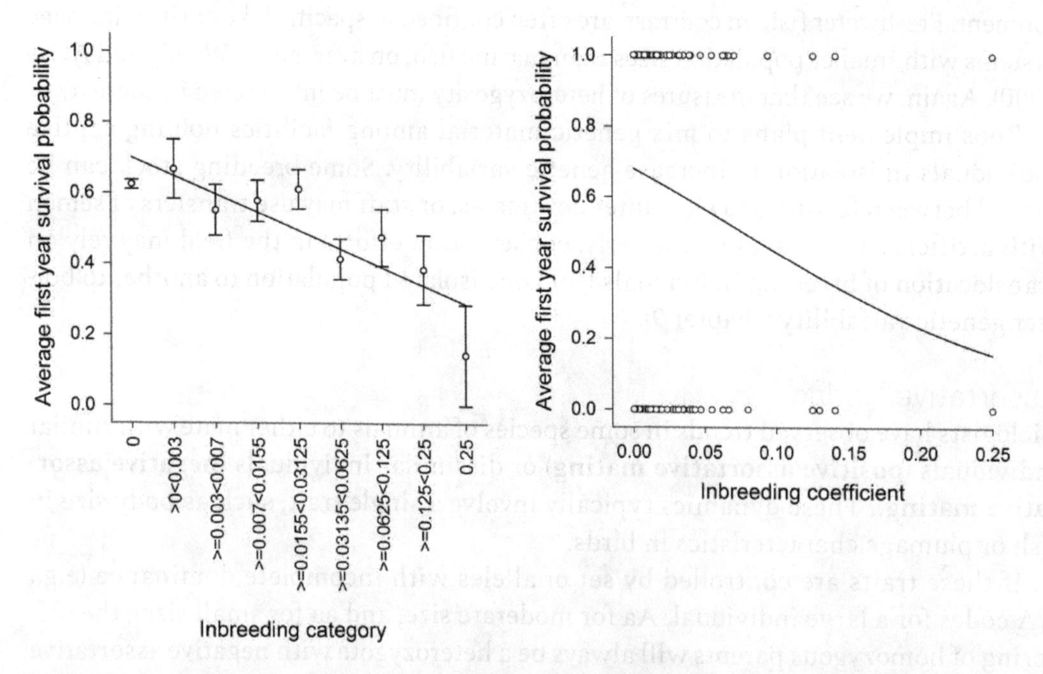

FIGURE 8.2 The association between an offspring's inbreeding coefficient and its probability of first-year survival. Plot shows averages of raw data for offspring with inbreeding coefficients binned as detailed on the x-axis, with bars representing standard errors. Reprinted from Walling et al. (2011), Open Access publication.

lower the probability of inbreeding. However, as populations become isolated and small, the potential for inbreeding grows larger.

A population's inbreeding coefficient, F, is defined as the probability that two alleles at any randomly-chosen locus are identical by descent. Studies on a wide variety of wildlife species have shown evidence of **inbreeding depression**, negative effects of inbreeding on survival and reproduction. Inbreeding has the potential to increase the frequency of **slightly deleterious alleles**, alleles causing characteristics that result in lowered fitness, in the population (Zink 2014). In birds and mammals, the effects of inbreeding depression are most often realized as smaller birth weight, increased risk of environmental stress and predation, and reduction of survival, reproduction, and resistance to disease (Keller and Waller 2002).

Inbred offspring were typically at a disadvantage with regard to juvenile survival for 38 species of captive mammals (Ralls et al. 1988). First-year survival of juvenile red deer in a wild population on the Isle of Rum, Scotland was lower for individuals with higher inbreeding coefficients (Walling et al. 2011, Figure 8.2). Slate et al. (2000) showed that lifetime breeding success for male and female red deer on the same island was reduced for individuals with lower heterozygosity.

Biologists are still working to show the causes of inbreeding depression. In some cases, lower survival in juveniles may be the result of lethal, homozygous alleles that become more likely when related individuals mate. However, the exact mechanism for inbreeding depression remains unknown for many species. One team of scientists has shown that inbred guppies are more prone to be susceptible to parasites (Smallbone et al. 2016, Figure 8.3). Similarly, heterozygous Soay sheep were less prone to infestations of intestinal nematodes than homozygous sheep on the island of Hirta

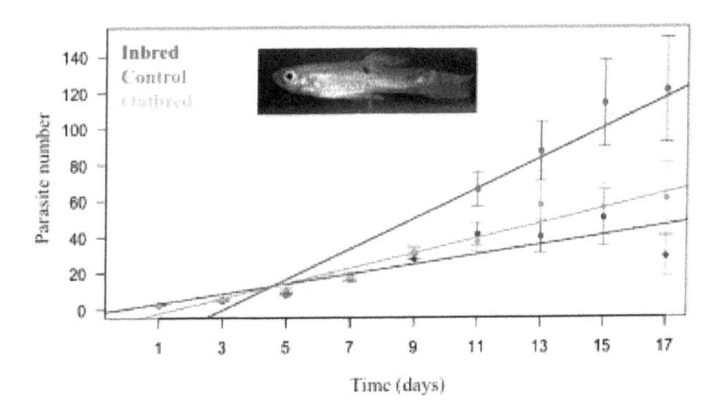

FIGURE 8.3 The effect of breeding regime—inbred (top line, red); outbred (middle, yellow); control (lower line, blue)—on the number (±SEM) of parasites (***Gyrodactylus turnbulli***) on guppies (***Poecilia reticulata***) over time (days). Reprinted from Smallbone et al. (2016), Open Access publication.

in the UK, and parasitic infections led to significant reductions in survival during the winter (Coltman et al. 1999).

Selection

Natural selection describes the differential survival or reproduction of genotypes coding for a specific set of traits. Heterozygosity is affected by the type of selection manifested for the trait.

Stabilizing selection results in more individuals in the population with a moderate phenotype, and individuals at the extremes are selected against. In an incomplete dominance scenario, such as if bird wing length were longest for AA, moderate for Aa, and shortest for aa, the result is higher levels of heterozygosity for a given trait. Conversely, **directional selection** for an extreme (long or short wings) or **disruptive selection** against a moderate trait condition will result in lower levels of heterozygosity (Figure 8.4).

At first glance, it could seem that selection is a background evolutionary dynamic that is not important to consider as populations become smaller. However, evolution is a constant process. The ability of species in small (and large) populations to adapt to changing environments may be critical to survival. How might a species' survival change for various phenotypes as climate warms and dries for example? Will a relatively low level of genetic diversity in polar bears, for example, provide challenges to survival as the arctic region changes in response to climate change (Miller et al. 2012)?

Long-term sets of data have potential to provide evidence of new selective pressures faced by species of wildlife as a result of anthropogenic influences. It is rare

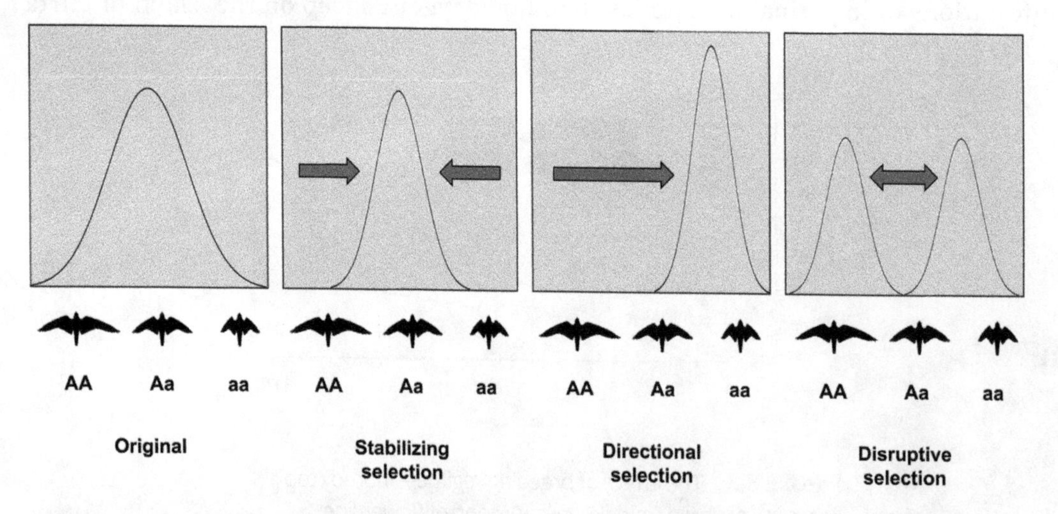

FIGURE 8.4 Comparison of types of selection in a hypothetical bird population. Distribution of genotypes (AA, Aa, or aa) and phenotypes (long-winged to short-winged) shown for the original population. Results of stabilizing selection, directional selection, and disruptive selection are shown with directionality of the selective force.

for long-term samples of genetic material to demonstrate changes in genotype, but phenotypes may provide clues to underlying changes in genetic structure. In western Nebraska, a team of biologists have been marking and measuring cliff swallows for over 30 years. The birds normally build mud nests on rocky cliffs, but the availability of bridges and other human-made structures has resulted in new nesting locations that are near highways. Vehicle collisions are a new mortality risk that was not previously a potential selective pressure for cliff swallows. During the past 30 years, wing length in the population has become shorter and the mortality rate ascribed to road kills has gone down (Brown and Brown 2013). Previously, we might have predicted that cliff swallows whose wings allowed them to escape predators and efficiently capture airborne insects would have higher levels of survival and reproduction. Now, the data suggests that slightly shorter wings are more advantageous to allow for quick turns to help avoid cars. Selection may occur in relatively short time periods.

Genetic Drift

The random loss of alleles occurs during breeding, which may be a distinct problem for species with small populations. Some wildlife species have relatively small litters or clutches of offspring, such that an individual breeder does not pass along every piece of its genetic code to its offspring. The alleles not passed along to offspring are referred to as lost.

Let us take a simple example of a trait at a single locus in the genetic code for a male leopard frog. This particular male is heterozygous, Aa, for this trait, and will produce sperm in equal numbers with either A or a alleles to be combined with eggs from a female to produce offspring. If the population is stable in size, each adult will produce one offspring to replace them, so this male frog will either contribute an A or an a to his one surviving offspring. If the offspring received the A, the male failed to pass along his a allele. Typically, this is not a problem in a large population, as any number of other adult leopard frogs in the population had the a allele, and chances are that many of them randomly passed along their a rather than their A allele. However, if the male frog lived as a member of a very small population in an isolated wetland, there is a much smaller chance that another individual will pass along the a allele. In some cases, a population becomes **fixed** for a single allele, meaning that the other form of the allele does not exist in the population. This loss of an allele is due to random chance, or genetic drift.

The cheetah may be the most well-known example of a species affected by genetic drift during a historic **population bottleneck**, a contraction of the population over an extended period of time. Decades of genetic analyses confirm extremely low genetic variability in cheetahs, and the loss of alleles is thought to have occurred during two population contractions: the first approximately 100,000 years ago when ancestors of modern-day cheetahs are believed to have migrated from North America to Asia and eventually to Africa, and the second 11,000–12,500 years ago during the period coincidental with the Pleistocene mammal extinction (O'Brien et al. 2017).

The Genetic Structure of Small Populations

Does mean heterozygosity, *H*, vary with the size of populations? In many species-specific cases, field data shows that small populations have less genetic diversity than larger populations. For example, genetic data from 26 locations throughout the range of the endangered red-cockaded woodpecker, from Texas to North Carolina, show that mean heterozygosity, measured by allozyme methods, is usually less than 10% and smaller populations have the lowest levels for *H* (Stangel et al. 1992, Figure 8.5).

Similarly, mean heterozygosity from microsatellite analyses among 194 species of birds was lower for species with smaller populations as indexed by their IUCN extinction risk. However, some at-risk species had high values of *H* while some low-risk

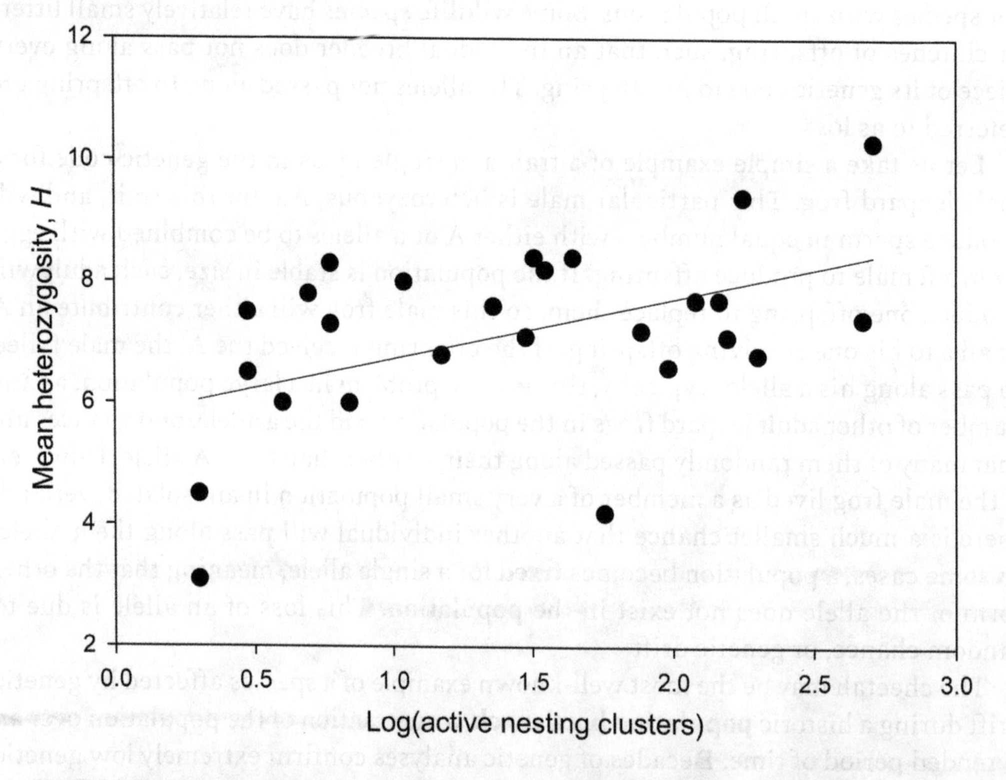

FIGURE 8.5 Genetic variability measured by allozyme analysis for 16 loci in 26 isolated populations of red-cockaded woodpecker. The number of nesting clusters within a population are an index to population size, with an average of 2.2 individuals per nesting cluster. Created with data in Table 8.1, Stangel et al. (1992).

species had low values of H (Evans and Sheldon 2008). The take-home message is that we need more information when making decisions for conservation than a single estimate of H for a species of concern.

Biologists are currently stymied by the fact that levels of genetic variability across taxonomic groups, derived using a range of genetic methods, show remarkably little effect of species' population size (Leffler et al. 2012). The result is that wildlife managers may be left wondering when to expect effects of low genetic variability in species of conservation concern. Although losses of genetic diversity may be found in smaller populations, low genetic diversity does not always result in lower survival or productivity.

For example, black-footed ferrets in the western United States demonstrated a loss of genetic diversity during a recent population bottleneck (Wisely et al. 2002). However, the remaining ferrets maintained levels of productivity similar to the period before the bottleneck, and the most critical threats to the species are loss of prairie dog colonies as habitat and non-native diseases (Belant et al. 2015). So, when does genetic diversity become an important criterion for conservation planning?

Decision-making (chapter 3) for management of species with small populations must incorporate an objective of minimizing probability of extinction. In this manner, genetic variability becomes an important factor in decision-making when a connection can be shown between genetic structure of a population and vital rates of survival and reproduction (chapter 9). For example, Robinson et al. (2016) had evidence that isolated populations of the endangered Red Hills salamander experienced inbreeding depression, and their team was able to prioritize habitat acquisition strategies that reduced landscape fragmentation and supported an increase in gene flow.

As the Red Hills salamander demonstrates, genetic concerns may often be associated with reductions in population because of habitat loss. The low genetic diversity of cheetahs is accompanied by evidence for inbreeding depression, but the cats also suffer from loss of habitat and effects of poaching (O'Brien et al. 2017). Conservation planners for cheetahs have participated in passionate arguments as to whether lack of genetic diversity (O'Brien 1994) or habitat loss (Merola 1994) is the most pressing threat. For managers, the appropriate decision-making process will involve use of the PrOACT process (chapter 3), which examines alternative strategies and their trade-offs.

We may see the potential for a regional approach to conservation planning in the case of the greater prairie chicken. The species shifted from the tallgrass prairies of Illinois and Iowa to the more arid Great Plains after row crop agriculture removed grassland habitat from its original range. In Illinois, the species lost specific alleles during this local population bottleneck (Bouzat et al. 1998). Meanwhile, in Kansas and Nebraska the species has stabilized and is not a federally listed species of concern. However, prairie chickens are still found in agriculture dominated areas, which tend to have fragmented grassland habitats.

A research team in Kansas used microsatellite analyses to evaluate a sample of greater prairie chickens in the state by using analyses of 11 polymorphic loci with a possible maximum of 22 alleles per individual. For each male captured, the team determined how many of the 22 alleles were present, as a measure of genetic variability. Males with more alleles present would tend to have higher levels of mean heterozygosity, *H*. The biologists also looked at the position of males on the booming ground, the site of the lek where males gather to display for females in the spring. Males that stake out and defend territories in the middle of the lek, known as primary males, can be expected to mate with over 70% of the females who visit the lek, so position represents expected reproductive success. Position also represents the ability of a male to defend his space on the lek against other males who want that prestigious location. Primary males at the middle of the lek tended to be higher in genetic diversity than unmated males at the edge of the lek (Figure 8.6), suggesting that genetic diversity in an individual conveys reproductive advantage. In contrast, those males with low genetic diversity are at a disadvantage (Gregory 2011).

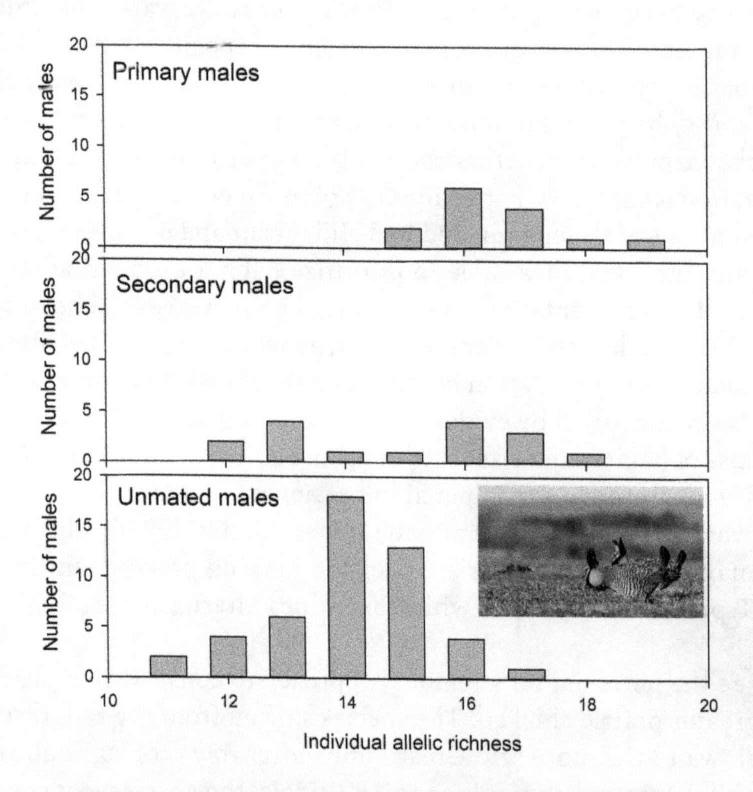

FIGURE 8.6 Comparison of allelic richness (possible maximum: 22) for primary males, secondary males, and unmated males at leks of greater prairie chickens in Kansas. Figure created with data from Gregory 2011, used with permission. Inset photo by Greg Kramos, USFWS public domain.

Allelic diversity in male greater prairie chickens in Kansas also contributes to variation in annual survival, which ranged from 20% probability of surviving a year for males with the lowest levels of allelic diversity to over 70% for males with the highest allelic diversity (Gregory 2011). The trend for lower levels of heterozygosity to be associated with lower annual survival has also been documented in the Zenaida dove in Barbados (Cézilly et al. 2016).

What does this mean for conservation planning for greater prairie chickens in fragmented grassland habitats in the prairies of the northern Great Plains? We know that prairie chickens need grassland areas, and previous work in Illinois suggests the potential for loss of genetic variability from genetic drift when local populations grow small. If we consider a struggling population in a region with highly fragmented habitats, the size of the population should decrease because of loss of habitat. Further, if the remaining males have lower genetic diversity, the dynamics observed in Kansas suggest that those males' annual survival will decrease, further increasing the chances of a local population extinction.

QUICK COMPREHENSION CHECK

What strategies might managers in fragmented grassland habitats use to preserve genetic diversity for greater prairie chickens and other grassland species of wildlife?

WRAPPING UP

Given what you have learned in this chapter, what effects would you predict that Luis finds for his isolated population of Cuban rock iguanas in our problem case? What approaches to genetic analysis are important for Luis to consider?

Decision-Making on the Ground

1: Santa Ana Seclusion: Mountain Lions Trapped behind an Interstate Highway

A genetic analysis using forty-six microsatellite loci revealed that mountain lions isolated in the Santa Ana Mountains in greater Los Angeles, California have lower genetic diversity than most other mountain lions in California (Ernest et al. 2014). Several individuals in the Santa Ana population display kinked tails, a sign of genetic stress among many cat species (Figure 8.7).

Mountain lions in the Santa Ana Mountains are at risk of experiencing negative effects due to loss of genetic variability because of their isolation. Current genetic modeling suggests that if the population would receive no immigrants, due to anthropogenic barriers, genetic drift may result in a reduction in heterozygosity

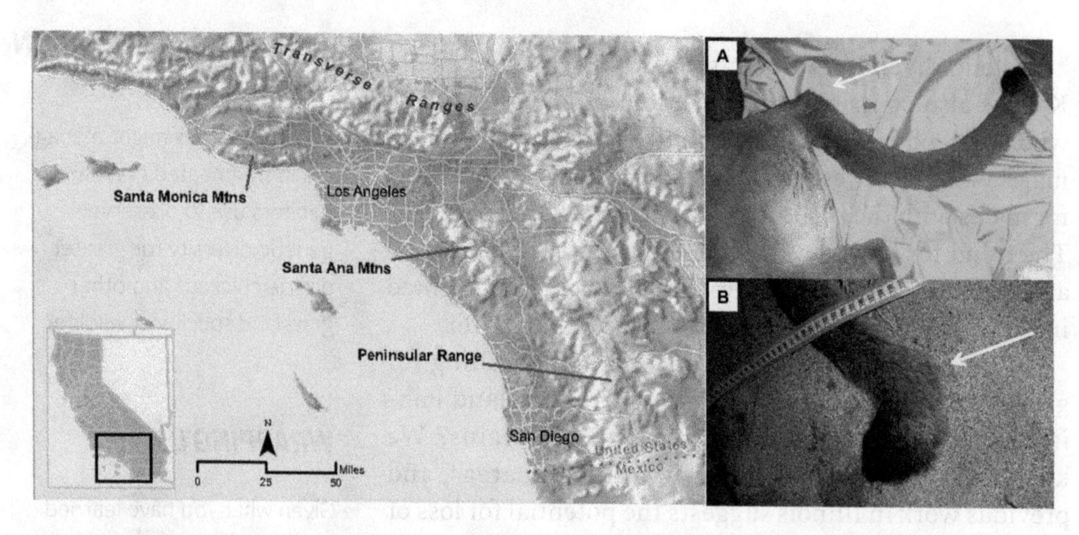

FIGURE 8.7 Location of mountain lions in the Santa Ana Mountains, California (left) and kinked tails found in the isolated population (right). Figure modified from Ernest et al. (2014), Open Access publication.

to the level at which Florida panthers experienced effects of population inbreeding (Benson et al. 2016). Population growth projections currently suggest a fairly stable population with less than a 20% probability of local extinction within 50 years (Figure 8.8). However, the risk of local extinction rose to greater than 95% when the impacts of inbreeding depression were included in the population model.

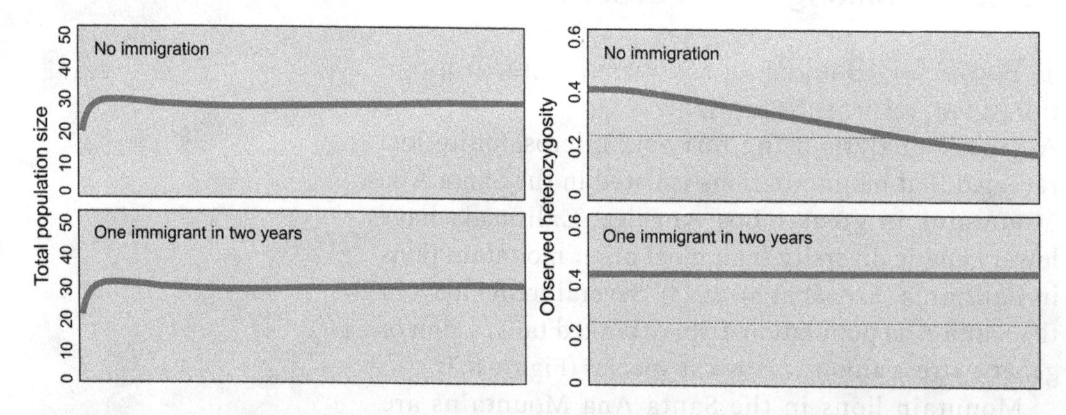

FIGURE 8.8 Predicted patterns of population size (left) and genetic diversity (right) in mountain lions in the Santa Ana Mountains of California under two immigration scenarios: no immigration (top) or one immigrant every two years (bottom). Dotted line in right panels denotes the level of heterozygosity at which Florida panthers experienced negative demographic effects due to inbreeding. Figures created from data presented in Benson et al. (2016).

APPLICATION, ANALYSIS, SYNTHESIS, AND EVALUATION

What dynamic will be responsible for the lower levels of heterozygosity in this isolated, small population over time?

Benson et al. (2016) note that they used different microsatellite loci than were used in a previous study of Florida panthers. Describe the use of microsatellite loci. If the authors wish to compare mountain lion heterozygosity levels to Florida panther levels, what problems might they encounter?

Describe the term "extinction vortex" and suggest how the Santa Ana Mountain population of mountain lions may be a classic example of this dynamic.

Develop strategies to consider as part of a conservation plan to manage the local population of mountain lions in the Santa Ana Mountains. What are your objectives? What possible actions do you think are necessary to avoid local extinction of the population?

A local radio personality suggests that plans to rescue the Santa Ana Mountain population of mountain lions are foolhardy and a waste of taxpayer money because the species exists in good numbers throughout other regions in California. Do you agree? Read some news stories about the Santa Ana mountain lions and the biological system. Justify your answer.

Sources of Information and Further Reading

Baker, A. "Animal ambassadors: an analysis of the effectiveness and conservation impact of ex situ breeding efforts." In: Zoos in the 21st century—catalysts for conservation? (Conservation biology.), vol 15, edited by Zimmermann A., Hatchwell M., Dickie L. A., West C., 139–154. Cambridge University Press, 2007.

Belant, J., Biggins, D., Garelle, D., Griebel, R. G. and Hughes, J. P. *The IUCN Red List of Threatened Species 2015*, e.T14020A45200314. 2015. Accessed online 4 September 2018 http://dx.doi.org/10.2305/IUCN.UK.2015-4.RLTS.T14020A45200314.en.

Benson, J. F., Mahoney, P. J., Sikich, J. A., Serieys, L. E., Pollinger, J. P., Ernest, H. B., and Riley, S. P. "Interactions between demography, genetics, and landscape connectivity increase extinction probability for a small population of large carnivores in a major metropolitan area." *Proc. R. Soc. B 283*, no. 1837 (2016): 20160957.

Bouzat, J. L., Lewin, H. A., and Paige, K. N. The ghost of genetic diversity past: historical DNA analysis of the greater prairie chicken. *The American Naturalist 152*, no. 1 (1998): 1–6.

Brown, C. R. and Brown, M. B. Where has all the road kill gone? *Current Biology 23*, no. 6 (2013): R233–R234.

Cézilly, F., Quinard, A., Motreuil, S., and Pradel, R. "Adult survival selection in relation to multilocus heterozygosity and body size in a tropical bird species, the Zenaida dove, Zenaida aurita." *Oecologia, 180, no.* 1 (2016): 127–136.

Coltman, D. W., Pilkington, J. G., Smith, J. A., and Pemberton, J. M. "Parasite-Mediated Selection Against Inbred Soay Sheep in A Free-Living Island Population." *Evolution 53*, no. 4 (1999): 1259–1267.

Cooke, F. and F. G. Cooch. "The genetics of polymorphism in the Snow Goose Ansercaerulescens." *Evolution 22* (1968): 289–300.

De Anna, E. B., Bonisoli-Alquati, A., and Mousseau, T. A. "The use of fluctuating asymmetry as a measure of environmentally induced developmental instability: A meta-analysis." *Ecological Indicators 30* (2013): 218–226.

DeWoody, J. A. and Avise, J. C. "Microsatellite variation in marine, freshwater and anadromous fishes compared with other animals." *Journal of fish biology 56*, no. 3 (2000): 461–473.

Ernest, H. B., Vickers, T. W., Morrison, S. A., Buchalski, M. R., and Boyce, W. M. "Fractured genetic connectivity threatens a southern California puma (Puma concolor) population." *PloS one 9*, no. 10 (2014): e107985.

Evans, S. R., and Sheldon, B. C. "Interspecific patterns of genetic diversity in birds: correlations with extinction risk." *Conservation Biology 22*, no. 4 (2008): 1016–1025.

Fisher, J., Simon, N., and Vincent, J. *The red book: wildlife in danger.* London: Collins Press, 1969.

Franklin, I. R. "Evolutionary changes in small populations." In *Conservation biology: An evolutionary-ecological perspective*, edited by M. E. Soule and A. Wilcox, 135–149. Sunderland, MA: Sinauer Associates, 1980.

Gregory, A. J. *Landscape genetics and behavioral ecology of Greater Prairie-Chickens* (Tympanuchus cupido) Doctoral dissertation, Kansas State University. 2011.

Hoelzel, A. R., Fleischer, R. C., Campagna, C., Le Boeuf, B. J., and Alvord, G. "Impact of a population bottleneck on symmetry and genetic diversity in the northern elephant seal." *Journal of Evolutionary Biology 15*, no. 4 (2002): 567–575.

IUCN. *IUCN Red List Categories and Criteria*, version 3.1. 2nd ed. Gland, Switzerland and Cambridge, UK: IUCN, 2012.

IUCN. *The IUCN Red List of Threatened Species.* Version 2018-1. Accessed on 26 August 2018. <http://www.iucnredlist.org>.

Jiang, Y., Bolnick, D. I., and Kirkpatrick, M. "Assortative mating in animals." *The American Naturalist 181*, no. 6 (2013): E125-E138.

Keller, L. F. and Waller, D. M. "Inbreeding effects in wild populations." *Trends in ecology & evolution 17*, no. 5 (2002): 230–241.

Lande, R. "Mutation and conservation." *Conservation biology 9*, no. 4 (1995): 782–791.

Leary, R. F., Allendorf, F. W., and Knudsen, K. L. "Developmental stability and enzyme heterozygosity in rainbow trout." *Nature 301*, no. 5895 (1983): 71–72.

Leffler, E. M., Bullaughey, K., Matute, D. R., Meyer, W. K., Segurel, L., Venkat, A., Andolfatto, P., and Przeworski, M. "Revisiting an old riddle: what determines genetic diversity levels within species?" *PLoS biology 10*, no. 9 (2012): p.e1001388.

McKinney, M. L. "Extinction vulnerability and selectivity: combining ecological and paleontological views." *Annual Review of Ecology and Systematics 28*, no. 1 (1997): 495–516.

Merola, M. "A reassessment of homozygosity and the case for inbreeding depression in the cheetah, Acinonyx jubatus: implications for conservation." *Conservation biology 8*, no. 4 (1994): 961–971.

Miller, W., Schuster, S. C., Welch, A. J., Ratan, A., Bedoya-Reina, O. C., Zhao, F., Kim, H. L., Burhans, R. C., Drautz, D. I., Wittekindt, N. E., and Tomsho, L. P. "Polar and brown bear genomes reveal ancient admixture and demographic footprints of past climate change." *Proceedings of the National Academy of Sciences 109*, no. 36 (2012): E2382–E2390.

O'Brien, S. J. "The cheetah's conservation controversy." *Conservation Biology 8*, no. 4 (1994): 1153–1155.

O'Brien, S. J., Johnson, W. E., Driscoll, C. A., Dobrynin, P., and Marker, L. "Conservation Genetics of the Cheetah: Lessons Learned and New Opportunities." *Journal of Heredity 108*, no. 6 (2017): 671–677.

Palmer, A. R. and Strobeck, C. "Fluctuating asymmetry: measurement, analysis, patterns." *Annual review of Ecology and Systematics 17*, no. 1 (1986): 391–421.

Ralls, K., Ballou, J. D., and Templeton, A. "Estimates of lethal equivalents and the cost of inbreeding in mammals." *Conservation biology* 2, no. 2 (1988): 185–193.

Robinson, O. J., McGowan, C. P., and Apodaca, J. J. "Decision analysis for habitat conservation of an endangered, range-limited salamander." *Animal Conservation 19*, no. 6 (2016): 561–569.

Slate, J., Kruuk, L. E. B., Marshall, T. C., Pemberton, J. M., and Clutton-Brock, T. H. "Inbreeding depression influences lifetime breeding success in a wild population of red deer (Cervus elaphus)." *Proceedings of the Royal Society of London B: Biological Sciences 267*, no. 1453 (2000): 1657–1662.

Smallbone, W., Van Oosterhout, C., and Cable, J. "The effects of inbreeding on disease susceptibility: Gyrodactylus turnbulli infection of guppies, Poecilia reticulata." *Experimental parasitology* 167 (2016): 32–37.

Soule, M. E. "Thresholds for survival: maintaining fitness and evolutionary potential." In *Conservation biology: An evolutionary-ecological perspective*, edited by M. E. Soule and B. A. Wilcox, 151–170. Sunderland, MA: Sinauer Associates, 1980.

Stangel, P. W., Lennartz, M. R., and Smith, M. H. "Genetic variation and population structure of red-cockaded woodpeckers." *Conservation Biology 6, no.* 2 (1992): 283–292.

Urban, M. C. "Accelerating extinction risk from climate change." *Science 348*, no. 6234 (2015): 571–573.

Vøllestad, L. A., Hindar, K., and Møller, A. P. "A meta-analysis of fluctuating asymmetry in relation to heterozygosity." *Heredity 83*, no. 2 (1999).: 206–218.

Walling, C. A., Nussey, D. H., Morris, A., Clutton-Brock, T. H., Kruuk, L. E., and Pemberton, J. M. "Inbreeding depression in red deer calves." *BMC Evolutionary Biology 11*, no. 1 (2011): 318.

Waples, R. S. "Conservation genetics of Pacific salmon. II. Effective population size and the rate of loss of genetic variability." *Journal of Heredity 81*, no. 4 (1990): 267–276.

Wisely, S. M., Buskirk, S. W., Fleming, M. A., McDonald, D. B., and Ostrander, E. A. "Genetic diversity and fitness in black-footed ferrets before and during a bottleneck." *Journal of Heredity 93*, no. 4 (2002): 231–237.

Zink, R. M. "Comparison of patterns of genetic variation and demographic history in the greater sage-grouse (Centrocercus urophasianus): relevance for conservation." *Open Ornithol J 7* (2014): 19–29.

Image Credits

Fig. 8.1a: Copyright © Dominic Scaglioni (CC by 2.0) at https://www.flickr.com/photos/dominic-scaglioni/7675367032/.

Fig. 8.1b: Copyright © Roman Boed (CC by 2.0) at https://www.flickr.com/photos/romanboed/8368745966/in/photolist-dKqwxV-dKqwSt-dKw1cy-dKqx2P-dKqwgr-dKqv1X-dKw13Y-dKqwnz-dKvZv9-dKvZU3-dKqv8r-dKqw2i-dKqvW6-dKw1By-dKvZzC-dKqq6e.

Fig. 8.1c: Source: https://www.flickr.com/photos/yellowstonenps/41491495920/in/photolist-27SU8rG-27SU6Uy-28TYKWS-28TYJEo-27SU3xU-28TYGbq-28TYE4Q-27As1yx-28TYAQq-27ArXu6-26dsMZC-26dsLcj-LDz3SS-28MkEHK-LDz2U9-28MkDzc-28MkCnH-ptxPEh-pvA4r8-pe6Z9e-pe5RwV-26dsJs7-DcUtjS-Gp3U6F-2.

Fig. 8.1d: Copyright © Pacific Southwest Region USFWS (CC by 2.0) at https://www.flickr.com/photos/usfws_pacificsw/16912323926.

Fig. 8.1e: Source: https://www.flickr.com/photos/usfwspacific/37198707652.

Fig. 8.1f: Source: https://commons.wikimedia.org/wiki/File:Eubalaena_glacialis_with_calf.jpg.

Fig. 8.2: Source: https://www.ncbi.nlm.nih.gov/pmc/articles/PMC3226574/.

Fig. 8.3: Copyright © Willow Smallbone, Cock van Oosterhout, Jo Cable (CC by 4.0) at https://www.sciencedirect.com/science/article/pii/S0014489416300807.

Fig. 8.5: Peter W. Stangel, Michael R. Lennartz and Michael H. Smith, "Woodpecker Inbreeding from Genetic Variation and Population Structure of Red-Cockaded Woodpeckers," Conservation Biology, vol. 6, no. 2. Copyright © 1992 by John Wiley & Sons, Inc.
Fig. 8.6a: Source: United States Fish and Wildlife Service.
Fig. 8.6b: Copyright © Greg Kramos (CC by 2.0) at https://commons.wikimedia.org/wiki/File:Greater_Prairie-Chickens_in_the_Flint_Hills_(7469130742).jpg.
Fig. 8.7: Copyright © Holly B. Ernest, T. Winston Vickers, Scott A. Morrison, Michael R. Buchalski, and Walter M. Boyce (CC by 4.0) at https://journals.plos.org/plosone/article?id=10.1371/journal.pone.0107985.
Fig. 8.8: JF Benson, PJ Mahoney, JA Sikich, LE Serieys, JP Pollinger, HB Ernest, and SP Riley, "Mountain Lion Population Genetics," Proceedings of the Royal Society B: Biological Sciences, vol. 283. Copyright © 2016 by Royal Society Publishing.

CHAPTER NINE

Managing At-Risk Species

Learning Outcomes

After participating in learning experiences related to this chapter, students should be able to:

- Describe the listing process for species under the Endangered Species Act.
- Define units of conservation used by the Endangered Species Act.
- Describe components of a recovery plan for threatened and endangered species.
- Compare benefits and disadvantages for *ex situ* and *in situ* approaches to conservation of critically endangered species.
- Describe components of a Species Survival Plan for captive animals.
- Compare decision processes for specific threatened and endangered species with those of other species.
- Assess how personal framing may affect the approach used to classify species of conservation concern during the listing process.

A One-Minute Summary

The Endangered Species Act (ESA) is a landmark piece of legislation that provides a system of protection for species of severe conservation concern and associated habitats in the United States. At the international level, the International Union for Conservation of Nature (IUCN) Red List is a record of status for more than 68,000 species of plants and animals, of which approximately 13,000 are threatened with extinction.

Anyone may petition the US Fish and Wildlife Service or the National Marine Fisheries Service to list a species as threatened or endangered. Species, subspecies, or distinct population segments may be considered for listing under the ESA. A species listed as threatened or endangered must have a Species Recovery Plan developed, which provides a plan for the species' recovery. Some species may be perceived to need a captive breeding program to support the population, a process that results in the decision to conduct conservation ex situ (in captivity) instead of in situ (natural, wild location). Zoos and aquariums are valuable partners in this process. A Species Survival Plan is used to plan, coordinate, and track the breeding programs' activities among cooperating facilities with captive animals.

The end-goal of captive breeding is to provide for release of captive animals back to the wild, but this decision is quite complex, relative to other wildlife management decisions. Biologists must decide how many individuals (including age and sex ratios) to release to create a wild population, and other decisions include where and when to release and whether to conduct future releases.

The decision to list a species as threatened or endangered is another complex decision that involves the integration of information about a species' status. Contemporary listing decisions that have been conflict-filled provide evidence that the individuals involved with listing a species may make different decisions based on the manner in which they frame their task to support the species of concern.

Principles for Your Toolkit

Units of conservation: The Endangered Species Act in the United States carries legal protections for animals and plants on the list. Therefore, it is critical to define what individuals are protected. The act covers lower levels of biological organization than species, so conservation managers work with a framework of "units of conservation." The Endangered Species Act uses species, subspecies, or distinct population segments as units of conservation to identify groups of individuals that will be protected by a listing decision.

Private landowner or stakeholder impact: A decision to list a species carries with it a set of costs to be borne by the conservation community (agencies, NGOs, individuals) to carry out the work to support recovery of the species. However, the decision will most likely result in direct or indirect costs of the regulations to private individuals or stakeholder groups who may have activities, such as agriculture, mining, or development, curtailed. Because many species can only be conserved by working with private landowners, the ESA provides two mechanisms to lessen the regulatory burden on private individuals: (1) The Safe Harbor Act and (2) the use of "non- essential population" status during reintroductions.

A Problem: Listing the Berry Cave Salamander

Gizela kicked off her boots in the mud room at the main office of The Nature Conservancy in Knoxville, Tennessee. She and another intern were returning from a day in the field, checking for evidence of the Berry Cave salamander on one of the conservancy's properties. Gizela definitely got her hands dirty during this internship, and after finding one of the salamanders her mind had been racing. On the drive to the cave in the morning, their supervisor told them about the rarity of the salamander, and Gizela remembered a paper she had read in her wildlife management course last spring about amphibian conservation.

"Amphibians are the taxonomic group with the highest proportion of threatened species in the IUCN Red List, but the US Fish and Wildlife Service lists fewer rare amphibians than other taxonomic groups," she told her fellow intern. "And, they receive less funding if they do happen to make it onto the ESA list. That doesn't seem fair."

After a short discussion, the two interns decided that they would write to their congressperson to attempt to convince them to vote to list the Berry Cave salamander as a threatened species. Not sure how species became listed, they started to search the internet.

"Wait a minute," Gizela's new friend called out, holding up his phone with a browser window open. "The Berry Cave salamander has already been petitioned for listing and denied. What are we supposed to do now?"

If someone has conservation concerns about a species, what is the process of getting the species listed as threatened or endangered? What level of concern qualifies a species to be listed as threatened or endangered in the United States? How might you help Gizela and her friend determine why the Berry Cave salamander was denied listing? By the time you finish this chapter, you should be able to find the answer.

Terms and Definitions[1]

CITES: The 1973 Convention on International Trade in Endangered Species (CITES) of Wild Fauna and Flora, regulating or prohibiting international commerce of plant and animal species believed to be harmed by, or that may be harmed by, international trade. The authority to implement this is under section 8 of the ESA.

Critical habitat: Specific geographic areas, whether occupied by a listed species or not, that are essential for its conservation and that have been formally designated by rule published in the *Federal Register.*

Delist: To remove an animal or plant species from the list of endangered and threatened wildlife and plants.

Distinct population segment: A subdivision of a vertebrate species that is treated as a species for purposes of listing under the Endangered Species Act. Standards require it to be separable from the remainder of and significant to the species to which it belongs.

---

[1] Because of the legal language in the Endangered Species Act, the terms and definitions used in this chapter come from the US Fisheries and Wildlife Service. Strict legal definitions may differ, but the definitions used here are working definitions used by professionals at federal agencies in the United States.

Endangered species: An animal or plant species in danger of extinction throughout all or a significant portion of its range.

Evolutionarily significant unit: A designation in the ESA used by NOAA fisheries to manage Pacific salmonid species. A stock that is substantially reproductively isolated from other stocks of the same species and which represents an important part of the evolutionary legacy of the species. Life history, ecological, genetic, and other information may be used to determine whether a stock meets these two criteria.

Experimental population: A population (including its offspring) of a listed species designated by rule published in the *Federal Register* that is wholly separate geographically from other populations of the same species. An experimental population may be subject to less stringent prohibitions than are applied to the remainder of the species to which it belongs.

Extirpated species: A species that no longer survives in regions that were once part of its range, but that still exists elsewhere in the wild or in captivity.

Listing: The formal process through which FWS or NOAA fisheries add species to the federal list of endangered and threatened wildlife and plants.

Non-essential populations: A status given to species rather than threatened or endangered when releasing a species of conservation concern into native habitat that has recently been devoid of the species.

Petition: A formal request from an interested individual to list, reclassify, or delist a species, or to revise critical habitat for a listed species under ESA. Critical habitat can be petitioned for designation under the Administrative Procedures Act.

Recovery: The process by which the decline of an endangered or threatened species is stopped or reversed, or threats to its survival neutralized so that its long-term survival in the wild can be ensured, and it can be removed from the list of threatened and endangered species.

Safe Harbor Agreement: A voluntary agreement signed by FWS or NOAA Fisheries and a property owner and any other cooperator that (a) sets forth specific management activities that the non-federal property owner will undertake or forgo to provide a net conservation benefit to species covered by the agreement, and (b) provides the property owner with the assurances of the Safe Harbor Agreement that are authorized in an enhancement of survival permit.

Species of concern: An informal term referring to a species that might be in need of conservation action ranging from periodic monitoring of populations and threats to the species and its habitat, to the necessity for listing as threatened or endangered. Implies no legal protection.

Threatened species: An animal or plant species likely to become endangered within the foreseeable future throughout all or a significant portion of its range.

Endangered Species

The United States and the Endangered Species Act

The management of threatened and endangered species is a critical component of the work done by wildlife and fisheries biologists worldwide. Although wildlife management's early focus was game management, state and federal agencies share a history of working together, along with non-governmental organizations (NGOs such as the National Audubon Society, World Wildlife Fund, Wildlife Conservation Society, or The Nature Conservancy), to support the recovery of species of conservation concern. The establishment of the Lacey Act (1900), the Migratory Bird Treaty Act (1918), and the Endangered Species Act (1966) are examples of early success stories that affected non-game species. The latter is the most significant legislation in the US to address conservation of threatened species.

In 1966, congress passed the **Endangered Species Preservation Act**. This legislation gave the Secretary of the Interior (the federal department housing nine bureaus including Bureau of Indian Affairs, US Fish and Wildlife Service, National Park Service, and US Geological Survey) the responsibility to determine which wildlife were facing extinction in the US. The act also called for the Department of Agriculture and the Department of Defense to protect listed species through habitat preservation. The Department of the Interior was authorized and encouraged to prioritize funds for research and habitat acquisition to support the new list of native species, and it gave the National Wildlife Refuge system the mandate to serve as protection areas for species of conservation concern. However, the 1966 act provided no funding for these activities, and it provided only limited protection for animals on the list.

The **Endangered Species Conservation Act** of 1969 built upon the Endangered Species Preservation Act of 1966. The new legislation prohibited the import of endangered animals and animal products from other countries. The 1966 act only applied to native species in the US, but the 1969 act included animals faced with worldwide extinction, and subspecies were allowed to be listed as **biologically significant units**. In many ways, the 1969 act served as a type of extension of the regulations in the Lacey Act of 1900, which prohibited interstate transport of illegally taken animals in the US.

The 1969 act also provided up to $15 million for habitat acquisition to support species on the list. Further, the act provided the framework to support the implementation of the **Convention on International Trade in Endangered Species** of Wild Fauna and Flora (**CITES**) in the United States—an agreement between 125 countries to protect approximately 30,000 plants and animals, with specific emphasis on trade. Still, the 1969 act only provided limited protection for species on the list of species of concern.

The **Endangered Species Act** (**ESA**) of 1973 extended coverage of the list of protected species to plants. The ESA also recognized protection of **critical habitats**, specific areas that could be designated as important to a species' recovery and, as such, could have restriction of specific activities (e.g., recreational use, logging, or mining).

The policymakers who wrote the ESA further defined the biologically significant units that could be listed, which went beyond the species and sub-species designation. For example, isolated populations such as the Florida panther could be determined to be biologically significant as **distinct population segments**. The ESA also defined what it means to be threatened and endangered. Although the definitions are short and simple, there is a lack of clear biological foundation:

- **Endangered**: faced with extinction
- **Threatened**: likely to become endangered

International Conservation Policy and Regulation

Beyond the United States, efforts to protect species also began in the 1960s. International trade in wildlife products, such as beaver pelts and bird feathers, occurred early in the history of the United States. In modern times, it is critical to have international partners and regulations to protect species because of pressures from the legal trade and illegal trade of animal products and live animals. Two major international efforts support conservation of threatened and endangered species at the international level.

The International Union for Conservation of Nature (**IUCN**; full legal name: International Union for Conservation of Nature and Natural Resources) established the IUCN Red List of Threatened Species in 1964. The international equivalent of the status levels found in the Endangered Species Act in the US includes status levels from least concern to critically endangered. The Red List is supported by scientific input, which includes consideration of specific probability statements used to define status levels (e.g., vulnerable: ≥10% chance of extinction in the wild in the next 100 years; see chapter 8). The list is used by conservation organizations around the world to set priorities for research and protection of species.

The **Convention on International Trade in Endangered Species** (**CITES**) **of Wild Fauna and Flora** is a multilateral treaty to protect endangered plants and animals (Figure 9.1). It originated in 1963 as a resolution at meetings of the IUCN and became active in 1975. Similar in purpose to the Lacey Act in the US, the aim of CITES is to ensure that international trade of plants and animals does not threaten wild populations. Regular meetings of CITES' Conference of the Parties allow decisions to be made to update the status of species as petitioned by members. CITES uses levels of endangerment to classify protected species (CITES 1983):

- **Appendix I:** Species threatened with extinction; trade permitted only in exceptional circumstances (e.g., red panda, shortnose sturgeon, all *Cheloniidae* species of sea turtles).

FIGURE 9.1 A graduate student in nature conservation examines animal parts and products for sale at a street market in Bangkok, Thailand. Photo by the author.

- **Appendix II:** Species not necessarily threatened with extinction, but for which survival depends on regulated trade (scalloped hammerhead shark, African penguin, guanaco).
- **Appendix III:** Species protected in at least one country that has requested international assistance for controlling trade (Colombia: raspy river stingray, India: golden jackal, United States: hellbender).

QUICK COMPREHENSION CHECK

How many "endangered species acts" were passed in the United States before our current legislation from 1973?

How might you define "endangered" and "threatened" in more specific terms?

Getting on the List

The first management decision to be made for a threatened species is whether to list the species as threated or endangered. The Endangered Species Act requires the designation of threatened or endangered when a species is at risk because of any of the following factors:

- Present or threatened destruction, modification, or curtailment of its habitat or range
- Over-utilization of the species for commercial, recreational, scientific, or educational purposes

- Disease or predation
- Inadequacy of existing regulatory mechanisms
- Other natural or manmade factors affecting its continued existence

Two federal agencies are designated to handle petitions to list a species under the ESA: Department of the Interior acting through the US Fish and Wildlife Service (USFWS) and Department of Commerce acting through the National Oceanic and Atmospheric Administration's (NOAA) National Marine Fisheries Service (NMFS). Anyone may petition the Secretary of Interior or the Secretary of Commerce to list a species under the ESA, including individual citizens, conservation groups, city governments, county governments, or state wildlife agencies. The Secretary of the Interior and the Secretary of Commerce also have emergency powers to begin the listing process without a petition, if necessary (Figure 9.2).

Once a petition is received, either the Secretary of the Interior or the Secretary of Commerce review the petition. The Secretary of the Interior and the USFWS have jurisdiction over a species decision for terrestrial and freshwater species, and the Secretary of Commerce and the NMFS typically have jurisdiction over marine and anadromous species. Some situations (e.g., sea turtles) necessitate that the agencies share jurisdiction.

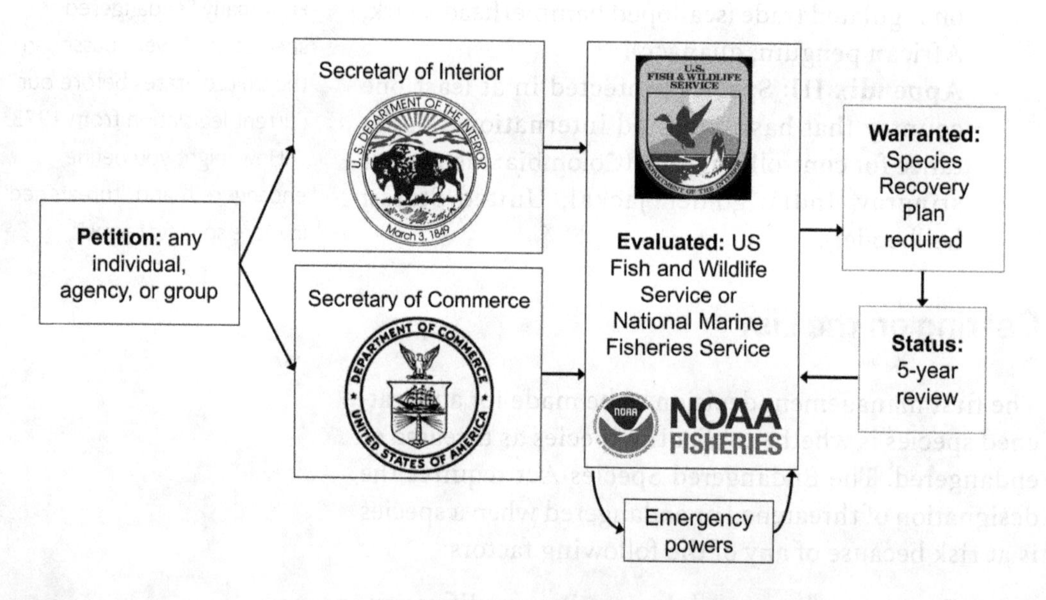

FIGURE 9.2 Flow diagram of the listing process for a species of conservation concern under the Endangered Species Act. Two federal agencies (USFWS or NOAA: NMFS) are used to consider petitions and declare warrant for listing. Each listed species has a 5-year status review.

Either agency then follows the steps below to determine if listing a species is warranted, once receiving a petition:

- A 90-day review period of investigation by the agency determines if the petition presents substantial information that the petitioned action may be warranted.
- Issuance of a negative or positive 90-day finding in the *Federal Register*, the official journal of the federal government with public notices.
- After a positive 90-day finding, the agency begins to compile a Status Review Document for the species, which will include the best available information on the species' biology, ecology, population trends, and existing or potential threats. During this time, the public has opportunity for input of relevant scientific or commercial information.
- Within one year (12 months) from receipt of the petition, the agency publishes a 12-month finding in the *Federal Register* as to whether the petition is warranted. A positive 12-month finding is also known as a Proposed Rule and will state which status is deemed appropriate. Public comments on the Proposed Rule are solicited on the proposal to list the species as threatened or endangered. One or more public hearings may be held at this time.
- Within one year of the Proposed Rule, the agency publishes a Final Rule. If the rule is positive, the species will be added to the list of threatened or endangered species.

Once a species has been ruled to meet the requirements to be listed, the responsible agency drafts a Species Recovery Plan which describes the process that biologists feel would lead to the species recovery, and eventual de-listing. Critical habitats will be established in the Recovery Plan, and the plan is important for on-the-ground wildlife managers, as it describes the goals and objectives relevant for management for the species and its habitats.

In addition to petitions to add species, the agencies also receive petitions to reclassify listed species from threatened to endangered or from endangered to threatened. A petition may be used to request the delisting of a species, thereby removing it from ESA protection. Finally, a petition may be used to revise an existing critical habitat designation. All forms of petitions go through the same process.

Wildlife biologists play many roles in the decision to list a species of concern. Population biologists determine if species are declining and identify causes of declines. Ecologists define a species niche and interactions with other species or the environment. What characteristics of its life history make it susceptible to endangerment? Geneticists can make determinations regarding what genetic material we would be conserving if we placed a subspecies or isolated population on the list. Would listing contribute to conserving a biological unit that is genetically unique? Habitat biologists work to assess habitats and make plans for habitat restoration, if needed.

It should be clear, however, that successful recoveries depend on more than biological information. In many cases, endangered species are tightly woven into controversies that involve economic effects of restricting activities (e.g., halting fishing, stopping logging practices, changing irrigation patterns). So, conservation biology involves more than biology! It includes intense input from sociologists, planners, economists and more.

Units of Conservation

The Endangered Species Act provides a listing of animals and plants within specific units of conservation. That is, a species, or segment of a species, can be listed if it qualifies under these criteria:

- **Species**
- **Subspecies**: One subspecies can be listed while other subspecies of the same species remain unprotected.
- **Distinct population segment**: A designation established by the US Congress in the ESA of 1973, which does not have a strict biological definition. Congress required these criteria for distinct segments: (1) discreteness of the population segment in relation to the remainder of the species to which it belongs, (2) the significance of a distinct population segment to the species to which it belongs; and (3) the population segment's conservation status.
    - **Evolutionary significant units:** An approach used primarily by the National Marine Fisheries Service to classify distinct population segments using a definition of groups of organisms that are substantially reproductively isolated and an important component in the evolutionary legacy of the species (Waples 1991).
    - **Management unit:** Terminology often used in Species Recovery Plans to describe an area of critical habitat, often described as a geographically designated population (isolated units) based on population exchanges of individuals.

Any attempt to classify groups of individuals below the species level is bound to encounter controversy (Waples 1998). On one hand, if a subset of individuals within a species is experiencing population declines in a distinct location, there is cause to believe that some component of the ecosystem is being challenged in such a manner to cause the local population to be at risk. Conservation measures would seem prudent and listing under the ESA is a mechanism to use for that purpose. However, those conservation measures often mean restricting use of habitat for purposes that may benefit humans, such as mining or agriculture. If the species as a whole is not threatened with extinction, conservation efforts at a local scale may be questioned by those affected by potential regulations.

A further complication is the designation of subspecies by "splitter" scientists (those who use differences to create new sub-species or species categories) or the collapse of subspecies into a single species by "lumper" scientists (those who assume differences are not as important as similarities among species). The tug-of-war between lumpers and splitters has been occurring ever since humans started to categorize the diversity of plants and animals into species groups. Even with genetic evidence, there are many situations in which there are no easy answers. As examples, ornithologists are known to frequently debate subspecies status, while fisheries and marine mammal biologists often debate the boundaries of distinct population segments.

Consider these examples of conservation of biological units lower than the species level:

> An example of a controversial ***subspecies*** designation under the ESA is the coastal California gnatcatcher (*Polioptila californica californica*), a subspecies of the California gnatcatcher (*Polioptila californica*). California gnatcatchers live in sage-scrub habitat in southwestern California and the Baja Peninsula of Mexico. The coastal subspecies (shown in Fig. 9.3A) is currently listed as threatened under the ESA. Habitat for the species is also where the rich and famous wish to build large ocean view houses, and land values may exceed $3 million per acre. Each gnatcatcher's territory is 10–15 acres, so the space for a pair of birds comes at a large economic cost, and this cost has led to a debate over whether the coastal California gnatcatcher is a true subspecies. The range of the California gnatcatcher is fairly continuous down the coast, and scientists originally noticed morphological and song differences between birds along the range. Various studies all suggested that the coastal California group of birds should be a subspecies. Today, California gnatcatchers are quite common in the Baja Peninsula, and it is only in California that their habitat has declined to the point that the birds are becoming locally rare. This rarity and their subspecies designation were enough to provide a spot on the endangered species list. However, geneticists provided evidence to suggest that gnatcatchers in California were not distinct from gnatcatchers in Baja (Zink et al. 1998, 2013). To date, the US Fish and Wildlife Service's review process has not delisted the coastal California gnatcatcher, suggesting that the genetic evidence is not strong enough to merit a change in the status of the subspecies.
>
> At least nine **population segments** of Chinook salmon (shown in Fig. 9.3B) are currently listed under the ESA as evolutionary significant units (ESU), based on the population's subdivisions caused by their fidelity to natal coastal rivers for spawning. The use of evolutionary significant units by the National Marine Fisheries Service has been opposed by some on the basis of the difficulty for objectively defining exactly what makes a population segment an ESU (Pennock and Dimmick 1997, Waples 1998).

Beluga whales in Cook Inlet on the southern coast of Alaska are a **distinct population segment** listed as endangered (shown in Fig. 9.3C). NOAA Fisheries has identified five stocks of beluga whales along coastal Alaska that are each unique and isolated from one another genetically and/or physically by migration routes and preferred habitats (O'Corry-Crowe et al. 1997). The other four stocks are protected under the Marine Mammal Protection Act but are not considered threatened or endangered. Similarly, the olive ridley turtle is listed as a threatened species throughout its range, except for Mexico's Pacific Coast population, which is a distinct population segment listed as endangered.

The Cumberland darter (shown in Fig. 9.3D) has nine **management units** designated in its recovery plan, and biologists consider them to be distinct population segments. The designation was made based on geography and knowledge of the species' range rather than genetic data. Not much is known about the Cumberland darter's specific habitat requirements. As shown in the figure below, the species typically occupies shallow pools or runs with gentle current over sand or sand-covered bedrock substrates with areas of gravel or debris in lower gradient streams.

FIGURE 9.3 Examples of species considered under the Endangered Species Act as conservation units lower than the species level: A) coastal California gnatcatcher (USFWS photo), B) Chinook salmon (USFWS photo by Michael Humling), C) beluga whale (NOAA photo), and D) Cumberland darter (Jeremy Shute, Conservation Fisheries, Inc.).

Conservation biologists will continue to use levels of designation lower than the species level as long as it is included in legal definitions in the ESA. The justification for inclusion of population segments and subspecies, regardless of level of genetic uniqueness, is that local rarity is indicative of loss of habitat or other detrimental population dynamic. These local groups of individuals are like a canary in a coal mine—the decline tells us that something is wrong. Thus, proponents of using lower levels of conservation units argue that we should use the ESA to force habitat restoration and protection. Alternatively, opponents in the conservation community would argue that ESA protection and limited funds available for recovery of species would be better spent on other species. Further, members of the public that have their activities (farming, mining, etc.) curtailed through the ESA restrictions are less than sympathetic when evidence suggests the protected population is not unique genetically from other thriving population segments.

These controversies are part of the decision process faced by scientists and managers implementing the Endangered Species Act. It is clear that wildlife biologists play a significant role in providing data to make defendable decisions for threatened and endangered species. It should also be obvious that defendable decision processes are important in situations that involve controversy!

The ESA Species Recovery Plan

Membership on the list of threatened and endangered species in the United States carries specific requirements that are intended to lessen the risk of endangerment and extinction, with the eventual goal of delisting a species. The Species Recovery Plan is at the heart of this planning process, and a Recovery Plan is required for all listed species.

Funding a Recovery Plan

Although the ESA requires establishment of a Species Recovery Plan for listed species, the ESA does not provide for complete or even partial funding for each species' recovery plan. Decisions for funding are at two levels, given a certain amount of funding provided in an annual budget by Congress: (1) which species should receive funding for recovery, and (2) how much of the proposed funding level in the recovery plan for each species should be allocated?

In 1995, the top 50 species of a possible 575 listed plants and animals received 86% of all funding, and 40% of listed species received no funding (Simon et al. 1995). An assessment indicated that it was more likely for a species to receive funding if a high level of conflict with human activities existed. Other considerations, such as genetic uniqueness or extinction risk level did not explain the presence or absence of funding. A larger proportion of mammals, birds, and fish received funding than other taxonomic groups, perhaps because of their role in conflict situations.

Disconnect between species' needs and funding for recovery has resulted in concerns that the mere presence of a Species Recovery Plan has not been helpful in species recovery. Australian scientists, for example, reported that the lack of ability to track expenses allocated for recovery of endangered species limited their ability to demonstrate how recovery planning impacted threatened and endangered species. Australian taxpayers, like taxpayers in the United States, have potential to lose confidence in federal ability to support recovery of species of concern when evidence of success is not available (Bottrill et al. 2011).

A study of 243 endangered species in the United States with recovery plans and budget expense reports suggested that a higher level of funding may lead to improvements in species status (Miller et al. 2002). A team of scientists categorized species as improving, stable, declining, or uncertain with regard to population trends. Species with improving populations had received an average of approximately 38% of requested funds from their recovery plan, while species with declining status had received approximately 15% of their requested funds. Although it is also possible that decision-makers were more kind with funding levels to species perceived to be improving, funding levels were similar for species with high or low potential for recovery as stated in the recovery plan used for the initial funding decisions.

The importance of the level of funding may vary by the type of threat facing a species (chapter 8). Within the same group of 243 endangered species, funding was especially important for recovery of species threatened by disturbances caused by logging, mining, and agriculture as well as those threatened by loss of habitat through development and human-caused mortality such as hunting or pesticide use. Higher funding levels did not result in higher recovery of species threatened by exotic species or altered disturbance regimes such as a lack of fire dynamics (Miller et al. 2002).

Seeking increased funding, therefore, may be an advantageous strategy to purchase or protect habitat for species that have lost habitat to mining or agriculture. However, some species' risks are not alleviated by higher funding levels, such as species threatened by invasive aquatic species, which are very difficult to control and cause expenditures to be less effective. Such information is extremely useful to decision-makers as they decide how to use limited budgetary resources. Threats to species vary spatially in the United States and other countries (Figure 9.3).

Structure of a Species Recovery Plan: Northern Spotted Owl

The structure of a Species Recovery Plan is instructive as we seek to understand how the ESA supports species recovery. We can examine the recovery plan for the northern

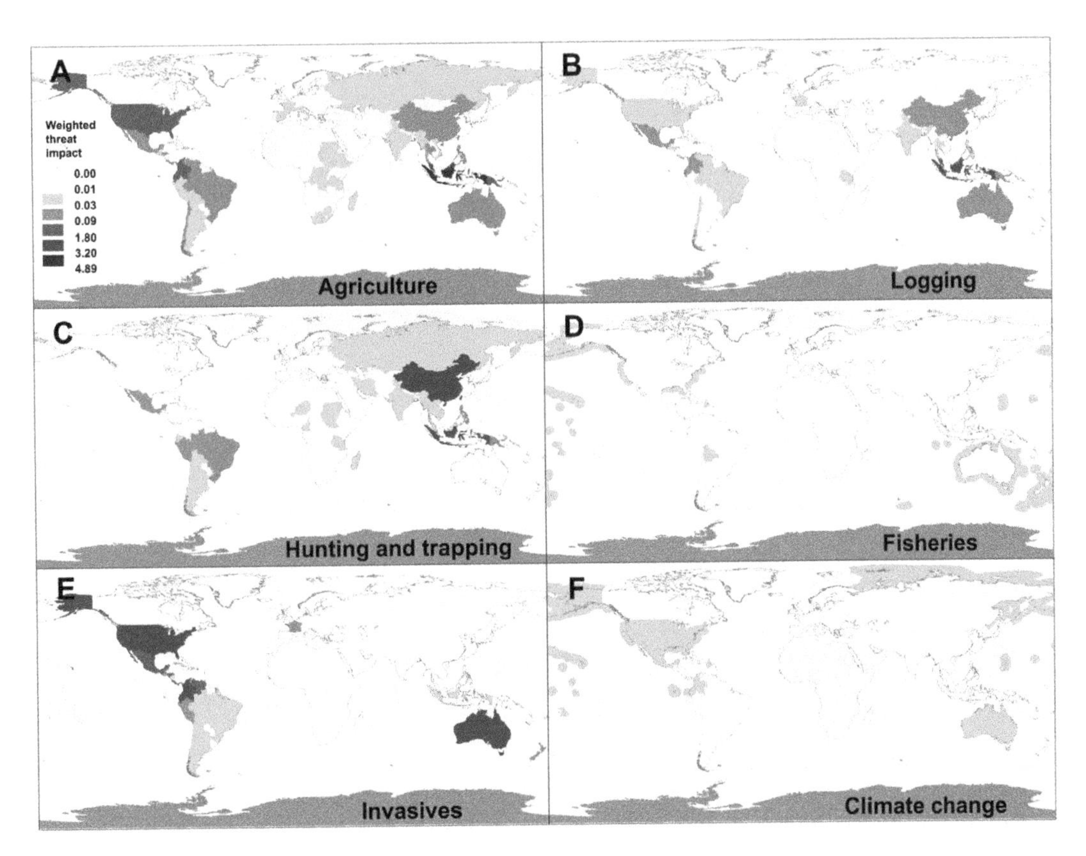

FIGURE 9.4 Contribution by country of six threats to the trends in the global conservation status of vertebrates. Shading indicates the weighted impact (darker = greater contribution to threat) of each threat type to the deterioration in global species conservation status, across countries. Reprinted from Rodrigues et al. (2014), Open Access publication.

spotted owl (Figure 9.5), a species at the heart of controversy with the logging industry in the Pacific Northwest in the United States (US Fish and Wildlife Service 2011).

The Endangered Species Act provides for five threat categories, or **listing conditions**, to consider when evaluating a species for listing:

- The present or threatened destruction, modification, or curtailment of the species' habitat or range
- Overutilization for commercial, scientific, or educational purposes
- Disease or predation
- Inadequacy of existing regulatory mechanisms
- Other natural or manmade factors affecting its continued existence

The document containing the recovery plan for the northern spotted owl begins with the current status of the species including the date of listing under the ESA, which occurred in 1990 as a threatened species for the owl. The plan also lists specific

FIGURE 9.5 Northern spotted owl. USFWS photo, public domain.

QUICK COMPREHENSION CHECK

Compare the threats listed for the northern spotted owl to the five threat categories used by the ESA as considerations for all species. Which of the five categories were seen as critical for the owl?

reasons for listing for the owl from the five categories, above. These threats must be reduced or eliminated before delisting:

- The widespread loss of spotted owl habitat across the spotted owl's range.
- The inadequacy of existing regulatory mechanisms to conserve the spotted owl.
- Competition from the barred owl (*Strix varia*) poses a significant and complex threat to the spotted owl.

We now have our justification: evidence suggests that the species would be at risk of becoming endangered without federal support. Next, the recovery plan lists the species' habitat requirements:

> Scientific research and monitoring indicate spotted owls generally rely on mature and old-growth forests because these habitats contain the structures and characteristics required for nesting, roosting, and foraging. Although spotted owls may disperse through highly fragmented forested areas, the stand-level and landscape-level attributes of forests needed to facilitate successful dispersal have not been thoroughly evaluated or described.

When will we delist the northern spotted owl? Recovery plans then outline a **strategy** to be used to achieve delisting. In the case of the northern spotted owl, the strategies, which are action items, include:

1. Completion of a range-wide habitat modeling tool
2. Habitat conservation and active forest restoration
3. Barred owl management
4. Research and monitoring

The **objectives** of the northern spotted owl recovery plan are succinctly stated as:

- Spotted owl populations are sufficiently large and distributed such that the species no longer requires listing under the ESA.
- Adequate habitat is available for spotted owls and will continue to exist to allow the species to persist without the protection of the ESA.
- The effects of threats have been reduced or eliminated such that spotted owl populations are stable or increasing and spotted owls are unlikely to become threatened again in the foreseeable future.

The last step in stating how the northern spotted owl can be delisted is to describe the objectives as measurable criteria (chapter 3), which can be important during legal proceedings that can arise during work with threatened and endangered species:

> **Recovery Criterion One:** ***Stable Population Trend*:** The overall population trend of spotted owls throughout the range is stable or increasing over ten years, as measured by a statistically reliable monitoring effort.
>
> **Recovery Criterion Two:** ***Adequate Population Distribution*:** Spotted owl subpopulations within each province (i.e., recovery unit) (excluding the Willamette Valley Province) achieve viability, as informed by the HexSim population model or some other appropriate quantitative measure.
>
> **Recovery Criterion Three:** ***Continued Maintenance and Recruitment of Spotted Owl Habitat*:** The future range-wide trend in spotted owl nesting/roosting and foraging habitat is stable or increasing throughout the range, from the date of Revised Recovery Plan approval, as measured by effectiveness monitoring efforts or other reliable habitat monitoring programs.
>
> **Recovery Criterion Four:** ***Post-delisting Monitoring*:** To monitor the continued stability of the recovered spotted owl, a post-delisting monitoring plan has been developed and is ready for implementation within the states of Washington, Oregon, and California, as required in section 4(g)(1) of the ESA.

The recovery plan for northern spotted owl is 277 pages in length. Each strategy and recovery criterion is explained in detail, and an adaptive management plan (chapter 3) is outlined.

Throughout the document, biologists differentiate between **proximate** and **ultimate** causal factors in a framework that will allow an effective response.

Proximate factors, the most obvious and immediate factors causing decline of northern spotted owls, are:

- Logging, which reduces habitat
- Fragmentation of forests, which affects the structure of the landscape and dynamics of movement for the owls
- Barred owls, which have started to compete with spotted owls

The proximate factors are important, but it is also important for conservation planners to recognize that the proximate factors are a result of **ultimate factors**, the underlying or root causes of the problem. In the case of the spotted owl, society has a much higher demand for timber products, which has caused the land use and economic structure of the region to change. An effective recovery will not move forward without consideration of the ultimate factors. In many cases, the ultimate factors involve impacts of human populations and societal dynamics.

The last section of a Species Recovery Plan is to list the proposed recovery actions, detailed steps to be taken to support the species. The Species Recovery Plan for northern spotted owls lists 34 actions. Some actions are organizational and agency-oriented in nature (establishing working groups, for example), others are targeted at habitat protection and improvement, and others may be focused on the species' biology through direct population management. It is easy to see evidence for the principle of the three-legged stool of wildlife management (chapter 1): managing people, habitat, or wildlife. Some selected actions for northern spotted owl:

- **Establish** an inter-organizational spotted owl working group ("NSO Work Group") to oversee the implementation of the recovery plan.
- **Continue monitoring** the population trend of spotted owls to determine if the population is decreasing, stationary, or increasing.
- **Establish** a network of Managed Owl Conservation Areas (MOCAs) that are of sufficient size and spacing to achieve long-term recovery of spotted owls.
- **Manage** habitat-capable lands within MOCAs to produce the highest amount and highest quality spotted owl habitat the lands are capable of producing.
- **Establish** a comprehensive incentives program to develop creative opportunities for non-federal landowners to engage in management strategies consistent with the recovery objectives.
- **Monitor** for avian diseases (e.g., West Nile Virus, avian influenza) and address as necessary.

- **Create and implement** an outreach strategy to educate the public about the threat of barred owls to spotted owls.
- **Manage** the negative effects of barred owls on spotted owls.
- **Develop** a post-listing monitoring plan ready for implementation with the states of Washington, Oregon, and California.

The recovery actions are comprehensive and purposeful. A working group will bring all of the agencies (state, federal, regional, count, and/or city) together to coordinate use of their public lands and the individual efforts of each agency. Monitoring is critical to future decision-making (chapter 3). Owls need forests that are not fragmented, so a network of public lands that is protected for owls is important. Because the US Fish and Wildlife Service is responsible for the recovery plan, the recovery actions show evidence that the core area to be managed for owls will be federal lands managed by federal agencies such as the US Forest Service, National Park Service, Bureau of Land Management, or US Fish and Wildlife Service. However, the region has many acres of private land owned and managed by individuals or timber companies. Because the owl will most likely not recover completely if we rely only on federal lands, the recovery actions call for engagement of private landowners with monetary incentives.

The recovery plan ends with a **projected timeline** for recovery, which is needed for a second additional component: the **cost** for the efforts of delisting. For the northern spotted owl, biologists projected that if all actions are implemented and effective, the species could be delisted in 30 years at a cost of $489.2 million.

Managing for Recovery

Captive Species Management

The United States has 214 zoos and aquariums, accredited by the Association of Zoos and Aquariums, and these facilities house approximately 800,000 animals from 6,000 species. Approximately 1,000 of those species are threatened or endangered species, and the AZA members spend $216 million in support of conservation projects each year.

Zoos are private ventures, which need to generate income to support their staff, feed animals, build and maintain facilities, and support conservation efforts. Almost 200 million people visit zoos and aquariums annually, which is 50 million more people than view professional baseball, basketball, hockey, and football combined each year in the United States.

Modern zoos are transitioning from being collections of exotic creatures that are meant to astound and entertain to well-managed collections of critical species intended to support education, research, and conservation goals. The transition has

FIGURE 9.6 California condor eggs in incubation as part of the captive breeding program at Los Angeles Zoo, in coordination with Hopper Mountain National Wildlife Refuge. USFWS, public domain photo.

been slow, as zoos still have the need to house individuals that will attract visitors. Worldwide, the percentage of animals in zoo collections that are threatened or endangered species are 8% for birds, 23% for amphibians, 27% for mammals, and 40% for reptiles (Conde et al. 2011).

When an animal is taken from the wild and placed in captivity, it transitions from a status of ***in situ*** to ***ex situ***: literally "in position" to "out of position." The decision to place an animal in captivity is an example of a complex decision, and is normally taken only in specific situations to increase the chance of survival for the individual or the species. Worldwide intervention by zoos has prevented the extinction of species such as California condor (Figure 9.6), the European bison, and the Przewalski's horse. Of the 33 animal species classified as extinct in the wild by the IUCN Red List, 31 species are housed and actively bred in zoos. Examples include the scimitar-horned oryx and Wyoming toad.

Of course, all else equal, conservation biologists would rather conservation occur *in situ* than *ex situ*. Both in situ and ex situ efforts have context-specific benefits, risks, and limits (Snyder et al. 1996, Balmford et al. 2011) as explored in Table 9.1.

Some conservation planners are hesitant to list *ex situ* conservation strategies as an option for decision-makers, as they believe that moving animals away from conflict-ridden situations may be a politically acceptable compromise to relieve conflict but enable continued ecosystem degradation such as habitat loss to agriculture or

TABLE 9.1 ***Comparisons of critical considerations for success of ex situ and in situ conservation programs***

	TYPE OF CONSERVATION PROGRAM	
CONSIDERATION	EX SITU	IN SITU
Primary concerns	• Individual must adapt to artificial environments or diets. • Reintroductions are difficult, and success rates vary by species and circumstance.	• Animals will be left in environment that has led to their current threatened state. • Suitable habitat and an area of protection needs to be identified and delimited from monitoring. • Habitat may need to be restored.
Expense and logistics	• Expense of housing animals and establishing breeding programs is high. • High level of coordination needed for removal of animals to captive facilities and establishment of breeding program among facilities.	• Property must be acquired if public lands are not already supporting the species. • A legal framework must be developed to control human activities, and law enforcement must be engaged to enforce the rules on human activity (including poaching).
Animal behaviors	• Animals may become domesticated and lose fear of humans, which may limit the opportunity for reintroduction to the wild. • Abnormal behaviors may develop in captivity, which may affect potential for reintroduction.	• Leaving individuals in the wild allows for normal behaviors and avoids concerns of modifications of behavior in captive facility.
Intraspecific competition, predation	• Removal to captive facility removes this concern.	• Species that compete with or prey upon the species of concern may need to be managed and potentially eliminated from the site.
Genetic diversity	• Breeding may be managed and planned in captive population. • Breeding population may be limited by space constraints in zoos or aquaria, so breeding population may be smaller than *in situ* population potential.	• Translocation of individuals to other sites may need to be considered to improve genetic diversity. • The number of alternative sites available for some species may be limited.
Disease transmission	• Monitoring of disease is easier in captivity. • Disease transmission, including human-transmitted diseases, is a concern in captive facilities.	• Monitoring of diseases in the wild may be difficult, and disease outbreaks may be disastrous for small populations.

QUICK COMPREHENSION CHECK

Review Table 9.1. What do you see as 3–4 of the most important considerations in the decision whether to remove a species from the wild to a captive breeding program?

development. Imagine, for example, a representative of the logging industry participating in a public meeting regarding the listing of the northern spotted owl: "We can continue our logging to support our economy, because we can raise that owl in zoos."

People may oppose *ex situ* conservation on ethical grounds (chapter 5), suggesting that they believe it to be more ethical for a species to be allowed to go extinct rather than expose it to the risks and confinement associated with captivity. Some even argue that a species that exists in a zoo is not really "alive." As such, the exploration of captive breeding may create an ethical dilemma to be discussed and evaluated (chapter 5).

Others are concerned that *ex situ* conservation seems to favor the hairy and scary species. Do we use our captive facilities to conserve species that have highest priority for conservation, or is our selection for the limited spaces in facilities a biased process?

These arguments against *ex situ* conservation actions have merit to consider as we work through complex decision processes for species of conservation concern. However, *ex situ* management of species allows for a variety of actions to increase reproductive output that are impossible in the wild. Individual animals with good levels of nutrition will often reproduce more times per year and have larger clutches or litters than their wild counterparts. Captive situations allow for artificial insemination or embryo transfer or actual movement of animals to facilitate planned breeding programs for maximum genetic diversity. And, lessons are often learned in zoos from research that may benefit *in situ* conservation efforts.

Species Survival Plans

The Association of Zoos and Aquariums developed **Species Survival Plans** in 1981 to support the coordination of breeding programs in facilities holding captive animals. Species Survival Plans are specific to captive animals, and they are not to be confused with Species Recovery Plans developed by federal agencies for threatened and endangered species under the ESA.

Species Survival Plans are one part of a three-part system used by accredited zoos and aquariums to manage breeding of captive animals. **Taxon Advisory Groups** are assembled to provide input on groups of species, such as amphibians, tapirs, small carnivores, and wild cattle and camelids. Some advisory groups cover entire taxonomic orders of animals, while others cover families or functional groups (e.g., raptors, freshwater fishes). The Taxon Advisory Group develops Species Survival Plans for species within its purview, and the **Studbook Program** records all breeding plans and activities and keeps pedigrees of each individual for a species in captivity. The Studbook Program also proposes how planned breeding will take place—either transfer of animals or artificial insemination with sperm transferred to other facilities.

There are currently more than 500 Species Survival Programs, each managed by their corresponding Taxon Advisory Groups. Each Species Survival Plan includes a **Breeding and Transfer Plan** that identifies population management goals and recommendations to ensure the sustainability of a healthy, genetically diverse, and demographically varied population of captive animals at accredited facilities.

Species Survival Plans were developed to bring zoos and aquariums together to leverage space and breeding animals found at different sites, rather than individual facilities acting as isolated islands with their own small populations of animals.

Another function of the Species Survival Plan is to establish priorities and resolve potential conflicts between zoos. For example, consider two zoos that house critical collections of eastern lowland gorillas with large males that are often named and are well-known local attractions. A third smaller zoo has a collection of only three gorillas. It might accomplish a genetic objective to move one of the males from the larger zoo to the smaller zoo, but the larger zoo may not want to lose an income-generating animal. The Taxon Advisory Group would use the Species Survival Plan to work through that problem with the participating zoos.

QUICK COMPREHENSION CHECK

Describe how a Species Survival Plan uses the Studbook Program and the Breeding and Transfer Plan.

Species Survival Plans often link to the ESA's Species Recovery Plans by integrating plans for eventual reintroduction of individuals to wild populations. In many cases, members of the two planning teams overlap, which is helpful.

Release Programs

Conservation planners may use three types of release programs to meet recovery goals for threatened or endangered species:

- **Reintroduction**: The release of individuals into an area from which the species has disappeared, or has been extirpated.
- **Augmentation:** The release of captive-bred individuals into a population experiencing decline to increase the local population size and/or enhance genetic diversity. Translocation of wild individuals may be used to augment another wild population.
- **Introduction:** The release of captive individuals into an area outside of their native range. Translocation of wild individuals to new sites may also be used.

Reintroduction of wildlife into their native range is a very complex decision process for a wildlife manager. In contrast to a more typical (but still potentially complex) management decision to be made to manage a population already in place, the complete absence of a population requires considerations on multiple fronts (Converse et al. 2013):

- Numbers to release
- Age classes to release
- Sex ratio of released animals
- Temporal pattern of releases
- Spatial pattern of releases
- Numbers for supplemental releases
- Age classes for supplemental releases
- Temporal pattern of supplemental releases
- Spatial pattern of supplemental releases
- Need for harvest or control of the reintroduced population
- Post-release habitat management

Reintroductions involve high levels of risk, and a failure in any one of these actions could potentially erode the success of the reintroduction. The use of a formal decision process (chapter 3) is critical, and the decision team will most likely need to explore the potential consequences of alternatives using a simulation model for the population (chapter 6). Adaptive management (chapter 3) may be effectively used for threatened and endangered species, especially when additional information is

FIGURE 9.7 Release of one of 30 endangered black-footed ferrets onto a private ranch in Colorado in 2013 under the Safe Harbor Agreement process, allowing private and Tribal landowners to volunteer their lands for reintroductions of endangered species without affecting their land-use activities beyond mutually agreed-upon measures.

gathered that may improve the potential to make better decisions to support species (Runge 2011).

An example of a successful use of *ex situ* conservation is the black-footed ferret (Figure 9.7), once considered to be extinct. After being rediscovered when a dog brought a dead ferret to a rancher's doorstep, an outbreak of canine distemper lowered the wild population to 18 individuals. All animals were taken into captivity in an effort to save the species in the context of the disease outbreak. A captive breeding program has been successful, and at least six zoos or breeding centers were involved, which included developing techniques to successfully produce kits that would survive in captivity. In less than ten years since the species was rediscovered, releasable individuals had been produced in captivity, and multiple reintroduced populations have been established since the first release in 1991. Reintroductions occurred in active prairie dog colonies, as ferrets depend on prairie dogs for food. Ferrets also use prairie dog burrows as dens.

The Species Recovery Plan for black-footed ferrets includes a focus on *ex situ* breeding programs including the need to develop capability for artificial insemination in preparation for release at multiple reintroduction sites. Now viable in the wild, the ferret is an example of a species that, at one time, was completely held in captivity.

The story of black-footed ferrets in the United States reads a bit like a soap opera, with peaks of enthusiasm and confidence mixed with valleys of despair and resignation. Such emotions are typical of work with species of conservation concern (Black-footed Ferret Recovery Program 2018).

Black-footed Ferret Recovery Timeline

1851: The species is described by John James Audubon and Rev. John Bachmann, but it not seen again for 26 years.

1964: After thought extinct in the 1950s, a population found in Mellette County, South Dakota and thought to be the last black-footed ferrets.

1967: Black-footed ferrets listed as endangered on the first list of endangered species.

1972: Nine individuals from Mellette County, South Dakota taken into captivity. They produce no kits in captivity.

1974: The last wild ferret in Mellette County dies.

1979: The last captive ferret dies, and the black-footed ferret is thought to be extinct.

1981: Wild ferrets are rediscovered, first by a ranch dog who brings a dead ferret back to his owner in Meeteetse, Wyoming.

1984: The Meeteese population peaks at 129 ferrets.

1985: Fleas at the Meeteese site test positive for sylvatic plague. After debate, mangers capture six ferrets due to the declining population. All six captive individuals die from canine distemper virus. Additional individuals are captured.

1986: The IUCN, US Fish and Wildlife Service, and Wyoming Game and Fish Department design a captive breeding program. New captive animals are bred, but no kits are produced.

1987: The Meeteese wild population dies out, but not before a total of 11 males and 7 females have been captured. These individuals are the only black-footed ferrets on earth, and the species is considered the rarest mammal. Two litters of ferret kits are born at Sybille Wildlife Research Center, marking the first time black-footed ferret kits survive in captivity. The total population of ferrets is now 25.

1989: 78 kits are born, bringing population total to 120.

1991: First release of 49 ferrets in Shirley Basin, Wyoming.

1992: Two wild-born litters reported in Shirley Basin, the first known wild reproduction since the Meeteese population died out.

1994: 228 ferrets were released during 1991–1994 in Shirley Basin, but an outbreak of plague stops releases at the site.

1996: Releases occur in South Dakota and Arizona.

1997: Releases occur in Montana.

1998: A banner year of 452 captive births and 339 kits survive to weaning. 210 individuals are released in a single year. More ferrets exist in the wild than in captivity for the first time since the captive breeding program began.

1999–2009: New release sites in Utah, South Dakota, Montana, Colorado, Mexico, Arizona, and Kansas including several native reservations.

2013: First release occurs on private land using a **Safe Harbor Agreement.**

The use of the **Safe Harbor Agreement** on private lands is an effective tool available under the ESA. This voluntary agreement involves private or other non-federal property owners who assist in the recovery of species listed under the ESA. The US Fish and Wildlife Service or the National Oceanic and Atmospheric Administration provides formal assurance to property owners that, in return for fulfilling the conditions of the Safe Harbor Agreement, the federal agencies will not require any additional or different management activities by the participants without their consent. At the end of the agreement, the land may be returned to the baseline condition when the agreement was signed. In the case of an introduction of a species, the baseline condition of the species in question may be considered to be zero.

For example, a mining company that sets aside a portion of their land to support a species of concern may ask, under the proposed agreement, to continue operations throughout the rest of their property. Although the agreement allows some potential habitat to be developed or used in ways that conflict with the species' needs, the portion of the habitat that is available contributes to the overall recovery of the species. Landowners who agreed to allow reintroduction of black-footed ferrets agreed to set aside specific zones of their ranch (~1,500 acres) for black-tailed prairie dogs and black-footed ferrets. They continued to use their ranch for cattle grazing and other activities as they wished in return for contributing to disease prevention and maintenance of prairie dog colonies needed by the ferrets.

If a rancher wanted to abandon the agreement, the US Fish and Wildlife Service asked that they be able to come trap the ferrets that remained to remove them to another area. The baseline condition of zero ferrets from the beginning of the agreement would then be allowed to resume without penalty. The Safe Harbor Agreement is a valuable tool as human population increases, because it facilitates positive collaborations with private landowners who provide food, mineral, or other resources to support society.

Most releases of black-footed ferrets at reintroduction sites managed by federal agencies were carried out with a designation of **non-essential, experimental**

populations. That is, the released ferrets were not considered threatened or endangered, rather they were officially "non-essential, experimental populations." The US Fish and Wildlife Service may use this designation when reintroducing threatened or endangered species into areas in which they have been extirpated but within their native range. Designation in this manner allows more flexibility when working with local landowners who may be apprehensive about the endangered species spreading from a federal National Wildlife Refuge to their land. The lowered restrictions on current and future land uses may lower barriers in the reintroduction process when stakeholders are apprehensive.

Making Difficult Decisions about T&E Species

The risk categories used in the Endangered Species Act of 1973 (16 USC 1531 et seq.) are "endangered," "threatened," and "not warranted." The act states that a species should be classified as endangered if it "is in danger of extinction in all or a significant portion of its range" and threatened if it "is likely to become endangered within the foreseeable future in all or a significant portion of its range."

Place yourself in the role of the biologists at the US Fish and Wildlife Service or the National Marine Fisheries Service who must incorporate input from monitoring, survey data, expert opinion, and other sources to decide which of the three categories is warranted for a species in a given petition brought before the agency. Not only is there potential for uncertainty or even a lack of useful information for species of conservation concern during this process, but the ESA is written in language that requires some interpretation.

Cummings et al. (2018) identified five common ways in which natural resource professionals may frame the process for assigning species' risk status. As you might guess, the way in which a person frames or views the decision process may affect the outcome of the listing process. Consider the details of the five frames:

Framing Your Role as a T&E Manager

Putting Species in the Right Bin

The literal approach to the job of classifying species is to concentrate on the species and the possible choices and apply a logical approach to make sure the species is placed in the proper category, or bin. Many people using this framing for the task may view the job of classification as extremely important to "get right the first time." We would expect the individual using this framing to examine data thoroughly and potentially err on the side of caution to protect the species.

Three levels of interpretation are required in this framing of the assessment process:

> First, the **metrics to define each risk category must be properly identified**. For example, "danger of extinction" might be interpreted as a relatively high probability of extinction.
>
> Second, the **metrics for definition of risk must be defined in a manner that allows assessment**. Probability of extinction, for example, must be further defined for each risk category: what range of probabilities of extinction do we ascribe to "endangered," "threatened," and "not warranted?"
>
> Third, a subtle but important interpretation is to **establish the costs of wrongly assigning another status to a species**. Biological costs may be incurred if a species is misclassified and is not supported as it should be supported. Societal and real economic costs may result from imposing regulatory burdens in a region where the species' recovery plan is enacted. Conservation costs money to carry out, so creating concern where concern is not warranted is a direct cost to taxpayers.

Doing Right by the Species Over Time

A second approach to framing the task of assigning status level to species of conservation concern is to see the task as recurring over time. If the decision will be revisited periodically, the main answer to determine is what classification for the species is warranted at the present given the available information.

The interpretation tasks are the same for this framing as in the *putting species in the right bin* framing, and costs are similar. However, because the decision is revisited over time, there is less concern over future costs and more concern about present costs. A person using this framing might not be drawn to err on the side of caution, because of the ability to revisit the decision in the near future.

Saving the Most Species on a Limited Budget

The third manner by which to frame the task of categorizing a species of conservation concern is to consider a group of species, or at least consider a single species in the context of many other species. What set of categorizations will result in support in the most cost-effective manner? The individual using this framing process is aware of limited resources available to support species recovery and uses that paradigm to shift classifications of species to allow for distribution of funds in a manner that may constrain the total number of species listed.

Rather than interpreting each species' risk factors for extinction in isolation, the interpretation tasks under this framing may result in quite different objectives, to the point of ignoring some language in the ESA. A person using this manner of framing may try to maximize the number of species that persist into the future, rather than attempt to maximize each species' chances of persistence. Suddenly, the anticipated budgets for recovery (although not available before the listing process is completed and the Species Recovery Plan is developed) are incredibly important, and a biologist might attempt to create a portfolio of species that can be supported within budget constraints. Just as triage as a hospital's emergency room may require some subjective decisions on the fly, a person using this framework may select species based on perceived value relative to cost of recovery. Indeed, critically endangered species that are expected to have a low probability of recovery might remain unlisted under this framing.

Weighing Extinction Risk against Other Objectives

A fourth approach to the decision of classifying species of conservation concern is to consider objectives of extinction risk in tandem with other objectives, such as minimizing impact of regulations on societal costs. Although criticisms of the ESA commonly suggest that consideration of multiple objectives would be preferred, the language in the ESA seems to constrain to making listing classifications "solely on the basis of the best scientific and commercial data available."

A person using this framing would need to create metrics to represent the other objectives, along with the same needs for extinction risk metrics found in the earlier frames. In addition, the objectives would need to be weighted in importance, relative to each other. Although the ESA may not explicitly allow multiple objectives, Cummings et al. (2018) stated that some decisions made during the listing or delisting processes for the gray wolf, polar bear, and greater sage-grouse appeared to be made by individuals who adhered to the multiple objective manner of framing their role in classifying those species. Certainly, each of these were controversial processes, and we can see the potential to be swayed by objectives other than extinction risk in such situations.

Strategic Classification to Advance Conservation

The last approach for species classification is to view the listing process as only one component, albeit important, in a set of negotiated actions among multiple parties, including outside stakeholders. A person using this framing might weight listing outcomes higher if they maximized participation of stakeholders. For example, perhaps listing a species as threatened rather than endangered could allow more regulatory flexibility in future interactions with landowners, which might prove beneficial over the long run for the conservation of the species.

The interpretation needed for this manner of framing the conservation listing task is complex. Not only must the listing team interpret the risk of extinction of the species, but the team must also predict the actions of stakeholders under all three scenarios of listing outcomes (endangered, threatened, not warranted). We might view the interactions under this framing as game theory or a type of negotiation in which the stakeholders have a reason to suggest they would cooperate at higher levels if regulations were limited, for example. Recent high-profile listing decisions, such as greater sage-grouse and New England cottontail, seem to fit this manner of framing (Cumming et al. 2018). In those cases, the US Fish and Wildlife Service made unwarranted findings following commitments to conservation from stakeholders.

Decisions to support species of conservation concern are certainly not made in a vacuum. Biologists must find management actions that have potential to support a species' recovery in the context of our modern world. In chapter 3, we discussed decision-making as a process, and establishment of objectives is the second step in that PrOACT process. Here, we see evidence that the manner in which objectives are framed may have real effects on the outcome of conservation decisions. Given the complexity of the additional decisions to be made as a Species Recovery Plan is developed, it seems critical to establish a common reference for how the listing process should proceed.

The ESA will soon see its 50th year of existence in 2023. In recent years, the ESA has been challenged from a variety of political positions. Management of threatened and endangered species is one of the most critical roles for wildlife managers in the United States and around the world. As the human population grows, there is a high level of certainty that more species will be added to the lists of threatened and endangered species. Thus, the manner in which the ESA is transformed and implemented in the next two decades will be critical to management of the large number of threatened and endangered species in the United States.

WRAPPING UP

Can you explain the petition and listing process for the Endangered Species Act to Gizela as she ponders a salamander of concern in our introductory problem case? What options might she have for action in the future?

Decision-Making on the Ground

A Recovery Plan for the Lesser Prairie-Chicken

The lesser prairie-chicken can be found in the southern portion of the Great Plains, generally from Kansas and to the south. Its cousin, the greater prairie-chicken, is found in the northern plains. Lesser prairie-chickens seem to be more sensitive to habitat fragmentation, energy development, and overgrazing. Lesser prairie-chickens were listed as a threatened species by the US Fish and Wildlife Service in 2014, but removed from that status after a lawsuit. Although public lands such as national parks, national wildlife refuges, or national forests provide a refuge for other threatened or endangered species, the southern Plains has few public lands and most states have >90% ownership by private individuals such as farmers and ranchers.

Lesser prairie-chickens are now found in only a portion of their former range (Figure. 9.8). Given the concern for lesser prairie-chickens and the lack of federal protection, several federal agencies and state wildlife agencies are working together in a Lesser Prairie-Chicken Initiative to support conservation efforts.

FIGURE 9.8 Historic and current range (left) of the lesser prairie-chicken (right) in the southern Great Plains of the US. Map is USFWS public domain image, photo by Larry Lamsa, public domain under Creative Commons license.

APPLICATION, ANALYSIS, SYNTHESIS, AND EVALUATION

Review the US Fish and Wildlife Service's information online for lesser prairie-chickens. What threats appear to be the most critical for the species? Categorize these threats as proximate or ultimate in their nature.

Using the recovery actions listed in this chapter for the northern spotted owl as a guide, develop a list of five recovery actions that should be taken by managers in the southern Great Plains to support lesser prairie-chickens.

Do your proposed actions address proximate or ultimate threats to the lesser prairie-chicken?

Review the history of the listing process for lesser prairie chickens online by searching for the species from this page at Environmental Conservation Online System: https://ecos.fws.gov/ecp/. Compare the decisions made to the five models for framing the listing process in this chapter. What framing system seems to have been used by biologists involved in the listing process for this species? What evidence do you have to support your answer?

Can you or a student team propose an innovative, out-of-the box solution to address concerns with lesser prairie-chickens? What barriers exist to attempting that solution? Who would be on the list of stakeholders for that solution?

Sources of Information and Further Reading

Balmford, A., Kroshko, J., Leader-Williams, N., and Mason, G. "Zoos and captive breeding." *Science 332*, no. 6034 (2011): 1149–1150.

Black-footed Ferret Recovery Program. *History of the Black-footed Ferret: Rediscovery & Second Chances.* 2018. Accessed 21 September 2018: http://blackfootedferret.org/timeline

Bottrill, M. C., Walsh, J. C., Watson, J. E., Joseph, L. N., Ortega-Argueta, A., and Possingham, H. P. "Does recovery planning improve the status of threatened species?" *Biological Conservation 144*, no. 5 (2011): 1595–1601.

CITES. Text of the Convention (1973), as amended in Gaborone in 1983. CITES Secretariat, Geneva Switzerland. 1983. Accessed online 21 October 2018. https://www.cites.org/eng/disc/text.php#I.

Conde, D. A., Flesness, N., Colchero, F., Jones, O. R., and Scheuerlein, A. "Zoos and captive breeding—Response." *Science 332*, no. 6034 (2011): 1150–1151.

Converse, S. J., Moore, C. T., and Armstrong, D. P. "Demographics of reintroduced populations: estimation, modeling, and decision analysis." *The Journal of Wildlife Management 77*, no. 6 (2013): 1081–1093.

Cummings, J. W., Converse, S. J., Smith, D. R., Morey, S., and Runge, M. C. "Implicit decision framing as an unrecognized source of confusion in endangered species classification." *Conservation Biology 32* (2018): 1246–1254.

Miller, J. K., Scott, M. J., Miller, C. R., and Waits, L. P. "The endangered species act: Dollars and sense?" *BioScience 52*, no. 2 (2002): 163–168.

O'Corry-Crowe, G. M., Suydam, R. S., Rosenberg, A., Frost, K. J., and Dizon, A. E. "Phylogeography, population structure and dispersal patterns of the beluga whale Delphinapterus leucas in the western Nearctic revealed by mitochondrial DNA." *Molecular Ecology 6*, no. 10 (1997): 955–970.

Pennock, D. S., and W. W. Dimmick. "Critique of the evolutionarily significant unit as a definition for 'distinct population segments' under the U.S. Endangered Species Act." *Conservation Biology 11* (1997): 611–619.

Rodrigues, A. S., Brooks, T. M., Butchart, S. H., Chanson, J., Cox, N., Hoffmann, M., and Stuart, S. N. "Spatially explicit trends in the global conservation status of vertebrates." *PLoS One 9*, no. 11 (2014): e113934.

Runge, M. C. "An introduction to adaptive management for threatened and endangered species." *Journal of Fish and Wildlife Management 2*, no. 2 (2011): 220–233.

Simon, B. M., Leff, C. S., and Doerksen, H. "Allocating scarce resources for endangered species recovery." *Journal of policy analysis and management 14*, no. 3 (1995): 415–432.

Snyder, N. F., Derrickson, S. R., Beissinger, S. R., Wiley, J. W., Smith, T. B., Toone, W. D., and Miller, B. "Limitations of captive breeding in endangered species recovery." *Conservation biology 10*, no. 2 (1996): 338–348.

US Fish and Wildlife Service. *Revised Recovery Plan for the Northern Spotted Owl* (Strix occidentalis caurina). Portland, OR: US Fish and Wildlife Service, 2011.

Waples, R. S. "Pacific salmon, Oncorhynchus spp., and the definition of 'species' under the Endangered Species Act." *Marine Fisheries Review 53*, no. 3 (1991): 11–22.

Waples, R. S. "Evolutionarily significant units, distinct population segments, and the Endangered Species Act: reply to Pennock and Dimmick." *Conservation Biology 12*, no. 3 (1998): 718–721.

Zink, R. M. and Blackwell, R. C. "Molecular Systematics and Biogeography of Aridland Gnatcatchers (GenusPolioptila) and Evidence Supporting Species Status of the California Gnatcatcher (Polioptila californica)." *Molecular phylogenetics and Evolution 9*, no. 1 (1998): 26–32.

Zink, R. M., Groth, J. G., Vázquez-Miranda, H., and Barrowclough, G. F. "Phylogeography of the California Gnatcatcher (Polioptila californica) using multilocus DNA sequences and ecological niche modeling: Implications for conservation." *The Auk 130*, no. 3 (2013): 449–458.

Image Credits

Fig. 9.2b: Source: https://all-free-download.com/free-vector/download/us-department-of-the-interior_87530.html.

Fig. 9.2c: Copyright © Fry1989 (CC BY-SA 3.0) at https://commons.wikimedia.org/wiki/File:Flag_of_the_United_States_Department_of_Commerce.svg.

Fig. 9.2d: Source: https://commons.wikimedia.org/wiki/File:US-FWS-logo.png.

Fig. 9.2e: Source: https://commons.wikimedia.org/wiki/File:NOAA_Fisheries_logo_vertical.png.

Fig. 9.3a: Source: https://www.fws.gov/cno/newsroom/featured/2016/Orange_County_20th_Anniversary/images/CAGN-male.jpg.

Fig. 9.3b: Source: https://www.fisheries.noaa.gov/feature-story/endangered-salmon-california-very-measured-sip-cold-water.

Fig. 9.3c: Source: https://www.mmc.gov/sections/species-profile/.

Fig. 9.3d: Source: https://defendersblog.org/2013/04/coal-mining-drives-decline-of-freshwater-fish/cumberland_darter-usfws/.

Fig. 9.4: Source: https://journals.plos.org/plosone/article?id=10.1371/journal.pone.0113934.

Fig. 9.5: Source: https://www.flickr.com/photos/usfwspacific/4948984904.

Fig. 9.6: Source: https://www.flickr.com/photos/usfws_pacificsw/25866661580/in/photolist-4poY9q-7cZW4U-9JN6JZ-CrTc8S-BWBjdH-CU14DP-BWBrv8-CJsc2u-CLGKYv-CrT4kh-FpKpiNmroDiC-YpPxCw-mrmnYJ-mrkmUT-mrgatc-mrkrf6-mrkgLg-mrjsbB-mrh9eB-mrnZTs-mrk-bu4-mriWtu-mrhbiD-mriTic-mrmHuh-mr.

Fig. 9.7: Source: https://www.flickr.com/photos/usfwsmtnprairie/10596149535.

Fig. 9.8a: Source: United States Fish and Wildlife Service.

Fig. 9.8b: Copyright © Larry Lamsa (CC by 2.0) at https://www.flickr.com/photos/larry1732/5644328619/in/photolist-bi6MjB-5T5v4B-TspsMD-T4Qg9f-TAd9HS-9APzny-SpWutR-E63g6L-Dj5ZoZ-pp41mc-bi6Mii-Ee9Kms-x1Xq2F-cHRZN5-9ALEfF-9APyQu-GCEA88-SpW9aK-Dj62iF-DG-ZvBV-SpYsma-EgtNU8-SpWYZt-Dj6bTx-nAEPfQ-NNtAWS-DiKDBJ-D.

SECTION V

Over-Abundant Species Management

CHAPTER TEN

Introduced and Invasive Species Management

Learning Outcomes

After participating in learning experiences related to this chapter, students should be able to:

- Contrast concepts of introduced species and invasive species.
- Provide examples of how invasive species can have negative impacts on ecosystems.
- Describe how management of invasive species is a complex task.
- Differentiate the alternative management strategies of prevention, eradication, containment, and mitigation.
- Illustrate cases in which professional wildlife and fisheries biologists have supported the introduction of non-native species during the last 150 years in the United States.

A One-Minute Summary

Introduced species of wildlife are either purposefully or accidentally moved from their native range to a new region. Invasive species are those introduced species that persist and thrive to the point of causing economic or environmental harm.

Invasive species are one of the largest environmental threats on the globe, and they incur billions of dollars in real, economic costs. Ecosystems can be altered by invasive species, including habitat, trophic, and spatial alteration, gene pool deterioration, and disease introduction. Invasive species are quite hard to detect until they become a problem, which makes management complex.

As a species spreads into a new region, wildlife managers have a progressive set of alternatives to consider, starting with prevention prior to introduction, eradication of small, localized introductions, and containment and mitigation of larger invasions that cannot be eradicated.

Principles for Your Toolkit

The invasive curve: Invasive species often follow a stereotypical pattern of logistic growth after initial introduction or colonization. The ecological principles of intra-specific and interspecific competition guide management responses and predicted population growth of an invasive species. Each stage of population growth has a management solution that is the most optimal response. Prevention no longer works after initial introduction, and eradication is not an optimal response after the species has reached levels of population size that make eradication difficult. Containment and mitigation are responses that are available when eradication is not possible.

A framework of barriers to invasion: Invasion of a new region is not easy. In fact, many barriers prevent any species from becoming invasive. Geography is an initial barrier that separates species from other regions in which they might thrive. After a species finds a natural way to colonize a new location or is introduced by humans, the species must be able to survive and reproduce in the new region. If these basic ecological barriers are overcome, the introduced species must then disperse and expand its range and influence on the ecosystem to become invasive. Managers may use these barriers to assist with management of potentially invasive species, and the order in which the barriers are faced may be aligned with the management alternatives of prevention, eradication, containment, and mitigation to find solutions to invasive species problems.

A Problem: Introducing Feral Hogs to the North Woods of Maine

Lars opened a letter from his pile of "Maine stakeholder mail" as his assistant called it. He had let the pile get too large over the past couple of weeks while he spent time conducting track surveys of lynx in the snow. As a new blizzard swirled outside his office, it was time to get caught up on the mail.

"Dear Sir," the letter began. "I recently returned from Texas, where I participated in a hunt of wild hogs. My daughter and I had the time of our lives, chasing hogs through the open brush country on an ATV. I am of the opinion that it is time to introduce these highly exotic wild hogs to Maine's North Woods. Consider the economic advantage we would have—to keep hunters from heading south to Texas. We might even attract some out-of-state hog hunters to Maine. I know you might be worried the hogs would get out of hand and disturb native animals, but I don't think our cold winters would allow their populations to get too large. Please let me know what you think about this proposal."

"Yikes." Lars took a long breath. Maine was lucky to be one of a few states in the US without feral hogs, and Lars knew his direct supervisor thought ill of any suggestion to introduce any kind of non-native wildlife in Maine. However, his colleagues in the fisheries division were always stocking non-native fish in lakes to encourage angler participation. The stakeholder's point about economic revenue for the agency and the state was intriguing. Like many places in the US, Maine's economy had been slow to recover from the 2008 recession. Lars was lucky to still have his state agency position, and he had seen other positions cut after his colleagues retired. Maybe he should talk to some colleagues and draft some ideas to present to his supervisor.

Is introduction of feral hogs in Maine allowed? What professional policies guide decisions for introduction of non-native species? What management options exist if the hogs were to get out of control in Maine? How might you help Lars and his supervisor walk through a set of considerations to determine if an introduction of feral hogs in Maine is advisable? By the time you finish this chapter, you should be able to find the answer.

Terms and Definitions

Containment: A management strategy for invasive species that aims to keep a species limited to areas in which it currently resides.

Eradication: A management strategy for a newly discovered invasive species that aims to find and remove them from the system.

Exotic species: Species that evolved elsewhere and then were purposely or accidentally relocated.

Introduced species: See "exotic species."

Mitigation: A management strategy for invasive species that cannot be contained or eradicated; the aim is to protect other resources as much as possible and to reduce the effects of the invasive species on the ecosystem.

Nonindigenous species: See "exotic species."

Non-native species: See "exotic species."

Prevention: A management strategy for invasive species that aims to keep a species out of a region.

A Challenge for Wildlife Managers

Species that evolved elsewhere and then purposely or accidentally relocated are known as **introduced**, **exotic**, **non-native**, or **nonindigenous** species. For wildlife biologists, it may be useful to know that university animal science programs may refer to all wildlife as "exotic," relative to domestic species typically studies in these academic programs (beef cattle, swine, sheep, horses, dogs, house cats, etc.). This cultural difference in definitions may be confusing to the public.

Animal species can colonize new locations without human assistance. New species may arrive through shifts in migration paths, rafting on floating debris, or when previous constraints to movement are eliminated. However, humans have increased the scale and magnitude of species movements, leading to a world in which prior geographical boundaries between species groups are largely breaking down (Vitousek et al. 1996). Approximately 50,000 non-native species have been introduced into the United States (Pimental et al. 2000), which has led to proliferation of non-native species as a part of local diversity. Consider the state of Hawaii, which has 57 native species and 38 non-native species in its avian diversity. Hawaii only has 6 native species of freshwater fish, but 19 non-native fish species in its streams and lakes (Vitousek et al. 1996).

Invasive species are the subset of introduced species that persist, proliferate, and cause economic or environmental harm, or harm to human health (Mack et al. 2000). Not all introduced species become **invasive**. Some introduced species appear to be relatively benign, but others are strong competitors or voracious predators with devastating effects.

Humans love to move species to new places, and we have been doing it for centuries. As people moved between continents, they usually took domestic livestock with them, which is how honeybees moved from Europe to North America. Similarly, the Spanish introduced horses to the Great Plains and Rocky Mountain Indians (Wishart 2016).

Europeans also introduced European starlings and house sparrows in the eastern US because they wanted familiar sounds around them. In fact, a club of New Yorkers who had a goal of introducing every British bird mentioned in Shakespeare's plays introduced starlings. The starling is mentioned only once, but that was enough (Colautti et al. 2005). Ring-necked pheasants were introduced to Oregon in the 1880s to increase the number of game birds by sport hunters, and other species of game birds such as gray (often called Hungarian) partridge and chukars (Phillips 1928). Aquaculturalists introduced species of Asian carp in aquaculture ponds to keep algae levels low to allow efficient production of other fish species. Floods caused overflow of rivers into ponds and provided a way for escape of the new species (Cuddington et al. 2014). In some cases, species secretly hitch a ride to a new location, such as brown tree snakes invading Guam from cargo in salvage boats after World War II (Rodda et al. 1992).

Invasions are rather simple, in concept, from an ecological perspective, which provides a useful framework to assess a species and its current or potential invasion status. Population growth is a function of survival, movement, and reproduction (chapter 6), and introduced species follow the same rules as other species. An invasive

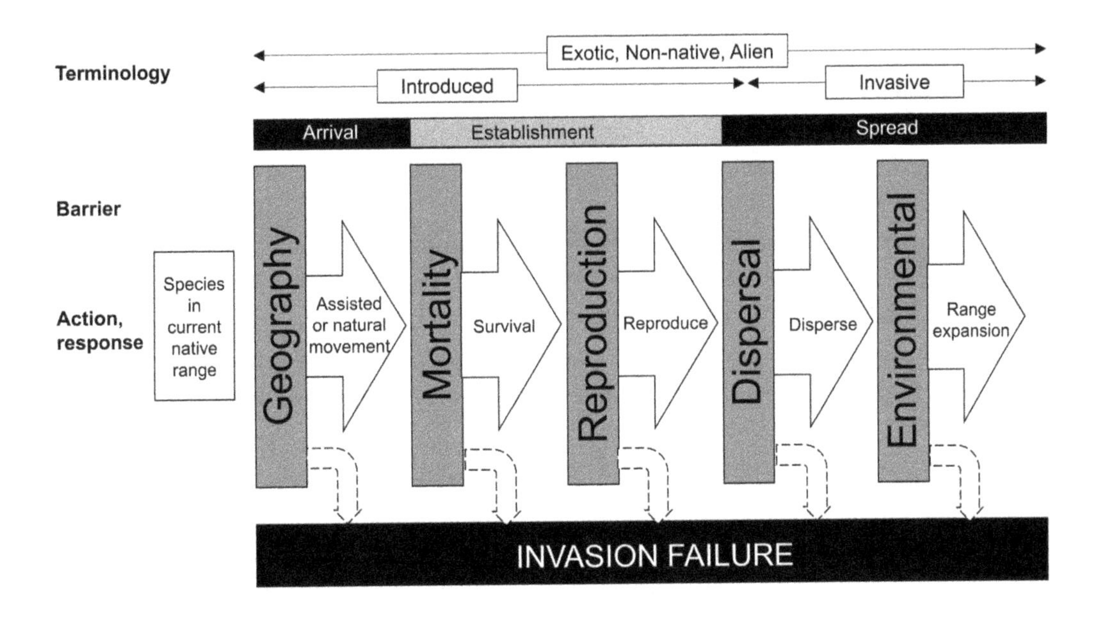

FIGURE 10.1 An ecological framework for an invasion, with potential barriers to a species during the arrival, establishment, and spread phases. Invasive species are successful in eliminating all barriers. Introduced species eliminate early barriers to establish a new population but do not expand range and population size to become invasive. Modified from Blackburn et al. (2011) and Hoffman and Courchamp (2016).

species often grows exponentially until it reaches a carrying capacity, the result of intraspecific competition.

Barriers of geography typically keep species from moving to other regions (Figure 10.1). However, once a species makes its way naturally to a new region or is transported by humans to a new region, it must survive and reproduce in that region to become established. Following establishment, a species must begin to grow in population size and increase its range to be considered invasive (Blackburn et al. 2011, Hoffman and Courchamp 2016).

Our emphasis in this chapter will be to highlight frameworks used by wildlife managers to respond to invasive species as an example of human-wildlife conflict. Throughout this text, our focus is on frameworks for decisions. How do managers arrive at the solution to problems? What techniques can be used? What alternative management responses are available?

The Cost of Introduced and Invasive Species

Decisions regarding introduced and invasive species are complex because an introduction is not always a negative occurrence. Some introduced (non-invasive) species are not particularly harmful and may even have economic benefits. For example, ring-necked pheasants are mostly harmless to ecosystems and provide millions of dollars to several states every year in the form of hunting licenses, guided hunts, hotel rooms, and restaurant orders. However, species that become invasive may also have negative effects on ecosystems. Simberloff et al. (2005) provide estimates of costs of $137 billion in annual economic damage in the US alone, or $335 billion in economic costs per year in the US, United Kingdom, Australia, India, South Africa, and Brazil.

The American Fisheries Society has designated five categories of potential impacts for introduced species in communities, which apply to aquatic and terrestrial situations equally: habitat alteration, trophic alteration, spatial alteration, gene pool deterioration, and introduction of diseases.

Habitat alteration: The introduction of plants to aquatic or terrestrial ecosystems may cause serious infestations, which affect human use of lakes and rivers, predator-prey dynamics, and water quality during plant decomposition. Exotic fish, such as grass carp, are often stocked to combat plant infestations, but such stocking efforts present a risk that native plants may be affected by herbivory of grass carp. If grass carp become too abundant and remove too much plant cover, they may negatively influence cover for juvenile fish. European immigrants stocked common carp early in the settlement of the United States, and millions of dollars have been spent to control and eradicate carp to combat their behavior of digging through lake bottoms in search of food, which decreases the clarity of water (Courtenay and Robins 1973).

Trophic alteration: The introduction of any species into a new environment has the potential to alter the structure of the community. The introduced fish species may have dietary overlap with native fish and exert pressure on the system through competition, or the introduced fish may be a predator that complicates the predator-prey dynamics in the system. In chapter 6, we noted that biologists were worried about diet overlap and potential competition between native filter feeding fish in the Mississippi River and invasive Asian carp. As an introduced predator in New Zealand streams, brown trout appear to have exerted pressure that resulted in declines in a native species, the common river galaxias (Townsend and Crowl 1991).

Spatial alteration: Competition for space by non-native and native fishes may lead to exclusion of the native species if the non-native species is more aggressive. In some stream and lake environments, nesting habitat is limited. Blue tilapia appear to have caused failure of recruitment of largemouth bass in Trinidad Lake, Texas after introduction of the tilapia (Noble et al. 1975).

Gene pool deterioration: The potential for stocked, non-native fish to hybridize with native fish depends on the relatedness of the species of concern. In some cases, closely related fish are brought into contact through introduction of one species to the other's native habitat. Walleye and sauger, for example, are highly managed species and either species may be the stocked species. The two species are prone to hybridize, and not all hybrids have distinct physical features for use in identification as a hybrid. Fisheries biologists risk deteriorating a gene pool with hybrid fish when collecting walleye or sauger breeding stock for a hatchery without conducting a genetic test (Billington et al. 1997).

Introduction of diseases: When a non-native individual is introduced to a new water body, there is potential for introduction of diseases caused by bacteria, viruses, and parasites. The American Fisheries Society suggested this aspect is one of the most severe threats that an introduced species may pose to a native community. The transfer of diseased rainbow trout from Europe to the United States is blamed for the introduction of whirling disease to North America (Bartholomew and Reno 2002). Whirling disease is caused by a microscopic parasite; the neurological damage causes fish to swim in an unnatural, whirling motion, which makes feeding difficult as well as making them quite vulnerable to predators.

QUICK COMPREHENSION CHECK

The examples provided for the five threats of invasive species on wildlife communities are for fish. Can you think of an example for the five categories from other wildlife taxonomic groups (amphibians, reptiles, birds, and mammals)?

Management Solutions at Stages along the Invasive Curve

Fish and wildlife agencies give high priority to solving invasive species issues because of the potential costs. However, arriving at solutions to prevent species from becoming invasive is difficult for three reasons:

> **For proposed introductions of exotic species, political or economic pressure may be hard to counter with ecological arguments.** There may be political reasons that sway decisions. Ring-necked pheasants are a non-native species, but it would be politically hard to eradicate them from a state given their economic benefits. In similar fashion, there were political reasons why US Forest Service biologists planted non-native Russian olive and Siberian elm in shelterbelts in the Great Plains during the Dust Bowl in the 1930s. They needed trees that could grow quickly to make their program appear successful

to politicians in the US Congress who were funding the work, and native trees tended to grow slower in the drought conditions (McShane et al. 2015).

It is hard to predict the effect of an introduction of a wildlife species in an ecosystem. Many species have been introduced yet failed to successfully survive or reproduce. Other species remain localized or at non-invasive levels in their new ecosystems (Figure 10.1). However, some species survive introduction and go on to have devastating effects.

Who would have predicted that the illegal release of a few pet pythons would have such an effect on the Florida everglades? Similarly, did the original people who released European starlings in New York City have any idea that they would start to outcompete native cavity-dwelling species for nests across the entire continent? Professional conservation and wildlife societies propose a species-by-species consideration for proposed introductions. However, it is very difficult for us to estimate the risk of introduced species. How negative could their presence be, and what is the likelihood that their introduction will result in negative consequences? Sugar cane farmers in Hawaii introduced small Indian mongooses to control brown rat populations, but there was very little way to predict that mongooses would turn to easier prey (bird eggs), which would lead to the near-extinction of the nene, or Hawaiian goose.

Inadvertent introductions are hard to detect. Often, the problem is found when ecosystem changes are so severe that people notice the problem, and it may be too late at that point to eradicate the species. Asian carp in the Mississippi River watershed were not a problem until they were a problem, which makes decision-making quite difficult.

With these difficulties, how do we manage invasive species? How do we make informed decisions about management actions? In addition, what are the available alternatives? Simberloff et al. (2005) suggested that wildlife managers and conservation planners could learn from the accumulation of experiences around the world, and that such experiences suggest that are **three main management alternatives for problems with invasive species**:

1. **Prevention:** Keeping invasive species out
2. **Eradication:** If invasive species get in, finding and trying to eradicate them quickly
3. **Containment:** If an invasive species cannot be eradicated, managing them at low levels

A fourth strategy, **mitigation**, involves resource protection and long-term management to reduce the effects of the invasive species on the ecosystem. Mitigation is a fallback strategy when the first three alternatives are not available once the

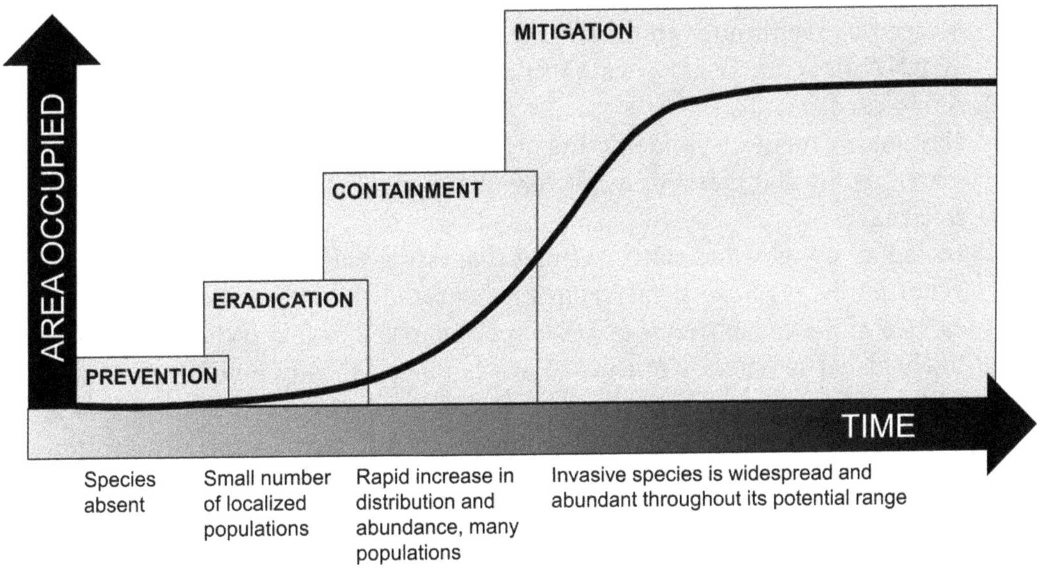

MITIGATION
CONTAINMENT
ERADICATION
PREVENTION
AREA OCCUPIED
TIME
Species absent
Small number of localized populations
Rapid increase in distribution and abundance, many populations
Invasive species is widespread and abundant throughout its potential range

FIGURE 10.2 The conceptual increase in population size and area occupied by an invasive species over time. Phase-specific management alternatives of prevention, eradication, containment, and mitigation are shown. Modified from Agriculture Victoria (2010) and Harvey and Mazzotti (2018).

invasive species becomes entrenched in a system (Agriculture Victoria 2010, Harvey and Mazzotti 2018) (Figure 10.2).

Prevention is the single best way to limit impacts of nonnative species. This alternative is the most cost-effective as well; some estimates suggest for every $1 spent, $100 in potential costs or damage to ecosystems can be avoided (Agriculture Victoria 2010). Prevention may be implemented by planned decontamination of freight, packaging material and transportation equipment that could contain unknown biotic hitchhiking invasive species. Similarly, countries may restrict deliberate imports of potentially harmful species. Most states in the US have invasive species education programs that work with boaters and anglers in the field to share methods to prevent introduction of baitfish or transfer of near-invisible larval forms of fish or zebra mussels in water left in live wells on boats.

Eradication may be feasible early in an invasion or in a restricted area, but this management option requires early detection and rapid response. State and federal agencies use planned, regular monitoring programs to identify new exotics soon after they invade.

Some approaches to enhance detection include (Simberloff et al. 2005):

- Molecular techniques to determine presence in a system (e.g., assessment of DNA floating in lake water to alert for presence of zebra mussels or Asian carp).
- Developing methods for detecting organisms hidden by containers or packing materials. Similar methods might have stopped the invasion of Guam by brown tree snakes.
- Introduce policies and control efforts that target pathways rather than species. What pathways have invasive species entered the US in the past, and how can we minimize entrance of other species in the future? Where are the most likely places for species to enter? For example, there are now bans on moving firewood from state to state or even throughout states to minimize spread of invasive insects that hitch rides in the fire wood, such as the current impact of emerald ash borer.
- Remote sensing imagery from airplane or satellite platforms may help identify the spread of invasive plant species or animals if they leave telltale signatures such as mounds of earth or other characteristics that may be picked up through imagery monitoring.

As a strategy, **eradication** is most likely to be successful if the following conditions are present:

- **The invasive species' range when found is limited**—as it is much easier to eradicate a small, local population than a large, extensive population. Some states have had success with early detection and eradication of small populations of feral hogs after citizens introduced the hogs for hunting purposes. However, if the feral hog population becomes too large, the chances of eradication drop significantly (McClure et al. 2015, Figure 10.3).
- **Funding and person resources must be adequate** to complete the eradication. An early attempt to eradicate the invasive gypsy moth in the eastern US failed because funding was withdrawn from the project in Massachusetts after moth numbers decreased. However, the eradication did not go to completion, and when the efforts to eradicate were not funded, the moth eventually increased in numbers and spread farther, making eradication impossible (Simberloff et al. 2005).
- There must be **clear legal grounds for the eradication**. It is important to remember that eradication usually involves culling the species, which may be contested by animal rights groups.
- The **biology of the invasive organism must be understood** to allow effective control. What do we know about the species' abilities to survive and reproduce in new environments (Figure 10.1)? How can we use its biology to make management recommendations?

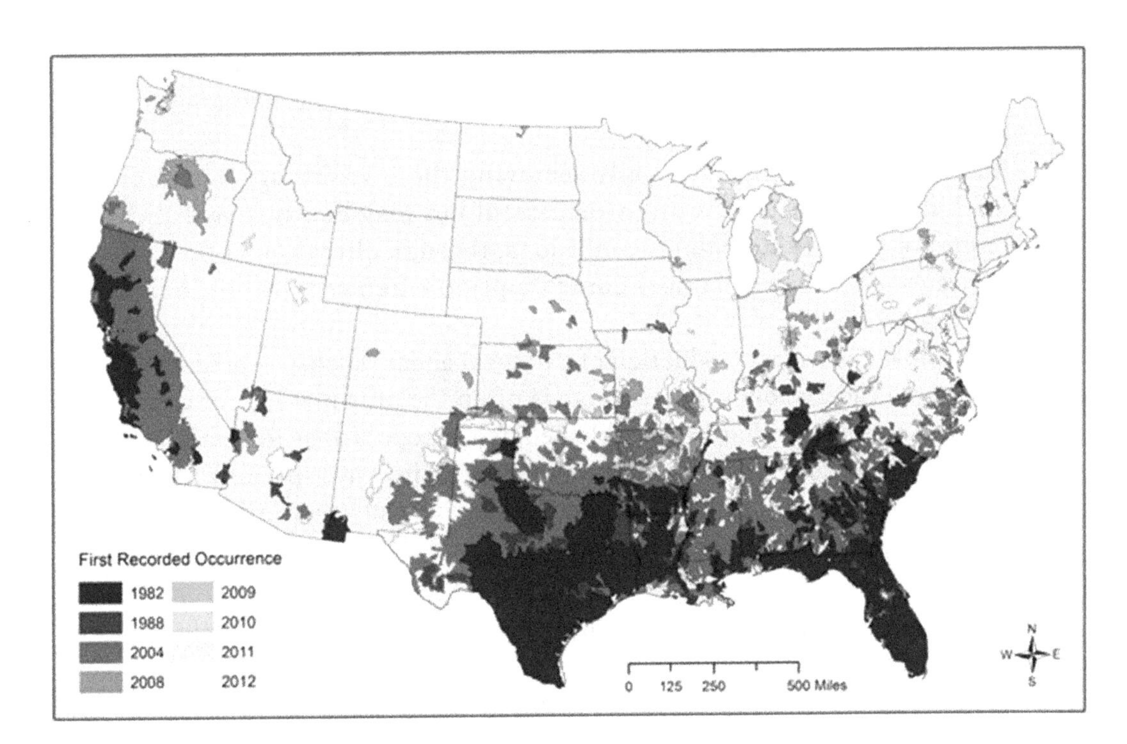

FIGURE 10.3 Cumulative documented occurrence of wild pigs from 1982 to 2012 based on Southeastern Cooperative Wildlife Disease Study records aggregated to watersheds. Areas occupied by wild pigs in a given year continue to be occupied in later years, with rare exception (image from McClure et al. 2015, open access).

- **Eradication should not do more harm than good.** What will happen when the invader is removed? Will another species take its place? On Santa Cruz Island, California, removal of introduced, non-native goats seemed like a good plan. However, the removal of the goats led to a sudden increase in exotic plants, and these weeds were harder to contain than the goats.
- Following a successful eradication, **restoration of native communities may be an important goal** for management, as a way to minimize the chances an area will be reinvaded. Many control techniques inherently create disturbance, which may increase the vulnerability of an area to subsequent invaders.

Containment prevents the further transport of existing exotics beyond the current location, and this can be an important tool to reduce the impact of an invasive species if eradication is not possible. Strategies for containment generally combine tools used in prevention and eradication. Containment methods may include any of the following:

- **Chemical control:** The use of pesticides, herbicides, or fungicides may be effective to kill invasive species, but it may be problematic due to impacts on non-target organisms, including humans. Prolonged use of chemical control is expensive and may be ineffective when target organisms develop resistance to certain chemicals.

- **Mechanical control:** Physically removing the invasive species or changing habitat conditions is often successful but may be expensive and labor intensive. Modifying habitat conditions, through alteration of fire or flooding regimes, is a mechanical control option when removal of individuals is infeasible.
- **Biological control:** Introduction of a natural enemy such as a predator or parasite from the invader's native range is often the only method for controlling an invasive species that has established dense populations over large areas. It may be an environmentally sound way to control invasive species with minimal expense, but some control agents do not survive and others attack non-target organisms or become invasive themselves.

Mitigation is necessary when prevention, eradication, and containment are not effective. However, mitigation may also be used when containment is effective, to treat the area in which the invasive species is contained. Long-term management of the species aims to either reduce populations of the invasive species to the lowest possible levels and/or to protect other components of the ecosystem that are affected by the invasive species.

For example, the Burmese python was introduced in the Florida Everglades ecosystem. The snakes eat a wide range of prey and biologists believe they are responsible for severe declines of mammals in the Everglades (chapter 3, Figure 10.4).

FIGURE 10.4 Two invasive species for which mitigation may be the best management strategy: left, Burmese python (photo by R. Cammauf, National Park Service), and right, northern snakehead (photo by USFWS).

However, no management option employed to date has been effective to eradicate pythons from the Everglades. It appears that long-term management and mitigation of their effects on other species is the only option at present (Harvey and Mazzotti 2018).

In some instances, the long-term management of an invasive species includes a combination of prevention, eradication, and containment. In the case of the northern snakehead, a popular food fish in Asia, biologists are working on several fronts to address concerns. The fish had been imported live to the US because of cultural tradition; diners in Asia would select the fish live from an aquarium prior to eating. However, snakeheads are voracious predators with a mouth full of impressive teeth structures (Figure 10.3), and they have high potential to affect vertebrate and invertebrate communities when introduced to new environments in the US. Therefore, in 2002, the USFWS prohibited important and interstate transport of the fish as an attempt at prevention. Several individual lakes and ponds on the east or west coasts of the US were found to have snakeheads, and eradication efforts were accomplished. A task force of fisheries biologists established monitoring protocols and eradication techniques for the species, and outreach materials were developed to try to confine the presence of snakeheads to the lakes in which it currently exists. Research on the species may also serve to help design better management alternatives (Northern Snakehead Working Group 2006).

The four-pronged framework of prevention, eradication, containment, and long-term management provide alternatives for PrOACT decision processes involving invasive species. Biologists continue to learn from successes and failures as they develop responses to new situations.

QUICK COMPREHENSION CHECK

Review Figure 10.1. Can you map the four management alternatives for invasive species to the ecological stages of an invasion? At what stage(s) does prevention work? Eradication? Containment? When is mitigation necessary?

How do the ecological barriers to invasion (Figure 10.1) provide assistance to managers who attempt prevention, eradication, or containment?

Shades of Gray: Our Professional Societies Have Supported Species Introductions

Members and representatives of The Wildlife Society and the American Fisheries Society have participated in introduction and continued supportive management of non-native species for sport angling or hunting. In fact, the primary purpose of early fisheries and wildlife agencies were to raise and stock fish and game animals, many of which were non-native species. Before the 20th century began, striped bass from New Jersey had been introduced in California and rainbow trout from rivers in the western US had become established in eastern states. Even fish species from Europe, such as brown trout and common carp were becoming favorites of anglers throughout North America. The propensity for stockings of non-native species by agencies may have conditioned the public to not perceive the potential threats of non-native species, and agencies are now struggling to control the public's purposeful introductions of non-native fish to lakes and rivers (Rahel 2004).

With time and wisdom that grows from experience, our professional societies have reevaluated policies for introductions of non-native species. Although political and economic forces still maintain some weight that supports non-native species that are not invasive, the realities of dynamics of introductions in our modern world has forced a conversation to critically examine how we make management decisions with regard to non-native species.

Certainly, all 50 US states and the rest of the world have never been so closely connected through commerce, tourism, and media as we are now. Pathways exist for the purposeful or accidental transfer of species that did not exist in previous decades, and not all invasive species travel to the US. The pet trade and some purposeful introductions for "faunal improvement" has delivered the North American raccoon to Europe, where it has reached extremely high populations in Germany and has spread among 20 other European countries as well as Russia. Raccoons have brought threats of disease (Beltrán-Beck et al. 2012) including the spread of canine distemper virus and raccoon roundworm.

In addition, the dynamic of a public group of stakeholders that travel extensively and experience angling and hunting activities in other countries creates new demand for introductions and the potential for purposeful and illegal international transfers by the angling and hunting public.

The magnitude of the spread of introduced species on a global scale has led some to suggest that the world is headed towards a single, global biota with lower overall diversity and fewer unique local species within continents (McKinney and Lockwood 1999). One thing is clear: humans have been responsible for movement of animals from their native ranges to other locations, and the management questions surrounding future decisions are complex and important for our future.

Decision-Making on the Ground

1: Policies on Introductions of Non-Native Species

Policy of the American Fisheries Society on Introductions of Aquatic Species[1]

Introductions of species to aquatic communities are commonly employed as a fisheries management tool or occur as a result of escapes from aquaculture or ornamental fish holding facilities. It is not feasible, nor desirable, to legislate against all such introductions. What is needed is more education on the role that introduced species can and should play in the context of aquatic resources management. The more informed natural resources managers are about such issues, the less likely that mistakes will be made or that legislation will be necessary to enforce an "attitude of caution." The following actions toward that end are recommended.

A. The membership reaffirms its endorsement of the 1972 "Position of the American Fisheries Society on Introductions of Exotic Aquatic Species" with modifications as indicated:

Position of the American Fisheries Society on Introductions of "Introduced" Aquatic Species

Our purpose is to formulate a broad mechanism for planning, regulating, implementing, and monitoring all introductions of aquatic species.

Some introductions of species into ecosystems in which they are not native have been successful (e.g., coho salmon and striped bass) and others unfortunate (e.g., common carp and walking catfish).

[1] "Courses of Action," AFS Policy Statement # 15: American Fisheries Society Position on Introductions of Aquatic Species. Copyright © by American Fisheries Society.

WRAPPING UP

What tradeoffs should Lars consider with regard to introducing feral hogs to Maine for hunting opportunities for state residents? Can you make a convincing argument against this practice?

If feral hogs were introduced (illegally) in Maine, what management strategies should Lars consider?

Species not native to an ecosystem will be termed "introduced." Some introductions are in some sense, planned and purposeful for management reasons; others are accidental or are simply ways of disposing of unwanted pets or research organisms.

It is recommended that the policy of the American Fisheries Society:

1. Encourage fish importers, farmers, dealers, and hobbyists to prevent and discourage the accidental or purposeful introduction of aquatic species into their local ecosystems.
2. Urge that no city, county, state, province, or federal agency introduce, or allow to be introduced, any exotic species into any waters within its jurisdiction which might contaminate any waters outside its jurisdiction without official sanction of the exposed jurisdiction.
3. Urge that only ornamental aquarium fish dealers be permitted to import such fishes for sale or distribution to hobbyists. The "dealer" would be defined as a firm or person whose income derives from live ornamental aquarium fishes.
4. Urge that the importation of fishes for purposes of research not involving introduction into a natural ecosystem, or for display in public aquaria by individuals or organizations, be made under agreement with responsible governmental agencies. Such importers will be subject to investigatory procedures currently existing and/or to be developed, and species so imported shall be kept under conditions preventing escape or accidental introduction. Aquarium hobbyists should be encouraged to import rare ornamental fishes through such importers. No fishes shall be released into any natural ecosystem upon termination of research or display.
5. Urge that all species of exotics considered for release be prohibited and considered undesirable for any purposes of introduction into any ecosystem unless that fish species shall have been evaluated upon the following bases and found to be desirable:
    a. RATIONALE. Reasons for seeking an import should be clearly stated and demonstrated. It should be clearly noted what qualities are sought that would make the import more desirable than native forms.
    b. SEARCH. Within the qualifications set forth under RATIONALE, a search of possible contenders should be made, with a list prepared of those that appear most likely to succeed, and the favorable and unfavorable aspects of each species noted.
    c. PRELIMINARY ASSESSMENT OF THE IMPACT. This should go beyond the area of rationale to consider impact on target aquatic ecosystems, general effect on game and food fishes or waterfowl, on aquatic

plants and public health. The published information on the species should be reviewed and the species should be studied in preliminary fashion in its biotope.

d. PUBLICITY AND REVIEW. The subject should be entirely open and expert advice should be sought. It is at this point that thoroughness is in order. No importation is so urgent that it should not be subject to careful evaluation.
e. EXPERIMENTAL RESEARCH. If a prospective import passes the first four steps, a research program should be initiated by an appropriate agency or organization to test the import in confined waters (experimental ponds, etc.).
f. EVALUATION OR RECOMMENDATION. Again, publicity is in order and complete reports should be circulated amongst interested scientists and presented for publication in the Transactions of the American Fisheries Society.
g. INTRODUCTION. With favorable evaluation, the release should be affected and monitored, with results published or circulated.

Because animals do not respect political boundaries, it would seem that an international, national, and regional agency should be involved at the start and have the veto power at the end. Under this procedure there is no doubt that fewer introductions would be accomplished, but quality and not quantity is desired, and many mistakes might be avoided.

A. The society encourages international, national, and regional natural resource agencies to endorse and follow the intent of the above position.
B. The society encourages international harmonization of guidelines, protocols, codes of practice, etc., as they apply to introductions of aquatic species.
C. Fisheries professionals and other aquatic specialists are urged to become more aware of issues relating to introduced species.

Position Statement of The Wildlife Society on Invasive Plants and Animals[2]

Invasive and feral species present unique challenges for wildlife management. The Wildlife Society defines an invasive species as an established plant or animal species that causes direct or indirect economic or environmental harm within an ecosystem, or a species that would likely cause such harm if introduced to an ecosystem in which it is non-indigenous as determined through objective, scientific risk assessment tools

[2] "Final Position Statement: Invasive and Feral Species." Copyright © 2016 by The Wildlife Society. Reprinted with permission.

and analyses. Feral species are those that have been established from intentional or accidental release of domestic stock that results in a self-sustaining population(s), such as feral horses, feral cats, or feral swine (wild pig) in North America. Feral species are generally non-indigenous and often invasive.

Whereas invasive species are typically non-indigenous, not all non-indigenous species are perceived as invasive. For example, species introduced as biological control agents and some naturalized wildlife species, provide significant economic benefits while not resulting in significant or perceived harm to native ecosystems. Similarly, some indigenous species may be perceived as invasive when population increase or range expansion beyond historical levels disrupt ecosystem processes, resulting in economic or environmental harm. Determination of an invasive species may vary across regions based on the presence of local economic or environmental harm.

The extent to which invasive and feral species harm indigenous species and ecosystems may be difficult to determine, and few laws and policies deal directly with their control. Many invasive and feral species are wrongly perceived as natural components of the environment and some have the support of advocacy groups who promote their continued presence in the wild. Invasive and feral species may negatively affect public trust resources, including indigenous and naturalized wildlife, which are managed by government agencies for society's benefit.

Effects of invasive and feral species on the natural world and their economic costs to society are increasing. Some known effects of these species include negative impacts to biological diversity, ecosystem productivity, environmental integrity, wildlife health, human health and safety, and property. Impacts vary widely depending on species and ecosystems affected. Negative effects of invasive and feral species on indigenous wildlife populations occur through direct competition, predation, habitat alteration and/or degradation, disease transmission, and diversion of conservation funds for control and research efforts. Many invasive and feral species also exhibit high reproductive potential and minimal natural regulation in the ecosystems in which they become established.

Cumulative impacts of invasive and feral species can be substantial. Resources are limited in all ecosystems and introduction of invasive and feral species to systems where indigenous species are already stressed may have significant negative effects. Even after control and/or removal of invasive and feral species, recovery of ecosystems may take considerable time and may require direct management efforts, depending on type, intensity and duration of disturbance.

The policy of The Wildlife Society regarding invasive and feral species is to:

1. Promote maintaining indigenous biological diversity and ecosystem integrity and function. Oppose introduction or maintenance of invasive species and feral species that threaten the survival of indigenous species. Land and

resource management agencies should place primary emphasis upon management needs of indigenous wildlife and plants and resist efforts to sustain invasive and feral species on public or private lands.

2. Acknowledge that some introductions of non-indigenous species have contributed to conservation and society's appreciation for wildlife or have been used as biological control agents.
3. Encourage programs to monitor invasive and feral species to inform and target future management strategies, especially those that include the key elements of early detection, rapid response, containment of spread, and eradication where possible. Support sharing technical data and cooperation among agencies and other partners to manage invasive and feral species.
4. Encourage and support increased funding for scientific research by public and private agencies and organizations to control, minimize, or eliminate negative impacts of invasive and feral species.
5. Support cost-effective control and/or eradication programs for invasive and feral species that exhibit timely results without sustaining or causing additional ecosystem harm.
6. Encourage the enactment, expansion, and enforcement of laws and regulations focused on eradicating and controlling the spread of invasive and feral species, and the introduction of harmful wildlife pathogens carried by non-indigenous species.
7. Urge strict control of known invasive and feral species in livestock and agricultural industries to prevent their accidental escape into the wild and consequent negative impacts.

APPLICATION, ANALYSIS, SYNTHESIS, AND EVALUATION

Review the policy guidelines of the two professional societies. What similarities do you see between the two societies' policy statements? Do you see any contrasts between their approaches?

How does the American Fisheries Society appear to treat the potential stocking of large-mouth bass in a lake in Nevada in which it does not naturally occur?

How does The Wildlife Society appear to treat the priority of ring-necked pheasant relative to native species? If a native predator was responsible for reducing populations of pheasants, would the society approve of predator control to support pheasant populations?

How do the two policies compare with regard to international movement of species that are potentially invasive? Consider examples in the chapter that reveal potential pathways of movement of reptiles, birds, or mammals between countries. The Wildlife

Society has seven numbered policy statements regarding invasive and feral species—can you write an eighth statement that sets a policy or action for society members who work internationally to assist in prevention of the spread of invasive species?

Sources of Information and Further Reading

Agriculture Victoria. *Invasive Plants and Animals Policy Framework*. State of Victoria, Australia, 2010.

Bartholomew, Jerri L., and Paul W. Reno. "The history and dissemination of whirling disease." *American Fisheries Society Symposium 26* (2002): 1–22.

Beltrán-Beck, B., García, F. J., and Gortázar, C. "Raccoons in Europe: disease hazards due to the establishment of an invasive species." *European Journal of Wildlife Research 58*, no. 1 (2012): 5–15.

Billington, N., Brooks, R. C., and Heidinger, R. C. "Frequency of natural hybridization between saugers and walleyes in the Peoria Pool of the Illinois River, as determined by morphological and electrophoretic criteria." *North American Journal of Fisheries Management 17*, no. 1 (1997): 220–224.

Blackburn, T.M., Pyšek, P., Bacher, S., Carlton, J.T., Duncan, R.P., Jarošík, V., Wilson, J.R. and Richardson, D.M. "A proposed unified framework for biological invasions." *Trends in ecology & evolution 26*, no. 7 (2011): 333–339.

Colautti, R. I., Muirhead, J. R., Biswas, R. N., and MacIsaac, H. J. "Realized vs apparent reduction in enemies of the European starling." *Biological Invasions 7*, no. 4 (2005): 723–732.

Courtenay Jr, W. R., and Robins, C. R. "Exotic organisms: an unsolved, complex problem." *Bioscience 25*, no. 5 (1975): 306–313.

Cuddington, K., Currie, W. J. S., and Koops, M. A. "Could an Asian carp population establish in the Great Lakes from a small introduction?" *Biological invasions 16*, no. 4 (2014): 903–917.

Harvey, R. G., and F. J. Mazzotti. *The Invasion Curve: A Tool for Understanding Invasive Species Management in South Florida*. University of Florida Extension Publication WEC347, 2018.

Hoffmann, B. D. and Courchamp, F. "Biological invasions and natural colonisations: are they that different?" *NeoBiota 29* (2016): 1–14.

Mack, R. N., Simberloff, D., Mark Lonsdale, W., Evans, H., Clout, M., and Bazzaz, F. A. "Biotic invasions: causes, epidemiology, global consequences, and control." *Ecological applications 10*, no. 3 (2000): 689–710.

McClure, M. L., Burdett, C. L., Farnsworth, M. L., Lutman, M. W., Theobald, D. M., Riggs, P. D., Grear, D. A., and Miller, R. S. "Modeling and Mapping the Probability of Occurrence of Invasive Wild Pigs across the Contiguous United States." *PLOS ONE 10*, no. 8 (2015): e0133771.

McKinney, M. L., and Lockwood, J. L. "Biotic homogenization: a few winners replacing many losers in the next mass extinction." *Trends in ecology & evolution 14*, no. 11 (1999): 450–453.

McShane, R. R., Auerbach, D. A., Friedman, J. M., Auble, G. T., Shafroth, P. B., Merigliano, M. F., Scott, M. L. and Poff, N. L. "Distribution of invasive and native riparian woody plants across the western USA in relation to climate, river flow, floodplain geometry and patterns of introduction." *Ecography 38*, no. 12 (2015): 1254–1265.

Noble, R. L., Germany, R. D., and Hall, C. R. "Interactions of blue tilapia and largemouth bass in a power plant cooling reservoir." *Proceedings of the Twenty-Ninth Annual Conference, Southeastern Association of Game and Fish Commissioners 29 (1975): 247–251.*

Northern Snakehead Working Group. *National control and management plan for the northern snakehead* (Channa argus). Washington, DC: Department of the Interior, 2006.

Phillips, J. C. "Wild birds introduced or transplanted in North America." *Technical Bulletin 61*. Washington, DC: US Department of Agriculture, 1928.

Pimentel, D., Lach, L., Zuniga, R., and Morrison, D. "Environmental and economic costs of nonindigenous species in the United States." *BioScience 50*, no. 1 (2000): 53–65.
Rahel, F. J. "Unauthorized fish introductions: fisheries management of the people, for the people, or by the people?" *American Fisheries Society Symposium 44*, no. 43 (2004): 1–443.
Rodda, G. H., Fritts, T. H., and Conry, P. J. "Origin and population growth of the brown tree snake, Boiga irregularis, on *Guam." Pacific Science 46* (1992): 46–57.
Simberloff, D., Parker, I. M., and Windle, P. N. "Introduced species policy, management, and future research needs." *Frontiers in Ecology and the Environment 3*, no. 1 (2005): 12–20.
Townsend, C. R., and Crowl, T. A. "Fragmented population structure in a native New Zealand fish: an effect of introduced brown trout?" *Oikos* (1991): 347–354.
Vitousek, P. M., C. M. D'Antonio, L. L. Loope , and R. Westbrooks. "Biological invasions as global environmental change." *American Scientist 84* (1996).: 468–478.
Wishart, D. J. *Great Plains Indians*. Lincoln, NE: University of Nebraska Press, 2016.

Image Credits

Fig. 10.3: Meredith L. McClure, et al., "Wild pig map, from 'Modeling and Mapping the Probability of Occurrence of Invasive Wild Pigs across the Contiguous United States,'" PLOS ONE, 2015.
Fig. 10.4a: Source: https://www.usgs.gov/media/images/burmese-python-everglades-national-park-0.
Fig. 10.4b: Source: https://usfwsnortheast.wordpress.com/2016/02/22/cooking-up-creative-ways-to-stop-invasives/.

CHAPTER ELEVEN

Human-Wildlife Conflicts

Learning Outcomes

After participating in learning experiences related to this chapter, students should be able to:

- Draw a diagram of the decision process for human-wildlife conflicts that includes stakeholder notification of a problem.
- Assess a conflict situation to identify the proximate problem and the ultimate problem.
- Describe components of an integrated response to human-wildlife conflicts.
- For a given human-wildlife conflict situation, describe a series of potential management alternatives for consideration.
- Detail important steps in a conflict resolution process.
- Describe why community-based management holds promise for long-term solutions in human-wildlife conflict situations.

A One-Minute Summary

Human-wildlife conflict situations have potential to test the skills of the best wildlife manager because of the emotions generated by stakeholders when wildlife damage property or when disagreements between two groups of people occur over a management direction. The traditional field of wildlife damage management has blossomed into a broad area of research and study of human behavior to create solutions in cases of human-wildlife conflict.

Stakeholders typically notify decision teams of a problem in human-wildlife conflict situations, and the complaints may initially be about proximate factors that are important to the individuals involved. However, the roots of the conflict (ultimate problems) may be difficult to address and solve, and conflict resolution requires the decision team to look beyond a single reported incident. In human-wildlife conflict situations, economic factors may lie at the heart of the conflict.

Responses to human-wildlife conflict are unique to each situation. Integrated solutions draw on biological, social, and economic considerations to attempt to address proximate and ultimate factors in the conflict. Community-based management is a form of integrated solution that draws on peer relationships within the affected community to plan and carry out a solution. Communication skills and management of people are critical for wildlife managers who engage to solve human-wildlife conflicts. Wildlife managers must also be innovative to find solutions that address the concerns of a community while providing for sustained support of a species of conservation concern.

Principles for Your Toolkit

Integrated response: An integrated response is a solution to human-wildlife conflict that is multi-dimensional in nature. Some situations call for multiple techniques to be used to reduce wildlife damage simultaneously. In other circumstances, an integrated response involves biological, social, and economic considerations to develop a plan that is sustainable in a community.

Conflict resolution: Wildlife managers benefit from basic training in conflict resolution when working with situations of human-human conflict over wildlife management. Conflict resolution involves an initial step to become familiar with the conflict from the stakeholder perspective. The manager must then look beyond each stakeholder's view to find common issues that underlie the situation. The facilitation process then involves a request for solutions, and stakeholders are consulted in public meetings or open sessions. These conversations allow people to identify solutions that can be supported by the group, and an agreement on a way forward.

Community-based management: Natural resource managers engage in community-based management as a technique to reduce conflict and solve natural resource problems. Rather than impose a solution on a community from a governmental institution, the strategy is to involve the community in the decision-making process from start to finish.

A Problem: Attack of the Birds

"I don't know how much longer I can come to work in these conditions."

Belinda stared at the last line in an email from a colleague and glanced up to see a line of European starlings on her window ledge. She was the vice president of a bank that was enjoying its second year in a new, 45-story building in downtown Milwaukee,

Wisconsin. In recent weeks, however, birds had overshadowed the joy of working in a new commercial center. It seemed like tens of thousands of starlings had decided the south-facing side of the building with its warm window ledges was the perfect roosting site during the winter.

The sidewalks were covered in bird feces. Windows were streaked with feces as well. People were using umbrellas to enter the building to avoid being hit by falling feces. It was costing about $10,000 per week to clean windows and sidewalks to prevent potential spread of disease. As the email on Belinda's computer indicated, the employees were starting to consider other options.

A local We-Treat-Wildlife business had suggested hanging ropes down the side of the building to deter the birds, to no avail. Loud propane canons had been proposed, but there was concern of waking downtown residents late at night as the birds settled to roost. Belinda was concerned about the bank's community relations; even if the birds were deterred from their building, they would likely just settle somewhere else. Their gleaming, new building had gone from a symbol of development in the downtown area to an eyesore and object of ridicule.

Perhaps they could try poisoning the starlings. How and where to attempt this? Would thousands of dead starlings on city sidewalks be any better than a new layer of bird droppings every morning? A wildlife biologist with the state agency suggested that the best solution would address the ultimate problem rather than proximate problems, which had Belinda's head spinning with terminology. The biologist talked at length about the need for an integrated approach to the problem, which sounded promising. Belinda had gotten the contact information for the nearest USDA APHIS Wildlife Services office, and she picked up the phone. It was time to give them a call.

How might you help Belinda work through her problem? What is meant by an integrated approach to management of the situation? What is the ultimate problem in this situation? How can Belinda manage the damage to the bank building while addressing the larger issue of starling over-population in downtown Milwaukee? By the time you finish this chapter, you should be able to find the answer.

Terms and Definitions

Community-based management: A bottom up approach of organization that can be facilitated by an upper government or NGO structure. It aims for local stakeholder participation in the planning, research, development, management, and policy making for a community as a whole.

Mitigation: The action of reducing the severity, seriousness, or painfulness of something.

Stakeholder: A person with an interest or concern in something.

Too Many Animals, or Too Many Humans?

In chapter 1, we defined **wildlife management** as *a human decision and action that affects a wildlife population*. Throughout this text, we have seen that management decisions are always made in the context of human social and political constraints. Perhaps no other topic conveys the strength and power of social and political constraints as much as **human-wildlife conflict**. The opportunity for human and wildlife interests to be in conflict has increased with the ever-larger size of the population of humans, and predictions of a world-wide population of over 9 billion by 2050 suggest that the next three decades will involve more management problems to solve.

The wildlife profession initially referred to management of human-wildlife conflicts as **wildlife damage management**. From a historic viewpoint, early conflict between wildlife and humans was center around agricultural damage caused to crops or livestock by wildlife (Frank and Conover 2015). In the United States, the first federal response to wildlife damage was to establish the Animal Damage Control program in the US Department of Agriculture (USDA) in 1931. The Secretary of Agriculture was given authority for investigation, demonstrations, and control of mammalian predators, rodents, and birds that were perceived to be a threat to humans. In 1939, the program was moved to the United States Department of Interior's Fish and Wildlife Service, and in 1996, the Animal Damage Control program was transferred back to the USDA and placed under the Animal and Plant Health Inspection Service (APHIS) in a program known as Wildlife Services (Clay 1996).

Throughout the 20th century, the relationship between humans and wildlife grew more complicated than simple concerns about agriculture. Today, we prefer to use **human-wildlife conflicts** to describe situations where interests of humans and wildlife do not align. The vast majority of these situations involve a wildlife population that has become too large or too intrusive from a societal viewpoint. A recent survey of published research found that 95% of authors used the term *human-wildlife conflict* to report on animal damage to entities of concern to humans, while **human-human conflict** over wildlife-related issues accounted for the remainder of the research topics (Peterson et al. 2010). Further, the damage-causing situations usually involve reptiles, amphibians, birds, or mammals, and especially the latter two types of vertebrates (Hygnstrom et al. 1994). Fish are rarely implicated as causing damage to human resources.

Another category of human-wildlife conflicts includes situations involving threatened and endangered species (chapters 8, 9) when the needs of a species with a small population conflict with human economic interests or alternative land or water uses. These broader human-wildlife conflicts involve all taxonomic groups of wildlife.

Whatever the source of the conflict, human-wildlife conflict issues typically involve two elements:

- There is an ecological problem to solve in order to manage the size or impact of a population that is perceived as either too large or too small. We have discussed management responses and decision processes for population management in chapters 6–10.
- There is a unique human perspective to consider in a conflict context. As such, the third leg of the proverbial three-legged stool of wildlife management (chapter 1) becomes critically important in managing humans.

Today, the field of human-wildlife conflict continues to broaden and respond to changing attitudes towards wildlife by society. Segments of our profession still deal with problems of damage caused by wildlife, which is literally a human-wildlife conflict. The decision-making process in wildlife damage situations does not typically involve human-human conflict, rather it is simply a perception by humans that wildlife are doing something that is not valued (i.e., causing damage). The management solution is to find a strategy to stop or curtail the level of damage.

However, our profession is shifting through emphasis on human dimensions towards understanding that the inherent conflict in disputes over wildlife is often human-human conflict (Peterson et al. 2010). The more difficult type of conflict resides in these situations—disagreements within a large- or small-scale community over the way forward to live with wildlife. This chapter will cover both of these issues.

QUICK COMPREHENSION CHECK

The animal damage control authority at the federal level in the United States rests with the US Department of Agriculture. Why is the USDA invested with this authority? What potential conflicts between USDA and US Fish and Wildlife Service might exist?

What examples of human-wildlife conflict have you encountered in your lifetime and experience?

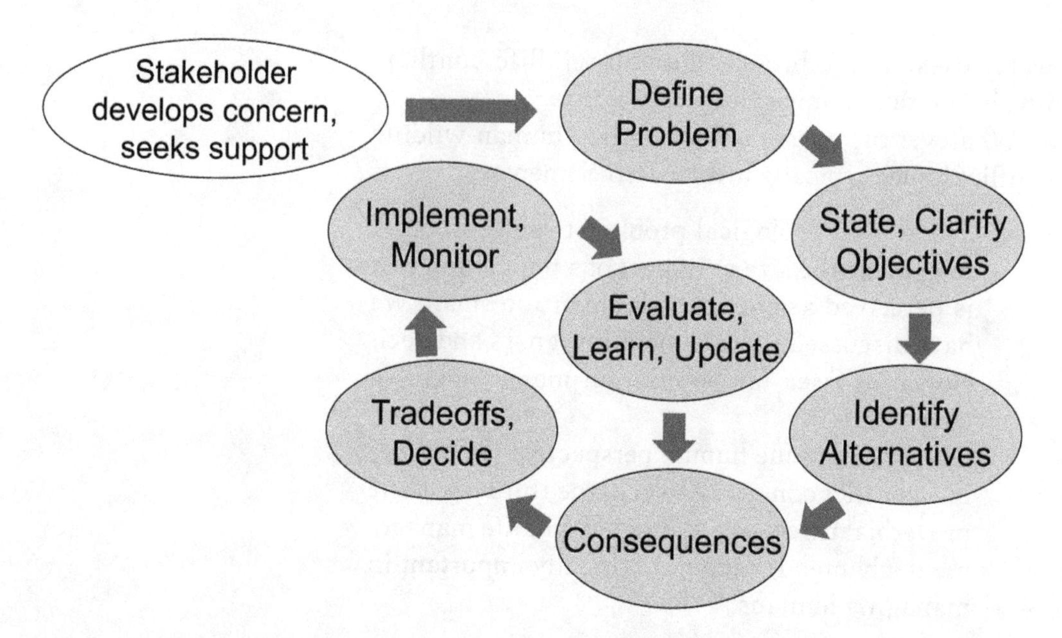

FIGURE 11.1 The PrOACT decision-making process, modified for human-wildlife conflict situations in which the problem is brought to the decision team's attention by stakeholder input or contact.

Problem Definition in Decision-Making for Human-Wildlife Conflicts

The **stakeholder** is an important concept to wildlife management in general. However, in the realm of human-wildlife conflicts, the stakeholder plays a key role of defining the problem. Without a perceived problem, there would be no conflict. The recognition of a perceived problem by a management organization often happens following a complaint from a stakeholder. Therefore, the model for decision-making and adaptive management in human-wildlife conflict has an additional component (Decker et al. 2002, Figure 11.1).

Problem definition is an extremely important step in human-wildlife conflict, because of the manner in which a perceived problem is identified. It is typical for a stakeholder to identify a superficial problem, for which there is a deeper, underlying problem. Therefore, we return to the concepts of ultimate and proximate factors that we first encountered in chapter 9 regarding solutions to declining populations of threatened or endangered species.

Proximate factors are often the most obvious and immediate factors causing a complaint from a stakeholder. **Ultimate factors** describe the root cause of the conflict, and, as a result, may be more difficult to address and solve (Madden and McQuinn 2014).

We might look at **urban wildlife** as an example of human-wildlife conflict to illustrate the importance of problem definition with regard to proximate and ultimate factors.

Consider the blooming wildlife control industry in urban centers. A large number of homeowners, especially in towns and cities, experience damage from a variety of wildlife species to their home, garden, outbuildings, yard, ornamental trees, and even their pets. Fox squirrels chew on drain spouts, woodpeckers make holes in siding, deer chew on newly planted shrubbery, red foxes kill pet chickens or ducks, or groundhogs dig holes on the lawn. These species of wildlife are well adapted to urban habitats, and the problems reported are important to property owners because of economic loss experienced.

For urban wildlife damage, the problems identified by stakeholders are usually proximate issues. Wildlife control professionals can install better fence on chicken pens, find ways to dissuade squirrels from chewing on metal drain spouts, and show landowners how to protect against deer browsing on shrubs. However, the animals causing the problem will mostly likely just shift their focus to the neighbor, who will be calling the wildlife control business the next week.

The ultimate factor with many urban problems is the expanding populations of wildlife that are found in urban environments. How can we address this ultimate factor? Certainly, it will not happen at the single homeowner level, and cities cannot halt growth to reduce conflict with wildlife. Cities must work to address these issues through urban design or city regulations. For example, the provision for corridors for some species to move around a city rather than through it may be a solution. A city ordinance against feeding deer corn in the winter may be a solution.

However, some ultimate factors are not possible to eliminate. Therefore, in similar fashion to the **mitigation** measures used for invasive species when eradication is not possible, some human-wildlife conflicts must be managed at the proximate level. Squirrels and woodpeckers are going to be a part of the urban environment, but an assessment of mast-producing trees (e.g., oaks, hickories, walnuts) in the city forestry plan might reduce the number of acorns available to support a larger population of squirrels.

An example of city planning can be found with rock doves, or pigeons, in the barrio of Old San Juan, Puerto Rico. Pigeons are known hosts of 60 disease pathogens and can transmit diseases to humans and domestic animals (Haag-Wackernagel and Moch 2004). Virtually every city in the world has large numbers of pigeons. Stakeholders may complain about pigeons perching or depositing fecal material on buildings and sidewalks. These health hazards and nuisances are proximate in nature, and there are many solutions that have been developed in an attempt to affect how pigeons use urban space. Spikes can be installed on window ledges or rooftops. Birds can be poisoned, although the effect

FIGURE 11.2 Pigeons in Old San Juan, Puerto Rico. Feeding by tourists (left) and nesting sites found in old walls (right) promote population growth through high reproductive output and high levels of survival. Photos by the author.

on non-target species must be considered. In the end, most approaches just move the problem to another location.

Of course, the pigeon problem exists because pigeons survive and reproduce well in urban environments—the ultimate factors. If we make a critical assessment of San Juan, Puerto Rico we may find some design flaws in existing policies and city structures, and these flaws are found in cities around the world that experience similar problems with pigeons.

- Some residents make a living selling food in city squares to tourists who find feeding pigeons to be an exciting activity. What child does not enjoy coaxing wildlife close (Figure 11.2)? Of course, this increases the potential for spread of disease and the food helps to supplement the survival and reproductive health of an already robust pigeon population.
- Segments of the city walls of Old San Juan appear to be specially made for nesting pigeons (Figure 11.2). While residents are complaining about pigeon populations, the urban system is supporting the existence of the species.

Planning of structural architecture and regulations on feeding pigeons could be a start to addressing the population ecology of pigeons to mitigate the human-wildlife conflict. *Without recognition of the ultimate factor in this issue, the conflict will never be addressed in a satisfactory manner because the objectives and alternatives will only be aimed at the proximate problems of birds perching where people do not want them to perch.*

QUICK COMPREHENSION CHECK

For the pigeon problem (Figure 11.2), list evidence of the proximate and ultimate problems that a city manager might encounter through interactions with citizens

Integrated Responses to Human-Wildlife Conflict

Wildlife managers who specialize in the field of human-wildlife conflict, especially related to damage caused by wildlife, often recommend the use of **integrated management** to maximize the potential to achieve the management objective. However, the term "integrated" has had a range of uses in our profession through the years:

- **Multi-faceted approach:** The choice to select simultaneously more than one alternative management action. To reduce damage of Canada geese on a golf course, a superintendent might hire a person with a specially trained dog to harass geese on the course, while planting vegetation between the lake and a playing surface to prohibit movement of geese, while also selectively applying chemical retardants to high-value turf surfaces (Powell et al. 2004).
- **Systems approach:** The consideration of management strategies that would simultaneously address issues for a variety of damage-causing species. An aquaculture facility may be at risk of economic loss of fish from diving and wading birds and aquatic mammalian predators. Rather than design species-specific protections, a systems approach would emphasize facility design to protect fish from any potential natural predator (Hygnstrom 1990).
- **Biological and social considerations:** The evaluation of a conflict situation that includes a human dimensions assessment. To develop a successful

set of protocols to address conflicts between black bears and humans in urban areas, a management team might conduct surveys of the public to determine their attitudes toward bears and their expectations and preferences for management responses (Don Carlos et al. 2009).

- **Non-lethal and lethal alternatives:** The inclusion of non-lethal alternatives in consideration for approaching problems of damage-causing animals. A consultant called to solve a problem with raccoons invading trash in a neighborhood might have used trapping or shooting in the early period of animal damage control, but modern approaches would consider a suite of actions to eliminate the potential for conflict without killing the raccoons. A key consideration in this paradigm is the realization that the problem may likely be caused by humans and not the raccoons (Fall and Jackson 1998). For example, behavioral modifications for neighbors, including use of trash cans with pest-proof lids and improvement of sanitary conditions, may make the neighborhood less attractive to foraging mammals.

Although the definition of "integrated management" may vary, it is clear that the pronouncement of such a technique usually means a more complex approach to the problem than simply targeting the animal, often with lethal control. Indeed, **Integrated Wildlife Damage Management (IWDM)** is a modification by wildlife biologists of the concept of **Integrated Pest Management** (IPM), often applied to plants and their diseases. IPM was developed as a holistic approach to combat plant pests and diseases to minimize the application of chemical pesticides (Stenberg 2017). In the case of Integrated Wildlife Damage Management, managers use a holistic approach to minimize the use of lethal control in situations in which wildlife cause damage to property.

USDA APHIS (2004) defines Integrated Wildlife Damage Management as:

> The integration and application of all approved methods of prevention and management to reduce wildlife damage. The IWDM approach may incorporate cultural practices, habitat modification, animal behavior management, local population reduction, or a combination of these approaches. The selection of wildlife damage management methods and their application must consider the species causing the damage and the magnitude, geographic extent, duration, frequency, and likelihood of recurring damage. In addition, consideration is given to non-target species, environmental conditions and impacts, social and legal factors, and relative costs of management options.

There are numerous alternatives to consider for an integrated management plan for human-wildlife conflict (Table 11.1). Each alternative may be evaluated based on its perceived effectiveness in a given situation during the PrOACT decision process (Figure 11.1).

TABLE 11.1 ***Summary of technical management alternatives used to mitigate human-wildlife conflict (modified from Dickman 2010, used with permission).***

CONFLICT MITIGATION APPROACH	TECHNIQUES	EXAMPLES
PHYSICAL SEPARATION OF CONFLICTING SPECIES AND RESOURCES	Fencing/enclosing resource	Livestock enclosures; placing fences, electric fences, trenches, flagging, trenches, netting or other defense structures around resource
	Repellents/deterrents and scaring devices	Visual repellents, acoustic repellents, chemical repellents (including odor and taste repellents), rubber bullets or other projectile deterrents, radio-activated guard boxes
	Fencing protected areas	Electric fencing or other fencing around boundaries of protected area
GUARDING ASSETS	Guarding and warning animals	Specialized livestock guarding dogs, other guardian animals such as donkeys and llamas, local dogs to warn of predator presence
	Human guardians	Human guarding of resources, for example staying in crop fields to scare away herbivores, herders going out with stock or staying in/around enclosures to protect from carnivores
	Physical devices on livestock	Protection collars, king collars, cyanide collars
HABITAT USE AND MODIFICATION	Habitat manipulation to reduce conflicts	Mowing vegetation around airports to reduce bird strikes, increasing heather on grouse moors to reduce grouse predation, burning vegetation to reduce cover for wild animals
	Habitat zoning	Demarcate habitat into different land use zones to prioritize human or wildlife use
BEHAVIOR MODIFICATION OF CONFLICT-CAUSING SPECIES	Physical aversion	Electric collars on conflict-causing animals to avert them from approaching resource
	Conditioned taste aversion	Lithium chloride and other chemicals applied to resource, to cause discomfort and aversion after consumption
BEHAVIOR MODIFICATION OF HUMANS RESPONSIBLE FOR RESOURCE	Livestock management	Synchronizing breeding, more conscientious herding, guarding, enclosing stock, carcass disposal, and avoidance of conflict hotspots
	Education and awareness	Reducing own risk factors (e.g., reducing driving speed to avert deer-vehicle conditions, increasing knowledge of the ecology of conflict-causing species and the best techniques for reducing conflict, use of conflict verification teams to help people correctly identify species causing conflict)

(continued)

TABLE 11.1 ***(Continued)***

CONFLICT MITIGATION APPROACH	TECHNIQUES	EXAMPLES
USE OF BUFFER RESOURCES	Buffer crops	Planting of buffer crops to reduce consumption of important resources
	Relocation of people	Local people encouraged or made to move out of wildlife areas
	Artificial provision of alternative food sources	Diversionary feeding for conflict-causing species
	Maintenance of alternative food sources	Maintenance of wild prey for carnivores, maintenance of wild crops for herbivores to avoid consumption of human resources
LETHAL CONTROL OF CONFLICT-CAUSING SPECIES	Population control	Widespread killing of conflict-causing species to avoid conflict, selective culling to limit population growth
	Retaliatory killing	Killing of conflict-causing species as a response to ongoing conflict
	Problem animal control	Targeted lethal control of "problem animals"
NON-LETHAL CONTROL OF CONFLICT-CAUSING SPECIES	Sterilization	Contraception, physical sterilization of conflict-causing animals
	Removal of problem animals	Translocation, relocation, placement of wild conflict-causing animals into captivity
REDUCING COSTS OF CONFLICT	Alleviating economic costs of conflict	Compensation schemes for wildlife losses, insurance cover for resources
	Economic incentives to maintain conflict- causing species	Direct payments for conservation of conflict-causing species
	Alternative income generation	Diversifying income sources away from pure dependence upon resource under competition
	Increasing benefits of wildlife	Increasing economic benefits of wildlife (e.g., through tourism, revenue-sharing schemes or wildlife-related employment, and/or increasing lifestyle benefits such as providing recreation opportunities through activities including wildlife viewing or hunting, or provision of meat from wildlife hunting)

Conflict Resolution

Conflict at some level is a part of all management decision-making processes in natural resources, and we refer to stakeholder disagreements during decision-making (chapter 3), population management (chapter 6), harvest management (chapter 7), planning to support threatened and endangered species (chapter 9), responses to invasive species (chapter 10), and management of habitat (chapter 14). However, human-wildlife conflict, by definition, requires further exploration of processes that may be used to manage people involved in conflict situations with wildlife.

The American Management Association defines five steps to mitigate conflicts between individuals and group, which we can adapt for human-human conflict about wildlife:

Step One: Identify the Source of the Conflict

The problem must be defined in full, following initial problem recognition. In the context of a stakeholder complaint or a community request for help, the decision team must become familiar with the concerns. Public meetings and discussions to gain information is critical at this stage. Stakeholder buy-in to the eventual solution can be increased by encouragement to share their story and perspective on the issue.

Step Two: Look Beyond the Incident

Stakeholders are likely to relate their perspective as proximal factors of the issue. It is completely within the realm of human experience to be selfish and see the world through our own perspective. While gathering the stories and perspectives in step one, the decision team needs to take the collection of statements and build a whole from the parts. What common issue underlies each proximal concern? What is the ultimate problem that seems to be causing the problem?

Step Three: Request Solutions

Working with stakeholders to develop potential management alternatives is critical for eventual participation in the solution. Stakeholders may provide ideas for how to improve the situation. If the decision team spawns a potential solution, the team can get stakeholder feedback on the realistic implementation of that alternative. This step develops ownership of the problem. In situations where stakeholder groups are aggressive in their

QUICK COMPREHENSION CHECK

Consider the problem of pigeons in Old San Juan, Puerto Rico from earlier in this chapter. Using Table 11.1, what possible solutions could be attempted to reduce the human-pigeon conflict?

disagreement, this step may carefully turn the discussion away from finger pointing towards alternatives that could resolve the conflict.

Step Four: Identify Solutions Both Disputants Can Support

Following the brainstorming of potential solutions, which in the case of human-wildlife conflict may be featured in Table 1, the community must decide which alternatives are mutually acceptable. The decision team can influence this discussion through providing potential tradeoffs and predictions for how each alternative might affect the system. This step is the most critical when a community is not in agreement, and not all situations will magically have a compromise alternative that appears to please everyone. In many cases, a mediator or professional facilitator may be necessary to find compromise and build cooperation (chapter 3).

Step Five: Agreement

The action phase of the conflict situation should start with an active process to bring all parts of a community together to support the action. A vote or a signed proclamation or other active request to have participants declare their support can be critical. In some cases, a formal agreement may actually be a part of the solution (e.g., ranchers agreeing not to shoot predators if they are reimbursed for losses to their livestock).

Community-Based Management for Conflicts

Community-based management is a common principle, worldwide, to reduce conflict and solve natural resource problems. Rather than impose a solution on a community from a governmental institution, the strategy is to involve the community in the decision-making process from start to finish. As such, community-based management is, at its heart, an exemplary application of the PrOACT decision-making process (chapter 3, Figure 11.1), but the focus on stakeholders is critical to success.

We typically use *community* to refer to the group of affected citizens close to the problem, but community-based management can occur at multiple scales, from neighboring ranchers to a local village to an entire region. As scale increases, communication between community members becomes more difficult. Support of agencies and NGOs can be critical to the success of community-based management at the landscape scale (Powell et al. 2017).

Human-human conflicts are at the heart of many modern human-wildlife conflicts, which may involve relationships between authorities and local people, or between people of different cultural backgrounds. For example, the regulation of endangered species by a wildlife government agency can create economic impacts on a community. A region may be impacted by invasive species and demand action by the authorities. Or, a group of indigenous people may use lethal control of predators that is satisfactory to them but causes worldwide alarm because of a threat to a species of conservation concern.

We can often trace conflict to social factors in a community, and these issues may be disproportionate to the level of damage caused by wildlife. Thus, it is important that wildlife managers come to the table with an understanding of the complex social fabric that is involved in a conflict issue. Understanding the mechanisms of conflict may help to identify solutions that solve the ultimate factors underlying the conservation problem (Dickman 2010). As trained biologists, wildlife managers are often aware of the environmental influences of the ecosystem, the management context, the population size, and the behavior of the animal. However, we also must consider social factors such as power structures and inequality in an affected community, the poverty level and vulnerability of community members, the levels of distrust of authorities or distrust between community groups, and beliefs and values of a community that impact their perception of costs of the human-wildlife conflict (Dickman 2010, Figure 11.3).

Community-based management should involve a facilitator to be highly effective (Figure 11.4). Regardless of the level of formal mediation, a wildlife manager can work to ensure the following characteristics of a functional, collaborative decision are present in a decision-making process (Gamman 1994, McGinnis et al. 1999):

1. **Representation and assistance for weaker parties**. A process can only be successful if all of the agencies, groups, and individuals with a stake in the outcome are represented at the negotiating table. This means that any party who possesses veto power (e.g., has legal standing and can file a lawsuit or make an administrative appeal to block a decision) needs to be included in the negotiation. In addition, representatives to the negotiation who lack technical and financial resources require support (Figure 11.4).

QUICK COMPREHENSION CHECK

Consider the five steps in conflict resolution. Compare them with the PrOACT decision-making process for human-wildlife conflict (Figure 11.1). What similarities do you see? What PrOACT steps are involved in conflict resolution?

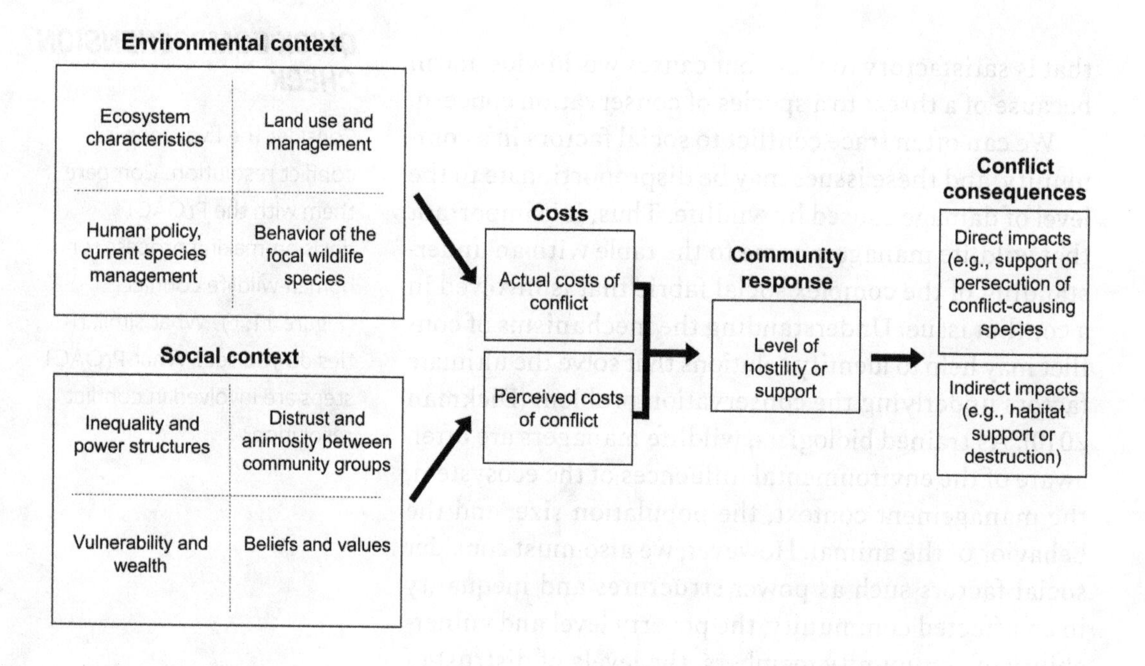

FIGURE 11.3 Relationship of environmental and social context to actual or perceived costs that lead to various levels of hostility or support in a human-wildlife conflict. Modified from Dickman 2010.

2. **Equal access to scientific information.** Informed decisions are dependent on the development and use of high-quality, clear, and well-documented scientific information. The path of gathering scientific information should be made accessible to participants in watershed organizations.
3. **Participation.** Once representation is assured, participants have to be given a full and fair opportunity to participate in the negotiation process.
4. **Accountability and legitimacy.** Participants in a collaborative process need to be held accountable for decisions they make and agreements to which they are a party. This requires that representatives at the table report regularly to their constituency to ensure broad buy-in to agreements. To provide the necessary legitimacy, the process should: (a) account for the attitudes and perceptions of the participants, (b) represent the interests of all participants, and (c) show participants what they can gain from participation.
5. **Commitment to the process.** Participants and the organizations they represent must be fully committed to the collaborative process. This includes offering resources for the use of the negotiation process (scientific, educational and political resources) to ensure that agreements that emerge from it will be implemented.

FIGURE 11.4 Public meetings are key to management of situations involving human-wildlife conflict. Left, a public meeting in June 2017 at Mattamuskeet High School, Swanquarter, North Carolina to begin the scoping process for an environmental review of the only red wolf population that exists in the wild (USFWS photo, public domain). Right, a public meeting held in July 2009 on the Ehirovipuka Conservancy in Namibia to discuss a grazing management program to support livestock protection from predators (photo by the author).

6. **Sustaining cultural values.** Watershed and ecosystems include human inhabitants and communities that possess social values and concerns. The citizenry places different values on how to organize and conduct human activities in the watershed and ecosystem.
7. **Creating adaptive decision-making**. As ecosystems are better understood, this information needs to be fed back in to the collaborative decision-making process. Successful negotiation processes change the nature of the relationship between human culture and ecology. Organizations developing new management strategies as an outcome of collaborative processes should therefore be flexible and allow experimentation, in order to adapt to these changing cultural values, perceptions, political pressures, scientific data, and ecological conditions.

QUICK COMPREHENSION CHECK

What key features support potential success of community-based approached (Figure 11.4) to human-wildlife conflicts?

Digging Deeper: Wildlife-Livestock Conflict

Damage to items that are of economic value to people have high potential for conflict, and wildlife and livestock conflicts are a common problem on every continent. African lions kill cattle and goats in southern Africa, tigers are a threat to cattle in Southeast Asia, red foxes kill sheep in Europe, and coyotes kill sheep and calves in North America.

The United States has a long history of lethal control of livestock predators, especially coyotes. In fiscal year 2017, USDA APHIS Wildlife Services employees killed 68,913 coyotes and destroyed an additional 393 dens. Also killed in 2017 were 355 gray wolves, 316 cougars, 2,062 gray foxes, 1,513 red foxes, and 353 American badgers (USDA APHIS Wildlife Services 2017). The number of coyotes killed has varied between 50,000 and 110,000 annually since 1939 (Bergstrom 2017).

Much of the lethal control of wildlife occurs on private land, at the request of the landowner, to solve a damage-causing situation. However, lethal control of predators by a government agency creates its own human-human conflict, due to public concerns about the use of lethal techniques (Figure 11.5, Arthur 1981). The preference for non-lethal techniques has spurred the development of Integrated Wildlife Damage Management responses. Further, many lines of evidence suggest that lethal removal of predators is ineffective to reduce local populations due to density dependent responses that result in higher productivity in remaining individuals, as well as immigration of new individuals from surrounding areas (Bergstrom et al. 2014).

Predator control efforts have been used successfully in European countries such as the United Kingdom, and these programs aim to completely remove predators from a large landscape for the benefit of gamebird production. However, teams of full-time gamekeepers are employed to carry out this time- and labor-intensive task. Predators return to managed areas as soon as the control efforts decline or stop, and predator control

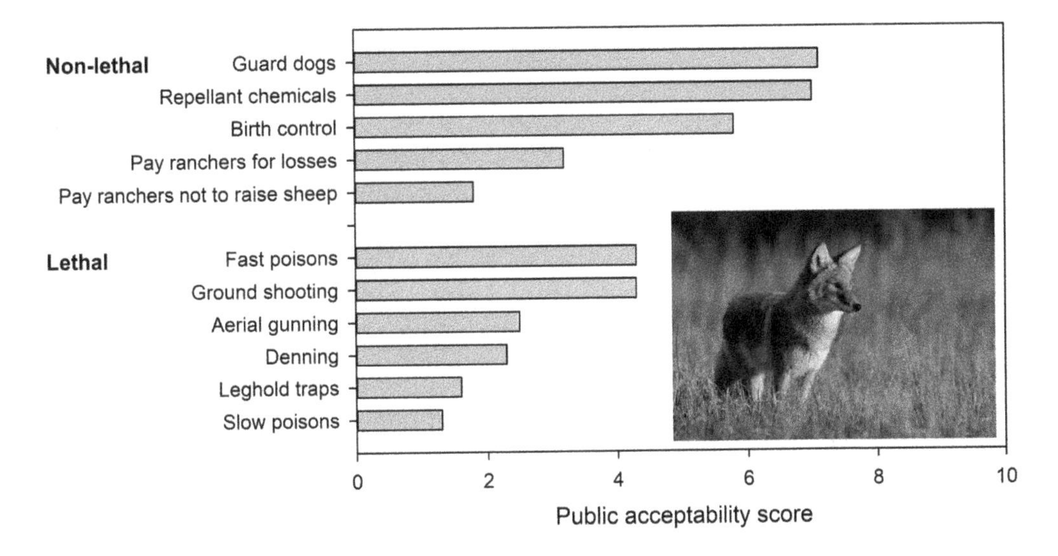

FIGURE 11.5 Comparison of acceptability (0: very unacceptable, 10: very acceptable) for a selection of non-lethal (top) and lethal (bottom) management alternatives to address coyote predation on sheep. Data from Arthur 1981, inset photo by Peter Eades, USFWS public domain.

efforts in the US typically are not implemented at a large spatial scale and with constant effort over time (Riley and Schulz 2001).

In addition to considerations of the effective nature of predator control, wildlife managers also find that predator control is complicated. Removal of predators has ecosystem-level effects, and predators can serve valuable roles to regulate other populations that cause economic damage. For example, in 1887 hawks and owls were shot regularly for rewards by the state government in Pennsylvania, and a government biologist used the stomach contents of these raptors to show that the $90,000 in bounty paid to shooters had saved $1,875 in chickens but cost the state $3.9 million in lost value of rodent and insect control (Robinson 2005). Current removal of coyotes in Arizona to reduce losses of calves for livestock producers has been linked to increases in jackrabbits, which reduces forage available for cattle. Thus, the trade-offs of a decision to implement predator control are often difficult to predict.

The joint downsides of current public opinion towards lethal control (Figure 11.5) and the economic hurdle to provide expensive, constant pressure to ensure the success of predator control often combine to encourage managers to seek other, non-lethal options to solve wildlife-livestock conflicts. Throughout the world, integrated responses to wildlife-livestock conflicts have been innovative, and many of the exemplary cases include community-based management. Consider the following examples of success stories.

Yellowstone National Park: Wolf Reintroduction and Cattle Ranchers

In the 1980s, biologists had worked to lay the groundwork for reintroduction of wolves to Yellowstone National Park. One large hurdle stood in the way: the wolves would ignore park boundaries and eventually kill livestock owned by ranchers who had cattle on private land or on grazing allotments on public land. Sentiment among members of the public in the region was against the reintroduction.

President Ronald Reagan's director of the National Park Service, William Mott, pushed for the reintroduction, and encouraged conservation groups to work towards development of a fund to compensate ranchers for their losses. "Economics makes ranchers hate the wolf. Pay them for their losses and you'll buy tolerance and take away their only legitimate reason to oppose wolf recovery," he stated (Nylus et al. 2003).

Defenders of Wildlife (DOW), a not-for-profit conservation organization, had established a **compensation program** for livestock losses to wolves prior to the first release of wolves in Yellowstone in January 1995. When a loss occurs, a rancher contacts the state or federal agency. A trained biologist investigates within 48 hours to determine if wolves were responsible for the incident. If warranted, the DOW team contacts the rancher to develop a payment amount, based on the value of the livestock. University extension personnel provide a value if the rancher disputes the offer from DOW. No paperwork is required from the rancher, and the program aims to have checks in the hands of ranchers within two to four weeks.

After some complaints that the standards for verification were too high, the program added a category of *probable losses.* Losses in this category were given payment of half the market value, to account for cases in which strong circumstantial evidence suggested wolf predation (Nyhus et al. 2003).

If compensation schemes for wildlife-livestock conflicts are not structured properly, they may result in more risky behavior on the part of the livestock owner. For example, the use of shepherds or nightly round-ups to prevent predator damages may be discontinued in favor of dependence on compensation when damage occurs. However, such programs have been successful around the world to protect tigers, gray wolves, Canada lynx, snow leopards, and grizzly bears, among others. Successful compensation schemes include the following elements (Nyhus et al. 2003):

- **Quick, accurate verification of damage:** Training of verifiers is critical, as is the process to establish trust among participants to ensure the process is fair.
- **Prompt, fair payment:** Payments should be based on market value or other unbiased source, and timely payments may relieve tensions and further conflict.
- **Sustainable funding source:** A compensation program that runs out of money may cause more problems than it initially solves.

- **Local specificity:** The location of a potential compensation program and the stakeholders must be used in the planning process, and the community should be involved in the establishment of the program and its rules.
- **Clear guidelines:** Compensation should be linked to sound management practices, and the compensation program should discourage risky behavior by the livestock producer. Successful programs often require the documentation of sound management practices before payment is approved.
- **Measures of success:** The compensation program should set objectives (e.g., fewer predators killed by livestock producers over time) and be evaluated like any other management decision.

Namibia: Predator Persecution by Farmers

Private farmers in Namibia often kill cheetahs and other predators such as leopards and hyenas in response to livestock damages. In fact, surveys suggest that an average of 19 cheetahs are removed per farm per year (Marker et al. 2003). The Cheetah Conservation Fund (CCF), a not-for-profit conservation organization, has taken a unique approach to reduce shooting and trapping of predators. Realizing that the ultimate issue for farmers is the economic loss incurred during a predation event, CCF has developed farmer training courses on animal husbandry to improve profits for farmers. The logic used in this approach is that farmers who make more money are less likely to see the loss of a single calf or sheep as an event that merits retribution by killing cheetahs or other predators.

Through interviews and surveys of farmers, CCF staff determined that calving rates in many cattle herds were less than 50% cows giving birth each year. Through training courses, farmers are taught techniques that improve calving rates by 20–30%. More calves are born on farms, increasing profits. The integrated approach by CCF also includes a guard dog program that trains and provides guard dogs to farmers to protect sheep and goat herds, and farmers reported financial savings of US $3,000 per farm after adopting guard dogs (Marker and Boast 2015).

South and Central Asia: Snow Leopards and Local Communities

Snow leopards are endangered, and their range includes 13 countries in South and Central Asia, including Afghanistan, Bhutan, China, India, Kyrgyzstan, Kazakhstan, Nepal, Mongolia, Pakistan, Russia, Tajikistan, and Uzbekistan. The predators hunt in high elevation rangelands, and thus frequently encounter grazing livestock. The livestock owners are typically poor with annual incomes less than US $500 per year, and their rangelands are not productive. The residents are scratching a living in a harsh environment.

Human-wildlife conflict occurs when snow leopards kill livestock, and estimates suggest that snow leopards, on average, take less than 5% of herds per year. However, resentment occurs when, on occasion, snow leopards enter a livestock corral and kill an entire flock of sheep or goats in a single night. Retribution killing of snow leopards often results. The use of protected areas or law enforcement to protect snow leopards is extremely prone to failure in the remote, harsh range of the snow leopard.

Instead, a consortium of conservation organizations has worked to implement integrated, community-based responses to protect snow leopards and to respond to economic concerns of the local people. The approach used by the conservation workers is to treat every culture and community as unique. A suite of community-based solutions is available from which to select a management response in a given situation (Jackson et al. 2010):

- **Incentive programs** have been developed in which conservation organizations provide markets for wool products (Figure 11.6) in return for moratoriums on snow leopard and ungulate poaching in Mongolia. Compliance may bring a bonus over the normal price for their products, and a single violation in a community may violate the entire community's bonus, which creates positive peer pressure to affect behavioral change.
- **Ecotourism development** has been successful in India, where conservation organizations provide training to villagers to run homestays for tourists and nature guiding, which may double their annual income. A portion of the income goes to the community for activities such as tree planting or garbage management, and the community is aware that the tourists come to have a chance to glimpse snow leopards and other local wildlife.
- **Educational initiatives** have been used in several countries within the snow leopard range to form youth clubs and provide material to school teachers to assist with learning experiences focused on conservation. Many local people are not aware of the uniqueness of their wildlife community or the plight of the snow leopard.
- **Training in grazing management** may impact rangelands to provide food for grazing wildlife that may normally be consumed by local livestock, thereby providing a prey base for snow leopards. Simple concepts such as rotational grazing plans or the use of a shepherd to guide flocks to allow rest of portions of the rangeland may result in high impact. The community benefits from increased livestock production and higher stocking capacity.
- **Sustainable trophy hunting**, marketed with the assistance of conservation organizations to an international audience, can provide food from the hunted animals and income distributed to the community. The presence of the hunts for species like ibex provides an incentive to local community members to protect the local ungulate population, and the assistance to create the market for hunting can carry with it a moratorium on snow leopard poaching. Conservation organizations must ensure that profits are spread through the community in a transparent fashion, as corruption may halt the effectiveness of the program.

FIGURE 11.6 Villagers in Sham Valley, Ladakh attend a handicraft training workshop organized by Snow Leopard Conservancy-India Trust (SLC-IT)/Panthera to supplement homestay incomes where participants learned the art of making toy animals (here, snow leopard and ibex) from locally sourced wool using a needle felting technique. These crafts are also sold at the SCL-IT souvenir shop in Leh, the main city in Ladakh. Photo credit: SLC-IT/Panthera, used with permission.

- **Animal husbandry training**, including the availability of inexpensive vaccinations to fight livestock disease, can promote profits for community members. In Pakistan, this method reduced disease losses in livestock by 90%, which doubled family income. As with other programs, the community must be involved in the planning and development of the program to insure buy-in and cooperation with agreements to halt the killing of snow leopards.

All of these alternative approaches to a community-based conservation program are designed to improve the economic condition of the community, which should reduce problems with poverty. Human-wildlife conflicts are exacerbated when poverty conditions exist, because the lost livestock represents a high proportion of annual income for the community member.

In these examples, we see evidence of the need to be able to identify and separate the proximate and ultimate problems in a situation. Successful programs start with the realization that a unique solution must be found for a particular time and place, and with the knowledge that the effort to work with the community has the potential to increase the success rate of any attempt to solve human-wildlife conflict. We also see the need for passionate, innovative wildlife managers who are motivated to find solutions to protect species of conservation concern.

QUICK COMPREHENSION CHECK

For each of the alternative approaches to community-based conservation of snow leopards, can you identify a dynamic or event that might cause failure of the program? What might be done to avoid dynamics that lead to failure?

WRAPPING UP

Can you describe the idea of an integrated approach to human-wildlife conflicts to Belinda, the bank vice president in our initial problem case? How might she work with the community stakeholders to find a solution to the problem?

Decision-Making on the Ground

1: Conflict Caused by Predators of Livestock on Grazing Allotments on Public Lands

Public lands, such as national parks, national forests, national wildlife refuges, or lands managed by the Bureau of Land Management (BLM) require grazing management by cattle (Figure 11.7) in the absence of bison or other native grazers. Rather than government ownership of large cattle herds, public land managers use a system of permits and leases that allow private ranchers to graze their cattle on public lands. Areas designated for this purpose are known as **grazing allotments**.

As one example of the area affected by grazing allotments, the BLM administers nearly 18,000 permits and leases held by ranchers who graze their livestock, mostly cattle and sheep, at least part of the year on more than 21,000 allotments under BLM management.

Grazing leases have economic value to ranchers. Ranchers frequently sell these permits to one another and banks loan money based on the value of the grazing allotment. Applicants typically must own other base property and livestock to prove they have land to move cattle during periods when grazing is not allowed on the allotment. The allotments are difficult to get, as not many are available. Most allotments have been leased for more than one generation by a family.

Wolf and grizzly bear populations are faring well in Yellowstone National Park and adjacent wilderness areas that comprise their primary range in the Yellowstone ecosystem. From the rancher perspective, grizzly bear and gray wolf depredation of livestock is high in some specific grazing allotments on public land near

FIGURE 11.7 Cattle grazing in an allotment east of the Owyhee River Canyon near Soldier Creek, Oregon. Photo by Greg Shine, Bureau of Land Management, public domain photo.

Grand Teton National Park and Yellowstone National Park. Loss of livestock creates lower profitability for ranchers in these lease areas, and human-wildlife conflicts arise from the potential for bears and wolves to be killed. In fact, conflict with domestic livestock is one of the leading sources of wolf and bear mortality. In most cases, the loss of bears or wolves runs counter to the conservation programs designed to support their populations.

At first glance, it might seem as if public land managers could just cancel specific leases at the end of a lease agreement period to create buffer zones around the parks where cattle are not grazed. However, the value of the lease areas to ranchers makes it impossible to withdraw the allotment from offer.

When federal agencies created public land grazing allotments more than a century ago, they were permitted almost anywhere with acceptable rangelands. However, as the mission of public lands expanded to provide for conservation of threatened and endangered species and protection of watersheds, public land managers had to balance competing uses of land.

Status of grizzly bears in Yellowstone:
In September 2009, the Federal District Court in Missoula issued an order enjoining and vacating the 2007 delisting of the Greater Yellowstone Area grizzly population. This order was reaffirmed in part in 2011, supporting the threatened status of grizzly bears. In 2017, the USFWS ruled to delist grizzly bears, but that ruling was

vacated by the courts in 2018, so the grizzly bear remains a threatened species in the continental US.

Status of gray wolves in Yellowstone:

Initially, gray wolves were reintroduced in 1995 as an "experimental" population with endangered species status. By 2011, gray wolves were delisted and managed by individual states. However, no hunting has been allowed in Yellowstone National Park. In December 2014, two court orders required the USFWS to reinstate regulatory protections for the gray wolf in Wyoming as an endangered species under the ESA . In 2017, a US Court of Appeals order mandated the delisting of wolves in Wyoming. As of 2018, gray wolves in the Northern Rocky Mountain distinct population segment are delisted (not threatened or endangered) and therefore under state management.

APPLICATION, ANALYSIS, SYNTHESIS, AND EVALUATION

Review the problem facing managers and ranchers in Yellowstone and discuss with a classmate. List at least three stakeholders in this conflict.

List a proximate solution for ranchers to lower predation on their livestock. Consider alternatives to human-wildlife conflicts listed in Table 11.1.

What is the ultimate problem facing wildlife managers in this situation? Propose a solution that might solve conflict. Consider examples of solutions for wildlife-livestock conflict in this chapter.

For each of your proposed solutions (proximate and ultimate), list a benefit as well as a potential pitfall that might cause the solution to fail.

The National Wildlife Federation became involved in this issue and created a program to solve the conflicts on grazing allotments. To evaluate the program they created, do an internet search for National Wildlife Federation Wildlife Conflict Resolution Program. What are the components of their solution? Compare their solution to solutions used by other conservation organizations in this chapter.

It seems clear that not-for-profit conservation organizations are playing a key role, worldwide, in solutions for human-wildlife conflict. Why are these organizations well positioned to help fund support programs? Why are they better suited for the task than government agencies?

Sources of Information and Further Reading

Arthur, L. M. "Coyote control: the public response." *Journal of Range Management 34*, no. 1 (1981): 14–15.

Bergstrom, B. J., Arias, L. C., Davidson, A. D., Ferguson, A. W., Randa, L. A., and Sheffield, S. R. "License to kill: reforming federal wildlife control to restore biodiversity and ecosystem function." *Conservation Letters 7*, no. 2 (2014): 131–142.

Clay, W. H. "An Overview of Animal Damage Control (ADC) Assistance to The Vertebrate Pest Management Industry." *Proceedings of the Seventeenth Vertebrate Pest Conference 17* (1996): 51–53.

Decker, D. J., Lauber, T. B., and Siemer, W. F. *Human-Wildlife Conflict Management: a practitioner's guide*. Ithaca, NY: Cornell University, 2002.

Dickman, A. J. "Complexities of conflict: the importance of considering social factors for effectively resolving human-wildlife conflict." *Animal conservation 13*, no. 5 (2010): 458–466.

Don Carlos, A. W., Bright, A. D., Teel, T. L., and Vaske, J. J. "Human-black bear conflict in urban areas: an integrated approach to management response." *Human Dimensions of Wildlife 14*, no. 3 (2009): 174–184.

Fall, M. W. and Jackson, W. B. "A new era of vertebrate pest control? An introduction." *International biodeterioration & biodegradation 42*, no. 2–3 (1998): 85–91.

Frank, M. G. and Conover, M. R. "Thank goodness they got all the dragons: wildlife damage management through the ages." *Human-Wildlife Interactions* 9, no. 2 (2015):156–162.

Gamman, J. K. *Overcoming obstacles in environmental policymaking: Creating partnerships through mediation*. New York: State University of New York Press, 1994.

Haag-Wackernagel, D. and Moch, H. "Health hazards posed by feral pigeons." *Journal of Infection 48*, no. 4 (2004): 307–313.

Hygnstrom, Scott E. "The evolution of vertebrate pest management—the species versus systems approach." *Proceedings of the Fourteenth Vertebrate Pest Conference 14* (1990): 20–24.

Hygnstrom, S. E., R. M. Timm, and G. E. Larson. *Prevention and Control of Wildlife Damage*. Lincoln, NE: University of Nebraska-Lincoln, 1994.

Jackson, R. M., Mishra, C., McCarthy, T. M., and Ale, S. B. "Snow leopards: conflict and conservation." In *The Biology and Conservation of Wild Felids*, 417–430. 2010.

Madden, F. and McQuinn, B. "Conservation's blind spot: the case for conflict transformation in wildlife conservation." *Biological Conservation 178* (2014): 97–106.

Marker, L. L. and Boast, L. K. "Human-wildlife conflict 10 years later: lessons learned and their application to cheetah conservation." *Human Dimensions of Wildlife 20*, no. 4 (2015): 302–309.

Marker, L. L., Mills, M. G. L., and Macdonald, D. W. "Factors influencing perceptions of conflict and tolerance towards cheetahs on Namibian farmlands." *Conservation Biology 17* (2003): 1290–8.

McGinnis, M. V., Woolley, J., and Gamman, J. "Bioregional conflict resolution: rebuilding community in watershed planning and organizing." *Environmental management 24*, no. 1 (1999): 1–12.

Nyhus, P., Fischer, H., Madden, F., and Osofsky, S. "Taking the bite out of wildlife damage the challenges of wildlife compensation schemes." *Conservation in Practice 4*, no. 2 (2003): 37–43.

Peterson, M. N., Birckhead, J. L., Leong, K., Peterson, M. J., and Peterson, T. R. "Rearticulating the myth of human-wildlife conflict." *Conservation Letters 3*, no. 2 (2010): 74–82.

Powell, L. A., M. J. Conroy, G. D. Balkcom, and J. N. Caudell. "Urban Canada geese in Georgia: assessing a golf course survey and a nuisance relocation program." In *Proceedings of the 2003 International Canada Goose Symposium, edited by* Moser, T. J., R. D. Lien, K. C. VerCauteren, K. F. Abraham, D. E. Andersen, J. G. Bruggink, J. M. Coluccy, D. A. Graber, J. O. Leafloor, D. R. Luukkonen and R. E. Trost, 135–139. Madison, WI: 2004.

Powell, L., R. Kharuxab, L. Marker, M. Nghikembua, S. Omusula, R. Reid, A. Snyman, C. Weaver, and M. Wykstra. "Coordination of large landscapes for cheetah conservation." In *Cheetahs: Biology and Conservation*, edited by L. Marker, L. K. Boast, and A. Schmidt-Küntzel, 239–250. Academic Press, 2017.

Riley, T. Z. and Schulz, J. H. "Predation and ring-necked pheasant population dynamics." *Wildlife Society Bulletin 29*, no. 1 (2001): 33–38.

Robinson, M. J. *Predatory bureaucracy: the extermination of wolves and the transformation of the West.* Boulder, CO: University of Colorado Press, 2005.

Stenberg, J. A. "A conceptual framework for integrated pest management." *Trends in plant science 22*, no. 9 (2017): 759–769.

United States Department of Agriculture Animal and Plant Health Inspection Service. *The Wildlife Services Integrated Wildlife Damage Management Program*. WS Directive 2.105. Washington, DC: US Department of Agriculture, 2004.

United States Department of Agriculture Animal and Plant Health Inspection Service. *The* Wildlife Services. *Program Data Report G – 2017.* Washington, DC: US Department of Agriculture, 2017.

Image Credits

Fig. 11.3: A. J. Dickman, "Levels of Hostility from Complexities of Conflict: The Importance of Considering Social Factors for Effectively Resolving Human–wildlife Conflict," Animal Conservation, vol. 13, no. 5. Copyright © 2010 by John Wiley & Sons, Inc.

Fig. 11.4a: Source: https://www.flickr.com/photos/usfwssoutheast/34356924743/in/photolist-fUMMNk-ftPpjS-uGsA61-26jADHf-LWvGNs-27GfapB-2959C96-26jj31q-26jj2Vq-2959C6a-2959BCr-26jj2q7-26jj2eA-2959Bg4-fURgWk-darUGF-ftQdAd-ftQcus-ftQez9-fUMPE7-27Gf7Kt-26jj2kY-2959Bx6-2959BqH-26j.

Fig. 11.5: Copyright © Peter Eades/USFWS (CC by 2.0) at https://www.flickr.com/photos/usfwsmtnprairie/27784783047/in/photolist-JkfgZz-KR8d9q-EVncLu.

Fig. 11.6: Tom McCarthy, "Woman with Wool Figures." Copyright © by Tom McCarthy. Reprinted with permission.

Fig. 11.7: Copyright © Greg Shine/Bureau of Land Management (CC by 2.0) at https://www.flickr.com/photos/blmoregon/35598758355/in/photolist-WeJWBM-UwZxie-Ux6qDa-VbeFch-Vbh12N-Ux6JPt-UtYeM3-Ux2ezz-VyXPWB-ToYYBX-TwMqis-VbmgJS-VyZ4ai-24woULp-fLaDKG-Vbrpxs-VvKkbd-a7Ssma-6RoUu-a7Sw1g-ZaNb95-fLaDMU-a7Vnk9-a7StnT-a7SvNK-fLaDPy-kqWrM-bR.

SECTION VI

Habitat Management

CHAPTER TWELVE

The Ecology of Habitat Management

Learning Outcomes

After participating in learning experiences related to this chapter, students should be able to:

- Describe how soil quality affects plant and animal growth.
- Describe patterns of wildlife abundance and diversity relative to levels of soil quality.
- Describe ecological dynamics that lead to management strategies used for wildlife habitat.
- Draw the stages of terrestrial and aquatic succession.
- Provide a list of alternative management strategies for a given problem in grassland, forest, wetland, or reservoir systems.
- Evaluate components of a simple habitat assessment model.

A One-Minute Summary

The quality of soils effect plant and animal production, and wildlife abundance and diversity are strongly influenced by the distribution of soils in the US. High quality soils are useful for growing agricultural crops, so wildlife abundance is lower in these regions despite having high potential. Food and cover are critical resources that can be affected by wildlife management, and population dynamics are modified indirectly by managers through habitat improvements. Levels of predation, nutrition, and physiological responses to extreme conditions are mechanisms that are manipulated by successful habitat management.

Grassland, forest, wetland, and reservoir management are four of the main fields of habitat management for wildlife. Each area of habitat management allows for specialization, and wildlife managers can become experts at predicting how management decisions will affect a specific system. Regardless of the system, however, a series of ecological, biological, physical, and geological principles are behind the strategies selected for effective habitat management.

Grasslands are managed by aiming disturbances to set succession back to early stages of development. The growth point of grasses allows fire and grazing to be used to reduce woody species, while allowing for recovery by grasses.

Forests are managed through a series of silvicultural methods that provide for different spatial patterns of disturbance on the landscape. Shade tolerant and intolerant tree species respond differently to the silvicultural methods. Economics plays a role in decisions for harvesting trees because of the long periods of time that trees need to grow to harvestable size.

Wetlands are managed through water level decisions, which are critical for plant growth or inhibition as well as the response of various types of wildlife. Wetland succession must be managed to keep wetlands effective for focal species of wildlife.

Reservoirs also experience succession, and siltation and nutrient loads are the largest threats to the life span of reservoirs. A series of watershed management tools may prevent problems from reaching reservoirs, and in-reservoir management may be used to manage water quality to benefit fisheries.

Principles for Your Toolkit

Ecological succession underscores habitat management: The process of change in the plant species structure of an ecological community over time is critical to timing and methods for habitat management. Wildlife species in terrestrial and aquatic habitats respond to the dynamics of plant species structure and soil formation that occurs over time. Wildlife management may target a certain stage of succession as being the most optimal habitat type for a species of interest. Grassland management often involves methods to remove woody tree encroachment. Wetland management may involve removal of emergent vegetation that crowds open water areas or silt removal to deepen pools. All habitat management is based on a knowledge of ecological succession dynamics in a system.

A Problem: Where Did All the Pheasants Go?

Josef, 47, sat at his breakfast table with his daughter, Adriana. She had started her senior year at university, and she looked forward to graduating with a degree in wildlife management. Josef was a farmer in the Oklahoma panhandle, but Adriana had always dreamed of being a manager of a USFWS National Wildlife Refuge.

"My stars!" Josef exclaimed while reading the newspaper. "What are those agency biologists doing to the pheasants in the state?"

Adriana peeked over her father's shoulder and read the story in the sports section:

> Oklahoma pheasant forecast—Similar to other states in the Great Plains this year, pheasant hunters in Oklahoma's panhandle region will likely find fewer birds than last year. Statewide, brood counts were down 10%. The populations are still recovering from last summer's drought. Historically, surveys of pheasant populations in Oklahoma show current levels are six times lower than the 1950s.

"It doesn't look good," Adriana agreed. "But I'm not sure the state wildlife agency is to blame."

"How could the state biologists not be to blame?" her dad asked. "I remember days when we had to beg people to come hunting with us, just to have people to shoot the birds we'd see. Pheasants were like raccoons—you'd always see a dead one on the roads. In the last few years, I haven't seen a pheasant on our road."

Adriana grinned. Some of the state's biologists had given lectures in her university classes, and they did not seem inept. "I think you're being a bit unfair," she replied to her father. "Less than half a percent of Oklahoma is managed by state wildlife biologists. Over 90% is in private farms and ranches. Many of our private rangelands have too many eastern redcedars for pheasants, and modern methods for herbicide use in corn and wheat fields can result in areas with no weeds to attract insects for pheasant broods."

Josef frowned. He knew about government farm incentive programs like CRP, and he was not a fan because he didn't like paying taxes. "You know that our neighbor with the grasslands in the CRP uses the program because their soil can't grow good crops! I haven't seen more pheasants around here after they put their land in CRP, and, you have to agree that if it can't grow crops, it can't grow pheasants."

Adriana reached for her coffee. Her dad had a good point—soil quality certainly could be important to wildlife populations. However, Adriana was sure that their neighbors' land was some of Oklahoma's better soils, which had matched up with areas of large populations of pheasants in the 1950s. She could not help wondering—was the habitat available for pheasants in Oklahoma really the same as the "good old days" that her dad remembered? On the other hand, had there been changes to the landscape that her dad had not noticed? Were the state biologists doing a bad job managing pheasants?

What would you need to learn to determine the cause of decline for pheasants in Oklahoma? What critical resources might available grasslands not provide for pheasants? By the time you finish this chapter, you should be able to find the answer.

Terms and Definitions

Cover: Physical shelter or protection.

Ecosystem services: Benefits that humans gain from the natural environment and from properly functioning ecosystems.

Endothermic: An organism (birds and mammals) capable of the internal generation of heat; compare to ectothermic organisms, which cannot use internal sources of heat to control body temperature.

Eutrophication: Excessive richness of nutrients in a lake or other body of water, frequently due to runoff from the land. The process often results in dense growth of plant life.

Meristem: A region of plant tissue, found chiefly at the growing tips of roots and shoots and in the cambium, consisting of actively dividing cells forming new tissue.

Sedimentation: The process of settling or being deposited as a sediment.

Silviculture: The growing and cultivation of trees.

Thermonetural zone: The range of ambient temperatures where the body can maintain its core temperature solely through regulating dry heat loss (i.e., skin blood flow).

Understory: A layer of vegetation beneath the main canopy of a forest.

Watershed: An area bounded peripherally by a divide that ultimately drains to a particular watercourse or body of water.

Soils and Wildlife

There is a close relationship between the success of wildlife management on private lands in the United States and our nation's farm policy. Soils are in the middle of that story, as they are at the heart of the farm and ranch, which make up the land base of many states in the US.

Local soil conditions vary across the US (Figure 12.1), which affects expectations for plant and animal production (Albrecht 1957). Herds of domestic livestock produce more milk, wool, and meat on better soils, and logic follows that wild animal production should follow the same trends. A major factor in soil quality is the clay content of the soil—soils are made of clay, silt, and sand, and the proportion of each varies from location to location. From a soil nutrient standpoint, clay content is important because it attracts and holds nutrients, such as calcium (Ca), potassium (K), magnesium (Mg), and ammonium (NH_4). Many important nutrients are positively charged, and they bind to the negatively charged clay particle.

As precipitation falls and enters the soil, it leaches nutrients from the top soil strata to the bottom strata, which reduces the soil nutrient levels. For example, tropical soils are ironically very nutrient poor, even though the rainforest deposits a lot of decaying vegetation on the surface of the soil because the near-constant rains leach the nutrients quickly into lower soil levels. Soils with higher clay content tend to hang onto nutrients during leaching because the nutrients are bound to the clay.

Soil pH is also a factor in soil quality. Acidic soils have many hydrogen (H+) cations, and hydrogen bonds are strong. The H+ tends to replace other cations that

FIGURE 12.1 General soils map of the continental United States showing soil color at a 25-cm depth. Data source: USDA, Natural Resource Conservation Service, public domain image.

initially bind to the soil's clay particles, and the nutrients are then leached away by rain. Farmers often apply calcium carbonate, or lime, to the soil to make the soil more basic. The lime treatment reduces the number of free H+ cations and increases the soils potential to hold onto its nutrients.

Wildlife benefit from soil nutrients directly and indirectly. Deer, as an example, use soil nutrients directly at "licks," locations where critical nutrients are available at the surface of the soil. Although wildlife typically get nutrients from their diet, spring foliage is sodium-poor (Na); water and potassium (K) levels are high during this period, and deer seek out mineral licks to obtain necessary sodium.

Soils also are responsible for the distribution of public and private lands in the US. Many of our nation's public lands are found in mountainous or arid regions (Fig. 12.1) that are not suitable for farming, and public land areas are often more marginal for livestock production as well. Therefore, soils are at the heart of a dichotomy of wildlife management approaches for managers who work either on public lands (e.g., national forests, national parks, and national wildlife refuges) or in landscapes with private farms and ranches.

Soil nutrients affect the distribution and movements of animals, and these nutrients can be manipulated by managers. People often use salt blocks to encourage wildlife to visit certain areas (for legal or illegal baiting, wildlife viewing, etc.). Auto/moose collision rates in Quebec, Canada are higher during the winter because the moose visit the highways when they are treated with salt (Grosman et al. 2011). Recent analysis of deer movements has shown that multiple individuals visit mineral licks frequently and these deposits serve as potential sites for disease transmission (Plummer et al. 2018).

Early wildlife biologists in Missouri documented the relationship between soil quality and wildlife quality measures (Crawford 1950). Pelts of Virginia opossum were larger in counties with higher soil fertility. Eastern cottontail femur bones were

COMPREHENSION AND APPLICATION

Scenario for consideration: Biologists assessed the use of mineral licks by adult and yearling male and female white-tailed deer in Indiana. Adult females use licks twice as often as other age/sex classes (Atwood and Weeks, 2002, Am Mid Nat). Female use of licks was especially high during May–July. Why might female deer have different mineral needs at this time of year than male deer?

longer and thicker and had a higher breaking strength in counties with high soil fertility. Fox squirrels had larger litters in areas with higher soil fertility. Certainly, domestic livestock producers are also aware of the relationship between soils and animal production.

Wildlife management should have different goals and expectations with regard to harvested animal production in some circumstances. For example, different soil regions of the state of Mississippi produce deer with varying sized antlers and body size (Table 12.1), and the number of acres needed per individual varies considerably

TABLE 12.1 ***Statistics from harvested white-tailed deer in Mississippi by soil regions of the state, ranked from best to poorest quality soils. Data from Mississippi Wildlife, Fisheries and Parks.***

	MEAN FOR 4.5+ YEAR-OLD BUCKS				
SOIL REGION	LIVE WEIGHT	POINTS	MAIN BEAM (IN)	INSIDE SPREAD (IN)	ACRES PER 3.5+ YEAR-OLD BUCKS
BATTURE	196	8.5	20.9	16.7	251
DELTA	199	8.5	20.4	16.3	381
UPPER THICK LOESS	196	8.4	20.2	16.1	404
LOWER THICK LOESS	183	8.5	19.6	15.4	270
UPPER THIN LOESS	170	8.2	18.5	14.8	529
LOWER THIN LOESS	177	8.2	19.0	15.0	372
BLACK PRAIRIE	174	8.3	18.6	14.8	609
INTERIOR FLATWOODS	173	8.4	18.9	14.9	520
UPPER COASTAL PLAIN	166	8.0	18.2	14.5	673
LOWER COASTAL PLAIN	157	8.0	17.7	14.3	874
COASTAL FLATWOODS	147	7.1	15.8	12.2	1,797

as well. In poor soil regions, a deer requires almost seven times the acres as in the best soil quality regions of the state. Further, the deer that take more space to grow in the poor soil regions will be smaller with lower-ranking antlers. A person wanting to establish a hunt club or hunt lease should definitely consider soil quality as they look at land to purchase. Soil can indirectly influence the quality of animals that live on the land.

Soil and Land Use

As **soil quality** goes from low to high (Figure 12.2, top), the intensity of land use increases. Areas with higher soil fertility can support row crops, large pastures, or

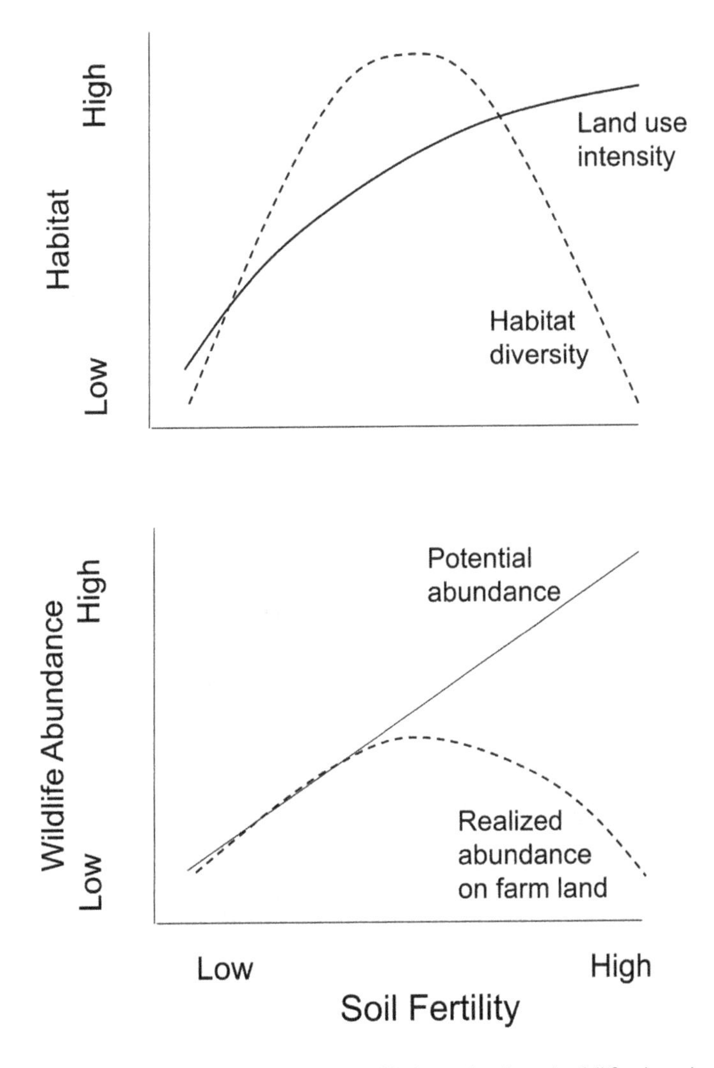

FIGURE 12.2 Relationship between soil fertility and habitat (top) and wildlife abundance (bottom). After concepts in Crawford (1950).

pine plantations, depending on location. Agricultural production areas are often treated with insecticides and herbicides, and the result is often a large area of monoculture habitat, with very little native habitat interspersed. The economics of agriculture are at the root of this dynamic, and the private landowners who have invested in the land use the most efficient methods to produce commodities to sell to feed their families.

Therefore, habitat diversity peaks at mid-soil fertility levels (Figure 12.2, top). Poor soils usually support a simple habitat structure (e.g., arid land areas), and the habitats on the best soils have been modified to be much simpler than their potential.

We might guess that wildlife might also peak in diversity on mid-grade soils, as well, and this turns out to be generally true. Wildlife are limited by low soil quality, just as domestic livestock are limited. All else equal, wildlife densities increase as soil quality increases. We might expect wildlife to be at highest density and diversity on the best soils, but those soils' habitats have been modified and simplified, reducing their potential to support wildlife. Thus, the realized pattern is for wildlife managers to expect mid-grade soils to support more wildlife than poor- or high-quality soils (Figure 12.2, bottom).

A natural experiment was provided for our assessment as agriculture increased in intensity in the United States. Early wildlife biologists documented these simple trends. For example, in Jasper County, Illinois, grasslands in farmland regions were eliminated and brushy fencerows were reduced by 84 percent between 1939 and 1974. Greater prairie chickens disappeared completely from this highly productive landscape with good soils. The northern bobwhite population in 1974 was only 22% of

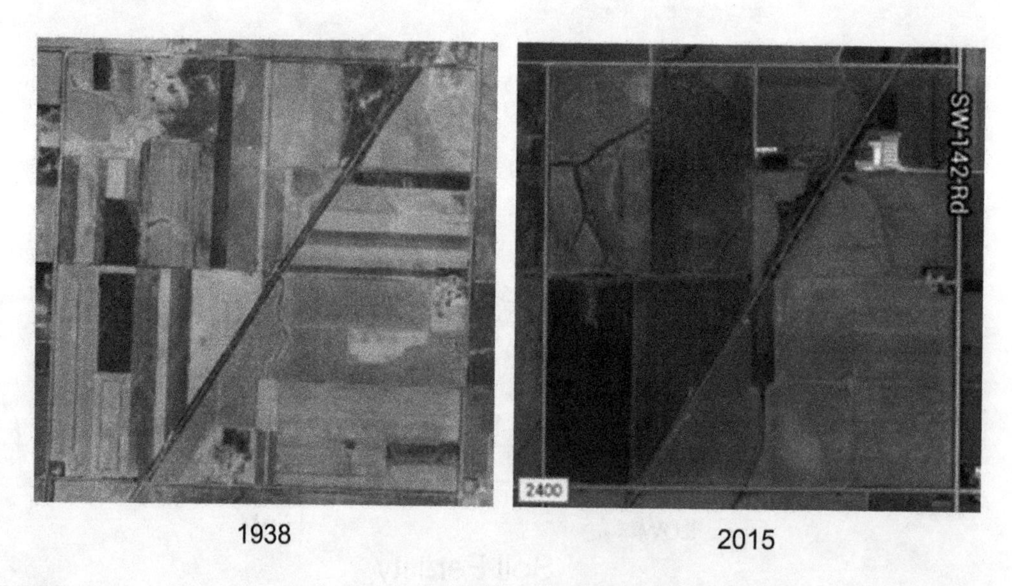

FIGURE 12.3 Comparison of farm landscape in a square mile in Saline County south of DeWitt, Nebraska between 1938 and 2015. Public domain photos from Nebraska's Conservation Survey Division (left) and GoogleMaps (right).

the population in 1939. Similarly, the population level of cottontail rabbits in the county was only 4% of the level found in 1939 (Vance 1976).

What happened? The habitat changed. The soils did not appreciably change in 40 years, so the land had the same potential. That potential was not realized because the landscape was used intensively for crop production. Pastures disappeared. The amount of small grains was also reduced as corn became more widespread. Thus, the types of agricultural habitats that can also support wildlife (e.g., pastures and small grains) were removed from the landscape, leaving mostly row crops. If we returned to the landscape today, more than 40 years after the 1974 data were collected, we would predict the landscape would be further modified. For example, row crops in 1974 still had weedy fields, and soybeans were just appearing as a new crop on the landscape. Small grains, wildlife friendly crops, were still found in some regions. Most corn and soybeans planted today is modified to allow herbicide use to eliminate weeds, which increases yields but leaves little food or cover for wildlife. Farm fields continue to get larger with fewer types of crops planted on the landscape. Corn and soybeans dominate most farm regions (Figure 12.3).

QUICK COMPREHENSION CHECK

In a region, if there is a range of soil quality, can you predict differences in land use in areas of high-quality soils and low-quality soils? How might soil affect deer that are in the low-quality soil regions?

Cover and Food

The BIDE model (chapter 6) emphasizes that survival and reproduction are key elements to wildlife population change. Habitat serves to support the demography of a species when habitat suitability is high. Likewise, lower quality habitat may result in lower survival and lower rates of productivity. Habitat managers often refer to “cover and food” as essential functions of habitat.

Cover is important to conceal animals from predators. In aquatic habitats, cover may be in the form of submergent vegetation, rock crevices, or woody debris, and cover may be provided by dense grass, shrubs, or trees in grasslands and forests. For fossorial animals, subterranean crevices or burrows may provide protection from predators. The choice of a nesting location for birds or birthing location for mammals is often based on available cover, relative to the landscape.

Further, cover provides thermal protection. Birds and mammals, as **endothermic** organisms, use internal, physiological processes to maintain their body temperature. As such, energy demands for birds and mammals are typically constant during a range of environmental temperatures known as the **thermoneutral zone** (Figure 12.4). When ambient temperatures deviate colder or hotter, energy demands rise for individuals, and energy requirements may accelerate during wet conditions that cause animals to lose body heat faster than normal. Cold, wet spring weather is especially bad for survival of chicks of grassland birds (Flanders-Wanner et al. 2004), while sharp-tailed grouse build their nests in shade of shrubs, which provides thermal protection (Raynor et al. 2018). Recent work in the field of thermal ecology suggests

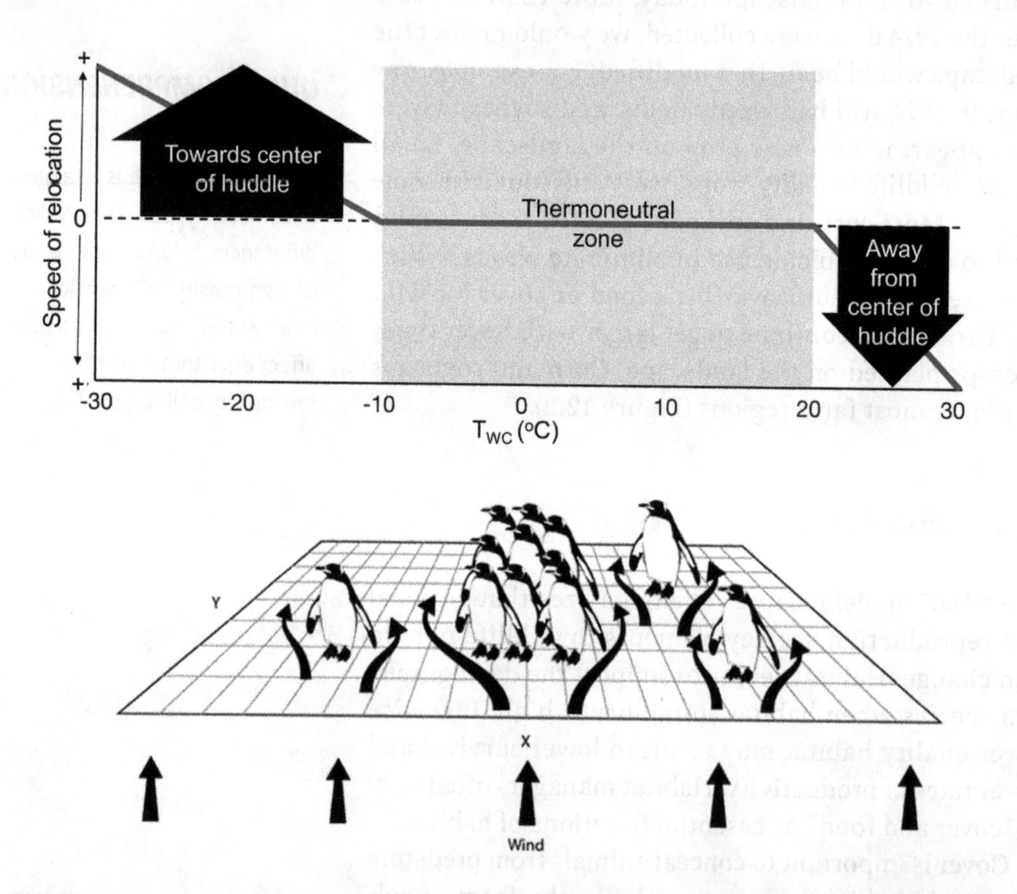

FIGURE 12.4 Characterization of the thermoneutral zone for emperor penguins in breeding colonies in Antarctica. Penguins are affected by wind and cold (bottom) and are more likely to move towards the center of a huddle when wind-chill temperatures (T_{WC}) drop below their thermoneutral zone (top). Red line depicts predicted speed at which penguins move towards or away from thermal cover of the huddle. Modified from Gu et al. (2018).

that wildlife from fish to mammals routinely position themselves in habitat structures that provide thermal protection, replacing previous ideas that predator protection and food availability are primarily responsible for habitat choices (Clarke 2017).

As an example of the need for thermal cover, consider emperor penguins at their Antarctic breeding locations on ice connected to the coastline. Because of a complete lack of structural cover in their habitat, penguins huddle in groups during especially severe periods of cold and high winds. Penguins have a thermoneutral zone from approximately −10°C to 20°C. At wind-chill temperatures lower than −10°C, penguins are likely to huddle, and when they become cold at the edge of the huddle, they are more likely to move at a quicker pace to the center of the huddle, to find thermal cover. Conversely, at temperatures above 20°C, penguins are more likely to move away from other penguins to reduce the temperature of their thermal environment (Gu et al. 2018; Figure 12.4).

Wildlife species meet energy demands with **food resources**. Food also provides the nutrients needed to maintain body functions and support growth. Protein content of diet is especially important to juveniles as they add body mass at impressive rates. Researchers often use body condition metrics, such as lack of fat reserves or atrophied muscle tissue, as a signal of poor health. Droughts, winter storms, and disease may

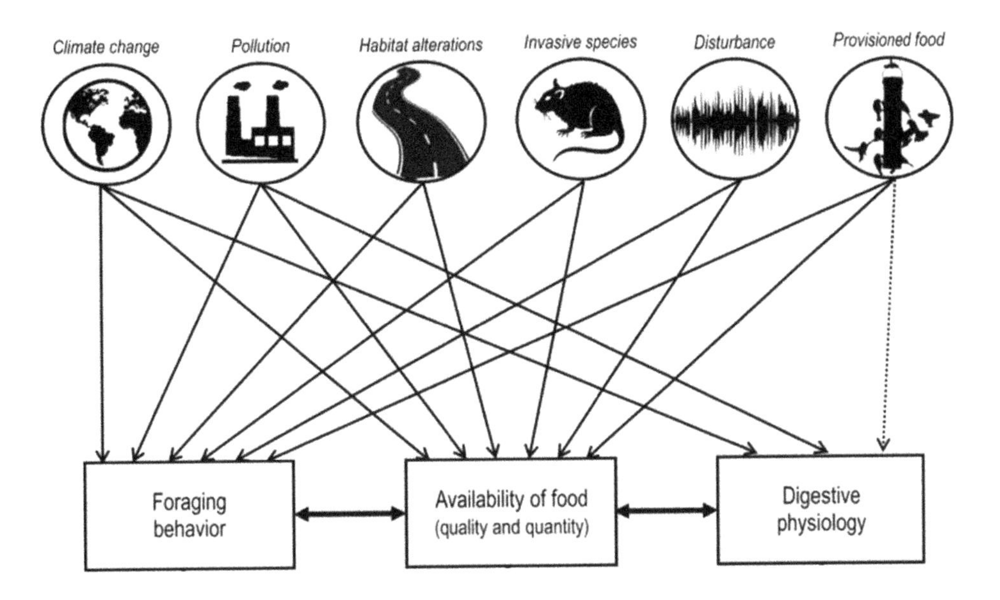

FIGURE 12.5 Anthropogenic effects on components of animal nutrition. Human presence has altered the environment through climate change, pollution, invasive species, habitat alterations, disturbance and human-provisioned food, which affect aspects of nutrition through effects on foraging behavior, food availability and digestive physiology (solid black arrows represent links already established in the literature; dotted arrows represents hypothetical link). From Birnie-Gauvin et al. (2017), Creative Commons license.

cause animals to lose body condition when food is in short supply or body physiology is compromised. Most free-ranging species of wildlife will attempt to maximize ability to intake energy while minimizing energy costs of movement or other activities, and these strategies may change by season (Parker et al. 2009).

Managers of wildlife must account for food needs of the species of concern, and the availability of food for wildlife has become a more complicated topic as anthropogenic effects to ecosystems increase. Human activity may affect food availability through several mechanisms (Birnie-Gauvin et al. 2017). Animals in modified habitats are affected by many stressors (invasive species, habitat loss, lowered water quality, modified temperature regimes, etc.) that affect competition, movement, and levels of predation. Likewise, food availability is a function of many of the same underlying anthropogenic pressures to ecosystems. Successful habitat management will consider the responses of food availability to the set of management alternatives during the decision process.

Grassland Management

Grazed native grasslands, or **rangelands**, can be found in central Florida and throughout the Great Plains and western United States (Figure 12.6). Grasslands are typically an intermediate stage in the successional process between bare ground and forests.

FIGURE 12.6 Rangelands (orange) in the continental United States. Areas dominated by federal lands are shown as gray. USDA NRCS map, public domain.

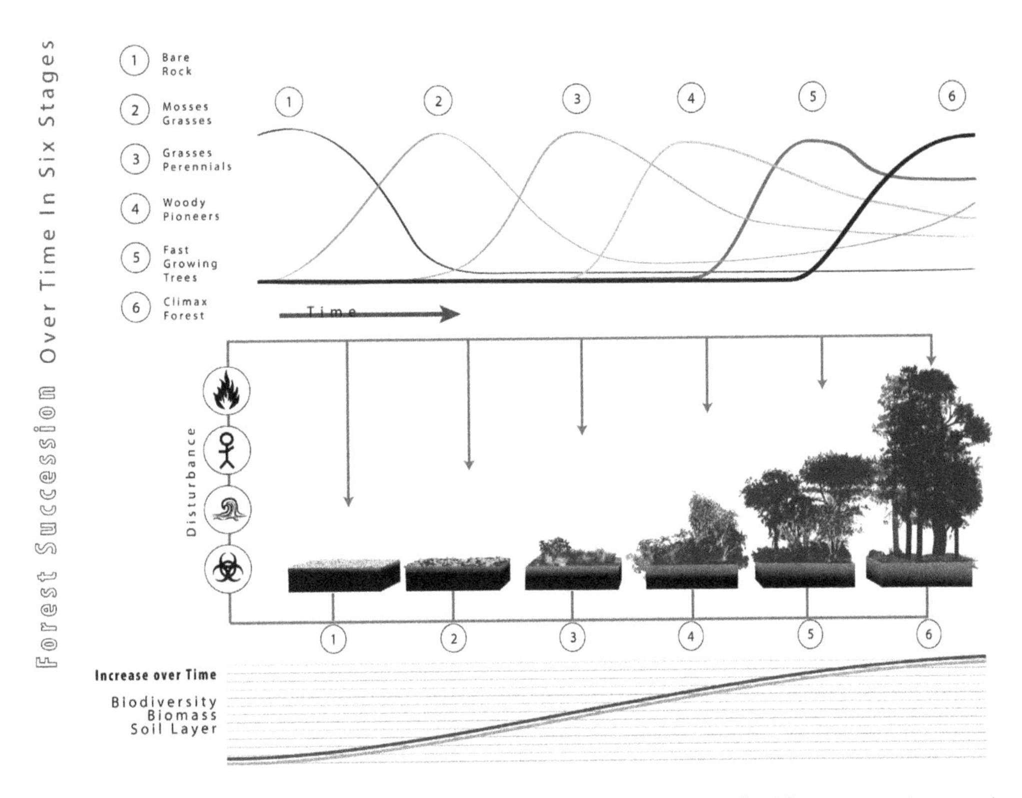

FIGURE 12.7 Linear depiction of the process of ecological succession to a final forest stage. Increase in biomass, biodiversity, and soil thickness are also shown, as well as the fluctuation of different plant communities over the process of succession. Created by L. Frey, WikiCommons.

Therefore, the management of grasslands involves keeping grasslands from transitioning to shrub lands or forests (Figure 12.7).

The biology of grass, shrubs, and trees is critical to the management approaches used in grasslands. Plants grow from a tissue known as **meristem**. Shrubs and trees grow from meristem that occurs at the tips of older stems. Grasses, in contrast, grow upward from the base of the plant, and the meristem is protected from disturbances such as fire and grazing animals, which may remove the tips of stems.

Examples of management for grasslands include (Tunnell 2004, Alldredge et al. 2013):

- **Interseeding** grass-dominated patches with legumes and forbs after discing to set back succession to an early grassland stage with the goal of increasing flowering plants and attracting insects to support production of birds
- **Mechanical tree or shrub removal** to prevent spread of encroaching woody species such as eastern red-cedar
- **Grazing** by wildlife to reduce biomass of vegetation and create openings
- **Prescribed burning** as a disturbance to set succession back to the earliest stage

Prescribed fire is useful in grassland systems as a disturbance to maintain the grassland stage of succession. Fire damages the meristems of woody plants and may completely kill shrubs or trees if the fire is severe enough. Woody plants take many seasons to mature and produce seeds, while grasses grow rapidly, mature rapidly, and produce seeds within one year. Thus, a fire removes many years of growth from shrubs and trees while grasses lose only one or two years of growth.

Rotation period is important to consider for grassland management with fire, with consideration of the timing of the dynamics of succession. A plot that is burned every year will rarely have any development of woody species, but grasses may dominate frequently burned plots because perennial forbs do not have time to establish. Plots burned less frequently have potential to develop woody species as well as thick stands of dead, unpalatable stems of grass that were not removed by grazing animals. A wildlife manager much have knowledge of the local system, plant species, conditions, and goals for the plot in question to determine the rotation length between fires.

Similarly, the **rotation of grazing animals** on grasslands may affect plant growth. Constant, heavy grazing pressure does not allow grasses to develop deep roots because the energy powerhouse of the plant is kept to a small size. Ranchers and grassland managers may use rotational grazing systems with multiple fenced paddocks to provide rest for plants between grazing bouts (Figure 12.8).

FIGURE 12.8 Fences are used to create a rotational grazing system with four paddocks using a central water storage facility in Texas. USDA NRCS photo, public domain.

Another consideration for the manager of grasslands is the stocking density of cattle used. Grazing pressure in a pasture is measured in **Animal Unit Months** (AUM). One animal unit is equal to one mature, 1000-pound cow (including with a calf up to six-months of age). The assumption is that a cow of this size will consume 20 pounds of forage per day. The AUM standardizes the grazing pressure on a monthly basis as (Tunnell 2004):

$$AUM = \frac{\#\,of\ cattle \times average\ weight}{1000} \times \frac{\#\,of\ days\ grazed}{30}$$

The **timing** of the use of fire and grazing is also critical for proper management of grasslands. Some grasses are warm-season grasses (e.g., big bluestem, Indian grass), while others are cool-season grasses (e.g., smooth brome, Kentucky bluegrass). Cool-season grasses metabolize better between 60–75 degrees F, while warm-season grasses grow more optimally between 80–95 degrees F. Therefore, cool-season grasses are the first to begin production in the spring, while warm-season grasses become productive in the summer in temperate regions.

A burn conducted in the spring, before the cool-season grasses start to grow, will accomplish the following:

- Remove dead plant material from the previous year
- Provide cool-season grasses with a flush of nutrients
- Encourage growth of cool-season grasses
- Warm-season grasses may be out-competed by the dominance of cool-seasons grasses supported by the burn

In contrast, a burn conducted later in the spring, after the cool-season grasses start to grow, will have the following influences:

- Remove dead plant material from the previous year
- Injure cool-seasons grasses after they have begun to expend stored energy to create new growth
- Inhibit growth of cool-season grasses
- Warm-seasons grasses may find a competitive advantage with the injury to cool-seasons grasses by the burn

Therefore, the objectives for management are critical to establishing the timing of a prescribed fire.

QUICK COMPREHENSION CHECK

How does a prescribed burn affect grass and woody vegetation differently?

If you wanted to encourage growth of warm-season grasses, when would you burn a grassland?

Forest Management

The forests of the US cover the eastern and mountainous western regions of the country. Forests are a climax successional stage of ecological succession (Figure 12.7), and management of forests involves a longer time period for regrowth than management of grasslands. The southern US has high levels of forest production per area, because of a longer growing season and higher temperatures.

Forest management can be roughly divided into two types of **silviculture**, a management scheme applied to a forest stand over its life (Figure 12.10). **Even-aged forest management** creates forests that were generated after a single disturbance, with a single, dominant age class of canopy trees (Ek et al. 2007). Even-aged forest management techniques include:

- **Clearcuts:** All trees are removed in a large patch, requiring planting for regeneration.
- **Seed-tree:** Rather than removing all trees as in a clearcut, seed trees are left intact for a few years to provide for natural regeneration.
- **Stand selection:** Smaller patches of forest are removed than a clearcut.

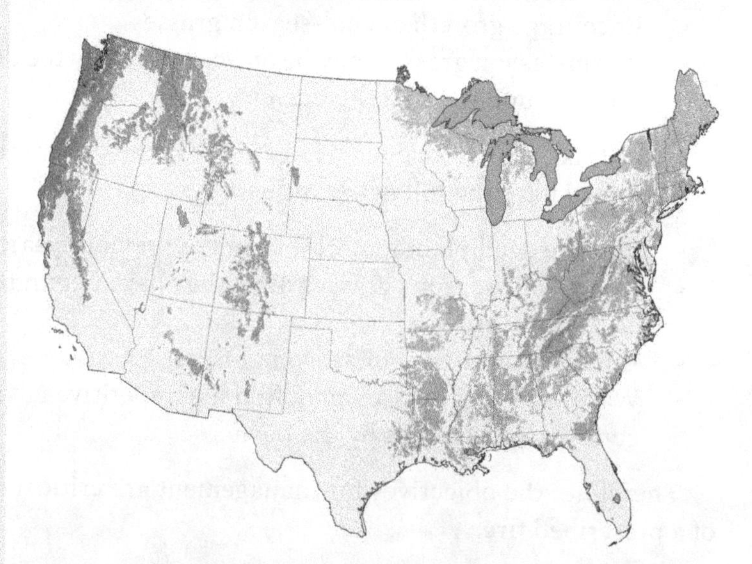

FIGURE 12.9 Forested areas of the continental United States. Darker colors indicate taller forests. NASA forest height data, public domain.

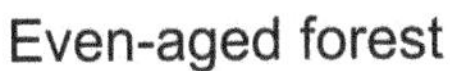

FIGURE 12.10 Comparison of stand structure of even-aged (left) and uneven-aged (right) forests. Images from US Forest Service, public domain.

These silvicultural techniques mimic larger, natural disturbances such as fire or wind damage, and favor species of wildlife that prefer early successional forest stages. Management of this type produces stark contrast and edges between remaining forest and open, newly-harvested areas, which can benefit species of wildlife that prefer a variety of habitats or edge habitats. Larger disturbances allow sun-loving, or **shade intolerant**, tree species to regenerate. Many pines, such as ponderosa pine, are shade intolerant and cannot regenerate under a full canopy; thus, pine silviculture requires even-aged management techniques that provide gaps in the canopy (Gruell et al. 1999). For hardwoods in the northeastern United States, American beech is very tolerant of shade and can regenerate under a full canopy, while paper birch and aspen species are intolerant and will only regenerate in gaps created by natural forest disturbance or forest harvest regimes (Leak et al. 2014).

The decision of management technique used on private lands can be important to the landowner's income. The income generated from timber sales from a clearcut on a large tract of land can be large, but it may take 50–80 years for trees to reach maturity before more profit can be derived.

Uneven-aged forest management creates forests with a variety of age classes because of a history of smaller disturbances within the forest (Ek et al. 2007). Uneven-aged management techniques include:

- **Shelterwood:** Groups of trees are removed in small patches, and the method may be used for trees especially prone to wind damage because the method allows the forest to remain largely intact and protect against wind damage.
- **Single tree selection:** Individual trees are identified for removal within an intact forest.

Silvicultural techniques for management at smaller scales mimic smaller, natural disturbances such as insect outbreaks or natural tree death. Wildlife species that

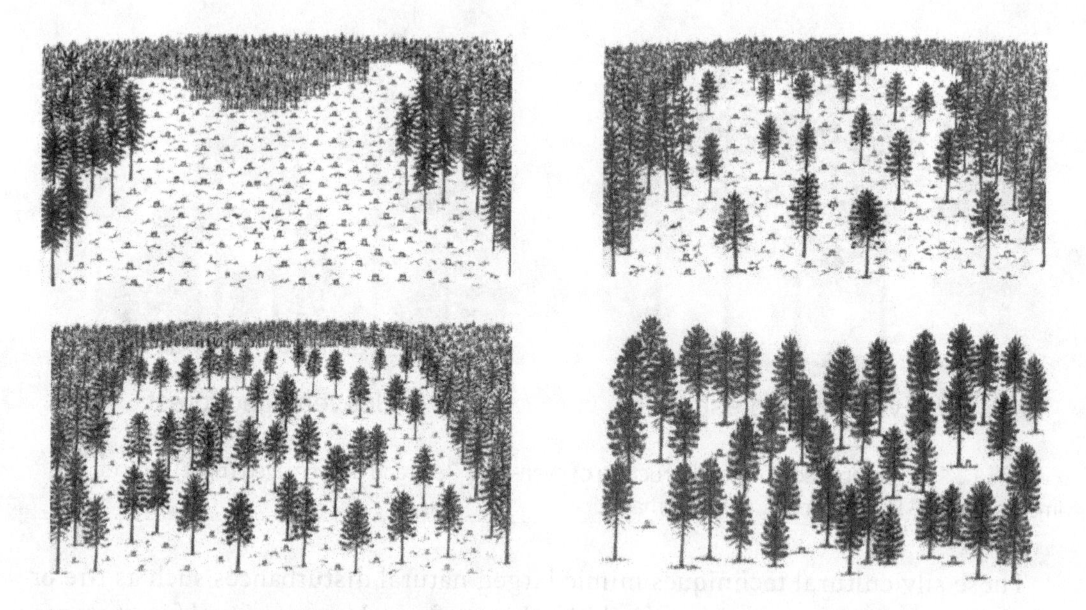

FIGURE 12.11 Silvicultural techniques for forest management include clearcutting (top left), seed-tree (top right), shelterwood (bottom left), and single-tree selection (bottom right). Images from US Forest Service, public domain.

prefer mid- to late-successional forest habitat are favored because the forest canopy remains largely intact. Shade-tolerant tree species are selected by these systems, as shade-intolerant species will not be able to regenerate. Profits from forest products will be smaller, but more continuous, although some damage may be done within the forest to make roads to allow for harvest of the small areas.

The **understory** of the forest can be managed for simple or complex layers of understory through thinning and prescribed burning. Reduction of understory and/or reduction in density of canopy trees should reduce competition and encourage faster growth of the dominant trees. However, simpler understories provide fewer niches for wildlife.

Forest structure is also affected by the rotation length between harvests. These choices have economic tradeoffs for the timber owner, and the forest products are different for trees harvested as pole timber (smaller trees at least five inches in diameter) or saw timber (trees suitable for producing logs that can be processed into lumber). If a forest stand is harvested at optimal rotation lengths for lumber production, the trees may not develop cavities that can be used for nests by mammals or birds. This dynamic is behind the conflicts over northern spotted owls in the Pacific Northwest, and public land managers may therefore choose to set longer rotation lengths. As with all wildlife management decisions, setting objectives is key to the decision-making process (chapter 3).

Wetland Management

Wetlands are one of the most threatened natural systems (Turner 1991), although they account for only 5% of the global land area. Wetlands provide important **ecosystem services** (chapter 13) for water filtration. Urban and agricultural development have eliminated wetland area through draining, filling, or other modifications, so the management of wetlands typically involves intensive levels of management to restore or maintain system function.

Water level in wetlands is highly variable, and the water level affects vegetation growth. This simple geological and physical phenomenon is key to selecting alternatives for managing wetlands. Vegetation in wetlands can be killed by flooding with deep water, or vegetation can be encouraged to grow by temporarily draining a wetland to allow moist soils to germinate seeds in the seed bank. Muddy flats left by draining are highly preferred by migrating shorebirds (Figure 12.12). Shallow flooding after plants germinate in a wetland basin can provide perfect habitat for migrating waterfowl, with a matrix of open water and food-bearing plants along with a new invertebrate community (Fredrickson 1991).

In a system that has lost **hydrologic function** because of draining and manipulation of a watershed, levees may

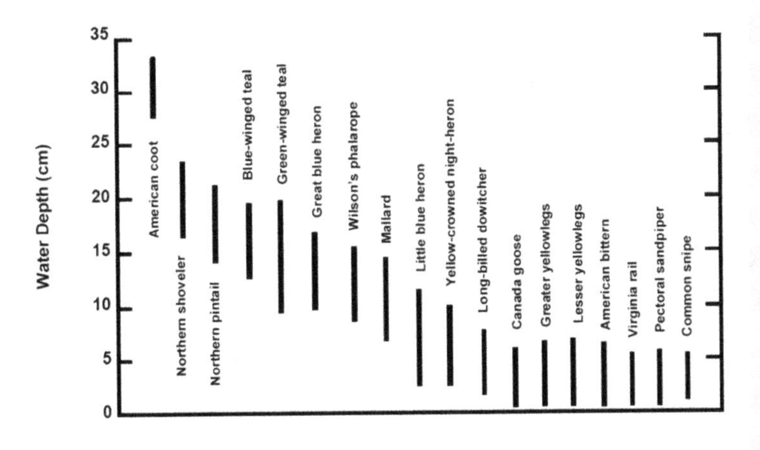

FIGURE 12.12 Preferred water depths for wetland birds commonly associated with moist soil habitats. Reprinted from Fredrickson (1991), USFWS publication, public domain.

QUICK COMPREHENSION CHECK

For what wildlife management objectives is a clearcut an important management choice?

FIGURE 12.13 A control system upgrade at the Savannah National Wildlife Refuge in Georgia and South Carolina. Previously, wildlife managers with the US Fish and Wildlife Service could only route water to 3,000 acres of wetlands for waterfowl. With replacement of wooden structures and automation, the water management area has doubled to 6,000 acres.

be built to create an artificial basin. A water control structure is used to hold or drain water (Figure 12.13), depending on management strategy, and a pumping station is vital for adding water during times of drought or when natural hydrology has been compromised.

Wetlands are subject to the processes of aquatic succession in which sediments are deposited in the basin and a series of plant communities develop within the wetland. Eventually, a wetland basin can become shallow and clogged with vegetation to the extent it may be less useful to focal wildlife species (Figure 12.14). Fish cannot survive in shallow waters that freeze during the winter, and waterfowl will not use wetlands without open waters.

Managers have several options to set succession back in wetland systems:

- **Prescribed burning** may remove vegetation that has closed a canopy in the wetland basin.
- **Grazing** may be used to thin vegetation density.

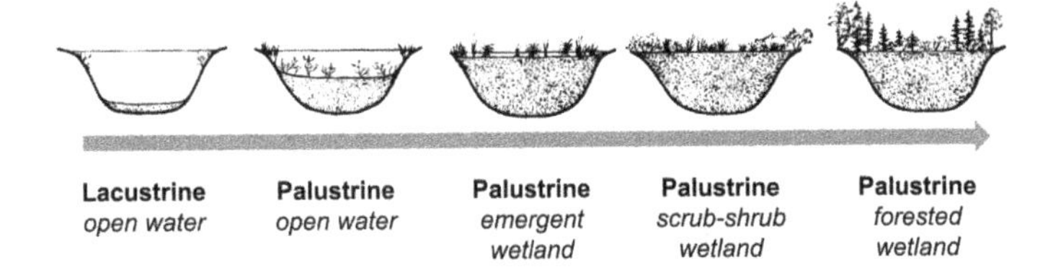

FIGURE 12.14 Stages of wetland succession in the eastern United States. Modified from Metzler and Tiner (1992).

- **Mechanical disking** may be used to cut through root systems of cattails, bulrushes, or similar wet-soil plants to create openings.
- **Dredging** or **scraping** to remove sediment with heavy equipment may create a deeper basin and reset aquatic succession to its earliest stage.
- **Herbicide treatments** with chemicals labeled for aquatic use may be used to create openings in thick vegetation, including invasive plant species.

QUICK COMPREHENSION CHECK

Why is a variety of wetland depths important for migrating birds?

Wetland managers have a variety of tools with which to approach management problems. Determination of goals is critical, and wetland systems are complicated because of natural variation in water levels that occur in time and space.

Reservoir Management

Reservoirs are artificial lakes, so their creation is a management decision. A reservoir is typically built where no lake previously existed, and most are built for a combination of purposes, including flood control, water storage, fishery creation, and aquatic recreation. As reservoirs are filled following construction, new terrestrial habitats are inundated causing a release of nutrients and creating diverse habitats for aquatic organisms that thrive and increase in abundances.

As the reservoir ages, the abundance of many aquatic organisms declines as habitats are degraded by the processes of **eutrophication** and **sedimentation** similar to the processes followed in wetland succession

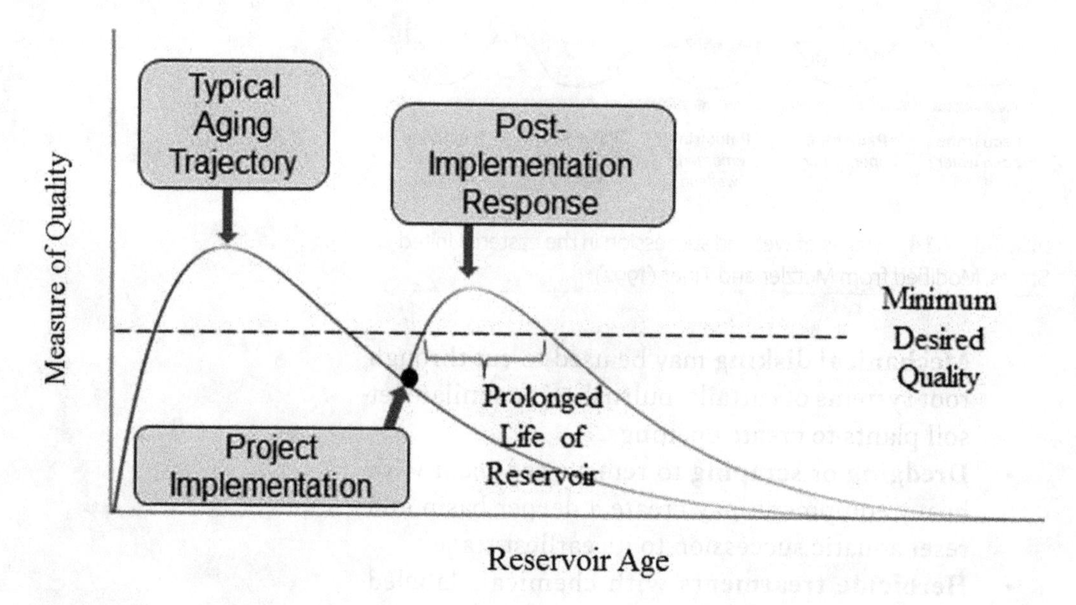

FIGURE 12.15 Conceptualization of the aging process in lakes and reservoirs and response of amplitude, rate, and duration to implementation of a rehabilitation technique. From Pegg et al. (2015), USGS publication, public domain.

(Figure 12.14). Human activities, such as upstream soil erosion and nutrient run-off from cities, farm fields, livestock facilities, and forests often accelerate the succession process. Management of reservoirs typically strive to mitigate the effects of aging and attempt to re-set lakes and reservoirs to earlier, more desirable states (Pegg et al. 2015, Figure 12.15).

Reservoirs in the United States are typically between 40–120 years old (Miranda 2017), which means many reservoirs are reaching the end of their life span (Figure 12.16). Rehabilitation of older reservoirs is critical to continued function. However, reservoir rehabilitation projects typically do not bring lake quality back to the original peak quality, and quality declines faster after rehabilitation than after initial construction (Figure 12.14). Most reservoirs cease to function at peak levels without management after 50 years (Pegg et al. 2015).

Management of reservoirs includes two categories of management tools:

- A **suite of management strategies to work within the watershed** above the reservoir to reduce problems such as silt, woody debris, and high nutrient loads from reaching the reservoir
- A set of **in-reservoir tools** to improve function of the reservoir

Modern reservoir management includes management beyond the boundaries of the lake. The goal is to halt, eliminate, or alter anthropogenic practices causing reservoir degradation. **Watershed management tools** may include (Miranda 2017):

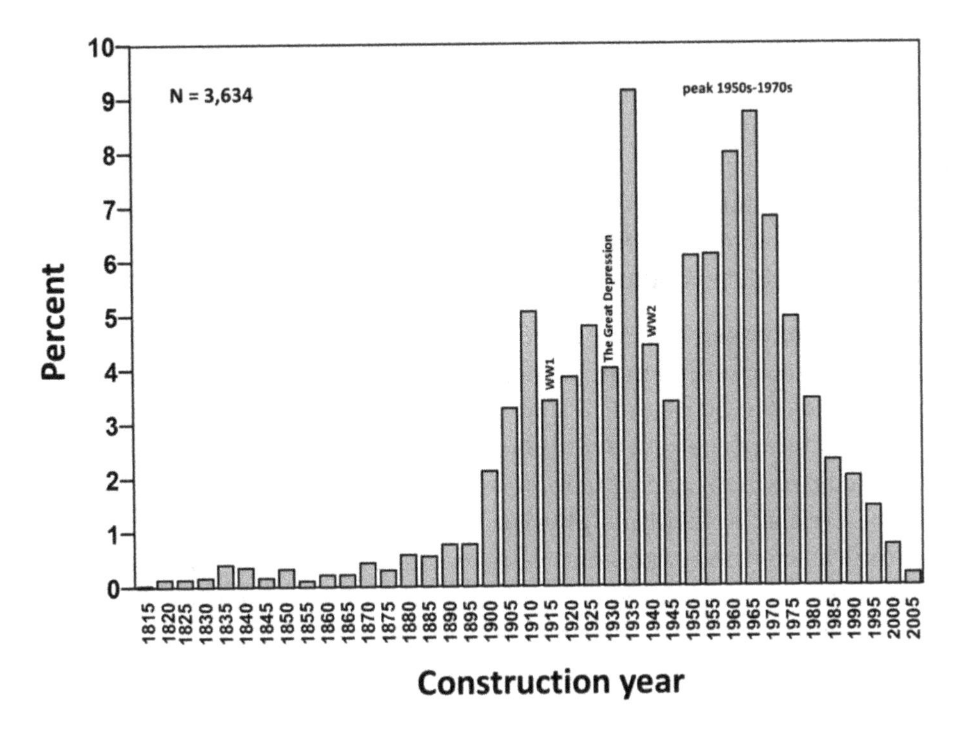

FIGURE 12.16 Distribution (percent by year) of reservoir construction in the US, 1815–2010. N represents the sample size of reservoirs ≥ 250 acres. Selected historic events are identified within the plot (WW = World War). Reprinted from Miranda (2017), USGS publication, public domain.

- **Partnership building:** The scale and context of the watershed often mean that a variety of city, county, state, and federal agencies, NGOs, and private individuals and corporations may affect human behaviors in the watershed.
- **Creation of structures:** Physical additions or modifications to assist with ecosystem function and prevention of harmful materials reaching the reservoir (e.g., bank stabilization, filter strips in agricultural fields, sediment basins to trap sediment, tree planting, fencing to reduce livestock impact on stream banks, or wetland restoration projects upstream; Figure 13.10).
- **Nonstructural practices:** Behaviors and processes that improve water quality entering the reservoir (e.g., conservation tillage, manure management systems, lawn fertilizer management in cities, pet waste programs).
- **Regulatory support:** Rules and laws to improve water quality (e.g., tax incentives for conservation practices, wetland protection, forest harvest permit process, land-use zoning in cities, wastewater treatment in cities).

In-reservoir management tools may be very similar to those strategies used by managers of fisheries in natural lakes, which also undergo aquatic succession (Figure 12.14). **Sedimentation** is a major concern as it reduces the volume of the reservoir. **Eutrophication**, the state of high nutrient levels in water, is also a concern of fisheries biologists at reservoirs. Although early stages of eutrophication may enhance fish growth, the subsequent water quality changes associated with higher trophic states are not beneficial, including hypoxia, phytoplankton blooms, reduced water clarity, and altered fish communities. **Water clarity** may affect fish communities, plant growth, and recreational use of the lake.

In-reservoir management alternatives include (Miranda 2017):

- **Sediment management: Sediment basins** may be constructed just above the reservoir to trap sediment in a more convenient location for removal, and **sediment dikes** can be placed to slow water velocity and settle sediment at the upper reaches of the reservoir (Figure 12.17). Once sediment is in the reservoir, **dredging** may be used to remove sediment from open water, or the basin may be drained to facilitate **physical excavation** before refilling the basin.
- **Eutrophication management:** Nutrient levels are best managed through watershed management. Many reservoirs have been recently altered at their upper end to include **systems of wetlands** (Figure 12.17) to allow vegetation to remove nutrients as water enters the system, and some reservoir managers have installed mini-reservoirs (a process known as **pre-dams**) above the main reservoir to trap water to allow nutrient processing before it flows to the main basin. Once nutrients are in the reservoir, often the result of storm run-off that overpowers upstream control measures, a reservoir manager may be able to use **routing** of water through the dam without allowing mixing with the majority of reservoir water or use **dilution** of high-nutrient water with a low-nutrient water

FIGURE 12.17 A water control structure regulates stream flow and wetland depth on a USDA Wetlands Reserve Program project in Hill County, Montana. Photo by USDA NRCS, public domain.

source from a water control structure. **Floating wetland islands** in the reservoir are a relatively new technique for removing nutrients once they have entered the reservoir. **Sediment removal** is also used as a long-term solution to nutrient build-up in reservoirs, as many nutrients are bound up in sediments at the bottom of the basin.

- **Water clarity management:** Turbid water may be caused by erosion of the reservoir shoreline, so **shore erosion control** may be used to stabilize soils along the edge of the reservoir. **Offshore breakwaters** are rock or concrete structures that cause approaching waves, created by boat traffic or wind, to break before they lead to erosion along the shoreline. **Flocculation** is used to control suspended clay particles in the water column. Flocculants may be organic in nature; however, the standard flocculent used is aluminum sulfate (alum).

QUICK COMPREHENSION CHECK

What dynamic seems to be the most critical problem for a reservoir manager?

Why are watershed management tools important, in addition to in-reservoir management strategies?

Models for Habitat Assessment

During the decision-making process for habitat management, it is important to evaluate consequences and tradeoffs of the alternative management actions. A **wildlife habitat assessment** model may be used as a tool to guide habitat evaluation and to assess predicted habitat conditions following management. Habitat models are available in a variety of styles. Habitat Suitability Indices (HSI) became popular in the 1970s and 1980s, and represent a basic, conceptual form of a habitat model. Created by experts, HSI models were species specific and contained textual information known about effects of habitat on survival and reproduction for a species. The models also provided a quantitative way to assess current habitat through graphical suitability indices (Figure 12.18). A manager could look at current habitat conditions and predict habitat conditions under a handful of management options—the option for which the HSI score was maximized represented the best choice for a given species (Stuber et al. 1982, Newsome et al. 1987).

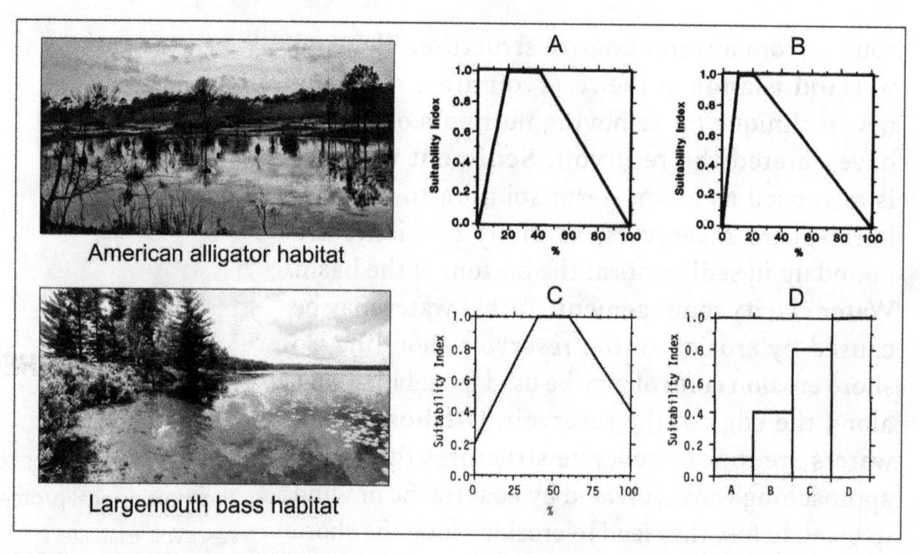

FIGURE 12.18 Select components of habitat suitability index (HSI) models for American alligator (top) and largemouth bass (bottom). Suitability is greatest for American alligator when (A) the percentage of wetland that is open water is 20–40%, and (B) the percentage of open water area in either bayous, canals, or ponds (>1.2 m in depth) is 10–20%. Habitat suitability for largemouth bass is greatest when (C) the percent of cover (aquatic vegetation, logs, debris) within waterbody during summer is 40–60%, and (D) minimum dissolve oxygen levels are often > 8 mg/l (other categories: frequently <2 mg/l, usually 2–5 mg/l, and 5-8 mg/l). Photos by Richard Elzey and Bailiwick Studies, used under creative commons license. Habitat models from USFWS.

The simple HSI models were easy to implement, although they were often very general to attempt to provide spatial coverage of species with large ranges. The general nature of the models caused poor performance in some cases, which was often complicated by a lack of methods to validate models in the field (Roloff and Kernohan 1999). However, the use of the HSI model was a step forward towards a common approach to collecting habitat data that could be used to assist managers with their decisions.

HSI models are not used commonly today, and one reason is that managers have moved beyond a single-species approach to habitat management. Although some situations require habitat management to focus on a single species, it is much more common for managers to think of habitat management from the systems perspective. For this kind of assessment, a different form of a model is needed: a **functional assessment model**. The main improvement over the older HSI models is the consideration of ecosystem function from a variety of angles. Experts develop the models by deciding on key functions of systems to assess, and each system function is evaluated with a clear rubric to provide a sub-score that can be added to a cumulative score for the site in question (Figure 12.19, Ward et al. 2003). As with HSI models, functional assessment models may also be applied to predicted conditions to determine the best path forward when several alternatives are available.

NE-CPA-45
7/04

FARM POND
HABITAT EVALUATION WORKSHEET

Client ______________________ County ______________________

Tract No. ________ Field No. ________ Section No. ________ Township ________ Range ________

Evaluator ______________________ Date ______________________

Enter the score for the conditions described that most closely resemble the present or planned condition of the site being evaluated. To meet the quality criteria requirements for wildlife habitat (food, water, cover, etc.) in Section III of the FOTG the planned system must provide a total rating of 0.5 or higher for the conservation treatment unit. For sites where a farm pond does not currently exist but will be constructed, score the site as 0.0 (present).

Note: This worksheet is intended to address habitat quality on "constructed" ponds including those formed by dams (embankments) and those created as dugouts (excavated). Do not use for naturally occurring ponds (wetlands).

Depth – Percent of surface area in deep, shallow, and intermediate water depths.

Give a rating of:
.2 If 25% or more is ≥ 12 feet deep **and** 25% or more is ≤ 3 feet deep with remainder at intermediate depths.
.1 If the majority is of intermediate depths but at least 10% is ≥ 12 feet deep **and** at least 10% is ≤ 3 feet deep.
.0 If the farm pond is shallow and intermediate water (90% or more of the surface area) with little or no deep water.
-.1 If the farm pond is deep and intermediate water (90% or more of the surface area) with little or no shallow water.
A. Rating for Depth Present ________ Planned ________

Size – Hydrology analysis should be used to determine water storage capabilities for constructed farm pond sites.

Give a rating of:
.2 If the farm pond is five acres or larger (average surface acres of water).
.1 If the farm pond is larger than one acre but smaller than five acres (average surface acres of water).
.0 If the farm pond larger than one-half acre up to one acre (average surface acres of water).
-.1 If the farm pond is one-half acre or smaller (average surface acres of water).
B. Rating for Size Present ________ Planned ________

Buffer – A minimum of five species (native grasses, forbs, and/or legumes) with at least one forb/legume with each comprising 10% or more of the stand and excluded from haying/grazing except for specific management purposes.

Give a rating of:
.3 If a buffer area 15.0 acres or larger immediately surrounds the farm pond (>100' wide).
.2 If a buffer area 10.0 acres to 14.9 acres immediately surrounds the farm pond (≥ 100' wide).
.1 If a buffer area 5.0 acres to 9.9 acres immediately surrounds the farm pond (≥ 100' wide).
.0 If a buffer area is a minimum of 100 feet wide but less than 5.0 acres and immediately surrounds the farm pond.
-.1 If the buffer area is less than 100 feet wide or does not meet species diversity or management requirements.
C. Rating for Buffer Present ________ Planned ________

Aquatic Habitat and Watershed Treatment – Aquatic habitat components should include desired emergent vegetation or rock reefs on a minimum of 25% of the shoreline **or** submerged trees/brush piles and/or islands across 10% of the surface area. A minimum of 75% of the watershed should be treated with appropriate soil erosion/water quality measures **or** a sediment retention facility should be installed immediately upstream of the farm pond.

Give a rating of:
.2 If at least one aquatic habitat component **and** watershed treatment are addressed for the farm pond.
.1 If only watershed treatment considerations are addressed for the farm pond.
.0 If only aquatic habitat components are addressed for the farm pond.
-.1 If the farm pond does not provide any aquatic habitat components and watershed treatment is not addressed.
D. Rating for Aquatic Habitat/Watershed Treatment Present ________ Planned ________

Water Control

Give a rating of:
.1 If a water control structure is present to allow for water level manipulations for management purposes.
.0 If no water level manipulations can be conducted to facilitate management.
E. Rating for Water Control Present ________ Planned ________

COMPOSITE RATING (A + B + C + D + E) **Present** ________ **Planned** ________

(180-vi-NPPH, Amend. NE12, July 2004) NE130e.03

FIGURE 12.19 System-level habitat assessment model for habitat of a farm pond. Habitat score is highest for large ponds with some depth, a vegetative buffer, active management, and a water control structure. Model provided by Nebraska USDA. NRCS is used to evaluate private ponds for management under federal habitat incentive programs.

WRAPPING UP

Can you help Adriana explain to her father how grassland habitat might be managed to provide critical resources for pheasants? How might landscape changes contribute to declines of the species?

Decision-Making on the Ground

1. Forest Management for Red-Cockaded Woodpeckers on the Carolina Sandhills Refuge

The red-cockaded woodpecker is listed as an endangered species. The woodpeckers are found in scattered locations throughout the southeastern United States, including on the Carolina Sandhills Refuge in South Carolina. The birds are cavity nesters and need live, mature pine trees for nesting, and they nest in groups with multiple nests within a small area (3–60 acres). Red-cockaded woodpeckers peck holes in the bark around their nesting cavity to cause the tree to exude resin that coats the tree and serves as a defense against black rat snakes, which are a common nest predator.

Nesting habitat for red-cockaded woodpeckers resembles a park-like setting, with large-diameter pine trees to provide potential nesting cavities and little to no understory to prevent nest predators from reaching the nest by using surrounding vegetation to negotiate around the resin on the nest tree.

APPLICATION, ANALYSIS, SYNTHESIS, AND EVALUATION

Given the description of red-cockaded woodpecker habitat, would a refuge biologist use even or uneven age forest management to create a forest stand that is eventually suitable for the endangered species' nesting needs?

What kind of management might be used to control the understory growth in the forest?

Other nesting forest birds are found at the Carolina Sandhills Refuge, and many of them may need understory trees or shrubs for nesting. From a landscape perspective, how can the refuge provide for the habitat needs of several species? Create a rectangular forest compartment of one square mile (640 acres)—how might you arrange habitat planning for multiple species within that square mile if there were two red-cockaded woodpeckers colonies using that area?

2. Reservoir Sedimentation in Northern Mississippi

Throughout the United States, the USDA Natural Resources Conservation Service has constructed more than 11,000 reservoirs since the 1940s for flood control purposes. Three small reservoirs installed in the Holly Springs National Forest east of Oxford, Mississippi have a forested watershed, and a study showed their sedimentation rates were slower than reservoirs found in agricultural (non-forested) or rangeland in Mississippi (Wren et al. 2007).

The Holly Spring National Forest, like several public land areas in the southeastern United States, was established on abandoned agricultural land that was rapidly eroding. The reservoirs were installed to slow water discharge to reduce erosion of riparian areas.

APPLICATION, ANALYSIS, SYNTHESIS, AND EVALUATION

Suppose the management objectives for the national forest changed, and a considerable proportion of the watershed for the three reservoirs was modified for grasslands rather than forest habitat. What would you predict would happen to the lifetime of the reservoirs' function (see Figure 12.15)?

What management actions could be taken in this scenario to modify the watershed to protect against sediment build-up in the reservoirs?

Now consider a scenario where the national forest lands near the reservoirs will remain in forest habitat, but a new manager arrives at the site from Montana. She has successfully used clearcutting as a management tool in her former job, and she suggests that the Holly Spring National Forest consider using more large-scale clearcuts to support northern bobwhite and deer populations. Why might clearcuts result in higher numbers of bobwhite and deer? What effect on sedimentation rates of the reservoirs might you predict from a change to clearcutting?

Sources of Information and Further Reading

Albrecht, W. A. "Soil fertility and biotic geography." *Geographical Review* 47, no. 1 (1957): 86–105.

Alldredge, B., L. Redmon, M. Clayton, and J. C. Cathey. *Native grassland monitoring and management.* College Station, TX: Texas A&M AgriLife Extension Service, Texas A&M University, 2013.

Birnie-Gauvin, K., Peiman, K. S., Raubenheimer, D., and Cooke, S. J. "Nutritional physiology and ecology of wildlife in a changing world." *Conservation Physiology* 5, no. 1 (2017): cox030.

Clarke, A. *Principles of thermal ecology: Temperature, energy and life.* Oxford University Press, 2017.

Crawford, B. T. "Some specific relationships between soils and wildlife." *The Journal of Wildlife Management* 14, no. 2 (1950): 115–123.

Ek, A. R., S. A. Katovich, M. A. Kilgore, and B. J. Palik. *Forest Management* 101*: a handbook to forest management in the North Central Region*. Minneapolis, MN: US Forest Service and University of Minnesota, 2007.

Flanders-Wanner, B. L., G. C. White, and L. L. McDaniel. "Weather and prairie grouse: dealing with effects beyond our control." *Wildlife Society Bulletin* 32 (2004): 22–34.

Fredrickson, L. H. "Strategies for water level manipulations in moist-soil systems. 13.4.6." *Waterfowl Management Handbook*. Washington, DC: US Fish and Wildlife Service, 1991.

Grosman, P. D., Jaeger, J. A., Biron, P. M., Dussault, C., and Ouellet, J. P. "Trade-off between road avoidance and attraction by roadside salt pools in moose: An agent-based model to assess measures for reducing moose-vehicle collisions." *Ecological Modelling* 222, no. 8 (2011): 1423–1435.

Gruell, G. E., Schmidt, W. C., Arno, S. F., and Reich, W. J. "Natural forest succession and fire history." In *Eighty-eight years of change in a managed ponderosa pine forest,* edited by Smith, Helen Y., Arno, Stephen F., 5–9. Ogden, UT: U.S. Department of Agriculture, Rocky Mountain Research Station, 1999.

Gu, W., Christian, J. K., and Woodson, C. B. "A novel coupled fluid-behavior model for simulating dynamic huddle formation." *PloS one* 13, no. 8 (2018): e0203231.

Leak, W. B., Yamasaki, M., and Holleran, R. *Silvicultural guide for northern hardwoods in the northeast.* Gen. Tech. Rep. NRS-132. Newtown Square, PA: U.S. Department of Agriculture, Forest Service, Northern Research Station, 2014.

Metzler, K. J. and Tiner, R. W. *Wetlands of Connecticut.* Hartford, CT: State Geological and Natural History Survey of Connecticut, Department of Environmental Protection, 1992.

Miranda, L. E. *Reservoir fish habitat management.* Totowa, NJ: Lightning Press, 2017.

Newsome, J. D., T. Joanen, and R. J. Howard. "Habitat suitability index models: American alligator." *Biological Report* 82, no. 10.136 (1987): 14.

Parker, K. L., Barboza, P. S., & Gillingham, M. P. "Nutrition integrates environmental responses of ungulates." *Functional ecology* 23, no. 1 (2009): 57–69.

Pegg, M. A., Pope, K. L., Powell, L. A., Turek, K. C., Spurgeon, J. J., Stewart, N. T., Hogberg, N. P. and Porath, M. T. "Reservoir rehabilitations: seeking the fountain of youth." *Fisheries 40*, no. 4 (2015): 177–181.

Plummer, I. H., Johnson, C. J., Chesney, A. R., Pedersen, J. A., and Samuel, M. D. "Mineral licks as environmental reservoirs of chronic wasting disease prions." *PloS one* 13, no. 5 (2018): e0196745.

Raynor, E. J., Powell, L. A., and Schacht, W. H. "Present and future thermal environments available to Sharp-tailed Grouse in an intact grassland." *PloS one 13*, no. 2 (2018): e0191233.

Roloff, G. J. and Kernohan, B. J. "Evaluating reliability of habitat suitability index models." *Wildlife Society Bulletin* 27 (1999): 973–985.

Stuber, R. J., G. Gebhart, and O. E. Maughan. *Habitat suitability index models: Largemouth bass.* US Department of the Interior, US Fish and Wildlife Service. FWS/OBS-82/10.16. 1982.

Tunnel, T. R. *Guide to native grassland management in Nebraska.* Wood River, NE: The Nature Conservancy and Platte River Habitat Partnership, 2004.

Turner, K. "Economics and wetland management." *Ambio* 20 (1991): 59–63.

Vance, D. R. "Changes in land use and wildlife populations in southeastern Illinois." *Wildlife Society Bulletin* 4 (1976): 11–15.

Ward, T. A., Tate, K. W., and Atwill, E. R. *Visual assessment of riparian health.* Davis, CA: Rangeland Monitoring Series. UC ANR, 2003.

Wren, D. G., Wells, R. R., Wilson, C. G., Cooper, C. M., and Smith, S. "Sedimentation in three small erosion control reservoirs in northern Mississippi." *Journal of soil and water conservation* 62, no. 3 (2007): 137–144.

Image Credits

Fig. 12.1: Source: https://gdg.sc.egov.usda.gov/GDGHome_DirectDownLoad.aspx.
Fig. 12.3a: Conservation Survey Division, Nebraska.
Fig. 12.3b: Google Maps.
Fig. 12.4: Copyright © Wen Gu, Jason K. Christian, C. Brock Woodson (CC by 4.0) at https://journals.plos.org/plosone/article/figure?id=10.1371/journal.pone.0203231.g004.
Fig. 12.5: Copyright © Kim Birnie-Gauvin, et al. (CC by 4.0) at https://www.ncbi.nlm.nih.gov/pmc/articles/PMC5516125/.
Fig. 12.6: United States Department of Agriculture, Natural Resources Conservation Service.
Fig. 12.7: Copyright © LucasMartinFrey (CC by 3.0) at https://commons.wikimedia.org/wiki/File:Forest_succession_depicted_over_time.png.
Fig. 12.8: Copyright © United States Department of Agriculture, Natural Resourses Conservation Service, Texas (CC by 2.0) at https://www.flickr.com/photos/139446213@N03/24489709423/.
Fig. 12.9: Source: https://earthobservatory.nasa.gov/images/44717/forest-canopy-heights-across-the-united-states.
Fig. 12.10: Source: https://www.nrs.fs.fed.us/fmg/nfmg/docs/fm101.pdf.
Fig. 12.11: Source: https://www.nrs.fs.fed.us/fmg/nfmg/docs/fm101.pdf.
Fig. 12.12: Source: http://digitalcommons.unl.edu/icwdmwfm/26/.
Fig. 12.13: Copyright © United States Army Corps of Engineers Savannah District (CC by 2.0) at https://www.flickr.com/photos/savannahcorps/6812097777.
Fig. 12.14: Source: https://www.ct.gov/deep/lib/deep/water_inland/wetlands/wetlands_of_ct.pdf.
Fig. 12.15: Mark A. Pegg, et al., "Reservoir Aging Process," Reservoir Rehabilitations: Seeking the Fountain of Youth. Copyright © 2015 by Taylor & Francis Group.
Fig. 12.16: Source: http://www.friendsofreservoirs.com/wp-content/uploads/2017/01/Reservoir-Fish-Habitat-Management-_Manual.pdf.
Fig. 12.17: Source: https://www.flickr.com/photos/160831427@N06/27300281919/in/photolist-RUJz2t-bnXMkF-9hdjnJ-QELLp4-RUKYVD-RF8vYj-RFapCj-Rk8Uu9-RHPeQV-QCfv97-QCdJw3-bnXLuP-bnXMvv-bnXM62-RUKRx2-bnXLWz-bnXMxM-HAr5FR-Rk7ZbL-dyzX2s-yCDm-So-RUKybP-RF8nb9-ySbZVu-yCBuLf-xYm5UZ-yCHA.
Fig. 12.18a: Copyright © Richard Elzey (CC by 2.0) at https://www.flickr.com/photos/elzey/16583946044/in/photolist-rgt4od-DGv2Kd-EdB8YE-Ed3piJ-26q9P8d-26q9Pyo-a2PZ8z-f3UiCQ-qgXA8J-pGrUFv-26q9PqN-dqL9RL-26q9PiU-2dzSUTw-pU76EX-nk27Rm-9AW9ua-21Ecrkr-pLs-1m-bH7LYr-9kxgHY-u3NJWf-ApEr1j-M4rTy-GLwaSV-q7jUq9-iG5dQj-M.
Fig. 12.18b: Copyright © Bailiwick Studios (CC BY-SA 2.0) at https://www.flickr.com/photos/raua/42146397905/in/photolist-27dkiJR-fuR1Uz-6QhR5C-8N7dNC-8N7dNj-2dkZmLo-26hFxsx-74aH74-2nWNcA-phHWab-dV6dUZ-8mFhxf-74eCY7-c5weSL-phJuPB-pym3XT-ppH5HR-puv2X-khDgBJ-74uKpS-e9DcYm-ppGrkL-phGVSD-phGQLB-Skn3MU-S7KNYR-6HHg99-pGdH.
Fig. 12.18c: United States Fish and Wildlife Service.
Fig. 12.18d: United States Fish and Wildlife Service.
Fig. 12.19: Source: https://efotg.sc.egov.usda.gov/references/public/NE/NE-CPA-45(Farm_Pond_Habitat_Worksheet).pdf.

CHAPTER THIRTEEN

Dichotomies of Public and Private Land Management

Learning Outcomes

After participating in learning experiences related to this chapter, students should be able to:

- Provide three ways in which society can affect decisions made on private land through public policy.
- Describe how conservation became a part of agricultural payment to farmers and ranchers.
- Connect corn prices to decisions affecting wildlife habitat made by farmers.
- Compare conservation incentive programs in the current farm bill with regard to their use by private landowners.
- Compare the mission statements of federal land management agencies and explain how each agencies' approach to wildlife management may differ.
- Describe the NEPA process and when an Environmental Impact Statement may be required.
- Explain why ranchers or timber companies may access public lands for grazing or timber harvest.

A One-Minute Summary

Private landowners on farms and ranches make decisions that affect wildlife on a vast majority of the land in the United States. These individuals weigh decisions based on a variety of factors including economic return on their investment in the land. Land owned by private individuals may also provide ecosystem services to the public, and activities on private lands may affect the public. For example, soil erosion or nutrient run-off from farms may affect public waterways. Public policy is a mechanism by which the public may influence decisions made on private lands, through regulations, incentives, and taxes.

Since the 1930s, agricultural incentive programs have included conservation measures, and wildlife habitat is affected by the type of programs provided by the federal government. The Conservation Reserve Program is the flagship program of the current farm bill, which provides ten-year lease payments to farmers who follow requirements to provide protective vegetation that conserves soil, water, and wildlife. The decision to enroll in a farm bill program is an economic decision, and current prices of commodities such as corn will affect the amount of lease payment required to incentivize farmers to participate in conservation programs.

On public lands managed by state and federal agencies, the work of wildlife biologists is influenced by the mission of their agency. These missions have considerable variation from between agencies. Compliance with environmental regulations is paramount during management decisions on public lands, and the National Environmental Protection Act (NEPA) provides a process for evaluation of environmental impact of management alternatives during the decision process. The use of grazing allotment permits and timber contracts with citizens near public lands provides an opportunity for partnerships between public agencies and private citizens. Collaborative programs among state/federal agencies, NGOs, and private landowners are critical for success of conservation if management is to occur over large spatial scales.

Principles for Your Toolkit

Laws, incentives, taxes: Public policy can influence decisions made by private individuals through three mechanisms:

- **Regulation** of what behaviors are legal or illegal
- **Incentives** to encourage behavior
- **Taxes** to discourage behavior

Partnerships: A relatively simple concept, but any wildlife biologist employed by an NGO or state/federal agency will tell you that collaborations are key to successful management of wildlife. Partnerships can be formed between public land areas and their neighbors or between conservation groups working across landscapes, regions, or national/international scales. Very few species of wildlife confine themselves within the boundary of single farms, ranches, or even larger public land areas such as refuges, parks, or forests. Partnerships leverage spatial scale by using contributions of a large group of participants. As Henry Ford said, "If everyone is moving forward together, then success takes care of itself."

Environmental impact planning: Federal employees who manage public lands are required to engage in assessments of the potential effects of each management action on the environment. The Environmental Impact Statement is a critical component of the planning process required by the National Environmental Policy

Act (NEPA), and the NEPA process embodies a subset of the steps of the structured decision-making process.

A Problem: A Home for a Little, Yellow Bird

Ingrid and Desmond shared an office suite at the regional office of the US Fish and Wildlife Service in Marquette, Michigan. After shoveling a path through the most recent deposit of lake-effect snow, the two wildlife biologists took a 15-minute break to prepare for their day. Ingrid showed Desmond a copy of a research paper about Kirtland's warbler that had just arrived in the mail.

The paper, authored by Brown et al. in 2017, described the progress made towards recovery of the handsome yellow and black songbird, an endangered species that breeds in northern Michigan and winters in the Bahamas. Both Desmond and Ingrid were aware of the years of tough work to improve the pine habitat needed by the species, as well as the never-ending work to remove brown-headed cowbirds from warbler breeding areas. Ingrid had been involved in some cowbird removal at the nearby Seney National Wildlife Refuge, and nest success of Kirtland's warbler had improved. The cowbirds were nest parasites, laying their own eggs in the nests of the warbler.

"I'm so glad our national wildlife refuges, national forests, and state wildlife areas can contribute to the recovery of Kirtland's warbler," remarked Ingrid. Besides her work on cowbird removal, she was often dispatched to help with habitat management at the lands managed by the refuge system in the Upper Peninsula, and a series of collaborative partnerships often brought her to meetings with biologists working with the US Forest Service and the Michigan Department of Natural Resources. The past years were proof that inter-agency partnerships could pay dividends for wildlife conservation.

Desmond looked up from peering through the paper with a worried look. "But, Ingrid," he remarked, "the simulations in this paper suggest that if the public land areas adopt a forest management strategy similar to the private land in the region, it could hurt warbler recovery efforts."

Desmond was familiar with private lands in Michigan—he worked with the agency's Partners for Fish and Wildlife program. In contrast to Ingrid, Desmond spent most of his time working with private owners of agricultural lands and forestlands in the region. He knew that the default management strategy in private forests was to use an even-age, "plantation" system to encourage the local jack pine to grow quickly to a harvestable size.

What would you need to learn to be able to talk about forest management with Ingrid and Desmond? What is even-aged forest management, and why do private forest owners tend to use it? What would you need to learn to help Desmond work with private landowners to support the at-risk species of warbler? By the time you finish this chapter, you should be able to find the answer.

Terms and Definitions

Conservation easement: A voluntary legal agreement between a landowner and a land trust or government agency that permanently limits uses of the land in order to protect its conservation values.

Cost share: A process, related to federal farm bill programs, in which the federal government pays a portion of the costs required to implement mandatory habitat management practices.

Ecosystem services: The benefits that humans gain from the natural environment and from properly functioning ecosystems.

Farm bill: A multi-faceted, multi-year law that governs an array of agricultural and food programs.

Incentive: A payment or concession to stimulate greater output or investment.

Public interest: A common concern among citizens in the management and affairs of local, state, and national government.

Public policy: The principles, written or unwritten, on which social laws are based.

A Tale of Two Careers

The choice to work with state or federal land management versus working to support wildlife on private lands offers a strong dichotomy of challenges, daily focus, and approach to wildlife management. Two individuals employed by an agency, such as the US Fish and Wildlife Service, may wear the same uniform, but a person tasked with federal and private land partnerships will use a very different set of strategies, or tools, for management than their colleague who supports management within a national wildlife refuge.

A manager who works on public lands, managed by state or federal government, typically is in a role defined by the mission of their agency. Public land managers are tasked with supporting some kind of protectionist mission with regard to wildlife. One of the reasons we have public lands is to provide for the habitat needs of wildlife (chapter 1), and this historic mission remains critical as private lands are under more pressure for development or commodity production.

Public land managers are also aware of the "public" adjective that describes the land in which they work. Visitors are important to the budgets of national parks and national wildlife refuges. The opportunity for private citizens to graze their cattle on national grasslands or harvest timber from national forests provides income to citizens as well as a service to managers who need cattle or timber harvesters to accomplish management goals for habitat. Hikers, climbers, and campers desire access to national parks or lands managed by the Bureau of Land Management, which requires trail maps, law enforcement, and other visitor services.

However, the relationship with public land areas is shifting with time. Despite a growing population in the United States, the number of visitors to national park service sites has remained fairly stagnant since 1990, and the number of hours spent by each visitor has declined since 1978 (Figure 13.1). Public land management agencies

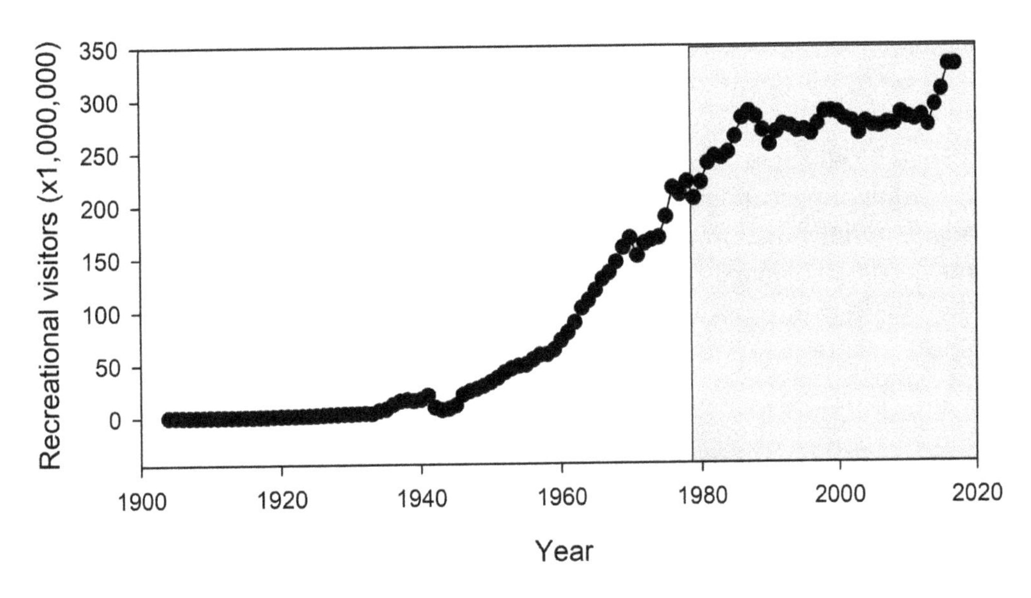

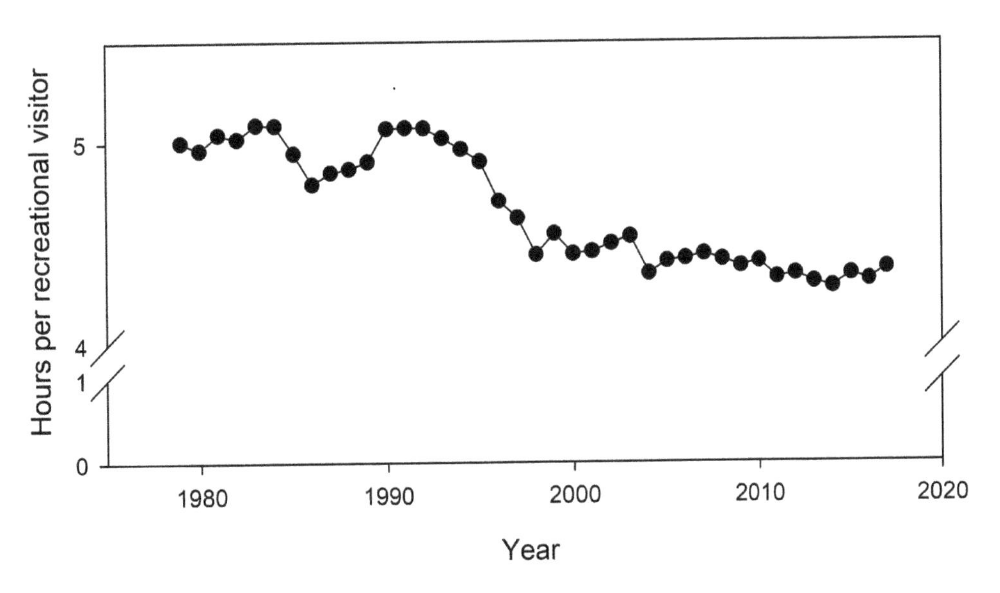

FIGURE 13.1 Visitor trends (top) for the National Park Service, 1904–2017, including (bottom) hours spent per visit during 1978–2017 (shaded area, top). Data provided by the National Park Service, and used with permission.

depend on Congressional support for their budgets, and a relative decline in public use could mean less interest in funding these agencies in the future.

A private lands biologist is in the unique role of reaching out to landowners who may have interest in developing management plans for wildlife on their land. Landowners typically have no requirement to participate in conservation measures, so incentive programs are useful tools for the private land manager. Landowners are especially tuned to costs and benefits as they keep their bottom line in mind. Farmers, ranchers, and private forest owners have large investments in their holdings, similar to any businessperson who has leveraged an initial capital investment in hopes of business success and profits. The estimated value of cropland in Illinois in 2018 was $7,450/acre (sale prices during the same period averaged $10,500/acre), and the value of pastureland in Texas in 2018 was $1,750/acre (USDA 2018). You can calculate how much it would take to purchase a 1,000-acre farm or a 20,000-acre ranch, which demonstrates the reason that agricultural producers often reflect that their main goal is not to support wildlife populations on their land (Sliwinski et al. 2018).

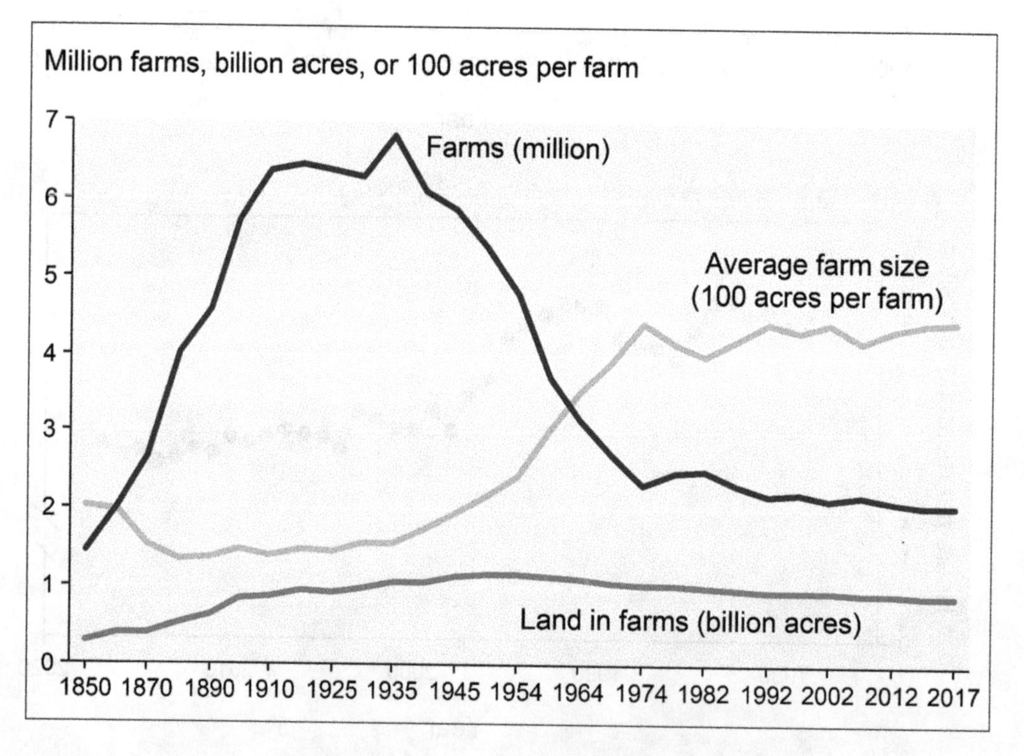

FIGURE 13.2 Trends in the number of farms (blue), average farm size (green), and the number of acres in farm operations (orange) in the United States, 1850–2017. Figure from USDA, National Agricultural Statistics Service.

Wildlife biologists who work in production landscapes also work with a changing dynamic of landowners and farm size. Although the amount of farmland has remained relatively unchanged since the 1920s, the number of farms has steadily decreased since the Great Depression in the 1930s. The average farm size has increased to approximately 450 acres/farm (Figure 13.2).

Farms in the United States are becoming increasingly specialized. USDA statistics show that the average farm sold 5 commodities in 1900, while farms in 2002 sold only 1.2 commodities per farm. This trend creates landscapes less useful for wildlife (Hiller et al. 2009), and specialization imposes heightened risk should commodity process fall. Perhaps for this reason, many landowners make their living from rental income rather than crop or livestock production. The USDA estimates that someone other than the owner operates nearly one-third of farms in the US. In fact, the owner may live in another county or state. These "absentee landowners" may be less concerned about the feelings of their neighbors than local owners and may be more likely to be detached from local concerns of watershed or ecosystem health.

The Role of Public Policy on Private Lands

Wildlife managers who support conservation on private lands are strongly affected by public policies for agriculture. In the western US, public lands make up a large portion of each state, and wildlife management can be effectively carried out through land management on federal and state lands. However, the proportion of public land drops as we move into the Great Plains and the eastern US (Figure 13.3). Conservation programs in these regions must have **private land partnerships** to be successful, because most wildlife in these states exists on private lands.

Two conflicting legal dynamics create some tension in areas dominated by private lands. The landowners control, through their ownership, the manner in which their land is used. However, as we noted in chapter 1, wildlife is a public resource. Therefore, we have a public resource that exists mainly on private lands, which affects the access to the resource and the decision processes that affects the wildlife resource. For these reasons, public **agriculture policy** is critically important.

A landowner can choose to make almost any modification to their land. Some of these modifications, such as planting crops, benefit the farmer (e.g., income based on sale of commodities). Agriculture production is also in the **public interest**, since food production for our nation is critical. However, agriculture entails cultivation, fertilization, and other decisions that affect people outside the farm. The public has interest in economic dynamics that lead to removal of wetlands or the use of farming methods that cause high rates of soil erosion. These outcomes might be seen to go against the public interest. Communities are currently facing high costs to filter water without wetlands, and turbid water in rivers affects fish populations and sediment

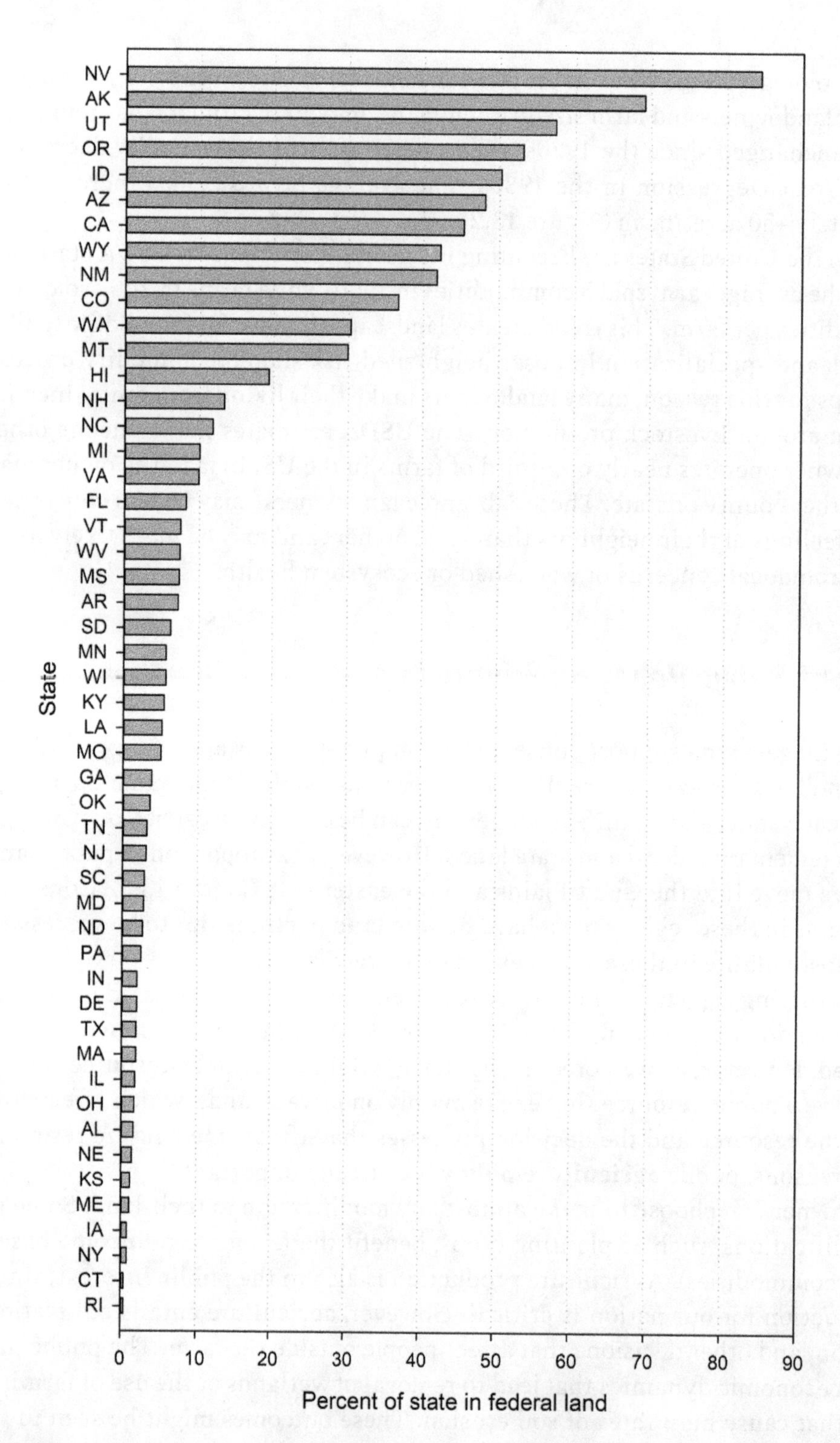

FIGURE 13.3: Percent of state in federal land, data from US General Services Administration, Federal Real Property Profile 2004.

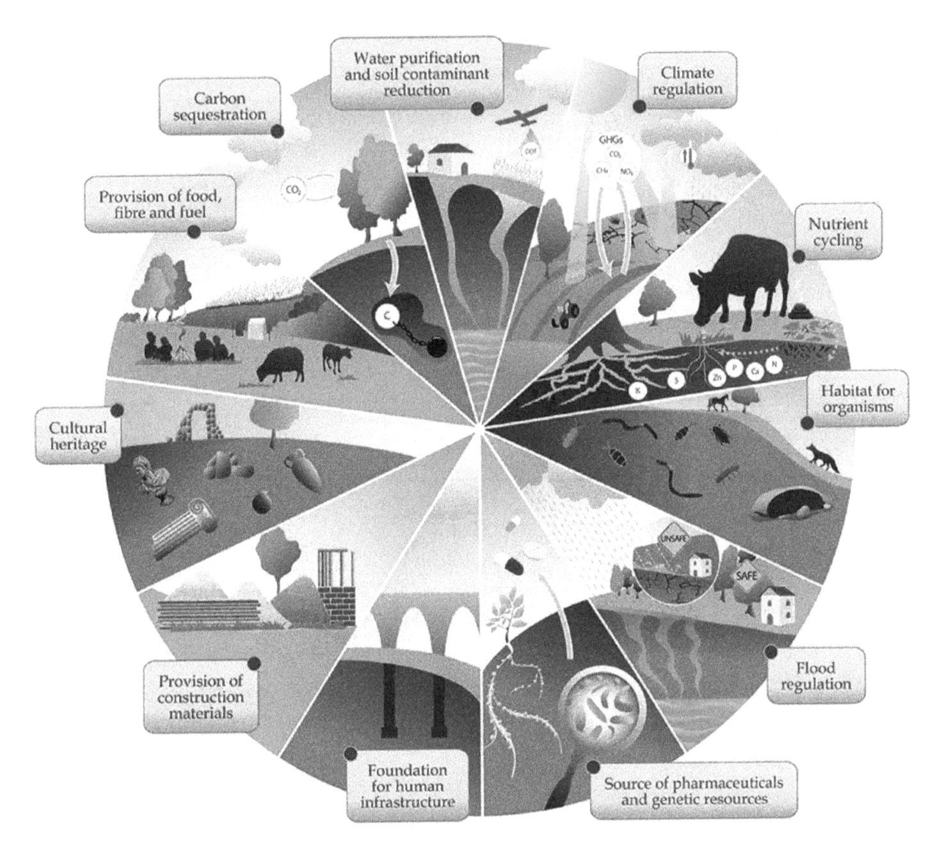

FIGURE 13.4 Schematic diagram of soil functions, reprinted from Baveye et al. (2016), Creative Commons license.

levels in public reservoirs. In addition to agriculture production, soils on farm and ranchland may also provide valuable **ecosystem services** to the region (Figure 13.4, Baveye et al. 2016).

The Landowner

How can society protect their interest on private lands? We start with the fact that the private landowner is a member of society, and the landowner chose to purchase land in the United States, rather than another country. Societies around the world make decisions about what they want to support and value, and these decisions become legislation and public policy. Therefore, society can make laws that can affect decisions made by landowners.

A landowner makes decisions based on a variety of factors using various types of decision processes (chapter 3), and most landowners highly value the tradeoff between benefits to self and costs to self. If it costs more to prevent soil erosion than a landowner can accrue through the benefits of preventing erosion, a landowner will most likely choose to ignore soil erosion, until soil erosion begins to cost too much (Figure 13.5).

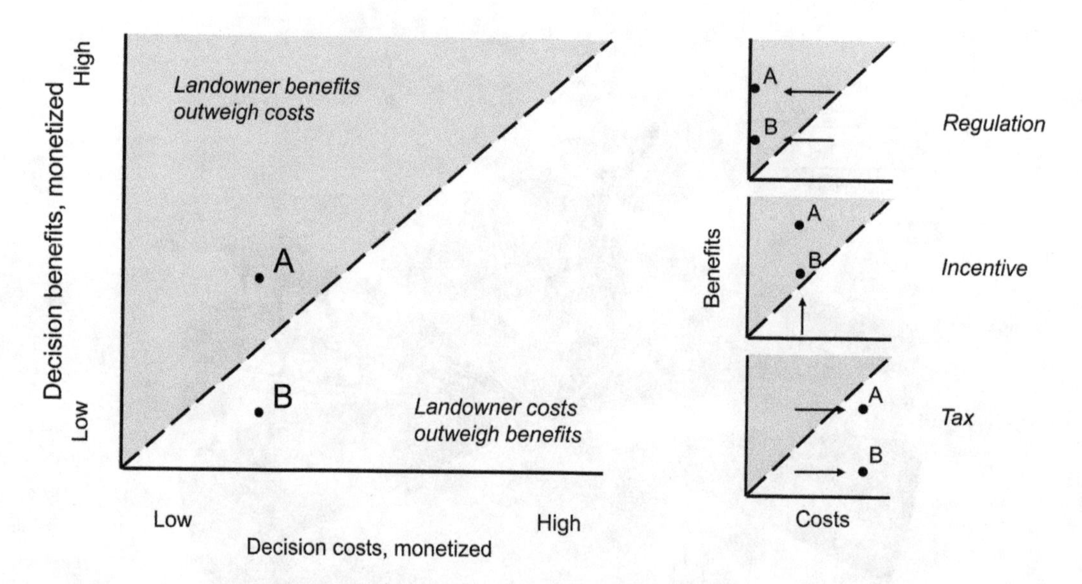

FIGURE 13.5 Simple cost-benefit comparison (left) for a decision made by a private landowner regarding use of their land. Area in green above the dotted line is where a decision's benefits outweigh the costs, below the line is opposite. On right, the effects of regulations (elimination of cost consideration), incentives (increased benefits per unit cost), and taxes (increased cost per unit benefit) on the decision (e.g., restore a wetland).

If the public good is served by a decision by a private landowner for which the benefits outweigh the costs to the landowner, the cost to the public for the service provided by the landowner is small or zero. However, if the public good is not served by a decision that benefits the private landowner, the costs to the public are potentially high.

Public policy has three basic tools at its disposal:

- **We can make certain practices unlawful.** If the public good is harmed by decisions that benefit private landowners (Figure 13.5), society can make that decision, or practice, illegal. Child labor laws and minimum wage laws are two examples of federal laws that govern labor practices set by society. The Clean Air Act and the Clean Water Act are examples that affect natural resources, and private landowners can be found in violation of these acts, regardless of the fact that they own the land.
- **We can provide incentives for practices that we support.** Cities give tax breaks to encourage companies to move to their town. We often refer to these incentives as **subsidies**. If a practice would cost a landowner more than it benefits them (Figure 13.5), society can add monetary benefit to encourage a certain behavior. For example, we can provide state or federal assistance to landowners who cut down cedar trees, plant native grasslands, restore wetlands, or use practices that reduce soil erosion. The subsidies offset the costs of these practices to the landowner.

- **We can tax a certain behavior to reduce its prevalence.** Cigarette taxes are meant to discourage smoking. Similarly, society can influence decisions made on private lands by taxing something that benefits the farmer more than it costs. In this way, the resulting benefits are less than before the tax. For example, a state might add a tax for proceeds from energy development (e.g., oil or natural gas) in landscapes decreed sensitive to development. The tax would reduce the profits from energy development and could affect the decision by the landowner (Figure 13.5).

The establishment of public policy is always controversial, as one segment of society feels regulated by other members of society. But public policy is an important part of any society. The advantage of living in a democratic society is that we have some level of input into public policy. Laws can be modified and changed as society's views change. It is in this context that we can consider farm policy and wildlife.

QUICK COMPREHENSION CHECK

Which of the three policy options to support conservation on private lands do you think is more appealing to the public? Why? Which is more appealing to the private landowner? Why?

Find your state in Figure 13.3. How does the percent of public land in your state affect the priorities for wildlife management in your state? How might it be different for a state with a different level of public land area?

The Farm Bill: Farm Policy and Wildlife

The federal government first became involved in supporting agriculture at a large scale during the Great Depression. Initially, the 1933 Agriculture Adjustment Act (AAA) sought to provide direct payments to farmers who reduced output of certain commodities to lessen the economic impact of the depression on rural communities. The reduction in production also attempted to stabilize markets and demand for agriculture products. However, the Supreme Court ruled that the AAA, which featured direct payments to farmers, was not constitutional because public money was being used to support individuals without a direct link to any public good.

However, politicians still wanted to relieve the strain on farmers, so conservation became a political tool. The Soil Conservation Act of 1935 paid farmers who used conservation practices to limit soil and water erosion,

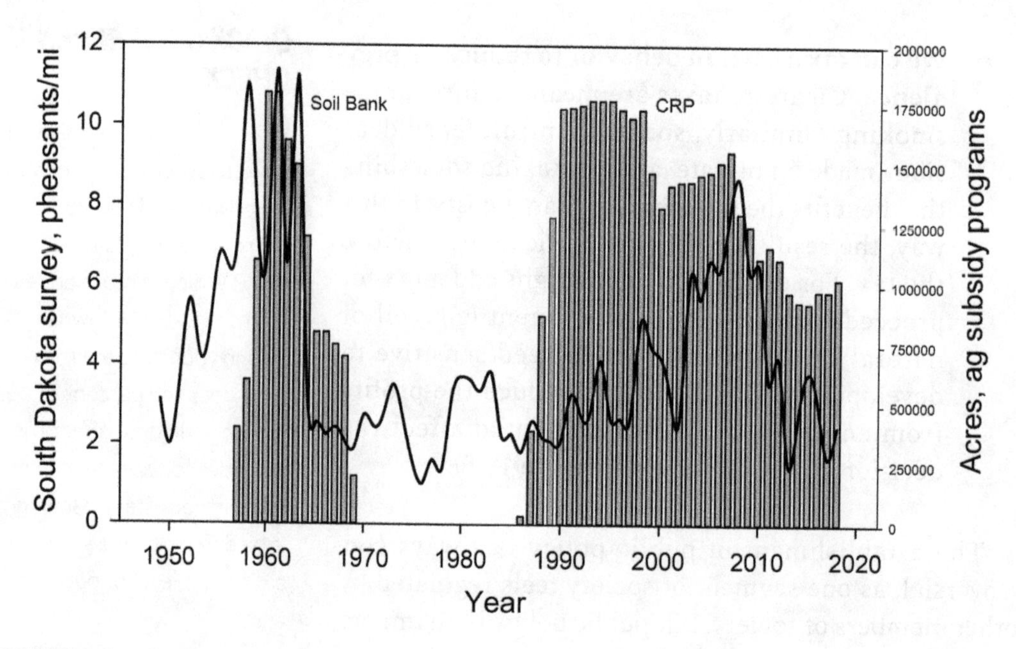

FIGURE 13.6 Ring-necked pheasant population levels in South Dakota during 1949–2018, as indexed by statewide, pre-harvest road surveys (pheasants seen per mile), relative to acres of land in South Dakota enrolled in either the Soil Bank or Conservation Reserve Program. Data provided by South Dakota Game, Fish, and Parks, used with permission.

which was clearly a public good to protect the soil that was needed to produce food for the country. These new payments were not challenged in court, and federal conservation programs were born as a legal maneuver to provide subsidies to farmers. The program included the development of a new federal agency, the Soil Conservation Service, which later become the Natural Resource Conservation Service, or NRCS (Cain and Lovejoy 2004).

Following World War II, the US markets encountered a surplus of crops as demand fell from wartime levels (Henderson et al. 2011), and a post-war recession emerged. During this time of economic stress on the farm, Congress passed the Agriculture Act of 1956, commonly referred to as the "Soil Bank" program. 29 million acres were removed from production in return for government rental payments under a ten-year contract. Programs promoted establishment of grasslands on farm fields to influence soil, water, forest, and wildlife conservation. Conservation, again, was the legal vehicle for federal payments to individual farmers.

Pheasant populations in South Dakota show the impact of the Soil Bank program on wildlife. As the soil bank acres increased, the pheasant population doubled, underscoring the potential for good soils to produce wildlife if habitat is available (Figure 13.7). Of course, when land came out of the Soil Bank program and returned to cropland, the pheasant population went back down.

The Farm Crisis of the 1980s was another severe economic time in rural America. Congress responded with the first of a string of appropriately named **farm bills** in 1985. One program within the 1985 farm bill was known as the **Conservation Reserve Program**, and it is still used today. The timing of this economic downturn resulted in a unique type of farm bill in 1985, as the 1970s had been a decade of public attention to the needs of the environment including the Endangered Species Act, Clean Water Act, and Clean Air Act. The 1985 farm bill went beyond concern for soils to protect the public food supply to introduce new goals: improve water, soil, and air quality for the public good. For the first time, a farm bill included acknowledgement of the role of the farm landscape in wildlife conservation in the language of the bill (Powell 2015). Similar increases in pheasant numbers were seen in South Dakota as acres were added in the Conservation Reserve Program (Figure 13.7).

Approximately 20 pieces of legislation could be labeled as farm bills since the 1930s. It is key to understanding the role of farm policy in conservation to note that

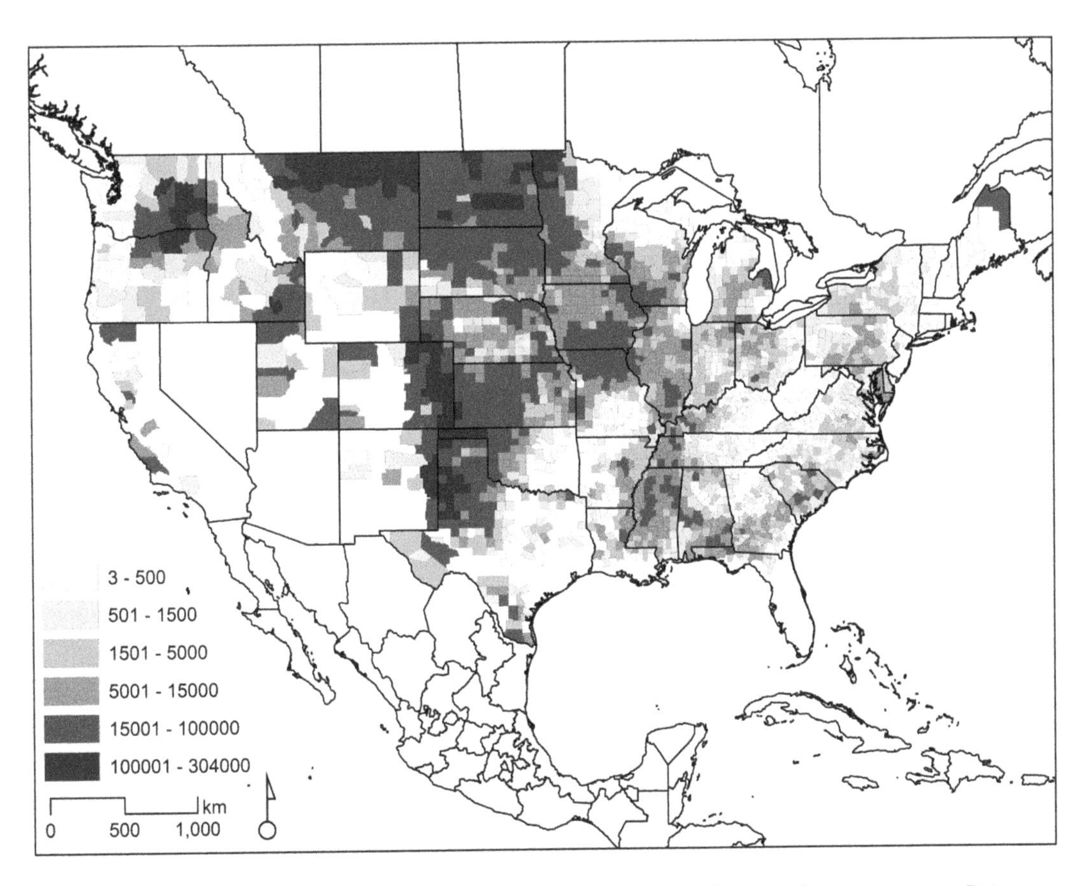

FIGURE 13.7 Cumulative acres enrolled in the Conservation Reserve Program by county, 2004. Data from USDA Farm Service Agency, provided by the Conservation Biology Institute.

the major innovations to the forms of agricultural policy occurred during economic crises in agriculture. Since the Soil Bank, the agricultural policy acts have included:

- Food and Agricultural Act of 1965
- Agricultural Act of 1970
- Agricultural and Consumer Protection Act of 1973
- Food and Agriculture Act of 1977
- Agriculture and Food Act of 1981
- Food Security Act of 1985
- Food, Agriculture, Conservation, and Trade Act of 1990
- Federal Agriculture Improvement and Reform Act of 1996
- Farm Security and Rural Investment Act of 2002
- Food, Conservation, and Energy Act of 2008
- Agricultural Act of 2014

The Conservation Reserve Program (CRP) provides farmers who successfully apply with ten-year contracts (Figure 13.7). The federal Natural Resource Conservation Service (NRCS) within the US Department of Agriculture administers the farm bill. The NRCS description of the Conservation Reserve Program is as follows:

- CRP reduces soil erosion, protects the nation's ability to produce food and fiber, reduces sedimentation in streams and lakes, improves water quality, establishes wildlife habitat, and enhances forest and wetland resources.
- CRP encourages farmers to convert highly erodible cropland or other environmentally sensitive acreage to vegetative cover, such as tame or native grasses, wildlife plantings, trees, filter strips, or riparian buffers.
- Farmers receive an annual rental payment for the term of the multi-year contract.
- Cost sharing is provided to establish the vegetative cover practices.

To enroll in the CRP, landowners sign contracts to remove highly erodible land, which has been scored high on the soil erodibility index (based on soil, climate, and topography of the land). Lands with a lower index may be approved if they are in a CRP conservation priority landscape. NRCS may give preference to protecting land in certain watersheds to protect water quality.

The farmer then establishes and maintains a specific type of cover: trees, shrubs, forbs, legumes, or grasses. The vegetation cannot be harvested commercially.

In return for participation in the CRP, an initial cost share provides up to 50% of the costs to establish the approved type of habitat on eligible cropland. Then, the landowner receives annual rental payments. The rental rates are based on the relative productivity of the soils within each county and the average dryland cash rent or cash rent equivalent. Farmers may also receive "maintenance payments" of up to $5 per acre per year as an incentive to perform certain maintenance obligations (such as discing, tree removal, or prescribed burning).

The maximum CRP rental rate for each offer is calculated in advance of enrollment. Producers may bid lower to increase the likelihood that the USDA will accept their offer. Farmers do not get rich on CRP rental rates, and, in most cases, a farmer may still receive more income by farming crops rather than participating in CRP. Such dynamics are especially true when grain prices are high.

To select lands for the CRP, USDA uses an Environmental Benefits Index to rank every application. The index includes the following components:

- Wildlife habitat benefits resulting from cover on contract acreage
- Water quality benefits from reduced erosion, runoff, and leaching
- On-farm benefits from reduced erosion
- Benefits that will likely endure beyond the contract period
- Air quality benefits from reduced wind erosion
- Is the land in a Conservation Priority Area?
- Cost

Other conservation programs in the 2018 farm bill in addition to CRP include:

Environmental Quality Incentives Program (EQIP): Applicants with highly erodible land or wetlands develop a plan to accomplish specific conservation objectives, and USDA assists with technical direction and project costs. Priority projects provide improvements for water quality, ground and surface water resources, air quality, soil erosion and sedimentation, and habitat for at-risk wildlife species. In contrast to CRP, EQIP provides payments for projects on working lands and does not take land out of production. Example projects include irrigation efficiency, animal waste facility improvements, installation of cover crops, grazing improvement plans, and forest stand improvement. Payments are made to producers once the conservation practices are completed. Two programs in previous versions of the farm bill, the Wildlife Habitat Incentive Program (WHIP) and the Conservation Stewardship Program (CSP) are now incorporated in the 2018 version of EQIP as critical incentive programs on working lands.

Agricultural Conservation Easement Program (ACEP): Provides financial and technical assistance through two types of easements. First, funding is available to support agricultural land easements that limit non-agricultural development of productive farm or grasslands. Second, wetland reserve easements may be supported if they protect and restore wetlands. Funding is provided to the partners who purchase the easement (*see easement description*). USDA pays a larger proportion of the purchase price and wetland restoration costs for permanent easements, compared to 30-year easements or other term easements.

Regional Conservation Partnership Program (RCPP): Supports conservation partnerships between agricultural producers and organizational partners such as local/regional governments, agricultural or silvicultural associations, farmer cooperatives, water and irrigation districts, universities, and NGOs. Almost half of RCPP funding is designated for national, multi-state projects, and all RCPP projects are intended to result in watershed or regional level projects that affect large landscapes rather than single producer holdings that are supported by other farm bill programs.

The farm bill is a large item in the federal budget at about 2% of all federal spending. The Congressional Budget Office projected that the 2018 farm bill would cost $428 billion over five years. The farm subsidy portion of the farm bill is about 20% of the total, with nutrition programs accounting for the other 80%. Political processes related to budget priorities and the federal deficit make for controversy each time the farm bill is renewed for another period.

The calculation for the cost of the farm bill program to taxpayers is directly related to land rent prices in the US, which rise when commodity prices are high (Figure 12.9). When corn prices are high, farmers can afford to pay higher rent. The widespread use of corn for ethanol has recently caused corn prices to jump to a new plateau, which

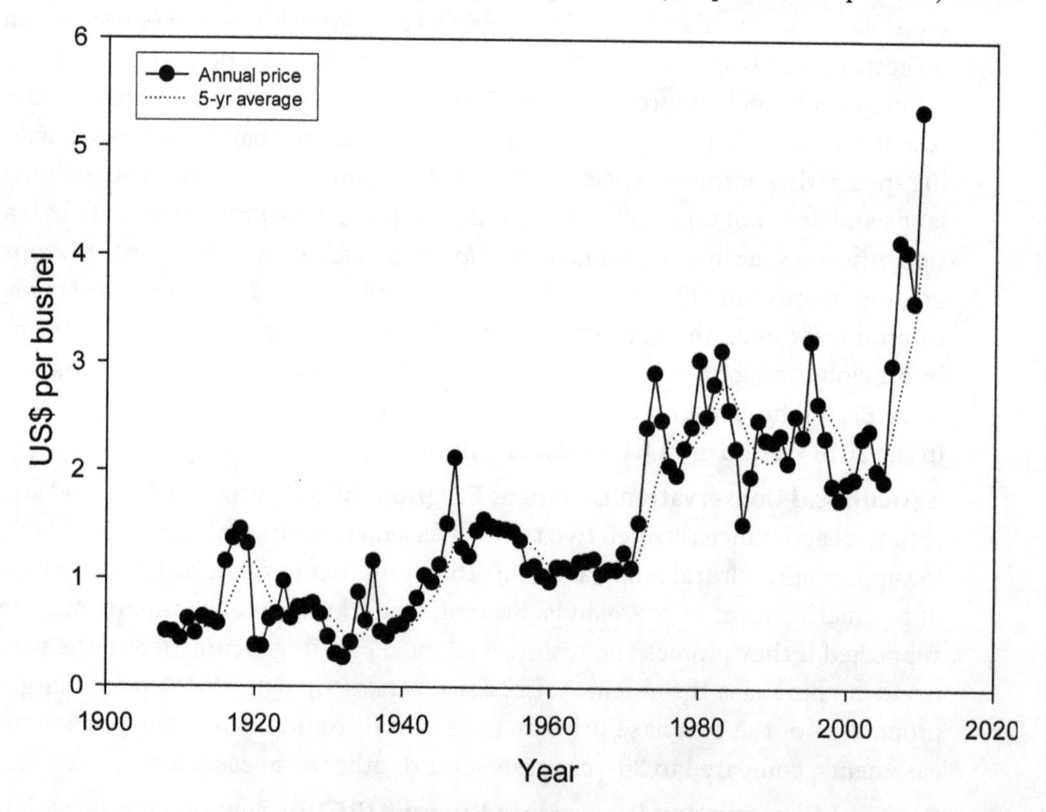

FIGURE 13.8 Average price of corn per bushel over time in Nebraska, US. Data from USDA National Ag Statistics Service, public domain.

will mean that farmers are less willing to settle for low rent prices. The next farm bills will be more expensive to taxpayers, and the rental prices offered will determine the pattern of participation by farmers, such as the variation seen in the past in South Dakota (Figure 13.8).

Farm policy is shaped by politics and economics, which are two of the most critical considerations for wildlife managers who work on private lands. Historically, wildlife habitat management on private lands is a by-product of soil conservation, and the future of wildlife habitat is tied to crop surpluses and prices.

The importance of public policy emphasizes importance of lobbying and politicians who understand conservation needs. Wildlife managers should be aware that 100 US Senators have the potential to have more impact on wildlife populations than 1000 wildlife managers. Farm policy changes our landscapes.

QUICK COMPREHENSION CHECK

Compare the maps of soils in the US (Figure 12.1) with the distribution of CRP (Figure 13.7). What common patterns do you seen? What causes those patterns?

More Tools for Conservation on Private Lands

The farm bill may provide a large share of the incentives for work on private lands, but other programs and legal tools are useful for managers who need incentive to create conservation plans on farms, ranches, and private forest lands.

Conservation Easements

An easement is a legally binding agreement in which certain rights are voluntarily sold or donated by the landowner. Conservation easements are a specific type of easement that limits development or types of uses as stipulated by the agreement. For example, a conservation easement of a property with wetlands may prevent drainage and wetland removal as well as limiting types of agricultural production that can occur on the property. A conservation easement on a coastal beach property may prohibit development for vacation homes or for wind energy. The land remains in private ownership, and owners retain most property rights to their land. The easement legally travels with the property when it is sold, and the new owner must abide by the easement (Merenlender et al. 2004).

A private organization or public agency agrees to hold the right to enforce the landowner's promise not to exercise the rights that are forfeited, such as development. Often land trusts or NGOs may purchase the easement with funds donated for conservation work. The farm bill's ACEP provides funding for easement purchases as well. The sale of an easement is an incentive to the landowner, and, in some cases, landowners donate the easement to the external organization in favor of receiving tax credits from the Internal Revenue Service.

Conservation easements protect land for future generations, while the property remains subject to property taxes. The value of the land may decrease if, for example, agricultural production is prohibited by the easement. In these cases, easements can be controversial in rural communities that rely on property taxes for schools and emergency services funding. This is especially true in areas with high density of wetlands or unique habitats that may be targeted in a landscape-level coordinated effort to protect large blocks of habitat. Although this strategy accomplishes conservation goals, the resulting loss of property tax income can have effects on the community and cause ill will towards conservation partners.

Conservation Banking

The US Fish and Wildlife Service uses conservation banks to allow some private landowners to purchase credits from bank owners when development results in unavoidable, adverse impacts on species of conservation concern. A partner landowner may offer property to be used as a bank by other landowners (USFWS 2012). For example, a rancher may reduce or eliminate grazing and install specific habitat for a species such as greater sage grouse or lesser prairie chickens and place lands under a conservation easement to create a bank. That rancher can then receive payments for credits that are purchased by other landowners that cannot avoid disturbing valuable habitat. The goal is to maintain an area of habitat for at-risk species, and the income serves as an incentive to the bank owner. The program allows some economic development to occur on the landscape, which may support the local economy and gain trust from critical partners in the community for conservation projects.

Safe Harbor

Safe Harbor Agreements are voluntary arrangements between the US Fish and Wildlife Service and non-federal landowners (chapter 9). The landowner provides information about the property, including information on species on the property that are listed under the Endangered Species Act. The USFWS describes baseline conditions that must be present at the end of the agreement, and the landowner agrees to perform a list of conservation actions in return for assurances that additional actions will be required in the future. Safe harbor is a useful tool for owners of critical habitat for endangered species that otherwise might worry about the limits for use of timber products, grazing area, or farmland. Safe harbor allows private lands to continue to provide income for owners in return for a set of conservation action plans, which may be limited to a portion of the property. Further, if conservation efforts result in increased populations of the at-risk species, landowners have assurances that they will not be required to perform additional actions beyond the original agreement. The program attempts to avoid the "shoot, shovel, and shut up" mentality often associated with discovery of at-risk species on private lands.

Partners for Fish and Wildlife

The US Fish and Wildlife Service provides technical assistance and cost share for habitat restoration on private lands through this public-private partnership. The program is often used in regions for specific initiatives. In the southern Great Plains, the program is used to create large blocks of suitable habitat that may include multiple landowners who engage in the removal of trees, prescribed burning, and rotational grazing practices to improve habitat for the lesser prairie chicken. The USFWS works with local USDA NRCS employees to engage with a large number of landowners in specific regions through this program.

Carbon Offsets

During the past three to four decades, the knowledge of carbon contributions to global warming and climate change have created demand for mitigation strategies for companies that build new factories that contribute additional atmospheric emissions. Groups of landowners may come together to restore vegetation (trees, grasslands, wetlands) in return for receipt of credits purchased by individuals or companies in voluntary carbon markets (Galik and Jackson 2009). Private lands used for carbon offsets can be grazed or harvested for timber as long as the management is done in accordance with estimates of carbon sequestered by vegetation on the properties. The unique nature of this program is that federal tax dollars are not used as incentives—rather private investments fuel the payments to landowners to support restoration and maintenance of habitat on the landscape.

Public Land Management

Perhaps your goal is to be a wildlife biologist or manager with a federal agency. There are plenty of choices, and each agency has its own unique mission and purpose to serve the public interests of the American people (Table 13.1). First, land management agencies are located within several federal departments, each with its own secretary who reports to the president. As a wildlife biologist, you can work near locks and dams operated by the Army Corps of Engineers in the Department of Defense. Alternatively, you might work in the National Wildlife Refuge program or in a national

TABLE 13.1 ***Mission statements of selected land management agencies of the United States federal government***

FEDERAL LAND MANAGEMENT AGENCY	MISSION STATEMENT: "OUR MISSION IS..."	PRIMARY RESOURCE RESPONSIBILITY
BUREAU OF INDIAN AFFAIRS	To enhance the quality of life, to promote economic opportunity, and to carry out the responsibility to protect and improve the trust assets of American Indians, Indian tribes, and Alaska Natives.	Human resources of tribes and villages, tribal lands and mineral resources
US FISH AND WILDLIFE SERVICE, NATIONAL WILDLIFE REFUGE PROGRAM	To work with others to conserve, protect and enhance fish, wildlife and plants and their habitats for the continuing benefit of the American people.	Wildlife and habitat conservation, wildlife-related recreation
US FOREST SERVICE	To sustain the health, diversity, and productivity of the Nation's forests and grasslands to meet the needs of present and future generations.	Forest products, domestic grazing, fish and wildlife habitat
NATIONAL PARK SERVICE	To preserve unimpaired the natural and cultural resources and values of the National Park System for the enjoyment, education, and inspiration of this and future generations.	Land, wildlife, and historical conservation
BUREAU OF LAND MANAGEMENT	To sustain the health, diversity, and productivity of public lands for the use and enjoyment of present and future generations.	Domestic grazing, mining, timber, energy extraction, fish and wildlife habitat
BUREAU OF RECLAMATION	To manage, develop, and protect water and related resources in an environmentally and economically sound manner in the interest of the American public.	Water resources and infrastructure of dams, power plants, and canals
ARMY CORPS OF ENGINEERS	To deliver vital public and military engineering services; partnering in peace and war to strengthen our Nation's security, energize the economy and reduce risks from disasters.	Improvements relating to navigation, hydroelectric power, and flood control for rivers, harbors, and other waterways

park within the Department of the Interior. The Bureau of Reclamation, Bureau of Land Management, and Bureau of Indian Affairs are also housed in the Department of the Interior. The US Forest Service is within the Department of Agriculture.

Funding of federal agencies is part of our political process. The Department of Defense may garner support in the congressional budget in years when other agencies receive cuts, but a different political climate may result in the opposite trend during the next budget season. Since 1980, the federal government has endured ten shutdowns that caused furloughs to federal employees, including a 35-day shutdown in 2018–2019. Federal budgets create complexities for federal land management agencies. State wildlife agencies have their own unique issues for their budgets (see chapter 2), which depend on a combination of state taxes and distributed federal funds.

The priority for wildlife management varies among federal agencies. For example, compare the Army Corps of Engineers with the US Fish and Wildlife Service. Wildlife refuges within the US Fish and Wildlife Service are specifically set aside to support migratory birds and endangered species, so wildlife management is at the top of their priority list. In contrast, the Army Corps of Engineers exists to support structural infrastructure such as dams on major rivers. As a result of these projects, the Army Corps ends up managing a considerable amount of floodplain habitat, and they make decisions regarding the release of water from dams in accordance with requirements of the Endangered Species Act, when applicable. However, wildlife management is not the Corps' top priority. The same could be said of the Bureau of Indian Affairs, which exists to protect assets of Native people, including management of land resources.

All work with wildlife and habitats by federal land management agencies is governed by three overriding legal mandates. Any employee of a federal agency spends considerable time working to ensure compliance during activities, and management decisions are often affected by these mandated priorities:

- Each wildlife refuge, national forest unit, land management unit, or national park has an approved management plan. The US Forest Service calls these documents Land and Resource Management Plans. The USFWS service establishes Comprehensive Conservation Plans for national wildlife refuges. National parks establish Management Plans. Regardless of the agency, each plan is developed under guidelines similar to those covered in chapter 4.
- The activities of federal land management agencies are guided by federal legislation, such as the Endangered Species Act (ESA, see chapters 8, 9), Clean Water Act, and Clean Air Act. This priority stems from the ideals of public lands serving the public trust mission of the federal government to the American people. For example, watershed protection and management of riparian areas are areas of emphasis in which modern public land managers may find themselves involved in evaluating impacts of alternative management strategies

for timber harvest or grazing on fish, mussel, and invertebrate populations in addition to water quality.

- All federal agencies (including agencies that do not manage large expanses of public land) are required to use an approval process for any project or development as required by the National Environmental Protection Act (NEPA). As one of the first broad environmental regulations, NEPA serves as a core responsibility and set of rules that apply whenever a federal agency proposes to take an action with the potential to affect the natural and physical environment. As such, NEPA is a procedural law that dictates the structure of a process that must be followed by agency personnel. NEPA does not dictate the decision that must be made, but rather how that decision is to be documented and justified with regard to environmental impacts.

The NEPA Process

NEPA requires federal decision-makers to include public involvement as part of the decision process, to investigate the environmental consequences of proposed actions, and to consider these consequences in determining courses of action. As such, NEPA represents a broad, deep dive into the alternatives, consequences, and tradeoff steps of the PrOACT decision-making process. Although private and state-level management decisions may not require NEPA consideration, if federal funds are not being used, components of NEPA have been incorporated over time to strengthen these non-federal decision processes.

NEPA allows for three levels of analysis of environmental consequences (Figure 13.9). The lowest level is Categorical Exclusion (CATEX). A more robust level of analysis is Environmental Assessment (EA), and the most robust analysis is a full Environmental Impact Statement (EIS, National Park Service 2015).

- Categorical exclusions are granted when actions do not have significant effects on the environment. Routine administrative action, routine real estate transactions, or routine law enforcement actions are examples of potential situations that may not require a more formal assessment.
- Environmental assessments are intermediate planning processes in which environmental impacts are expected but the strength of the impact is unknown. If the impact is determined to be significant during the EA process, the EA process is abandoned and the environmental impact statement process is begun (Figure 13.9). Public involvement is more substantial in the EIS process than the EA process, while the CATEX process does not involve public involvement. Therefore, NEPA provides an opportunity for stakeholders to engage regarding concerns or other input.

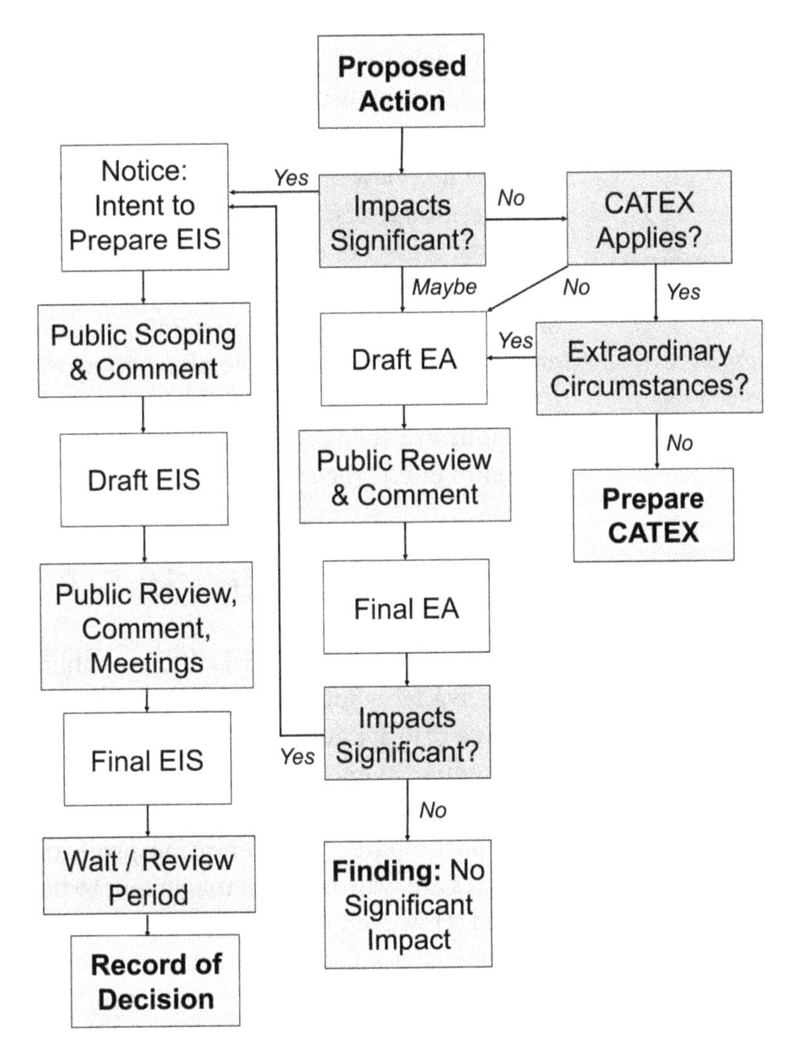

FIGURE 13.9 A flow chart of the NEPA process regarding three levels of analysis from Categorial Exclusion (CATEX), Environmental Analysis (EA), or Environmental Impact Statement (EIS). Figure modified from data provided by the US Navy.

- Environmental impact statements have a basic function in the NEPA process that should remind you of steps in the PrOACT process (chapter 3). Each EIS includes a purpose and need statement, which explains the reason the agency is proposing the action and what the agency expects to achieve. Then, the EIS describes a reasonable list of alternatives (means objectives) to accomplish the purpose (fundamental objective) of the proposed action. The EIS then turns its attention to the affected environment. Where will the project take place? What sensitive features are present in the environment? Terrestrial habitats? Species? Aquatic resources? Finally, the EIS describes the direct and indirect environmental consequences of the alternatives on the affected environment. The EIS is subject to review to ensure the treatment of concerns is complete and justified.

After a review of the final document, NEPA does not require an agency to select the most optimal alternative with regard to environmental concerns. Rather, the strategic objectives of the agency or the fundamental objectives of the project may guide a decision towards an environmentally acceptable alternative, even if it is not the alternative with lowest environmental impact. NEPA decisions are then recorded in the *Federal Register* as a matter of public record after a final public review period.

QUICK COMPREHENSION CHECK

In what way do the steps to complete an EIS remind you of the PrOACT process (chapter 3)?

More Tools for Conservation on Public Lands

One benefit of managing wildlife on public lands is that land is available for management, and wildlife management is a priority at some level for state and federal land management agencies (Table 13.1). In contrast to private land managers, who must go looking for willing landowners to participate in conservation projects, public land resources are waiting for management to be planned and enacted. However, a biologist on public lands faces two problems: (1) despite the large size of many refuges, parks, or forests, wildlife are not confined to land boundaries, and (2) the staff size on most federal lands is not large enough to carry out the habitat management that must be done. Therefore, managers have developed processes (tools) that allow wildlife managers to utilize and incentivize private citizens to assist with management, as well as collaborations that provide for coordination of management activities across larger regions and landscapes.

National and international conservation partnerships: When an agency develops a management plan for a specific unit (forest, refuge, park, etc.), the agency must consider the goals of existing national, regional, and ecosystem plans. Federal agencies must consider state-specific programs, and vice versa. The site-specific management plan is expected to be consistent with these existing plans, and the agency's planning should contribute to broader goals. In return, activities coordinated within the broader action plans will assist the park or refuge to meet some of its goals. For example, national wildlife refuges prioritize support for migratory birds, and the following partnerships are valuable to all wildlife refuges:

- North American Bird Conservation Initiative (coalition of state/federal agencies and NGOs)
- Partners in Flight Bird Conservation Plan (network of 150 partner organizations)
- US Shorebird Conservation Plan (developed by coalition of state/federal agencies and NGOs)
- Northern American Waterbird Conservation Plan (a coalition led by US Fish and Wildlife Service)
- North American Waterfowl Management Plan (led by USFWS and state agency biologists)

Public/private partnerships with neighboring landowners or land management agencies:

For the same reason that national and regional collaborations are critical to public land managers, partnerships are also necessary with surrounding landowners or agencies that manage nearby lands. Although we might imagine state and federal lands as large contiguous blocks, in fact, state and federal lands are often fragmented within the same wildlife management area, national forest, wildlife refuge, or park (Figure 13.10). For historic reasons, lands acquired for public use may be cobbled together from a variety of abandoned agricultural land, willing sellers, or other sources. For example, USDA acquired failed farms and ranches during the Great Depression of the 1930s that were transformed into the National Grassland system. Another reason for fragmented public lands is the checkerboard pattern of land ownership often seen in western states. To encourage quality railroad infrastructure during the 1800s, railroad companies were given land in a checkerboard pattern extending away from the path of the railway. Railroads could sell the lands to generate funds to support construction, and these private lands are now inholdings within public lands (Figure 13.10).

Worldwide, managers of national parks and other public lands often find it necessary to form partnerships with neighbors because of wildlife that leave park boundaries and graze on private grazing land or prey on livestock (chapter 11). In other situations, public land managers work with nearby landowners to increase the scale at which habitat management is accomplished for at-risk species. Public land biologists use some of the same tools listed earlier for use by private land biologists to provide incentives for their neighbors to support conservation in the broader landscape around the public land area.

Grazing allotments: Public lands, such as national parks, national forests, national wildlife refuges, or lands managed by the Bureau of Land Management (BLM) require grazing management by cattle (chapter 11) in the absence of bison or other native

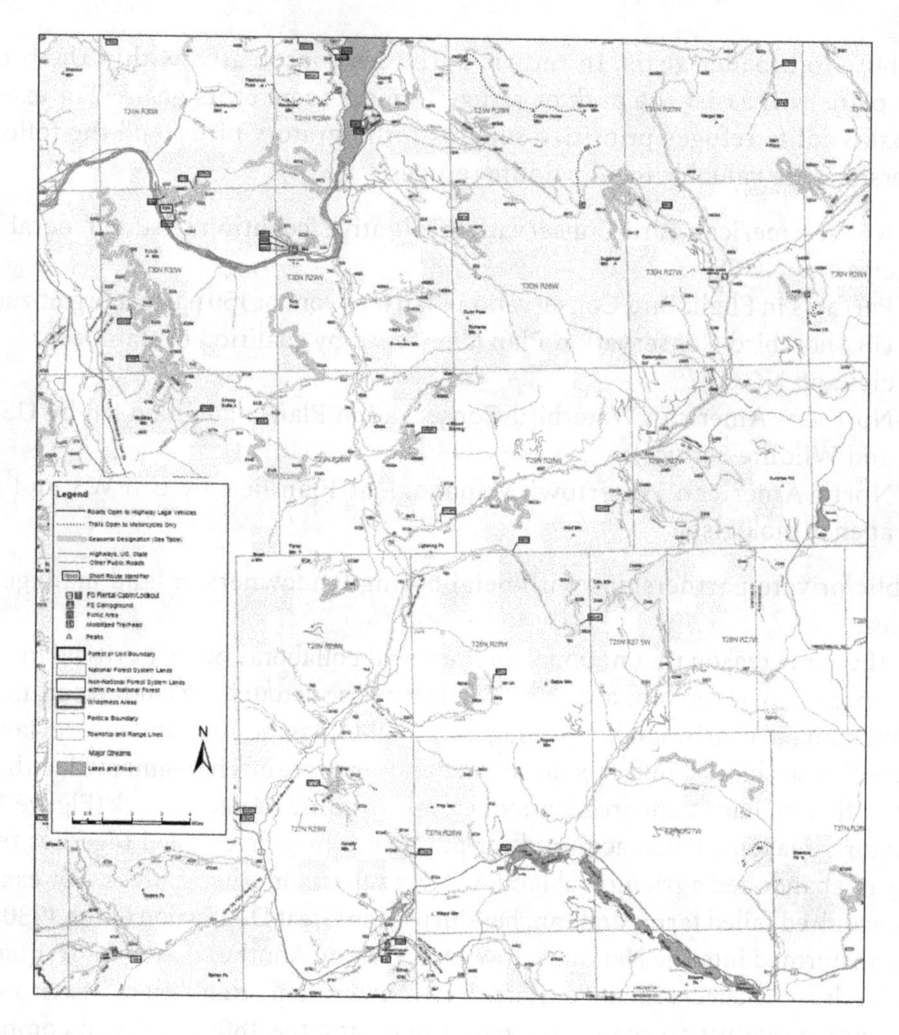

FIGURE 13.10 A section of the Kootenai National Forest near Libby, Montana with lands managed by the US Forest Service (gray) and surrounding lands managed by other agencies or private citizens (white). Map provided by the US Forest Service.

grazers. To allow habitat management by cattle in the absence of large site-specific federal staff to manage a herd of cattle, public land managers use a system of permits and leases that allow private ranchers to graze their cattle on public lands. Areas designated for this purpose are known as grazing allotments.

Prior to application for a grazing lease, a rancher must show proof of ownership of a base property where cattle can be taken in the off-season, as well as proof of ownership of cattle to use on the public lease site. Grazing leases have economic value to ranchers. Ranchers frequently sell these permits to one another and banks loan money based on the value of the grazing allotment. Public land managers must manage the logistics and payments for the grazing leases and monitor use by the landowner to ensure compliance with the AUMs (chapter 12) allowed under the management plan.

Leaseholders often assist federal agencies with monitoring soils, vegetation, and water quality. The cooperatively collected data helps drive future management decisions and allows the federal agencies and permittees to have defensible data to use for the permit renewal process. Both partners benefit from a smooth permitting process.

Timber sale contracts: The federal land management agencies do not employ timber harvesting crews, so private citizens and commercial timber companies are engaged when a forest management decision results in a need to thin or harvest trees. Companies bid for the opportunity, and the agency receives payment from the company in return for the opportunity of the company to harvest trees in a specified removal pattern as designated by the agency's foresters. The company then sells the timber product at market to recoup the costs of harvest.

WRAPPING UP

In our problem case, Ingrid and Desmond were worried about forest management for Kirtland's warbler on private and public lands. What strategies are available for them to use in each type of land system for conservation of this endangered species?

How would the endangered species figure in a NEPA consideration for a proposed harvest of timber on land managed by the US Forest Service?

Decision-Making on the Ground

1. Farm Bill Programs for the Jones Family Farm

The Jones family has come to the USDA Natural Resource Conservation Service in their county in Ohio for advice on enrolling all or portions of their farm in farm bill programs. Mr. and Mrs. Jones are in their 60's, and the farm is paid for. The children have jobs in the city, with no interest in farming now. The Jones family has heard about the CRP program in the farm bill, but do not know much about the other programs available.

The main farm is approximately 300 acres of corn, beans, pasture, and hay land. The crop fields are fairly level, with a 20-acre wet patch in the middle of the corn and soybean field that has always caused Mr. Jones fits when he tries to plant crops in the spring. The family tried to drain a wetland several years ago so that they could plant the additional acres to crops. The pasture and hay land are on a steep hillside, near a river. Mr. Jones has raised a few cattle and is considering selling that herd because of high corn prices that are causing feed costs to rise. If farm bill programs do not work out, the other option would be to lease the ground to neighbors.

APPLICATION, ANALYSIS, SYNTHESIS, AND EVALUATION

Describe why an incentive program for natural habitat on farmland is in the interest of the public in your state.

Consider the programs available in the current farm bill programs, and decide as a group which program(s) might be the most reasonable to pursue with an application to USDA. The main conservation programs in the 2018 farm bill are CRP, ACEP, EQIP, and RCPP. Use the table below to record information.

Evaluate each program in the current farm bill with pros and cons for each program. You can access fact sheets from USDA online to help you consider each program. What do the acronyms stand for? Which programs seem especially made for the Jones family's farm?

2018 FARM BILL PROGRAM	ADVANTAGES	DISADVANTAGES
CRP		
ACEP		
EQIP		
RCPP		

2. Three Creeks Partnership: Allotment Consolidation

The Bureau of Land Management and the US Forest Service manage 64% of all land in Utah. To manage grassland and shrubland habitat, public land managers have historically issued permits to owners of private lands to allow the owners to graze their livestock on public lands. The permits (allotments) are generally of ten-year duration and allow for an annual season of use. In semi-arid regions with sensitive riparian areas, annual grazing might not be a preferred alternative for optimum habitat management, but the tradition and economic reliance on the allotment made it difficult

FIGURE 13.11 Leaseholders in the Three Creeks Allotment Consolidation project move cattle into an upland pasture managed by Bureau of Land Management. Photo by Taylor Payne and used with permission.

to vary grazing pressure on the public land areas. To change grazing pressure for a new ten-year contract, a NEPA process was required, and the federal managers were overwhelmed by paperwork to the extent that response to changing range condition was not feasible for each new contract.

In Rich County, in northeastern Utah, the rangeland landscape is managed largely by the BLM and USFS using public grazing allotments. The rangelands are typically grazed May through September as large open pastures receive little rest during the growing period of the vegetation. Over time, habitat for greater sage-grouse became degraded and range condition declined for livestock. In an area known as Three Creeks, landowners have been utilizing ten grazing allotments (five BLM, five USFS) for multiple generations.

In 2010, the group of ranchers holding federal permits began a planning process to improve range conditions and avoid potential restrictions on grazing because of concerns of greater sage-grouse habitat and the potential for listing under the Endangered Species List. State employees of the Utah Department of Agriculture and Food's

Grazing Improvement Program worked with managers with BLM and the USFS to facilitate a discussion with the leaseholders. The group engaged in a watershed-scale planning effort that encompassed grazing, wildlife, water quality, habitat, recreation, legal, and policy issues. Most notably, the planning process addressed the social dynamics of working with 36 different grazing permittees representing ten different grazing allotments, and multiple government agencies. Considerations of the NEPA permitting process were also included in the discussions.

Because of the planning discussions, the group of private ranchers decided to consolidate the allotments of all permittees in a form of regulated, common land use, and the process is now known as the Three Creeks Allotment Consolidation. The ranchers formed a new company, which is now the permittee for the single, large allotment. The goal of the allotment consolidation is to improve rangeland, enhance ecosystem services, and provide for increased economic sustainability (Payne 2018). This arrangement is the first known attempt to consolidate allotments in the fashion approved by the group, representing a potential model for the future on public lands in the United States.

APPLICATION, ANALYSIS, SYNTHESIS, AND EVALUATION

Consider the social dynamics in communities near public lands. If a local BLM or USFS employee was to lower the number of cattle that could be grazed on an allotment by 20%, can you describe the reaction of the rancher when they met the BLM employee at the local grocery store or at church?

How is the challenge with changing the grazing pressure on allotments similar to the challenge of changing harvest rate quotas for marine fish and mammals discussed in chapter 7?

Why is a local partnership between federal agencies, state agencies, and private landowners critical to management of greater sage-grouse in northeastern Utah?

The ranchers involved in the Three Creeks allotment consolidation were members of a small community and had routinely helped each other with ranching activities such as branding or fence construction in the past. Why might the ten allotment owners' familiarity with each other lead to their agreement to join in a private company that holds the new grazing lease?

What personality and leadership traits might be useful for the local BLM or USFS employee who works with these ranchers and holds the agreement together in the future? Refer back to chapters 3 and 4 to evaluate traits of successful decision-making teams—can you find suggestions for the type of team that worked to create this unique partnership? What kind of people would you want on your team, if you were leading this process?

Sources of Information and Further Reading

Baveye, P. C., Baveye, J., and Gowdy, J. "Soil "ecosystem" services and natural capital: Critical appraisal of research on uncertain ground." *Frontiers in Environmental Science* 4 (2016): 41.

Brown, D. J., Ribic, C. A., Donner, D. M., Nelson, M. D., Bocetti, C. I., & Deloria-Sheffield, C. M. "Using a full annual cycle model to evaluate long-term population viability of the conservation-reliant Kirtland's warbler after successful recovery." *Journal of Applied Ecology* 54, no. 2 (2017): 439–449.

Cain, Z. and Lovejoy, S. "History and Outlook for Farm Bill Conservation Programs." *Choices* 19 (2004): 37–42.

Galik and Jackson. "Risks to forest carbon offset projects in a changing climate." *Forest Ecology and Management* 257, no. 11 (2009): 2209–2216.

Henderson, J., B. Glay, and M. Boehlje. "Agriculture's Boom-Bust Cycles: Is This Time Different?" *Economic Review*, Federal Reserve Bank of Kansas City. Fourth Quarter 2011: 83–105.

Hiller, T. L., Powell, L. A., McCoy, T. D., and Lusk, J. J. "Long-term agricultural land-use trends in Nebraska, 1866–2007." *Great Plains Research* 19 (2009): 225–237.

Merenlender, A. M., Huntsinger, L., Guthey, G., and Fairfax, S. K. "Land trusts and conservation easements: Who is conserving what for whom?" *Conservation Biology* 18, no. 1 (2004): 65–76.

National Park Service. *NEPA Handbook*. National Park Service, Department of the Interior, 2015. https://www.nps.gov/subjects/nepa/upload/NPS_NEPAHandbook_Final_508.pdf

Payne, T. "The Three Creeks Allotment Consolidation: changing western federal grazing paradigms." *Human-Wildlife Interactions* 12, no. 2 (2018): 272–283.

Powell, L. A. "Periodic corrections to agricultural land values provide opportunity for conservation." *Journal of Soil and Water Conservation* 70, no. 2 (2015): 39A–44A.

Sliwinski, M., Burbach, M., Powell, L., and Schacht, W. "Ranchers' Perceptions of Vegetation Heterogeneity in the Northern Great Plains." *Great Plains Research* 28, no. 2 (2018): 185–197.

United States Department of Agriculture. *Land Values: 2018 Summary*. Washington, DC: USDA, National Agricultural Statistics Service, 2018.

USFWS. *Conservation banking: incentives for stewardship*. Washington, DC: USFWS, Department of the Interior, 2012. https://www.fws.gov/endangered/esa-library/pdf/conservation_banking.pdf

Image Credits

Fig. 13.1: Source: National Park Service.

Fig. 13.2: Source: https://www.ers.usda.gov/data-products/chart-gallery/gallery/chart-detail/?chartId=58268.

Fig. 13.3: Source: United States General Services Administration.

Fig. 13.4: Source: http://www.fao.org/resources/infographics/infographics-details/en/c/284478/.

Fig. 13.6: Source: South Dakota Department of Game, Fish, and Parks.

Fig. 13.7: Source: United States Department of Agriculture, Farm Service Agency.

Fig. 13.8: Source: United States Department of Agriculture, Farm Service Agency.

Fig. 13.10: Source: https://www.fs.usda.gov/Internet/FSE_DOCUMENTS/fseprd488315.pdf.

Fig. 13.11: Taylor Payne, "Three Creeks Allotment Cattle." Copyright © by Taylor Payne.

APPENDIX ONE

For Further Study

Chapter 1: Public Trust Doctrine in the United States

Talk to a wildlife manager or search for recent legislative bills about wildlife in your state legislature. Can you find an example of how social or political biases affect the management of wildlife in your state?

◆◆◆◆◆◆

The chapter describes three constitutional platforms under which the federal government could argue to end discrimination of nonresidents for hunting and angling permits. Consider current political dynamics regarding states' rights versus federal control of controversial issues like medical marihuana, gun control, or abortion. Do you think there is a danger of future court challenges to higher nonresident license fees for hunting and angling?

◆◆◆◆◆◆

If you were a lawyer arguing to make nonresident license fees equal to resident fees, which clause of the Constitution provides for the best path for an argument?

◆◆◆◆◆◆

What are your responses to the following statements? Justify your responses as informed opinions:

- The federal government should have no role in any wildlife management policy in any state.
- If I want to hunt, I should expect to pay up to $300/day for access to private lands.

- I am glad that our wildlife laws tend to keep private citizens from being able to benefit economically from wildlife.
- In my state, outfitters should be able to receive a certain number of permits each year to guarantee their out-of-state clients can hunt in the state.

◆◆◆◆◆◆

This chapter shows how the history of the United States was important to the formation of the Public Trust Doctrine and our wildlife laws. Select a country beyond North America, and investigate how its history has affected its current wildlife management strategies and laws.

Chapter 2: Global Models of Wildlife Management

Find the online summary of the 2016 National Survey of Fishing, Hunting, and Wildlife-Associated Recreation. Which activities contribute the most to wildlife-related expenses?

◆◆◆◆◆◆

Compare the 2016 results to the previous survey by the same organization. Are wildlife-related expenses growing or declining?

◆◆◆◆◆◆

With the trends in wildlife expenses in mind, look at Figure 4.4 to evaluate trends in the purchases of hunting and angling licenses. How might the changes in income from licenses during the last two decades affect your state wildlife agency?

◆◆◆◆◆◆

Compare the models of wildlife management in other countries with the three distinctive characteristics of the North American Model for wildlife management. What similarities and differences do you find?

◆◆◆◆◆◆

Complete the table to allow comparison between the countries explored in chapter 2. Find answers in the text or explore trusted internet sources.

	UNITED STATES	NORWAY	NAMIBIA	THAILAND	GUATEMALA	ENGLAND
AVERAGE INCOME (US DOLLARS)						
POPULATION DENSITY (PEOPLE/KM^2)						
HUNTING ALLOWED?						
MAIN SOURCE(S) FOR FUNDING OF CONSERVATION EFFORTS?						
PUBLIC LANDS ACCESS?						
WILDLIFE OWNERSHIP OR DIRECT PROFIT FROM WILDLIFE?						
PRIMARY DECISION-MAKERS FOR WILDLIFE MANAGEMENT						
STRENGTH OF REGULATIONS AND LAWS						
STRENGTH AND PRESENCE OF WILDLIFE LAW ENFORCEMENT						

Chapter 3: Decision-Making Frameworks

Open the most recent online issue of *The Wildlife Professional* (published by The Wildlife Society) or *Fisheries Magazine* (published by the American Fisheries Society) or your state wildlife agency's monthly magazine. Find examples of management situations that fit the descriptions of "complex decisions" in the introduction to chapter 3.

◆◆◆◆◆◆

With the help of your instructor or academic adviser, reach out to an employee of a state or federal wildlife agency. Ask them about their decision-making strategies. How often do they use their gut for decisions, versus more formal decisions? How often does their job involve emergency decisions? Do they think about the manner in which they make decisions?

◆◆◆◆◆◆

Can you develop an expert system with three steps that allows a user to decide whether they should attend their wildlife management class on a given day? Compare your design with a classmate's design.

◆◆◆◆◆◆

Assume you are the manager of a set of ten small lakes along an interstate highway. The lakes are former gravel mines and are heavily used for fishing. Recently, anglers from all of the lakes report catching many small fish and very few large fish. Your supervisor suggests you use adaptive management as you address the issue. What kind of approaches to implement adaptive management (trial and error, step-wise, horse race) might you use and why? How might your approach affect the speed at which you find the management solution?

Chapter 4: Management Planning for Success

Consider the variety of management plans described in Table 4.1. For more insight into management plan structure and function, investigate the following:

- Gharials are a freshwater crocodilian species, endemic to the Indian subcontinent. The animals inhabit large, deep, fast-flowing rivers. They are now limited to 2% of their former range (IUCN Bangladesh 2016). Use an internet search to

locate the IUCN Species Action Plan, titled "Gharials of Bangladesh." What management actions are proposed by this plan?
- Commercial whaling has depleted the North Pacific right whale, and there are now fewer than 500 individuals. The whale was one of the species listed on the first list of endangered species, The Endangered Species Conservation Act of 1969 (National Marine Fisheries Service 2013). Use an internet search to locate the Species Recovery Plan titled, "Recovery Plan for the North Pacific Right Whale." What are the two objectives for the recovery plan?
- The bluefish is a migratory species found in temperate and tropical coastal oceans worldwide and along the entire east coast of the United States. The Mid-Atlantic Fishery Management Council responded to a substantial increase in recreational fishing for bluefish with a fishery management plan in 1990. Use an internet search to locate the regional fisheries management plan titled, "Fishery Management Plan for the Bluefish Fishery." How would you describe the input from stakeholders that was included in the planning process?
- New Hampshire has established a state wildlife action plan (New Hampshire Fish and Game Department 2015). Use an internet search to locate the plan, titled "New Hampshire Wildlife Action Plan." Review chapter 4 and find the most common risk factor for wildlife in New Hampshire.
- The city of Davis, California has experienced a significant increase of the number of resident wild turkeys during the past decade. Since the first nine birds were reported in urban areas in 2009, the population has increased to the level such that community members routinely complain about aesthetic impacts (e.g., feces, vehicle and landscape damage), traffic safety issues, and aggressive encounters. Use an internet search to find the plan, titled "Wild Turkey Population Management Plan, City of Davis." What management recommendations have been made to respond to the human-wildlife conflict?

◆◆◆◆◆◆

Select a state wildlife agency, a federal wildlife or land management agency, and a wildlife-related NGO. Use an internet search to determine if they have a published planning process. Compare the processes you find to the generalized process in Chapter 4. What differences do you find? If you find differences, why do you think the agency uses a slightly modified approach? Why might some steps be minimized, missing, or enlarged?

◆◆◆◆◆◆

In chapter 3, we noted that management of wildlife is based on decision processes that are similar to business decisions. The development of a management plan for wildlife may be remarkably similar to the basic structure recommended for a **business plan**. For example, an entrepreneur starting a new company or an existing company developing a new product would include the following information in their planning documents:

- *The Problem—worth solving?*
- *Current Environment—description of market, company finances and strengths, and competition*
- *The Solution—roadmap to the future*
- *Market Analysis—key customers, competitors, and future markets*
- *Execution—the marketing plan, sales plan, and resources required*
- *Financial Plan—sales forecast, expenses, and projections*
- *Milestones—key metrics for evaluation*

Compare the structure of a business plan with the structure of a wildlife management plan found in chapter 4. Map the sections between the two kinds of plans. How is a wildlife management plan like a business plan? How is the process of planning for a management project similar to planning for a business venture? What are important differences between the planning process used by a wildlife manager and a corporate manager?

◆◆◆◆◆◆

If a state fisheries program wished to restore populations of bluegill in a public lake, what feature of the bluegill population would be critical to monitor? Conduct an internet search and find at least one method that biologists commonly used for this type of monitoring.

Chapter 5: Values and Ethics in Wildlife Management

Refer to research summarized in chapter 5 on variation in value orientation among residents of 19 western US states. How might the differences described with regard to composition of state residents' education, rural/urban residence, and income affect a wildlife biologist who is making recommendations for regulations for harvesting bobcats with leg-hold traps or cable traps? Why might two wildlife managers in states with contrasting education, residence patterns, and income have two different experiences at public meetings on trapping?

◆◆◆◆◆◆

A local landowner writes a Letter to the Editor to complain about the Endangered Species Act's effect on his ability to harvest timber to support his family. "It's just not right," he writes. Can you identify in which category of value orientation in Figure 5.3 he most likely would be?

◆◆◆◆◆◆

A biologist at a university is engaged in a research project in which 30 bighorn sheep are captured and transported to a new location to repopulate an area in which bighorn sheep have disappeared during the last century. The research biologist will monitor individuals after release to evaluate habitat use. During the transport operation, two bighorn sheep die from capture myopathy, a physiological response to stress. The news of the deaths reaches a local animal rights group, who demands that the university abandon any future plans to translocate sheep. The biologist disagrees. What is at the heart of the contrasting ethical beliefs about what is right for bighorn sheep in this situation?

◆◆◆◆◆◆

Feral pigs were introduced on the Channel Islands, off the coast of California, and their population grew in size. The pigs modified the habitat and changed ecosystem dynamics (Roemer et al. 2002). Managers created a list of alternatives for managing the population, including (1) culling through shooting, (2) an expensive program to use remotely deployed contraceptives to eliminate reproduction, (3) introduction of a new predator to the island to control the pigs, or (4) no action. Use a role-playing exercise to determine how four different people, each in a different category in Figure 5.3, might approach the preferences for management alternatives. Would their value orientations matter?

◆◆◆◆◆◆

Use an internet search to find your state government's ethics standards. Are there any differences when compared to the federal standards shown in the Executive Order #12674 in chapter 5?

◆◆◆◆◆◆

Compare the Association of Zoos and Aquariums code of ethics with the code for The Wildlife Society. What unique statements do you see in each? Why might each group need its own code of ethics?

Chapter 6: Biology of Wildlife Populations

Consider the program to build bluebird nest houses in North America as you think about density dependent, regulating factors. Use an internet search to investigate the reasons behind the need for cavity boxes for bluebirds, and look at some Breeding Bird Survey data (Pardieck et al. 2017, Sauer et al. 2017) for bluebirds since the next program began in 1966. What factor might have been regulating the population prior to the start of the nest box program?

◆◆◆◆◆◆

Consider a manager of a wildlife management area who understands that cold winters can be a limiting factor on wild turkeys, ring-necked pheasants, and northern bobwhites. Use an internet search to learn about wildlife food plots. What is a food plot? How might a food plot assist the population during a harsh winter?

◆◆◆◆◆◆

Use Figure 6.9 to estimate recruitment, per capita, for a pair of muskrats breeding at low to high densities of ln(N) = 1, 2, and 4.

Multiply the levels of recruitment x2 to obtain the number of recruits for the pair of muskrats (x2 to change your per capita estimate to a "per pair" recruitment estimate). Add the 2 parents to their offspring/recruits to obtain the fall population size for the family. Now, use Figure 6.9 to find the probability of winter survival, given the population density: ln(N) = 1, 2, or 4.

Multiply the probability of survival by the size of the family. How many muskrats survived the winter? We started with 2 muskrat (parents) the previous year. Is the population growing or declining under each scenario?

◆◆◆◆◆◆

Read the section on predators' numerical response. Perform a calculation to see why a numerical response of predators is not enough to regulate a prey population. Assume a population of 1000 black-tailed jackrabbits and five coyotes who each eat ten jackrabbits per month. What proportion of the jackrabbit population is eaten each month? Now, assume a doubling of the jackrabbit population from a very good reproductive year to 2000 individuals. Assume a similar numerical response by coyotes, increasing from five to ten (also doubling). If the kill rate of jackrabbits per month remains the same, what proportion of the jackrabbit population is now taken by coyotes in one month? Is the predation pressure of coyotes on jackrabbits any different at the population level? Has the survival rate of jackrabbits changed?

What do you predict will regulate the jackrabbits—coyotes or food resources?

◆◆◆◆◆◆

Read about predators' functional response. Return to the previous example of 1000 black-tailed jackrabbits and five coyotes who each eat ten jackrabbits per month. Calculate, again, the monthly mortality rate at this density for jackrabbits. Now, allow the jackrabbit population to increase to 2000 and the coyote population to double as a numerical response to ten as before. But, now incorporate a functional response that allows each coyote to eat 20 jackrabbits per month (perhaps switching from porcupines or prairie dogs, in favor of abundant jackrabbits). Now what is the monthly mortality rate from coyote predation?

Compare this result to the result from above with only a numerical response. What do you believe would happen to the rabbit population now? If this continues, what do you believe would happen to the coyote population?

◆◆◆◆◆◆

Choose a species of interest to you and create a conceptual model of all factors that affect reproduction and survival of the species. Consider whether these effects are density-dependent. You may wish to use the BIDE model figure at the beginning of the chapter as the framework for your conceptual model by connecting known predators, diseases, parasites, welfare factors, and other influences to the appropriate segments of the figure.

◆◆◆◆◆◆

In a simple 2-age structure for a population, if $S_a = 0.6$, and $S_j = 0.4$, how many offspring, per capita, must be produced (*P*) in the population to maintain a stable population size (hint: stable population is when $\lambda = 1$)? Assuming an adult sex ratio of 50:50, how many offspring must each female produce to reach that per capita level of P?

◆◆◆◆◆◆

Review the stage-based model for fathead minnows. Miller and Ankley (2004) reported that exposure of minnows to minimum levels of an endocrine disruptor (17b-trenbolone) caused reductions of fecundity of 50%. Modify the Leslie matrix appropriately for an exposed population of minnows. What is the next year's population size? Calculate the discrete rate of population growth, λ.

◆◆◆◆◆◆

The general Leslie matrix model for population projection has constant birth and death rates. Therefore, does it represent an exponential model or a logistic model? How could you modify the process used to project population size with the Leslie matrix model to account for density-dependent birth or mortality?

Chapter 7: Harvest Management Decisions

Use a search engine to find the state legislative code for your state and make a list of all species of fish and wildlife that are legally harvested. Compare to another state. Hint: try the search strong "[state] legislative code hunting" or "[state] legislative code fishing."

◆◆◆◆◆◆

Population yield: Assume that the population in Figure 7.6 is a population of cottontail rabbits, and assume the population is at carrying capacity (1000 individuals). What level of growth is the population exhibiting? Can you find the appropriate data point on the yield figure to represent the current conditions at carrying capacity?

If the population is lowered through a disease or other mortality to 700 individuals, what will be the growth response in the following year?

◆◆◆◆◆◆

Use a search engine to review applications of MSY to commercial marine fisheries, such as Atlantic cod, Atlantic bluefin tuna, or Pacific salmon. Compare how MSY was used to set policy in each situation and evaluate the outcomes. How did politics, economics, and population biology interact in these scenarios?

◆◆◆◆◆◆

In the example used to explore Figure 7.8, the harvest rate for bobwhites was 10%. Use a harvest rate of 5% or 15% instead. Compare the predictions for the spring populations for bobwhites using a (1) no-harvest, (2) additive harvest mortality, and (3) compensatory harvest mortality model. Which of the three scenarios results in the most individuals alive in the following spring? Which model predicts the least number of individuals alive in the spring?

◆◆◆◆◆◆

Talk to a biologist with your state wildlife agency about processes used to set angling or hunting regulations. Does that process seem more similar to the formal decision-making process used in the North American Waterfowl Management Plan or to the deliberations of the "hunting subcommittee of the Mongol Supreme Command in the 13th century"?

◆◆◆◆◆◆

Refer back to chapter 3 and our discussion of when formal decision-making processes should be used, relative to risk of outcome. How might this explain why managers used a very formal process for waterfowl harvest in North America, but most states use very informal processes to set regulations for squirrel and rabbit harvests?

Chapter 8: Small Population Problems

Do an internet search and determine details of the non-natural threat factors apply to the six species shown in Figure 8.1.

◆◆◆◆◆◆

For each threat factor used by the IUCN, can you list two examples for a species of wildlife that is threatened (beyond those listed as examples in chapter 8)?

◆◆◆◆◆◆

Compare and contrast the IUCN's definitions for threatened and endangered species with definitions provided in chapter 9 from the United States' Endangered Species Act. Which set of definitions is more functionally useful in your opinion? Justify your answer.

◆◆◆◆◆◆

Analyze Table 8.A1. Can you provide examples of solutions to threats that match those categories in the table? Which threat factor in Table 2 appears to be the most difficult to address as an agency? What factors make it difficult to address the threats? Which threat factor in the table appears to be the easiest to address? Why?

TABLE 8.A1 ***Comparison of five threat factors for endangerment with regard to whether economic factors are motivations for the threat, the level of control by management agency, types of potential solutions, and potential recovery speed following the management solution.***

THREAT FACTOR	ECONOMIC MOTIVATION FOR THREAT?	LEVEL OF CONTROL BY WILDLIFE MANAGEMENT AGENCY?	TYPE(S) OF POTENTIAL SOLUTION(S)?	RECOVERY SPEED FOR SPECIES AFTER PROBLEM ADDRESSED?
	Yes, Often, Seldom, No	*None, Low, Moderate, or High*	*Biological, Political, or Cultural*	*Fast, Moderate, or Slow*
NATURAL CAUSES	No	None	Biological	Not applicable
UNWISE AND UNREGULATED HUNTING AND FISHING	Yes	High	Political, Cultural	Fast
INTRODUCTION OF PREDATORS	Often	Low, unless sanctioned by agency	Biological, Political	Moderate
OTHER SPECIES INTRODUCTIONS	Often	Low, unless sanctioned by agency	Biological, Political, Cultural	Moderate
HABITAT LOSS OR MODIFICATION	Yes	Low	Political, Cultural	Moderate

◆◆◆◆◆◆

Calculate expected heterozygosity, h, for a large population operating under Hardy-Weinberg assumptions with 5% A and 95% aa alleles.

For comparison, calculate expected heterozygosity, h, for a large population operating under Hardy-Weinberg assumptions with 50% A and 50% aa alleles. If this 50/50 composition of the two alleles is the most optimal in terms of genetic diversity, how does your calculation for h inform your interpretation of other values for h or H given in the chapter?

◆◆◆◆◆◆

Conduct a literature search to find another species of wildlife that has been found to have effects of genetic diversity on reproduction or survival? What genetic analysis methods were used to measure genetic diversity in the study?

Chapter 9: Managing At-Risk Species

The Endangered Species Act (ESA) uses general definitions for "threatened" and "endangered" species. Do these vague definitions help or hurt conservation efforts? Find an example that supports your answer.

◆◆◆◆◆◆

In 2008, the polar bear was listed as a threatened species under the ESA because of the threat of sea ice decline. The IUCN lists polar bears as vulnerable, citing scientific studies that suggest there are over 20,000 polar bears. Because of the relatively large population size, the status of polar bears and their critical habitat under the ESA has been contested in court more than once. Review the definition of "vulnerable" under the IUCN. What criteria do you think led the IUCN to adopt that status for polar bears?

◆◆◆◆◆◆

What do you think about the ethical arguments against captive breeding programs discussed in chapter 9? Share your thoughts with a classmate and listen to his or her opinions.

◆◆◆◆◆◆

Review the process for working through an ethical dilemma in chapter 5. Black rhinos are currently encountering high levels of poaching in the wild, and law enforcement is finding it difficult to protect the species. Using the guidance for decision process in chapter 5, would it be ethical and biologically prudent for conservation success to remove black rhinos to a secure captive facility funded by a philanthropist?

◆◆◆◆◆◆

Conduct an internet search on the web page of the closest accredited zoo or aquarium to your university or college. In which Species Survival Plans do they participate, and who functions and the keeper of the studbook for the zoo or aquarium?

◆◆◆◆◆◆

Contact your local zoo and ask the studbook keeper what plans they have for targeted breeding. Do they move animals or use transfer of sperm to accomplish these plans? What other zoos or aquariums participate in the Species Survival Plan with your local zoo?

◆◆◆◆◆◆

Review the five ways in which a manager of threatened and endangered species might frame their role in the listing process for the ESA. Now, review the value orientations we discussed chapter 5. How do the five models for framing the listing decision process compare with the value orientations listed in that chapter? Do you think a person with a utilitarian approach to natural resources might be more likely to adopt one of these framing approaches, for example? What about a person with a protectionist approach to natural resources?

Chapter 10: Introduced and Invasive Species Management

Consider invasion of brown rats on an island. Provide an example of chemical, mechanical, and biological control that might be used to eradicate or contain the rats.

◆◆◆◆◆◆

Do you think one vertebrate taxonomic group is more likely to have invasive species than another? What is your hypothesis? Support your answer with some online research.

◆◆◆◆◆◆

Imagine an aquaculture facility in Mississippi that is raising catfish for sale as a food product in regional restaurants. The owner is experiencing algal blooms in the ponds, because of high nutrient loads from uneaten fish food and catfish fecal material. One option is to use chemicals to kill the algae, but a stakeholder in the operation suggests introducing a new filter-feeding fish from South America. Describe the process that the owner should use to decide whether a non- native fish should be introduced to the ponds in Mississippi. List the potential concerns you might have.

Chapter 11: Human-Wildlife Conflicts

Consider an animal damage or human-wildlife conflict situation in your city or region. Write down the problem as stakeholders express it (the "complaint"). What is the cause of this issue? Have solutions been attempted in the past? Do they address the ultimate problem, or are they aimed at satisfying stakeholders through addressing a proximate problem?

◆◆◆◆◆◆

Develop a plan for pigeon management in your city or a city near you. Be creative. Determine the extent of the problem and use the PrOACT steps to develop your plan. Consider Table 11.1 for alternative management options, and use an internet search to see what solutions have been attempted in other situations to solve a similar problem.

◆◆◆◆◆◆

The case examples from the chapter on cheetahs and snow leopards were international conservation situations. Consider the spread of mountain lions, black bears, or wolves into new states in the United States during recent years. All three species have the potential to create human-wildlife conflicts with livestock. How might you apply the techniques used by managers in other countries to our local management problems?

Chapter 12: The Ecology of Habitat Management

Contact a habitat management specialist in your state wildlife agency. Ask him or her to describe the importance of soil maps to development of plans for state-managed wildlife management areas.

◆◆◆◆◆◆

Ask for your instructor's assistance to determine the location of the historic photo archive for your state. Using Figure 12.3 as an example, select four or five locations in your region and find a series of aerial photos dating back to the 1930s or 1940s. Evaluate the photos and describe the changes that you observe. Make hypotheses to explain the changes. What role did policy or social dynamics play in the changes you observe?

◆◆◆◆◆◆

Calculate the AUMs for a pasture that is grazed by 100 1105-pound cattle for 15 days.

◆◆◆◆◆◆

Select a species of wildlife that interests you. Do a search of published literature to determine what is known about the dietary needs for your species. How might management affect the quality and quantity of foods available for fish, amphibians, reptiles, birds, or mammals?

◆◆◆◆◆◆

Select a nearby forest or timber unit managed by a state or federal agency. Contact their management staff and obtain a copy of their management plan. What are the goals for the property? Do the silviculture methods used make sense given the management goals? If not, why might there be a mismatch? Hypothetically, change the goal for forests in the area. What management techniques would you use to reach that goal?

◆◆◆◆◆◆

Make a list of reservoirs near you. Can you find records that show the year in which they were created? Do the ages look similar to Figure 12.16?

◆◆◆◆◆◆

Use an internet search to find the HSI model for a species that interests you. The National Wetlands Research Center provides a web page with links to many species. After becoming familiar with the data needed to calculate the suitability index for your species, visit a local site and use the HSI model to determine habitat suitability. Look at the individual components for the overall index—which component gave the lowest score? What management technique could you use to improve that score for the area in the future?

Chapter 13: Dichotomies of Public and Private Land Management

Develop a public policy response in a situation where nitrate levels in a watershed have increased beyond safe levels. In this hypothetical case, evidence suggests that fertilizers spread by farmers in the watershed are to blame for the high nitrate levels. How could society persuade the upstream farmers to lower fertilizer applications, which would lower their profits from their fields?

◆◆◆◆◆◆

Take the list of programs from the 2018 farm bill, located in the table in "Farm bill programs for the Jones family farm." Using the USDA web pages, find current fact sheets for each program. Create a table for the four USDA programs that allows you to compare the following characteristics of each program: description of program purpose, length of contract with the landowner, eligibility for land enrolled, eligibility for the landowner, description of how applications are evaluated, the proportion of the costs that can be paid with cost share, and the total limits of funding.

◆◆◆◆◆◆

Use job search websites, such as those supported by the American Fisheries Society, The Wildlife Society, or the Texas A&M Fisheries and Wildlife Jobs Board. Look for jobs labeled "private lands biologist" and review the job description. What characteristics of this job seem to be unique to working with private citizens?

◆◆◆◆◆◆

Use USAjobs.gov to search for jobs of wildlife biologists with the federal agencies listed in chapter 13. Compare similar jobs in different agencies—do you see differences in job requirements, job duties, or descriptions of the positions? Compare the job descriptions to the mission statements provided in Table 13.1. Are there ways in which the agency's mission statement affects the duties or roles of their wildlife biologists?

◆◆◆◆◆◆

Search the Environmental Protection Agency's online database for Environmental Impact Statements for an EIS developed in your state. What kind of projects do you see listed with EIS statements? Select one and evaluate it. Find the executive summary section of the EIS—what management issues were being explored with the EIS? Why was an EIS required? Throughout the EIS document, what at-risk species were considered? What was the determination with regard to impact of the proposed action?

APPENDIX TWO

Scientific Names

COMMON NAME	SCIENTIFIC NAME	CHAPTER FIRST MENTIONED
alligator, American	*Alligator mississippiensis*	12
badger, American	*Taxidea taxus*	11
bass, largemouth	*Micropterus salmoides*	7
bass, striped	*Morone saxatilis*	10
bass, white	*Morone chrysops*	7
bear, black	*Ursus americanus*	Preface
bear, grizzly	*Ursus arctos horribilis*	11
bear, polar	*Ursus maritimus*	8
beaver, North American	*Castor canadensis*	1
beech, American	*Fagus grandifolia*	12
birch, paper	*Betula papyrifera*	12
bison, American	*Bison bison*	1
bison, European	*Bison bonasus*	9
bluefish	*Pomatomus saltatrix*	4
bluegill	*Lepomis macrochirus*	7
bluegrass, Kentucky	*Poa pratensis*	13
bluestem, big	*Andropogon gerardi*	13
bobwhite, northern	*Colinus virginianus*	6
box turtle, ornate	*Terrapene ornata*	1
brome, smooth	*Bromus inermis*	13
buffalo, bigmouth	*Ictiobus cyprinellus*	6
buffalo, Cape	*Syncerus caffer*	2
bullfrog	*Lithobates catesbeianus*	6

COMMON NAME	SCIENTIFIC NAME	CHAPTER FIRST MENTIONED
canvasback	*Aythya valisineria*	1
cardinal, northern	*Cardinalis cardinalis*	1
carp, bighead	*Hypophthalmichthys nobilis*	6
carp, common	*Cyprinus carpio*	10
carp, silver	*Hypophthalmichthys molitrix*	6
cat, feral	*Felis catus*	5
catfish, African sharptooth	*Clarias gariepinus*	5
catfish, channel	*Ictalurus punctatus*	1
catfish, channel	*Ictalurus punctatus*	7
cattle	*Bos taurus*	6
cheetah	*Acinonyx jubatus*	8
chukar	*Alectoris chukar*	10
coati, brown-nosed	*Nasua nasua*	6
cod, Atlantic	*Gadus morhua*	7
condor, California	*Gymnogyps californianus*	9
cottontail, Eastern	*Sylvilagus floridanus*	12
cottontail, New England	*Sylvilagus transitionalis*	9
coyote	*Canis latrans*	1
crane, sandhill	*Grus canadensis*	2
crappie, black	*Pomoxis nigromaculatus*	7
crappie, white	*Pomoxis annularis*	7
crow, American	*Corvus brachyrhynchos*	2
darter, Cumberland	*Etheostoma susanae*	9
deer, red	*Cervus elaphus*	8
deer, white-tailed	*Odocoileus virginianus*	5
dove, rock	*Columba livia*	11
dove, zenaida	*Zenaida aurita*	8
eland, common	*Taurotragus oryx*	2
elephant, African	*Loxodonta spp.*	2
elk	*Cervus canadensis*	1
elm, Siberian	*Ulmus pumila*	10
ferret, black-footed	*Mustela nigripes*	6

COMMON NAME	SCIENTIFIC NAME	CHAPTER FIRST MENTIONED
fox, crab-eating	*Cerdocyon thous*	6
fox, gray	*Urocyon cinereoargenteus*	11
fox, red	*Vulpes vulpes*	11
frog, lowland leopard	*Lithobates yavapaiensis*	6
galaxias, common river	*Galaxias vulgari*	10
garter snake, common	*Thamnophis sirtalis*	1
giraffe, reticulated	*Giraffa camelopardalis reticulata*	5
gnatcatcher, California	*Polioptila californica*	9
gnatcatcher, coastal California	*Polioptila californica californica*	9
goose, Canada	*Branta canadensis*	11
goose, Hawaiian (Nene)	*Branta sandvicensis*	6
goose, snow	*Chen caerulescens*	8
gorilla, eastern lowland	*Gorilla beringei graueri*	9
grass, Indian	*Sorghastrum nutans*	13
grass, reed canary	*Phalaris arundinacea*	4
groundhog	*Marmota monax*	11
grouse, red	*Lagopus lagopus scoticus*	6
grouse, ruffed	*Bonasa umbellus*	7
grouse, sharp-tailed	*Tympanuchus phasianellus*	7
guanaco	*Lama guanicoe*	6
gyrfalcon	*Falco rusticolus*	6
hare, showshoe	*Lepus americanus*	6
harrier, hen	*Circus cyaneus*	6
hellbender	*Cryptobranchus alleganiensis*	9
horse, feral	*Equus ferus*	10
horse, Przewalski's	*Equus ferus przewalskii*	9
iguana, Cuban rock	*Cyclura nubila*	8
iguana, green	*Iguana iguana*	8
jackal, golden	*Canis aureus*	9
jackrabbit, black-tailed	*Lepus californicus*	6
kudu, greater	*Tragelaphus strepsiceros*	2
leopard	*Panthera pardus*	2

COMMON NAME	SCIENTIFIC NAME	CHAPTER FIRST MENTIONED
leopard, snow	*Panthera uncia*	11
lion	*Panthera leo*	2
lionfish	*Pterois spp.*	6
lynx, Canada	*Lynx canadensis*	6
mallard	*Anas platyrhynchos*	7
marten, European pine	*Martes martes*	6
minnow, fathead	*Pimephales promelas*	6
mongoose, small Indian	*Herpestes auropunctatus*	6
moose	*Alces alces*	1
mountain lion (cougar)	*Puma concolor*	Preface
muskrat	*Ondatra zibethicus*	6
ocelot	*Leopardus pardalis*	6
olive, Russian	*Elaeagnus angustifolia*	10
opossum, Virginia	*Didelphis virginiana*	12
oryx	*Oryx spp.*	2
oryx, scimitar-horned	*Oryx dammah*	9
ostrich, common	*Struthio camelus*	2
owl, barn	*Tyto alba*	6
owl, barred	*Strix varia*	9
owl, northern spotted	*Strix occidentalis caurina*	3
paddlefish, American	*Polyodon spathula*	6
panda, red	*Ailurus fulgens*	9
panther, Florida	*Puma concolor coryi*	5
partridge, gray	*Perdix perdix*	10
penguin, African	*Spheniscus demersus*	9
penguin, emporer	*Aptenodytes forsteri*	12
perch, Nile	*Lates niloticus*	3
perch, white	*Morone americana*	6
perch, yellow	*Perca flavescens*	7
pheasant, ring-necked	*Phasianus colchicus*	Preface
pig, feral	*Sus scrofa*	10
pigeon, passenger	*Ectopistes migratorius*	1

COMMON NAME	SCIENTIFIC NAME	CHAPTER FIRST MENTIONED
pine, loblolly	*Pinus taeda*	4
pine, ponderosa	*Pinus ponderosa*	12
pipit, meadow	*Anthus pratensis*	6
prairie dog, black-tailed	*Cynomys ludovicianus*	1
prairie chicken, greater	*Tympanuchus cupido*	1
prairie chicken, lesser	*Tympanuchus pallidicinctus*	1
pronghorn	*Antilocapra americana*	1
ptarmigan, rock	*Lagopus muta*	6
python, Burmese	*Python molurus bivattatus*	3
quetzal, resplendent	*Pharomacrus mocinno mocinno*	2
raccoon	*Procyon lotor*	10
raccoon, crab-eating	*Procyon cancrivorus*	6
rat, brown	*Rattus norvegicus*	6
reindeer (caribou)	*Rangifer tarandus*	2
rhinoceros, black	*Diceros bicornis*	2
rhinoceros, white	*Ceratotherium simum*	2
roundworm, raccoon	*Baylisascaris procyonis*	10
sage-grouse, greater	*Centrocercus urophasianus*	8
salamander, Berry Cave	*Gyrinophilus gulolineatus*	9
salamander, Red Hills	*Phaeognathus hubrichti*	8
salmon, chinook	*Oncorhynchus tshawytscha*	9
salmon, coho	*Oncorhynchus kisutch*	6
sauger	*Stizostedion canadense*	10
sea cow, Steller's	*Hydrodamalis gigas*	1
sea turtle, green	*Chelonia mydas*	8
sea turtle, logger-head	*Caretta caretta*	6
sea turtle, olive ridley	*Lepidochelys olivacea*	9
seal, Northern elephant	*Mirounga angustirostris*	8
shad, American gizzard	*Dorosoma cepedianum*	6
shark, scalloped hammerhead	*Sphyrna lewini*	9
sheep, bighorn	*Ovis canadensis*	5
sheep, Soay	*Ovis aries*	8

COMMON NAME	SCIENTIFIC NAME	CHAPTER FIRST MENTIONED
snake, brown tree	*Boiga irregularis*	10
snakehead, northern	*Channa argus*	10
sparrow, house	*Passer domesticus*	10
springbok	*Antidorcas marsupialis*	2
squirrel, eastern gray	*Sciurus carolinensis*	6
squirrel, fox	*Sciurus niger*	1
squirrel, red	*Sciurus vulgaris*	6
starling, European	*Sturnus vulgaris*	Preface
stingray, raspy river	*Potamotrygon scobina*	9
sturgeon, shortnose	*Acipenser brevirostrum*	9
swallow, cliff	*Petrochelidon pyrrhonota*	8
tiger	*Panthera tigris*	5
tilapia	*Oreochromis spp.*	5
tilapia, blue	*Oreochromis aureus*	10
toad, eastern spadefoot	*Scaphiopus holbrookii*	1
toad, Wyoming	*Anaxyrus baxteri*	9
toad, Yosemite	*Anaxyrus canorus*	8
tortoise, desert	*Gopherus agassizii*	4
trout, brook	*Salvelinus fontinalis*	8
trout, brown	*Salmo trutta*	8
trout, rainbow	*Oncorhynchus mykiss*	8
trout, Yellowstone cutthroat	*Oncorhynchus clarkii bouvieri*	8
turkey, wild	*Meleagris gallopavo*	1
turtle, leatherback	*Dermochelys coriacea*	6
vole, common	*Microtus arvalis*	6
vole, field	*Microtus agrestis*	6
walleye	*Stizostedion vitreum*	6
warbler, Kirtland's	*Setophaga kirtlandii*	13
whale, beluga	*Delphinapterus leucas*	9
whale, North Pacific right	*Eubalaena japonica*	4
wolf, gray	*Canis lupus*	Preface
wolf, red	*Canis rufus*	11
woodpecker, red-cockaded	*Leuconotopicus borealis*	4

CPSIA information can be obtained
at www.ICGtesting.com
Printed in the USA
LVHW021824090723
751947LV00002B/57